Penguin Books
The Complete F-Plan Diet

As well as being the author of Britain's best-selling diet of all
time, *The F-Plan Diet*, Audrey Eyton is the woman who can
justly claim to have invented that now popular feature of every
magazine stall – the slimming magazine. When she and her
partner founded *Slimming Magazine* seventeen years ago it was
the first publication in the world to specialize in the subject. The
publication was an instant success and has continued to be the
dominating bestseller despite the many rival magazines which
have followed.

For many years Audrey Eyton edited *Slimming Magazine* herself,
and later became Editorial Director. During their years of
ownership (the company was sold in 1980) she and her partner
also started Ragdale Hall Health Farm and founded and
developed one of Britain's largest chains of slimming clubs. Mrs
Eyton continues to work as a consultant to the company.

During her many years of specialization in the problems of
weight control and healthy eating, Mrs Eyton has worked with
most of the world's leading nutritional, medical and psychological
experts. No writer has a greater knowledge and understanding of
the subject.

She has a nineteen-year-old son and lives in Kensington and
Kent.

Audrey Eyton

The Complete F-Plan Diet

The F-Plan
The F-Plan Calorie and Fibre Chart
F-Plus

Charts compiled and recipes devised by Joyce Hughes, B.Sc.
Research directed by Dr Elizabeth Evans

Penguin Books

Penguin Books Ltd, Harmondsworth, Middlesex, England
Viking Penguin Inc., 40 West 23rd Street, New York, New York 10010, U.S.A.
Penguin Books Australia Ltd, Ringwood, Victoria, Australia
Penguin Books Canada Limited, 2801 John Street, Markham, Ontario, Canada L3R 1B4
Penguin Books (N.Z.) Ltd, 182–190 Wairau Road, Auckland 10, New Zealand

Made and printed in Great Britain by
Richard Clay Ltd, Bungay, Suffolk

Contents

As with all slimming diets, if you suffer from any health problems at all, or intend to follow a strict regime of less than 1,000 calories, check with your doctor before embarking on a dieting programme.

Acknowledgements

In addition to my excellent collaborators, Joyce Hughes and Elizabeth Evans, I would like to express my warmest gratitude to Dr David Southgate of the Food Research Institute, to Derek Miller of London University's Department of Nutrition and to Dr Martin Eastwood of the Western General Hospital, Edinburgh, all of whom have been most generous with their help and encouragement. My thanks, too, to Sue Horsman, without whose supersonic typing I would never reach a deadline, to my research assistant, Simon Sharples B.A., and to my son Matthew who, even when I delve into the sombre depths of the lower intestine, can always be relied on to come up with the jokes.

Preface

In May 1982, a large proportion of the British nation began to behave in an unprecedented and totally uncharacteristic way. They went overboard about a diet.

Such phenomena are hardly unknown in America. Indeed, they are known nearly every year as the latest diet craze hits the country. But, as far as diets are concerned, the average Brit is soundly made of much more sceptical and less easily stirred-up stuff.

But in May 1982, stirred up they certainly were. And things happened which had never happened before – or since.

Never before had so many Britons embarked on the same diet at the same time – they were numbered in their millions. Never before had a diet appealed to such a diverse cross-section of the population, from national leaders like Dr David Owen, who proudly revealed his personal weight loss of a stone in three weeks, to the many works canteen enthusiasts who insisted on the diet meals being included on their menus. Never before had a diet been so much talked about and written about, as the media world, from Terry Wogan to *The Times*, got in on the act.

The diet, of course, was the now classic F-Plan. And now it can be said that never before has a diet made such a lasting change to the eating habits of a country.

What a diet-weary public appreciated with such perception and alacrity in 1982 was that the F-Plan was not just another diet, but the revelation of a complete revolution which upturned decades of outdated theories on dieting and healthy eating.

In no way was the F-Plan simply the pet theory of its author, Audrey Eyton. The revolution in nutritional thought was already revealed in scientific papers and research findings. But to the general public the new dieting guidelines were largely unreadable, and certainly unfollowable. The F-Plan brought it all down to easily understandable terms, and showed how the new way of weight-beating and healthy eating could be wheeled through the check-point in a supermarket trolley.

Diets come, and usually go. The F-Plan does not go. Having sold more copies than the sum total of all diet books in Britain over the previous twenty years, it remains, consistently, Britain's best-selling diet.

Its worth has been recognized throughout the world with at least sixteen foreign-language editions embracing cultures as far apart as Islam and Iceland. In America, the birthplace of the great dieting blockbuster, it was the first British diet ever to become a major best-seller, and is the only famous diet praised for its soundness in a new authoritative publication on the subject: 'The F-Plan is the direction in which national dietary recommendations are being focused, and rightly so.'*

Today, very many British doctors recommend the F-Plan to their patients and for very good reasons. If you are overweight it provides by far the easiest method of shedding surplus weight. All sound and healthy modern diets are simply adaptations of the F-Plan eating pattern. Those which aren't are simply here-today gone-tomorrow gimmicks, or short-term crash diets. If you *aren't* overweight it is also the diet you should be following, but without restriction on quantity of food. The F-Plan shows you how to shift the emphasis of your eating pattern from fatty food to fibre-containing food, to protect your health from today's most wide-spread serious ailments. Is it a slimming diet or a health diet? The answer is: both.

Since *The F-Plan* was first published it has been followed by two partner publications, *The F-Plan Calorie and Fibre Chart* and *F-Plus*. The former shows you how to work out your own daily menus, sufficiently high in fibre and low in calories to shed weight and improve health. The latter provides a side selection of daily F-Plan menus ready-planned for you.

Combined together for the first time in this volume, they provide a hugely comprehensive guide. Everything you need to know to lose weight on Britain's most successful diet of all time. Everything you need to know in order to make the switch from unhealthy and outdated eating habits to the new pattern of eating, unanimously recommended by all leading health authorities.

* *Popular Nutritional Practices: A Scientific Appraisal* by Jack Z. Yetiv, M.D.Ph.D.

The F-Plan

Introduction

Over the past years, many claims have been made suggesting that the inclusion of some particular food in a slimming diet would specifically help overweight people to shed weight more quickly and effectively. Grapefruit was a classic example. Grapefruit diets were popular for years. More recently, in an American bestseller, pineapple was invested with those magical weight-shedding properties. Sadly, *all* these claims in the past were based on fiction rather than fact – certainly not on any established medical fact! Apart from caffeine (which does have a small effect in speeding up the metabolism) no substance we eat or drink was proved by scientific methods to have any realistic effect in speeding away our surplus fat. Weight loss depended entirely on the calories we *didn't* eat.

Now, for the first time in the history of medical science, a substance has been isolated about which it is possible to say: 'If you base your slimming diet on this food you should shed weight more quickly and easily than on a diet based on the same quantity of any other foods.'

The substance is dietary fibre. This is what the F-Plan is all about. The F-Plan shows you how to cut your calorie intake and at the same time increase your intake of dietary fibre from the unrefined cereal foods and the fruits and vegetables which provide it.

When you follow the F-Plan you should:

1. Find slimming easier than ever before, because your diet will be considerably more satisfying and filling than any diet you have ever followed;

2. Lose weight *more quickly* than ever before, because a larger proportion of the calories you consume will remain undigested;

3. Gain all the well-established health advantages of eating meals high in dietary fibre content.

Who says so?

Not some earnest, eager and ignorant lady running a slimming clinic in Slough. Not some dubious doctor (all professions have their black sheep!) cashing in on some personal theory totally unsupported by scientific evidence. Who – or rather *what* – says so is a very large and growing body of evidence produced from medical research conducted by leading doctors and scientists of the Western world: experts whose reputation is beyond question and who have no cash benefit to gain from their findings.

This is what makes the F-Plan unique.

Quote: *'It seems likely that a diet in which sugars and starches are taken in natural fibre-rich form would contribute to the control of obesity by encouraging satiety at a lower level of energy intake, and to a lesser extent by increasing the amount of potential energy lost in the faeces.'*

What that means, in simple English, is that if you follow a high-fibre diet you will find that you feel more satisfied on fewer calories. And more of the calories that go into your mouth will, to put it bluntly, go straight through and down the lavatory.

Of course, the fewer calories the body uses from food the more it must draw from your surplus body fat, so this adds up to faster weight loss.

Another simple definition which will appeal to everyone who has ever tried to slim: More weight loss for less willpower!

Even more dramatic: *who* made the statement quoted above? The answer is that august, eminent and necessarily highly conservative body, the Royal College of Physicians. This statement is drawn from a special report they have compiled on the medical aspects of dietary fibre. The members of the Royal College need a very large quantity of scientific evidence indeed, drawn from many sources, before they will commit themselves so far. If they feel it likely that a high-fibre diet, which also reduces sugar and fat, will be particularly beneficial to slimmers – as they do – we need hardly say more. The F-Plan is the first slimming diet which enables you to follow this formula.

These discoveries are relatively recent for a particular reason: medical scientists only started seriously investigating the benefits of high-fibre little more than a decade ago. Before that time, only a minority of 'cranks' insisted on eating wholemeal bread, extolling the virtues of bran, and complaining of the ill-effects of a Western diet rich in refined carbohydrates.

When the authentic medical researchers started to get involved, they were looking for dietary answers to serious illnesses prevalent in Western societies but extremely rare in many less sophisticated communities in the developing world. Why was it that so many diseases, like cancer and other disorders of the bowel, heart disease and diabetes, were occurring frequently here, but not there? What were these people doing that we weren't doing, and vice versa? One of the answers which emerged was that they were eating diets high in natural fibre – while we, in the West, were stripping this cell-wall material from our day-to-day diet by refining our cereal foods and sugar.

In recent years the evidence for the health benefits of fibre, or 'roughage' as it used to be called, has grown so strong that it has filtered through from the medical journals and is now well known to the British and American public. These days it isn't just those health-food cranks who are scurrying off to buy their brown wholemeal loaves. Sales of this typical high-fibre food have hugely increased in recent years. The health connection was the motivation for the research that led to keen medical interest and the endorsement of the benefits of dietary fibre. The slimming connection emerged more recently, almost as an accidental byproduct of this research.

In addition to being relatively free from many major diseases, those people in developing countries, eating their high-fibre diets, were found to escape another major scourge of Western civilization – obesity. Even where food is plentiful, societies accustomed to a diet containing a high percentage of cereal foods, fruit and vegetables, all rich in natural fibre, do not become overweight.

This intriguing finding from the surveys led medical researchers to investigations into a whole new aspect of dietary fibre. Why were those high-fibre eaters keeping slim even when they were eating their fill? Could it be that the calories supplied by a diet high in natural fibre were being digested and utilized in a different way by the human body? The remarkable answer, revealed by many recent scientific experiments, is undoubtedly: YES.

However, today's enlightened experts realize that there is little point in discovering important diet guidelines unless these can be presented to the public in a form which makes them realistic and easy to incorporate into daily eating.

On this principle, Dr Elizabeth Evans has worked most diligently in supervising research, and Derek Miller, the distinguished nutritional expert, has made research information and facilities available to us at London University. At the Food Research Institute Dr David Southgate, who has made a special study of dietary fibre and whose research is the source of the scientific textbook fibre figures, has provided analytical values for the dietary fibre in a range of usefully fibre-rich canned and packaged foods, so that for the first time these products, which form such a major part of modern eating, can be realistically assessed and used for health value.

Another expert in the work on dietary fibre, Dr Martin Eastwood of Edinburgh's Western General Hospital, has generously given his advice and guidance, and Joyce Hughes, who lectures in nutrition at Croydon College, has compiled the F-Plan calorie and fibre charts.

There can be no doubt about the authenticity of the F-Plan and its claim that dietary fibre will help you slim. But on the basis that 'there has to be a snag', those who haven't taken much interest in the dietary fibre health factor to date may well become a little alarmed about what type of foods they will be required to eat on this diet. Somehow the words 'dietary fibre' do tend to conjure up an image of being put out to graze on food that has all the comfort and flavour of that consumed by a sheep or a cow.

When we tell you that baked beans on toast (as long as the toast is made with wholemeal bread) is one of the best high-fibre meals you can eat, it should give great reassurance to those who enjoy the more homely delights of the table. A quick glance at the recipes in this book should delight the gastronomically adventurous.

Dietary fibre is provided by a wide selection of easily available and palatable foods. The F-Plan will provide you with a wonderfully easy formula for boosting your intake to between 35g and 50g of fibre a day – at least twice most people's normal consumption – without sacrificing any pleasure in meals.

Those readers who are now sufficiently convinced that the F-Plan is the first realistically helpful medical advance in slimming, as indeed it is, may if they wish turn to page 91 of this book, where they will find all the rules for following the plan, followed by recipes, menus and charts.

The F-Plan calorie and fibre charts are the first charts to make it possible to keep to the correct number of calories and, at the same time, to choose the foods which will be of most help in making slimming both easier and speedier. For the health-conscious person, as well as those concerned about weight, they are a unique guide, making it possible to follow that major modern nutritional recommendation made by all leading medical authorities in the Western world: increase your intake of dietary fibre.

You will find three food charts in this book (in addition to a calorie chart of drinks) to make it triply easy to follow the new high-fibre low-calorie method of eating reduction and health benefit.

The first makes it easy to see which foods are low in calories and which are high in dietary fibre by listing the calorie and fibre content of average or easily recognizable portions of all the basic foods. You will see at a glance the number of calories and the quantity of dietary fibre (when present) in a whole average-sized eating apple, or a carrot, or a rasher of bacon. We call this chart the 'Instant Calorie and Fibre Guide'.

Our next chart, the 'Calorie and Fibre Guide to Packaged Foods', makes high-fibre low-calorie eating even easier. In this we reveal the number of calories and the quantity of dietary fibre present in the useful canned and packaged foods. The use of convenience foods need be no crime in health and weight control if the correct ones are chosen: in fact they can be a great asset. Here is the guide you need.

'Your Basic Calorie and Fibre Chart', reveals the calorie and fibre content (where present) of all those basic everyday foods on a per ounce basis.

However, we hope that you will take time to read the chapters that precede the recipes, menus and diet charts. Because if you do, you cannot fail to be deeply impressed by the very many ways in which high-fibre foods can help you to slim, and to come to the conclusion that the F-Plan is that major slimming breakthrough everyone has been seeking for so long.

What (and where) is dietary fibre?

Dietary fibre is a substance obtained from plant foods, as distinct from animal foods. All cereals, fruits and vegetables contain some dietary fibre, but, just as the calorie content of different foods varies to a great degree, so does the fibre content of different plant foods. Some are excellent sources, while the quantity contained in an average serving of others would be negligible. With cereal-based foods, fibre value depends to a large degree on how much has been stripped away in the milling and refining processes. Fruits and vegetables, even in their raw, unprocessed state, differ so much that you certainly can't say that *all* of them are useful sources of fibre.

But precisely what is dietary fibre? Well, it could be loosely defined as the cell-wall material of plants – but only loosely, because it also consists of substances associated with these cell walls. Dietary fibre can also be described as the carbohydrate material in plant foods (mainly derived from the cell walls) which is not digested by man. Note that phrase 'not digested by man', because it gives you your first clue to the slimming advantages of dietary fibre. Food which is not digested cannot be used to provide body fat or calories!

All plants and animals, ourselves included, are made up of cells, but the cell walls of plants are of a more rigid structure. This performs the function of enclosing cell contents, trapping water, stiffening the plant and conducting sap. It is tempting to think of dietary fibre as the tough stuff which holds the plant together, and this is true to a degree, but it can be misleading when it comes to locating high-fibre plants by guesswork. Cell walls are made up of a variety of substances of which only one, cellulose, is truly fibrous in the sense of being filamentous or threadlike.

Hence if you were to take a guess at selecting a high-fibre vegetable you might well think of something like celery, which seems to reveal its fibre content unmistakably. Yet peas, extolled by advertisers for their tenderness, in fact contain more than four times the fibre of celery, weight for weight.

Generally, however, high-fibre foods do require more chewing, which gives them yet another slimming advantage, as you will learn later in this book.

By far the richest source of dietary fibre is bran. This consists largely of cell-wall material from grain and contains between 40 and 50 per cent dietary fibre – a much greater percentage than any other food. Bran is a byproduct of the milling process used in making white and other extracted flours. It is largely because the bran is stripped from white flour that our Western diet has become low in natural fibre content. White flour, the basis of so many foods, is fibre-depleted flour. Similarly, sugar, as we use it, is sugar cane or beet totally divested of all its dietary fibre.

However, the F-Plan does not require you to obtain your dietary fibre from bran alone. Yesterday's message of 'bran alone' is now outdated and for some very good reasons. For one thing, bran is a bulky substance and it isn't easy to consume sufficient fibre from it without making your diet unpalatable. If you have tried sprinkling it on breakfast cereal and weighed the quantity, you will have discovered that you get a large volume for a quarter of an ounce – just about as much as you can palatably add to a single portion of breakfast cereal, without beginning to think that you are eating a bowl of sawdust!

Most people would only eat bran with breakfast cereal. Yes, there are enthusiasts who scatter it on to their scallops, mash it into their spinach and, quite possibly, stir it into their tea. But in the F-Plan we use bran only where it is palatable. No one ever goes on eating anything they don't like for long. There are, however, other important reasons why your dietary fibre should be obtained from fruit and vegetables as well as cereals. Dietary fibre differs in some degree from plant to plant. It is a complex substance and there is still much to be learned about it. Medical researchers are becoming increasingly aware of the health and weight-control benefits of dietary fibre in general – but the indications are that different forms of fibre may perform different beneficial functions.

Fresh fruit, for instance, being mainly water, provides only a dilute form of dietary fibre. Weight for weight it does not compare favourably with foods like cereals and nuts in fibre content, although it works out well when you take into account how much fibre you get for a modest number of calories. However, there is a substance called pectin, which is part of the fibre of fruit, which is not found in other plant foods. Medical experiments indicate that the presence of an appreciable quantity of pectin in the diet tends to increase the number of calories excreted in the stools in the form of fat. Obviously, the more calories you excrete the more calories the body is deprived of, and the more speedily you force it to shed weight.

For this and other known and yet to be investigated reasons, it is obviously a good plan to boost daily fibre intake – for health and slimming benefit – from a variety of cereal, fruit and vegetable sources, and this is what you do on the F-Plan. Although the benefits of dietary fibre are still in the process of scientific investigation, we want to make sure that you don't miss out on any of the advantages, both those which are known and those still to be fully revealed.

Although generally aware that bran, wholemeal bread (which has less of its fibre stripped away in the milling process than white bread) and muesli-type mixtures are rich sources of fibre, most people used to find it difficult to know where to locate that healthy high-fibre food. There is a good reason for this difficulty. Before the F-Plan was published it was impossible to find a really helpful and realistic guide to the sources of fibre in everyday foods. Scientific textbooks reveal the percentage of fibre in various cereal foods, fruits and vegetables. But this is only part of the story and can be very misleading.

To assess, realistically, how much fibre a particular food is likely to contribute to a daily menu, it is important to estimate what quantity of that particular food you are likely to eat. This varies a great deal from food to food.

Let us consider watercress as a typical example of how easy it is to be deceived. If you were to consult fibre charts, you would see that watercress (3·3 per cent fibre) appears to be quite a good source. It contains a higher percentage of fibre than cabbage, for instance, and more than twice as much as apples on a weight-for-weight basis. However, if you were to help yourself to a reasonably generous helping of watercress as part of a salad meal, it is unlikely that your portion would weigh more than half an ounce. You get plenty of watercress for half an ounce, but the quantity of dietary fibre in that weight is really too small to make any realistic contribution to your daily fibre intake. It provides you with just half a gram of fibre. If you were to serve yourself an average helping of cabbage, though, it would usually weigh at least two ounces if you were eating it raw as part of a portion of coleslaw, for example, or four ounces if you were serving boiled cabbage. If you were to pick up and weigh that apple you are about to eat, you would find it weighed about five ounces. So both these foods are useful sources of dietary fibre because, unlike watercress, they tend to be consumed in reasonably weighty quantities. The apple would provide more than two grams of fibre, and the cooked cabbage nearly three.

Why we eat what we do and how much we eat of any particular food is a fascinating subject. It depends a good deal on the bulk and 'fillability' of the food, of course. Hence many of the fibre-rich foods have inbuilt quantity controls because of their sheer bulk – fruit and vegetables in particular.

But there are many other factors involved. We tend to serve and finish off complete units of food as provided for us by manufacturers. If you are wondering, for instance, why The Instant Calorie and Fibre Chart lists only three quarters of an ounce of shredded wheat and then an ounce or more of other cereals, ask yourself whether you have ever seen anyone eat one and a quarter, or perhaps one and one third, shredded wheats . . . There are those who eat one shredded wheat and those who eat two. The world is precisely divided between those two groups with no grey areas in between.

Similarly, with potato crisps, have you ever known anyone *not* finish a packet they started? There are even some (not you, of course!) who have been known to lick the first finger of the right hand and dip it into the bottom of the packet, so that those tiny remaining crumbs of crisp can be finished off.

Nature does a neat packaging job with many foods, of course, and this also influences the quantity we normally consume. Where one unit is usually sufficient to satisfy the appetite and desire, we tend to keep to just one unit – one apple, one pear, one orange. Where mother nature has been meaner in her packaged quantity, with plums for instance, one unit does not have an inbuilt stop mechanism, so we often end up eating a good deal more than we would with a larger fruit. This has been taken into account in compiling The Instant Calorie and Fibre Chart, too.

How we buy food also has an influence on how much we eat of it at any one meal. If we buy half a pound we tend to eat either half a pound – or half that quantity.

The size of the dish or plate we use affects quantity as well, and this mainly accounts for the variation in quantities of breakfast cereals. Where a cereal is very light, like cornflakes, an ounce will comfortably fill the usual breakfast bowl. With Puffed Wheat an ounce would actually overflow in many bowls, so people tend to serve less than an ounce. Bran cereals and muesli are rather more weighty, so here people tend to serve out more than an ounce just so that it looks sufficient.

Price is another factor which influences quantity with some foods – mainly those we think of as protein foods. For example, most people will be quite content with a two-ounce portion of prawns, because they have become accustomed to eating a modest quantity of an expensive food, while with many fish – cod, for instance – six ounces would be a more usual serving. This factor applies less with foods rich in dietary fibre, because these foods – happily – tend to be inexpensive. But it might influence the quantities of grapes or strawberries consumed, for instance.

The amount of work we have to do in consuming any particular food influences the quantity too – both chewing (where high-fibre foods score so well) and manual work. Scientists discovered, in an experiment with overweight people, that when allowed to eat as much as they wanted, they ate considerably fewer peanuts in the shell than peanuts provided ready-shelled.

On the whole, the bulky form of foods rich in dietary fibre has a wonderful restraining effect on the quantity consumed – one of the great advantages of the F-Plan. But use self-control in relation to nuts (it's a good idea to buy them in shells) and take care with dried fruit – we have observed that some slimmers make frequent sorties into the pantry to nibble a handful of dried fruit. This way rather a lot of calories can be consumed; the chart gives the number of calories per ounce of dried fruit.

Dried fruit has been processed, of course, to some degree. It is interesting to note how often foods only become fattening when man has had a hand in processing them in some way. The foods which are consumed very much in the way they were grown – many of the fibre-rich foods – are rarely potentially fattening. It would appear that God did not intend us to be fat.

The best sources of all are those foods which have a high percentage of fibre and tend also to be consumed in reasonably large quantities ... without providing too many calories, if you are slimming! This is where, for instance, the good old baked bean in tomato sauce is unbeatable. These beans consist of more than seven per cent dietary fibre and most people would eat the contents of an 8oz can. This means that an average serving would contribute more than 16g of fibre to the diet, which is more than half the quantity that the average Briton consumes in a day on his fibre-depleted diet.

At the other end of the scale, one of the poorer vegetable sources of fibre is cucumber, which contains only 0·4 per cent of dietary fibre and tends to be consumed in modest servings. It has a low fibre content and a low portion weight, so its fibre contribution to the average diet is negligible.

Taking this essential 'how much is normally eaten' factor into account we have compiled the guide starting on page 213. This gives a truly realistic and helpful guide to the fibre content of foods. Based on average portions, it shows you a whole range of foods, from those which are enormously helpful to those which are virtually useless in boosting the fibre content of your diet.

2

The vital calorie factor

By including sufficient high-fibre foods in your diet you will actually help your body to shed surplus fat. But this doesn't mean that you can forget about calories. The strength of the F-Plan lies in the way it affects the calories you consume.

Never let anyone, or any diet, convince you that calories don't count in achieving weight loss. They do. They are what slimming is all about.

Calories are units of energy, the energy we need to keep going. We consume these calories in the form of food and use them up in maintaining the body's functions and movements. All foods supply calories, but in widely varying quantities on an ounce-for-ounce basis.

Sometimes – often, in fact – in the Western world, people consume more calories than they need to fuel the body with energy. A percentage of these surplus calories is then stored as body fat, and this is what makes people overweight.

The only way in which to reverse this situation and become slim again is to supply the body with fewer calories than it needs for its daily energy requirements, so that it has to draw on the emergency store of calories in its own fat. When you are slimming you are really eating your own body – eating away the part of it you don't want, that surplus fat! Apart from becoming highly energetic and making the body burn up many more calories daily – a possible but usually very slow method of shedding weight – there is no other way of losing weight than by depriving the body of calories.

All slimming diets which can possibly work are based on calorie reduction, but it is easy to see why people become confused about this. So many diets appear to have no connection with calories.

An example is the once highly popular low-carbohydrate method of slimming. Dieters were told that they only had to ration carbohydrates and then they could eat as much as they liked of other foods. These diets are now frowned upon by many medical experts because of their low fibre content. However, it is true that many people have succeeded in shedding weight on them in the past. (These diets could be said to have been half-right, in that they did cut out refined carbohydrates, but unfortunately without adding fibre-rich carbohydrate foods which we now know to be of such help to slimmers.)

The reason for weight loss, though, was calorie reduction. Because so many people in the West eat such a large proportion of their daily calories in the form of refined sugary and starchy foods, it was found that, when these foods were strictly rationed, daily calorie intake usually automatically dropped sufficiently to achieve weight loss. Although people were allowed to eat other foods freely, in fact when they were deprived of their refined carbohydrates they tended not to increase their intake of these alternative foods very much – not enough to make up for the calories they were saving.

Then there are those modern diets which tell you to ration only fats. Fats supply the most calories of all, very many more, weight for weight, than all other foods. All high-calorie foods are fatty, and all high calorie meals are fatty. So by rationing these foods you cut calorie intake. You are on a low-calorie diet. But since the foods allowed are still refined foods, the fibre content may not be high enough to meet present recommended levels.

Ah, but what about this remarkable new diet formula from America which tells you that you can eat vast quantities of melon and chicken, or spinach and prunes, or pineapple, or whatever, as long as you keep to this one food, or this combination of two foods, for the whole day? You may have actually heard people raving about the miracle weight losses they have achieved and attributed to these magical foods. Poor souls, all they were doing was cutting calorie intake – the hard way. You could say their success was based on the 'throw-up factor'. There is a limit to the quantity of any one particular food you can eat, and continue to eat without other foods, before beginning to feel bored with it and then almost sick at the thought of it.

More scientifically, variety has been found to be a factor in influencing the quantity of food we desire. It is partly because our Western diets are varied (and healthily so, because this ensures a wide range of necessary vitamins and minerals) that we are tempted to overeat. It's amazing how easy and tempting it is to eat a little more when we are offered food of a different flavour and texture – the dessert after a savoury meal, for instance. Interestingly enough, even hens and rats have been found to consume more calories when they are offered a varied diet than when they are fed 'the same old thing' all the time.

People eating 'the same old thing' eat fewer calories. Restrict a person to any one food and – even if that food is chocolate – they will almost certainly shed weight. But these diets are, by their nature, eventually self-defeating. After a certain time the very sight of the food allowed becomes off-putting and even repellent. Many people have experience of this from gorging sessions in childhood. My own son, as a small boy, allowed to graze freely on a strawberry field during a 'pick your own' expedition and aware that he, unlike our basket, would not be weighed and charged, once achieved a mammoth strawberry-eating feat. That was five years ago, and he hasn't been able to face a strawberry since!

So ALL diets, even those which come complete with generally useless injections and pills, achieve weight loss only by reducing calorie intake.

The F-Plan also reduces your calorie intake in order to allow you to shed weight at sufficient speed. But the radical difference between this and previous dieting methods is that it makes the food you consume more filling and also renders some of the calories it supplies non-fattening, as you will begin to learn in the next chapter.

3

The calorie–fibre connection

The most dramatic thing about the recent dietary fibre research is that it has, to a degree, altered the basis on which experts have been calculating potential weight loss over the past half century or so . . . the period during which overweight people have been begging diet doctors and dieticians to help them shed that surplus fat.

It is never possible to predict weight loss precisely. Even on the same diet, this will vary from person to person depending on many individual factors, including the amount of excess weight (the heavier you are the faster you tend to shed weight) and the degree of energy expended in physical activity. Nevertheless, there was a simple weight-loss equation on which it was possible to estimate the maximum amount of weight likely to be lost each week on any specific calorie allowance. This was based on subtracting the calories consumed in food from the calories required to keep the body going.

Let us assume that you are a woman of medium height, doing a job like housework, which requires a moderate amount of physical activity, and that you are about one stone overweight and just about to embark on trying to lose it. In these circumstances, it could be roughly assumed that you would be burning up around 2,000 calories a day.

If we were to put you on a slimming diet providing you with 1,500 calories a day, you would be 500 calories short of your requirement and these would have to be taken from your body fat. It has been scientifically estimated that a pound of your own body fat provides approximately 3,500 calories. So during a week you would be likely to shed one pound of surplus fat.

Obviously, if you followed a stricter diet, allowing you only 1,000 calories a day, you would draw an additional 500 calories a day from your body fat. So with a daily deficit of 1,000 calories you could expect to shed around two pounds a week.

As you see, expected rate of fat loss has always been estimated simply by counting the calories consumed in the form of food, any food, and subtracting them from the number the body requires for energy.

The recent findings about fibre introduce a new factor into this weight-loss equation.

As you read in the introduction to this book, when people eat high-fibre diets they excrete more calories in their stools (faeces). In several experiments, scientists have undertaken the task of analysing the stools of those following high-fibre diets and have found that the calories excreted are measurably greater in number than the calories excreted by those on the normal, varied Western diets, rich in refined carbohydrate foods – or, indeed, on any other pattern of eating. Tests indicate that the increased calorie content of the faeces amounts to nearly ten per cent when people follow high-fibre diets.

Obviously, those calories which are being flushed away are not being used by the body . . . which means that the body is having to use more of its own surplus fat to make up for them. So on a 1,000 calorie high-fibre diet the body is going to shed weight more quickly than on a normal 1,000 calorie diet of varied food – or on any other 1,000 calorie diet.

Before the fascinating high-fibre research findings it was assumed that weight loss depended entirely on *the number* of calories consumed compared with the number expended by the body. Now we have to add another factor to this simple statement.

Weight loss depends on the number and the *source* of calories consumed. The rate of weight loss will be influenced not only by the quantity you eat, in terms of calories, but also by which foods you choose to make up that calorie intake.

This is a great asset in favour of high-fibre dieting, but is very far from being the only advantage you gain when you follow the F-Plan slimming method. The benefit of this revolutionary diet is based not on just one advantage over other diets but on many factors which add up to faster, easier, more effective slimming. The fact is that from the moment you put fibre-rich food into your mouth it starts to give both physical and psychological advantages in filling you, satisfying you, protecting you from feeling hungry again soon, and speeding your weight loss.

The slimming benefits of the F-Plan diet start in the mouth, continue in the stomach, extend to the blood and reach a grand finale with that final flush!

So let's start with the first mouthful and work our way down the whole digestive tract, to explain fully the marvellous benefits of this new slimming method.

4

How fibre helps – in your mouth

Even before the foods which are rich in dietary fibre start to pass down your throat, they perform a multiplicity of functions which help to reduce the quantity of food you want to eat and they start to send helpful satiety signals to the brain. A whole range of slimming benefits, both physiological and psychological, come into play right there in your mouth.

One of these benefits is in slowing down your eating. This may not, at first glance, seem to be a major factor but in fact it is a crucial element in weight control. The rate at which you eat not only strongly influences how much you want to eat but – more surprisingly – it influences the length of time elapsing before you feel the desire to eat again. One of the most fascinating scientific experiments of recent years showed that when people ate meals at a rapid rate they became hungry again more quickly than when they ate precisely the same size of meal at a slower rate. Why this happens isn't fully understood. But it is well endorsed by general observation.

Never underestimate the role of eating-speed in slimming and weight control. It is very much more important than most people realize. If a group of people sitting at a dining table had their entire bodies shrouded under some tent-like garment, there are two ways in which the expert observer of eating behaviour could differentiate the fat from the slim. One of the things the expert would note would be that, however big the meal – and let us assume that over-large portions were served – some people would consume every morsel and leave an entirely clean plate. These would almost certainly be the overweight people, and this is something you can observe for yourself in almost any restaurant.

Overweight people, particularly the heavily overweight, rarely stop eating until they have finished everything on the plate. Slim people, in contrast, usually stop when they feel satisfied. In the case of an over-large meal this would mean that the slim people would put down their knives and forks and leave some food.

Overweight people seem to lack a 'stop mechanism'. This appears to be one of their basic problems. Effortlessly slim people are governed by their body's requirement for food and are bullied by messages from the body – 'That's it, old chap, I've had enough' – at the appropriate time. 'Honestly,' they say, 'I couldn't eat another morsel.' And they really mean it.

In contrast, overweight people seem to get much less strong and effective stop signals from the body, and this is largely because of the other factor, the major clue, which our eating-behaviour expert would be using in his 'guess who's overweight' game.

The overweight people would eat more rapidly than the slim people. This has been shown in several scientific experiments which invariably indicate that overweight people eat more quickly than slim people. A recent experiment in America showed that people of normal weight might start eating at a reasonably rapid pace at the beginning of a meal, when their hunger is at a peak, but this eating rate will steadily slow down as the meal progresses. The overweight people in this experiment, however, kept eating at the same fast pace throughout the meal.

Again, this is something you can observe for yourself in any public eating place. The overweight people tend to eat in a non-stop motion. As one mouthful of food is being chewed, the other is on the fork and on its way up – ready to be put in the mouth the second that the first mouthful starts on its way down the throat.

From my own observations, generally the greater the weight problem the faster the rate of eating. America, where there appear to be more grossly obese people than in Britain (by which I mean those around double their desirable body weight, rather than just a couple of stones overweight), is an excellent place to observe this eating-speed phenomenon. Once I sat with an American psychiatrist, a specialist in eating behaviour, and observed a hugely overweight couple (quite unaware that we were watching them) eating their restaurant break-fasts. The quantity of food collected from the help-yourself buffet was enormous and the speed with which it was consumed was almost supersonic. The husband not only forked food into his mouth with an almost non-stop movement of his right hand, but he also held a corn bun in his left hand so that food could be put into his mouth to fill the split second it took to reload the fork. Chewing must have been abso-lutely minimal. Needless to say, silence prevailed throughout the meal.

And at the end of it, after eating what must have been at least half-a-dozen scrambled eggs, plus bacon, sausages and several buns, the couple got up to reload their plates . . .

This is an extreme example. But most of us who have any kind of weight problem, however small, can benefit from slowing down our eating, for some very sound scientific reasons.

After food is put into the mouth it takes a few minutes (usually around five) even to start having any physical effect in satisfying the hungry body. At a fast eating pace and with a minimum amount of chewing – and very little chewing is usually required with refined sugary and starchy foods – an awful lot of calories can be consumed in five minutes.

As eating-time continues, the body sends out more and more satiety signals, but it is estimated that it takes about twenty minutes for a meal to have its full effect in filling our stomachs and sending out all the other physical signals of sufficiency. That is why speedy eaters, who eat their fill in perhaps ten or fifteen minutes, often feel over-full some minutes after the meal. Most of us, the slim as well as the overweight, have uttered that plaintive wail: 'Oh, I shouldn't have done it!', as we pat our far from comfortable stomachs after a particularly tempting feast, like Christmas dinner, and stagger off for the Rennies.

'Slow down your eating' is excellent classic advice for those with a weight problem – and many of those who have struggled long in the battle of the bulge have probably read it before, and even tried to follow it. Quite probably they have failed, or given up trying after a time.

Why? Because the rate of eating is a deeply established habit and all deeply established habits are very difficult to break. If you were advised to speak more slowly it would probably take months of effort, repeated conscious effort, before you succeeded in altering the speed at which you spoke. The same would apply to changing your accent. Think of the effort that Professor Higgins had to put in with Eliza!

Slowing down a habitual eating rate isn't easy and tends to need prolonged effort. And this is where a high-fibre diet starts to play its first function in helping you to eat less. It automatically slows down the rate of eating for you! And for a number of reasons – not just one.

First of all, plant foods in their natural form, unstripped of natural fibre in processing, tend to be bulky. You get a large volume or bulk of food for a small or moderate number of calories, and that in itself is going to necessitate considerably more chewing and take considerably more time. Take sugar and apples for comparison. The average Briton consumes about five ounces of sugar in a day. In the way it is grown and gathered, in cane or beet, sugar contains an appreciable content of dietary fibre, but this is stripped away completely in the refining process to leave no fibre at all in the sugar we buy in packets or consume in cakes, biscuits or drinks.

Many people consume a good deal of sugar in drinks. It takes hardly any time at all to swoosh down a can of cola, and neither does this seem to have any effect in satisfying the appetite. Most people find it easy to drink large quantities of calorific drinks, sweet or alcoholic, without in any way lessening or delaying their appetite for the next meal – and these drinks, and sugar itself, are perhaps the ultimate example of fibre-free calories. By consuming calories without any dietary fibre at all, you can get down a very large number of calories, at a very fast rate, with very little effect in satisfying the appetite.

Even when refined sugar is combined with refined flour to make cakes or desserts, the chewing required tends to be minimal.

It is somewhat unrealistic to imagine people gnawing away at sugar cane or sugar beet, so as an example at the opposite extreme let us consider apples. Apples are basically a mixture of water, sugar, dietary fibre and little else. Only the sugar in them supplies calories. You would have to eat about a dozen apples in order to obtain that average daily 5oz of sugar from this source; you can imagine how long that would take and how difficult it would be to eat all the remainder of your daily food. If the dietary fibre were removed, the apples would become apple juice. This way, those apple sugar calories could be consumed very quickly without the appetite-satisfying effect. So it *is* the dietary fibre which has the slowing down and filling up effect.

This principle is true of all foods. Dietary fibre, which is calorie-free, has the general effect of adding bulk, slowing down eating and satisfying the appetite in this and many other ways.

But this isn't the only way in which dietary fibre slows down eating. The texture as well as the bulk of fibre-rich foods helps to put on the brakes.

The pleasure of eating is largely the pleasure of taste. In natural fibre-rich foods the taste-evoking substances appear to remain intact within the cell walls which have not been stripped away by refining processes. Therefore the taste of an unprocessed food is not fully appreciated unless it is chewed. This may be one reason why fibre-rich foods are normally automatically chewed more thoroughly than processed foods.

There is *yet another* reason why many fibre-rich foods slow down eating and add to satisfaction. Food is not swallowed with comfort unless, or until, it is soft and moist. If it is dry and unyielding we automatically chew it until it becomes comfortable to swallow. Many high-fibre fruits and vegetables, nuts and dry breakfast cereals (shredded wheat, for instance, as opposed to porridge) need a good deal of chewing before they can be comfortably swallowed. Cooking, particularly boiling, reduces but does not wholly remove the firmness of food.

Scientists have done careful experiments to confirm the benefits of dietary fibre in slowing down eating. Sensibly comparing two foods of a very similar nature, they monitored a group of people eating a 'meal' consisting entirely of wholemeal bread, which contains 8·5 per cent of dietary fibre, and compared them with a group eating a 'meal' of white bread, which contains only 2·7 per cent dietary fibre. The wholemeal bread took 11 minutes longer to consume (45 minutes) than the white bread (34 minutes).

Dietary fibre means that a food requires more chewing but it *also* requires more swallowing. During prolonged chewing, more saliva is secreted and this adds to the volume of the food in the mouth. That obviously necessitates more swallowing movements.

Although it takes a few minutes for the body to send out any strong signals of satiety it is probable that chewing and swallowing movements do begin to send messages to the brain.

All of us, the overweight as well as the slim, have some body controls which limit our eating capacity. Otherwise, some people would indeed quite literally eat themselves to death – in fact there have been a few cases of disturbed people doing just that in recent years. However, the vast majority of people have inbuilt controls and these seem to differ only in their degree of effectiveness between the overweight and the slim. The major control mechanisms appear to be the state of fullness of the stomach, the level of sugar in the blood, and a satiety centre in the brain known as the appestat.

In experiments with rats, increased electrical activity was recorded in the satiety centre of the brain during chewing and swallowing. This indicates that chewing and swallowing at least start to bring our bodily eating controls into action by sending the first satiety signals to the brain – and that the more chewing and swallowing we do the more effective this is likely to be.

So far we have dealt only with the physical benefits of fibre-rich foods in the mouth. The psychological benefits might well be just as great.

Chewing gives psychological satisfaction, and even in scientific experiments the chewing of gum has been found to help reduce tension. Psychiatrists working in the area of weight control have discovered that we need our 'psychological fill' as well as our physical fill of food in order to feel content with what we have eaten.

When someone eats a snack while mentally absorbed in other things – perhaps a mother grabbing her own meal in between attempts to coax food down a baby, or a viewer eating a TV snack while totally involved in the latest beastly plots of 'J.R.' – it has been found that the food has little effect in satisfying hunger. Often, for instance, after the baby has been put to sleep the mother will sit down and eat another meal.

We seem to need to get a sufficient daily quota of conscious relaxation and pleasure from our food, and obviously this occurs while the food is in the mouth. Little wonder that a meal of mainly refined foods, gulped down in seconds, tends to lead to second helpings to extend the time of eating, or another meal or snack shortly afterwards to 'bulk out' the eating pleasure of the day.

In this chapter you have discovered many ways in which foods containing dietary fibre can make you feel more satisfied – and the food has not yet gone down the throat. See what happens when high-fibre food reaches the stomach . . .

5

How fibre fills your stomach –
and for longer

Dietary fibre is a sponge-like material which absorbs and holds water as it is chewed in the mouth and passes down the gastro-intestinal tract. This means that fibre-rich foods swell to a greater bulk, to fill the stomach, than any other foods.

The state of fullness of the stomach is obviously going to influence your appetite. A derivative of cellulose, one of the substances present in dietary fibre, has long been used as a 'slimming aid' for this reason.

Many of the pills and capsules which are sold to slimmers as appetite suppressants consist largely of methyl cellulose. The only problem is that you can't get enough of this material in pills and capsules to provide enough bulk to have any realistically helpful effect in filling the stomach.

However, when scientists Derek Miller and Dr Elizabeth Evans conducted tests at London University, adding 20g of cellulose to people's daily diet, they found this did indeed automatically reduce calorie intake. People consumed fewer calories without even trying to do so. So a sufficient quantity of cellulose does help you to eat less.

This large bulk of material in the stomach on a high-fibre diet is just one of the factors which makes you feel more satisfied on less food. Equally important is the fact that fibre-rich food *stays* in the stomach longer than fibre-depleted food. Those gastric acids have a much tougher job to do when they have to fight their way through fibrous cell-wall material. This produces two results – both beneficial in weight loss. Food in a fibre-rich diet stays in the stomach longer; and it seems probable that the food is less efficiently digested as it goes through the digestive tract.

The second factor is less obviously helpful at first glance – but what it adds up to is calorie saving!

The cell walls themselves are totally indigestible and do not provide calories. This factor is taken into account in giving the calorie values of carbohydrate foods. However, it seems highly likely that some of the calorie-supplying substances associated with the cell walls are not digested either when a diet is high in natural fibre. This would help to account for some of the extra calories expelled in the faeces of those consuming fibre-rich foods.

So when you eat your F-Plan fibre-rich diet you get a greater and more filling bulk of food in the stomach, the food stays there longer, and it is likely that fewer of those potentially fat-producing calories are digested.

Yet *another* advantage is the prevention of stomach discomfort, often the trigger for diet-breaking snacks. Unless stomach acids have a job to do in digesting food they tend to cause discomfort, and dieters often find themselves turning to extra food to quell that unpleasant acidic feeling when the stomach is largely empty. Fibre-rich foods keep the stomach acids under control for long periods because those acids have to work longer and harder at digestion processes.

It is only when the fibre-rich food leaves the stomach that it starts passing through the body at a faster pace, giving the well-documented health benefits. It stays longer where you need it to stay – in the stomach – and moves more swiftly where you need it to move more swiftly, through the intestine and bowel.

But we are far from being at the end of the chain of slimming benefits that are achieved by a diet rich in natural fibre. There is the blood factor, too, which can also provide a major benefit, as you will learn in the next chapter.

6

Rebound hunger – how fibre beats it

One of the major problems which gave carbohydrate foods in general the reputation of being fattening would be described by doctors as 'rebound hypoglycaemia'. The rest of us might put the same thing in much more simple terms by voicing that popular complaint, 'When you've eaten a Chinese meal you feel hungry again in a couple of hours.' This kind of comment might well follow a Chinese meal consisting largely of white processed rice. Carbohydrate foods – it used to be thought *all* carbohydrate foods – do indeed have a tendency to produce a rebound hunger. There is a scientific explanation.

One of the processes of digestion is to reduce food to a substance which can be absorbed in the bloodstream as sugar. Blood sugar needs to be kept up to the correct level in order to allow both body and mind to function correctly, and the body is very clever at informing us of its requirements. Hence when blood sugar drops below the required level the body sends out signals which are interpreted by the mind as 'I am feeling hungry.' Blood-sugar level is one of the major physical factors in determining the state of hunger. Generally, when the blood-sugar level is high we don't feel hungry – when it is low, we do.

All carbohydrates, sugars and starches are converted into blood sugar. The only difference is that sugars and starches, in the form of refined carbohydrate foods, are more quickly converted into blood sugar. After a meal consisting largely of refined carbohydrate food the blood-sugar level goes up very quickly, which would seem to be a good thing in satisfying the appetite. But then comes the snag.

The body has to have control mechanisms to regulate all its functions. Mechanisms to excrete an appropriate quantity of the water we drink, for instance; otherwise, since we tend to drink so much more than we require, we would eventually burst. Similarly, mechanisms to excrete at least most of the excess salt that we eat, since most of us consume about ten times the amount necessary for our bodily needs.

Blood-sugar level goes up on the digestion of food. But if it were to go up and up and up the blood would become absolutely saturated with sugar which would do us no good at all. Therefore we have a control mechanism to bring down blood-sugar level when it begins to reach unhealthy peaks. This control mechanism involves the substance called insulin, secreted by the pancreas.

When the blood-sugar level shoots up rapidly, the pancreas hurries into action and secretes a large quantity of insulin to keep the situation under control. Insulin in the bloodstream reduces the quantity of blood sugar. All is well for an hour or so. But after about two hours the excess amount of insulin in the blood tends to have an effect which isn't at all helpful to the person seeking to control hunger and food intake. It suppresses the blood-sugar level – not just back to the level before the meal, but even *lower* than the pre-meal level.

This is what is known as rebound hypoglycaemia. On the basis of this scientific fact you can readily understand why many doctors have for years discouraged overweight people from eating carbohydrate-rich foods. However, during all those years of 'cut your carbohydrates' advice, which impressed itself so much on the British public that many people are still overwhelmed with guilt at the sight of a slice of bread or a potato, all high-carbohydrate foods were grouped together as culprits in causing this rebound hunger which led to excessive eating.

More recent research has shown that it is only some carbohydrate foods which cause this problem, not all of them. No prizes for guessing that it is the refined sugary and starchy foods which cause this rebound hunger, and natural fibre-rich foods which do not. The latter are more slowly converted into blood sugar, mainly because of the digestive processes described in the previous chapter. This may well be the reason why the rebound hunger problem does not arise when carbohydrate foods are consumed in their natural fibre-rich form. Whatever the reason, repeated tests have shown that the inclusion of sufficient dietary fibre in meals prevents the excessive output of insulin which so often leads to hunger and snack-eating on diets in which the carbohydrates are processed and refined.

. . . Yet another reason why dietary fibre helps to control your hunger and your weight.

7

The fibre calorie saving

Once the residue of a meal rich in natural fibre leaves the stomach after its lengthy residence there, it speeds down the intestine at a faster pace. In doing so it saves the dieter from the common curse of constipation, mainly caused by lack of bulk in normal slimming diets. Medical research, which you will read about later in this book, indicates that this faster and more efficient transit may well be helpful in preventing many much more serious illnesses of the lower intestine and bowel, including cancer.

When the faeces are finally expelled, many studies have shown that this waste matter has a higher calorie content than that excreted by people following a normal Western diet containing refined carbohydrates.

Happily for most of us, who are inclined to overeat occasionally or frequently, all the calories consumed in food are not used by the body for energy or fat storage. There is a natural wastage of at least five per cent on any diet. But tests so far have clearly shown that dietary fibre increases the wastage and indicated that generally the higher the fibre content the higher the wastage of calories.

In one scientific experiment it was found that a daily increase of 10g of dietary fibre, by the addition of more fruit, vegetables and wholemeal bread to an ordinary Western diet, increased the number of calories excreted in a bowel movement by nearly 90. With still more additional dietary fibre, 32g a day, the stools were found to contain 210 calories on average. However, it must be added that these subjects were consuming quite a large quantity of food and were not attempting to shed weight.

Just why there are more calories in the human excreta following the intake of a high-fibre diet is less than fully understood at the present stage of scientific research. One source of these surplus calories excreted is obviously the non-digestible cell-wall material which forms much of the dietary fibre itself. This is taken into account when calorie figures are given for carbohydrate foods.

Scientific calorie charts, on which all those popular women's magazine calorie charts are based, speak of 'available carbohydrate calories'. This means that the non-digestible calories in the plant cell walls, which will eventually be expelled in the faeces, have already been subtracted in order to give a realistic calorie figure for each carbohydrate food. However, there are other, additional, calories in the faeces expelled after high-fibre eating, in the form of fat and protein. These are not accounted for in the calorie figures. Nor are they fully explained – although less efficient digestion in general is probably a reasonably accurate explanation.

But we have dwelt long enough on this final stage of the fibre slimming story. Suffice it to say that if you are cutting calories in order to shed weight at a speedy pace, every calorie counts. Every calorie that you *don't* make available to your body!

By following a normal mixed 1,000 calorie diet of protein, fat and refined carbohydrate foods you will be making most of those calories available to your body. But you will still shed weight at a good pace. By concentrating on the inclusion of a greater percentage of high-fibre vegetables, fruit and cereal foods in your diet you will be making less of those 1,000 calories available to your body. So you should shed weight at an even faster rate.

The dual aim of most dieters is to become slimmer *and fitter* by following a diet. No one wants to be slim and ill. These days the principal dietary health recommendations of all major nutritional bodies in the Western world are: Eat less fat, less sugar and more dietary fibre. That is precisely what you will do on the F-Plan. Later on in the book we discuss the fitness factor in detail. But now for your guide to losing weight the easy, speedy way – on the F-Plan.

8

How to get the calories right

If you are keeping strictly to 1,000 calories a day and not shedding surplus fat . . . then the chances are you are NOT keeping strictly to 1,000 calories a day.

This fact is not intended to hurt anyone's feelings, and still less, dear reader, to cast any aspersions on your honesty and integrity. The truth is that most of us eat (and drink) more calories than we think we are eating (and drinking) in the course of a day. What is more, it is very easy to make mistakes in counting calories. Then there is also that nasty little disorder called 'eating amnesia' which afflicts us all from time to time. Only recently I suffered a modest attack of it myself when recounting what I had eaten, or rather hadn't eaten, that day. 'Mummy,' my son observed after overhearing the conversation, 'if you aren't careful your nose will grow *very*, very long.'

So it is on the basis of us all (EVEN I!) being human and fallible that I have to announce that it is scientifically almost impossible not to shed surplus body fat when calorie intake is strictly limited to 1,000 a day. On the F-Plan it is even less possible – because if you are consuming 1,000 calories a day in the form of fibre-rich meals a percentage of those calories is not digested, as explained in previous chapters. Hence you are providing your body with less than 1,000 calories daily.

My confidence in making the opening statement of this chapter stems not only from scientific fact. Once when I was young, innocent and unaware of eating amnesia, 'weighers-wilt' ('I'll just take a guess at this – looks like two ounces . . . !') and other related disorders, I became so alarmed about all the people who couldn't seem to shed weight on 1,000 calories a day that I interviewed many of them, carefully selected a group of twenty of the most baffling and genuine cases, and incarcerated them in a health farm for a week. Then (somewhat sneakily) I had them fed not 1,000 but 1,500 calories daily.

All but two of them shed weight.

The reassuring message from this cautionary tale is that if you are overweight and use the F-Plan calorie tables correctly, as instructed, you simply cannot fail to shed surplus body fat. Health disorders which prevent weight loss are very rare. Almost certainly if you were suffering from such an illness you would have other symptoms to indicate that you were unwell.

The reason why people sometimes think they can't shed weight on a strict calorie ration of 1,000 daily is that they are guessing at the weight – and thus the calorie content – of their portions of food, or forgetting to add in the calories provided by little items like the butter spread on that bread, or the milk in all those cups of tea; or they fail to realize that innocent-looking things like that canned soft drink or glass of orange juice, or the mayonnaise coleslaw served in the office canteen ('Can't contain many calories – it's salad, isn't it!') can add a sizeable number of calories to the daily total.

When people guess at the calorie content of a portion of food they tend to underestimate the calories in meat and cheese, mainly because there was such a deeply entrenched fallacy, persisting for so many years, that 'protein foods' like this could not possibly be fattening. Most people also underestimate the calories provided by fatty foods and fat-containing sauces and dressings. This is simply because the calorie content of these foods is so amazingly high. All fats – butter, margarine, lard, and all the oils including vegetable oils – contain more than 200 calories an ounce. An astronomic figure, when you consider that sugar, for instance, provides, weight for weight, only about half that number of calories, and that potatoes contain only 25 calories an ounce. But again, schooled by the incorrect idea that it is the carbohydrate foods which are the most fattening, many people will very much underestimate the number of calories in the butter-based sauce on their slice of fish, which looks like such an innocent dish.

By the same token, many people *over*estimate the calories provided by potatoes (cooked without fat), cereal foods, and even fat-free sweet foods. Most sweet foods like chocolate, biscuits, cakes and many puddings have a high fat content as well as a high sugar content, so their calorie cost is, indeed, extravagant. However, when sugar is present without much fat or indeed with none, as in a packet of fruit pastilles or some light desserts like crème caramel, the calorie cost is often lower than people imagine.

Of comfort to those of lesser virtue is the fact that pub drinkers, guided only by guesswork, tend to overestimate the calories provided by alcoholic drinks, while innocent orange-juice drinkers, or saintly souls who will 'just stick to a bitter lemon, thanks', often underestimate the number of calories they are consuming. This based on the deeply entrenched conviction that if it looks naughty it must be very fattening, while if it looks innocent or healthy it cannot be. This is not a totally dependable theory when it comes to calorie counting.

I make the distinction of 'pub drinkers' because home drinkers often pour much larger so-called singles and therefore consume *at least* as many calories as they think they are taking in – frequently even more. This applies to spirits rather than wine, for obvious reasons. And, of course, if the bitter-lemon drinker is insisting on one labelled 'low calorie', he or she is consuming hardly any calories at all and is to be congratulated.

From my own observations, made over many years, another great area of calorie error is cold food. We all associate salads with slimming. So if we are eating, for instance, a slice of calorie-crammed quiche surrounded by salad vegetable concoctions oozing with oily or mayonnaisey dressings we are still eating a salad, aren't we, so that can't be very fattening, can it? YES IT CAN. Most people very much underestimate the number of calories in cold salad meals served in restaurants, canteens and cafés.

As you will see from all these examples of overestimating and underestimating, guesswork is dangerous, on the whole, when it comes to calorie counting. I use that qualifying phrase 'on the whole' because there are some foods which allow you to get away with it, some meals in restaurants where you can and indeed have to get away with it, and some people who can get away with it. Let us deal with the people first.

The honest truth, never before revealed, is that there are two types of slimmer. One type can get away with near murder, at least for a while, and still shed some weight. The second type cannot get away with anything, and must keep very precisely to a set number of calories, weighing and measuring food carefully, in order to shed weight. Obviously there must be a third type, hovering somewhere in the middle, but you will be able to work this out for yourself by considering the following characteristics of the two extremes.

The CAN-get-away-with-murder calorie counter: This dieter is heavily overweight (by several stones), large in height as well as bulk.

He or she has been eating a very large quantity of food and has recently embarked on a calorie-counting slimming programme.

Big people who weigh a lot and eat a lot tend to shed weight very easily and speedily when they start cutting down on calorie intake. So even if they are inadvertently or wilfully slipping down a couple of hundred more calories than they intend in the course of a day, they might still find themselves clocking up a decent weight loss on the scales each week.

My message to them: Good luck, and as long as you are satisfied with your weekly weight loss by all means continue to do your own thing. But do be aware that being a little easy-going in working out and rationing your calories can easily allow you to drift down the slippery slope towards being *too* easy-going to achieve weight loss. Such is the frailty of most of our natures that once we take a toe off the straight and narrow we tend to slide off it altogether.

Also, be aware that this happy state of reward for only relative virtue will not continue indefinitely. The body adjusts to lower calorie intake during prolonged periods of dieting, with the result that weight loss tends to slow down. This means that, as we continue to diet, we must reduce calorie intake a little more in order to go on achieving a satisfactory rate of weight loss. This in turn means being even more strict and exact in measuring out the food and counting up the calories. So if your regular weigh-ins start to yield disappointing news, you know what to do.

The CAN'T-get-away-with-anything (darn it!) calorie counter: If you belong to this category you are probably a little person. Things are very unfairly stacked against the short when it comes to slimming. Not only do we display even two or three surplus pounds in the form of an enormous bulge – tall people can often carry a surplus stone without showing it – but we also tend to burn up fewer calories than people of larger height and frame. That means we have to eat less than they do in order to shed weight.

Being only 5′ 2½″ tall myself I too feel very strongly about the unfairness of this, but there is absolutely nothing I can do about it except to warn you that in these circumstances you do need to be very accurate in counting calories in order to achieve a good rate of weight loss. The same applies to anyone, tall or short, who has been dieting for a lengthy period already, and generally to those who are only a few pounds overweight. Weigh, rather than guess, is the general rule to follow in this situation.

Those referred to at the beginning of this chapter, the dieters who think they can't shed weight on 1,000 calories a day, almost invariably belong to the can't-get-away-with-anything group and are not following the essential rules of calorie counting sufficiently strictly. So this is a timely moment to list those rules. Even if you belong to the getting-away-with-murder group, the time will come when you have to follow the rules precisely in order to maintain a speedy weight loss. So here we go:

1. *Be aware that ALL foods, not just some foods, supply calories.* Every single food you see in every supermarket, butcher's, greengrocer's and fishmonger's in the land has calories lurking within. Fibrerich foods provide calories, too. Because this book explains the many ways in which fibre-rich foods help you to shed weight, I don't want you to imagine that they are calorie-free. In the bad old days of lowcarbohydrate diets, many people did, indeed, imagine that those saintly 'protein foods' were calorie-free – I have even known poor souls pouring down vastly fattening cream under the mistaken impression that it was calorie-free because it lacked carbohydrate! Let no similar mistake arise with the F-Plan. The foods which supply you with fibre also supply you with calories. Some of those calories are, in fact, wasted and won't add to your weight. But as we don't yet know how many are wasted, be on the safe side: count the full number given in the F-Plan calorie and fibre charts, and reap the advantage in speed of weight loss.

2. *Weigh your food.* Calories are worked out on a per ounce basis (or in grams, for the modern metric-minded), so how many calories you eat in a portion of food depends on the weight of the portion of food you are eating. WEIGH IT is the key phrase for the calorie-counter. Not weighing it is the key crime. It simply isn't possible to follow a calorie-counting method of slimming without owning some dependably accurate weighing scales – ideally, dietary scales, because with some foods like fats you need to weigh out very small portions.

Most diet advisers sternly insist that you weigh every single thing before putting it in your mouth (cigarettes and fingernails, only, excluded). My own attitude, stemming from a kindly nature, is more permissive. Frankly I think you would look pretty silly weighing out your lettuce when an ounce provides only THREE calories. So what if you go berserk and eat an ounce more lettuce than you think you are eating! Let us be adult about this and accept that, in view of the fact that even the very strictest diets suggest that you eat not much less than 1,000 calories daily, those three calories aren't going to make a jot of difference to your weight loss.

Sometimes the vegetables which are particularly low in calories are not particularly high in fibre. This means they don't do you much good, but neither do they do you any harm. Some vegetables, like cucumber, radishes and lettuce, are mainly water with the occasional vitamin floating around here and there.

Dieters have asked whether they can add these low-calorie vegetables to the meals in this book, and the answer is: Yes. Eat the high-fibre vegetables for their value in health and weight control, but by all means add more variety and colour to your plate, if you wish, with these harmless foods which don't provide enough calories to slow your weight loss.

On the other hand – and this is where many people go wrong – that tiny bit of butter that you sneak onto a crispbread IS going to make a difference because there are such an enormous number of calories in such a very modest quantity of fat. The best tip in using fats like butter, margarine or their lower-calorie alternatives such as Outline or St Ivel Gold is to weigh out half an ounce or an ounce each morning and make that your ready-calorie-counted ration for the day – saves a lot of fiddling around with small quantities. Ditto for the milk you are going to use throughout the day in all those cups of tea and coffee. However, I digress . . .

Earlier in this chapter I explained that with some foods you CAN get away with guesswork about quantity, and weighing is unnecessary. Which foods these are will become clearly evident when you look through the Instant Calorie and Fibre Chart, showing average portions, which starts on page 217. I suggest that where an average portion provides less than 20 calories you let yourself off the chore of weighing while following the F-Plan slimming method. Apart from these, weigh all foods you eat when using the F-Plan calorie and fibre charts.

Listed in Chapter 13 are the meals you can calorie count by guess-work when eating out in restaurants.

3. *Remember that many drinks supply calories, too.* These are every bit as fattening as the calories in solid food, and must be taken into account in reaching your daily total calorie intake. Happily, many drinks are calorie-free or near enough not to matter, and you can drink as much as you like of these (see Chapter 11 and the Drinks Calorie Chart).

I mentioned earlier that it is nearly impossible not to shed surplus weight on a total calorie intake of 1,000 a day when you are following the F-Plan method. I cited that 1,000-calorie total because, to my knowledge, all adults in normal health and circumstances burn up *more* than 1,000 calories daily. Shedding surplus weight depends on providing your body with fewer calories than it needs to keep going. This is the only way in which it can be forced to feed on its own surplus fat. Never believe anything else, whatever silly things you may read or hear elsewhere.

Different bodies have differing calorie requirements to function and fuel their energy output. Size, in both height and weight, is a major factor, and this largely explains why men use more calories than women. The latest scientific investigations into how many calories the average Briton is burning up in this modern labour-saving, sedentary age are yielding somewhat depressing indications.

At one time I would have suggested that everyone would shed surplus fat on a ration of 1,500 calories daily. However, some of my medical and scientific friends now suspect that some women burn up only 1,500 calories daily – so obviously, on this intake, they would maintain weight rather than reduce surplus fat.

However, I am not personally aware of any research revealing that adult British people of either sex or any size can live on 1,000 calories daily without shedding weight, whether they are aiming to do so or not. For this reason 1,000 calories daily is a pretty safe, 'can't fail' figure.

This does not mean, though, that it is the ideal daily calorie quota for every F-Plan dieter. In the next chapter you will find guidance on your own ideal daily calorie ration.

Exercise counts

In answer to a common question from those about to embark on the F-Plan: No, it is not necessary to exercise in order to shed weight. The F-Plan method can make you slim without additional exercises. However, having said that, I am very strongly in favour of increasing physical activity and am among those who suspect that its value in weight control has been much underestimated.

In my experience, the major mistake that dieters make lies in deciding that they *will* exercise once they get slim, rather than starting to increase their physical activity as they start to diet. We had a typical example of this during the F-Plan trials at London University. One attractive but heavily overweight young lady revealed that she spent most of her evenings chatting to friends in a wine bar while dieting. She *did* intend to join a nearby sports club, where she could swim regularly, as soon as she was slim, but meanwhile shyly admitted to feeling too embarrassed to be seen in a swimsuit.

The situation arising from this all-too-common attitude was as follows: in the evening she was placing herself in a situation of maximum temptation as far as diet-breaking was concerned – with time on her hands and food and drink all too readily available. There is nothing quite as bad as watching other people eat and drink what you are trying to avoid. Had she embarked on an evening swim instead, she would have achieved all these advantages in helping her to keep to her diet:

1. She would have been kept busy and occupied, and well away from the sight, smell and temptation of food.

2. She would have experienced the undoubted lift in spirits that results from physical exercise. Depressed moods are the most difficult moods for dieting, and such is the mood-lifting effect of exercise that it is even being used medically as part of the treatment for depression.

3. She would have burned up extra calories, thus helping to speed her weight loss still more.

4. She would have experienced that glow of virtue which is so conducive to easy dieting. When we feel pleased with our achievements we tend to feel inspired to achieve even more in the way of health and figure improvement.

I am very well aware of the sensitivity of anyone who is overweight. It can often arise even when people are a mere few pounds overweight. But if you are contemplating increasing physical activity for still further benefit to your health and figure, try to realize that those vast crowds of people who will scream with laughter at the sight of you in a swimsuit, or on seeing you jogging, skipping, enrolling at aerobics classes or even taking a brisk daily walk, exist only in your mind. The best time to start exercising is at the start rather than at the end of a dieting campaign.

9

Calories: how low can you go?

Hunger is a problem that simply should not arise on the F-Plan, even though you are restricting the actual number of calories consumed each day. This does not mean that you cannot possibly be tempted by the sight of a chocolate bar or the scent of a fish and chip shop, but you will more easily be able to resist. Because the calories consumed are in the form of particularly bulky, filling and satisfying food your appetite will not be sharpened nor your willpower lowered by actual physical hunger.

We live in a world where food temptations flaunt themselves all around us. They pop up in the commercials on the T V screen, on the usherette's tray at the cinema, in every other shop window. In the Western world, unless you are sitting in a canoe in the middle of the Atlantic it is almost impossible to be far from the sight of food. Even in that situation you would probably be rescued by a passing cruise ship, on board which they would stuff you endlessly with food to compensate for the boredom of the interminable view of the sea. Food, in our society, is used for many reasons other than simply to satisfy hunger. It is used for comfort, pleasure, socializing, celebrating, time-filling, seduction – to name just a few of the alternatives.

Obviously, the person who is not actually hungry is considerably less vulnerable to the temptations of our food-filled Western world. Psychiatrists studying shopping behaviour have found – not surprisingly – that the hungry woman is much more inclined to succumb to impulse food buys. She generally fills her supermarket trolley more fully when she shops just before a meal than if she shops shortly after one, when her hunger is fully satisfied. Supermarket chiefs, always seeking new ways to cram more food down us, would be wise to offer a special shop-before-lunch discount!

When you are eating a fibre-rich diet there are restraining limits on how many calories you can actually manage to consume in a day – even if you aren't trying to shed weight. This was illustrated most illuminatingly by a recent study in which a group of people were asked to eat more than a pound of potatoes each day (baked in their skins, not fried) in addition to whatever other food they could manage to eat. By adding these potatoes, a bulky food of reasonably high-fibre content, they actually lost some weight over a three-month period! The potatoes were so filling that there wasn't a great deal of room left for all the other foods they usually ate.

This was impressive. But it certainly wouldn't be fair to claim that all you need to do in order to shed surplus weight is to add sufficient fibre-rich foods to your diet – or switch from refined carbohydrate foods to natural fibre-rich foods like wholemeal bread.

In the future, when you have become slim, the change from refined carbohydrate foods to their high-fibre alternatives should be sufficient to keep you that way. Certainly it will do so if you also put some restraints on your intake of fats. This is clearly indicated by the natural slenderness of those among the Third World societies who live on plentiful supplies of foods high in fibre content. So the F-Plan does have a great stay-slim bonus. Food preferences are very much dictated by habit, and those who get into the habit of choosing the fibre-rich foods gradually come to prefer them.

However, most people aiming to shed surplus weight are also aiming to do so reasonably swiftly. To be frank, the basic aim of most dieters is to shed two tons of weight by yesterday! This attitude is understandable, and slimming experts who drearily continue to tell us to 'be satisfied just to lose weight slowly: half a pound a week is enough' have little or no understanding of human psychology.

The F-Plan requires less actual effort than any other slimming diet you have followed before. But all slimming diets – the F-Plan included – require some degree of conscious effort and self-control. In order to sustain effort, in this and all other areas of life, we need the feedback of reward – ideally, short-term reward rather than some far distant pot of gold, way off at the end of the rainbow. The essential reward for the dieter is that weekly weight loss. There are few joys in life to compare with that of stepping on the scales and discovering that you weigh measurably less this week than you did last.

A miserable half pound is barely recordable. Any seasoned dieter knows full well that she can 'cheat' that weight off the normal set of bathroom scales by shifting her stance a little or rushing off to empty the bladder, remove the dentures and so on. Yes, don't think we weren't watching you . . . A measurable weight loss needs to be at least in the region of 2lb a week in order to provide that reward so essential to sustained effort. You can't 'cheat' off 2lb! In slimming, success tends to breed success and vice versa. Every slimming club leader knows that it is the member who registers a good weight loss at her weekly weigh-in who is most likely to keep up her dieting and return to the club next week, while the member who records a disappointingly low weight loss is the most likely to drop out. In dieting, failure does not make us try harder. Usually, it makes us give up.

On the F-Plan we are aiming for an average weekly weight loss in the region of 3lb in order to keep spirits up as weight goes down. The loss could well be considerably higher, particularly if you are male or heavily overweight; but over-high expectations can be just as demoralizing as very slow weight loss, so we are taking a restrained attitude.

On the F-Plan the calories will be consumed in food which is more filling, and your body will waste more of them than on other slimming diets. However, we recommend that you keep to the usual recommended calorie intakes for weight loss, and reap the additional advantages in ease and speed, rather than try to eat even fewer calories than usually recommended in a diet. Remember, most dieters fail to stay the course. The F-Plan's extra filling power can most help you by getting you right to slim-weight target. The 'easy' diet is the one that succeeds, because it is the one you continue to follow until you are slim.

Frankly, the only people I can think of who need to go as low as 850 calories a day in order to achieve a pacey weight loss on the F-Plan are small, rather sedentary women, only a few pounds overweight, and those struggling off the last few pounds of excess weight after a prolonged dieting campaign. In these circumstances, increasing energy expenditure helps, too – by which I mean generally moving around as much as possible, doing a lot of brisk walking and speeding this up to running pace if you are young.

To shed surplus weight with the F-Plan, allow yourself a maximum of 1,500 calories a day and a minimum of 1,000 calories (or less only if medically supervised) a day. You may choose to set your daily calorie intake anywhere between those two limits. These recommendations will guide you to your own ideal daily calorie limits for successful weight loss.

Allow yourself 1,500 calories daily

*   If you are male, of at least medium height, and more than half a stone overweight. Men have a greater daily calorie requirement than women, so they can shed weight on more generous slimming diets and generally record considerably larger weekly weight losses. This is unfair, but something that even Women's Liberation cannot change. Few men could fail to shed weight at a satisfactory rate on a daily allowance of 1,500 calories.

*   If you are female, more than two stones overweight, and just embarking on a weight-loss programme – as opposed to switching from another slimming diet on which you have already lost some of your surplus weight. The more heavily overweight people are, the more swiftly they can shed surplus fat on a slimming diet. This rate of loss tends to slow down as weight goes down and the metabolism adjusts, to some degree, to dieting. So if you are starting out with a good deal of weight to shed, it is wise to allow scope for reducing calorie intake in the later stages of dieting. Start on 1,500 calories daily, and work your way gradually down to 1,000 daily in order to maintain a good, encouraging rate of loss.

Set your daily calorie intake between 1,000 and 1,500 (if you wish) by taking into account the following:

These factors tend to increase speed of weekly weight loss on a diet
*   Being male.
*   Being heavily overweight.
*   Being at the start of a slimming programme, rather than at a midway stage.
*   Being in the habit of eating a generous quantity of food – the more you have been eating the greater the initial weight loss impact when you switch to a slimming diet.
*   Being involved in a job which necessitates a good deal of physical

activity (housework, unfortunately, does not rate high in this way, in these days of mod. cons.), or taking part in a good deal of sport or walking (that ten-minute daily dozen doesn't really rate here, either).

Allow yourself 1,000 calories daily

* If you are a small man, with only a few pounds of surplus weight, and are in a big hurry to lose it.
* If you are female and less than one stone overweight.
* If you are female and more than a stone overweight, but have already been dieting and have lost a stone or more on any other slimming method.

Reduce calorie intake to 850 if you must, but ONLY in these circumstances:

* If you are just thinking in terms of an occasional day, maybe a couple of days a week. Our desire for food tends to vary from day to day. On some days it is easy to eat very little, on others it is difficult to keep to even the most generous diet. It seems sensible to take advantage of the good days in order to make allowance for any excess eating on the difficult days, and dieting calorie intake can be averaged out on a weekly basis. If you eat more on some days and less on others, you will shed weight just as successfully as if you stuck to the same number of calories each day.

* If you are only planning to follow the F-Plan for a week or two to polish off a modest weight problem of just a few pounds. If you have been following a normal varied British pattern of eating you have probably been consuming less dietary fibre than you need for health protection, but it is unlikely that you are deficient in minerals and vitamins. In those circumstances, vitamin and mineral deficiencies do not crop up in a couple of weeks. However, on a calorie intake of below 1,000 a day it is a reasonable idea to take a multi-vitamin pill with iron – just to keep your mother, and me, happy.

These factors tend to slow speed of weight loss on a diet

* Being female.
* Being only a few pounds overweight.
* Being at the tail-end of a slimming campaign. Those last few pounds can prove the most stubborn, but the F-Plan will help.
* Having a naturally restrained appetite, which probably means that you are only a few pounds overweight and have gained this weight over a lengthy period. We all think we eat less than we do!
* Being a sedentary type of person. This doesn't just mean doing a sedentary job but refers rather to the type of person (who could well be a housewife, doing a basically non-sedentary type of job) who calls the children to bring something from the next room rather than getting up herself, or who goes to great lengths to avoid journeys up and down stairs, or who will drive round for five minutes to find a parking spot near the exit of the car park rather than walk for two minutes . . . The sum total of all those little movements makes a big difference to daily calorie expenditure and varies a good deal among individuals. The people who move a good deal are often described as being 'full of nervous energy'. It is not the so-called 'nervous' aspect that burns up the calories, but the frequent physical movement. These always-on-the-move people are usually slim.

10

Fibre: how high can you go?

Although statistics on dietary fibre intake were not recorded until 1919, the Royal College of Physicians thinks it probable that it has halved in Britain since the middle of the last century.

Today, the average intake of 20g a day puts us among the lowest fibre-consumers in the world. Indeed, it is quite difficult to find nations who eat less dietary fibre than the British, apart from the Swedes (14g daily) and Masai warriors, who are thought to eat practically none! U.S. citizens score a little higher than we do, with an average intake of 27g daily. But this is still modest compared with the quantity thought to have been consumed by our ancestors and the quantity being consumed, today, by societies in the underdeveloped world.

Surveys of these societies sometimes reveal remarkably high intake figures – 130g a day among the Kikuyu of Kenya and a staggering 150g daily among the Buganda of Uganda, for instance. Generally, however, people of the poorer African and Asian countries consume two to three times our quantity of fibre. Their intake of 40g to 60g daily is thought, by many medical experts and eminent medical authorities, to be highly significant in relation to the fact that major killers of the Western world, like cancer of the bowel and heart disease, are virtually unknown in these high fibre consuming societies. And so is obesity!

Just because you are British you can't even assume you are eating your 20g a day. This is an average figure. Individual variations are great. Surveys show that some Britons are consuming as little as 6g daily. What is worse, if you are concerned about your excess weight you are likely to be among the lower consumers of dietary fibre. Studies have indicated that the weight conscious, brainwashed by years of 'cut out those carbohydrates' advice, tend to avoid the bread and potatoes which supply a good deal of the fibre in most people's diets.

Dieting and nutritional fallacies die hard. As you embark on the F-Plan you might have to work quite energetically to convince yourself that the supposed virtues of the old low-carbohydrate method of dieting have been disproved by recent research. Medical experts no longer approve of this method of dieting – largely because of the limits it places on the intake of cereals, fruit and root vegetables. Bread (if it is wholemeal!) and potatoes are no longer considered the baddies in health and obesity. Fats and sugars have revealed themselves as the real villains.

And, when you think about it, did *you* succeed in getting permanently slim by struggling to cut out carbohydrates for all those years?

When you follow the F-Plan menus you can hardly fail to increase daily dietary fibre intake considerably – even if you don't bother to count the grams.

The average Briton's full daily intake of 20g is provided by the two pieces of fruit, and muesli-type mix called Fibre-Filler, which you are required to eat each day as part of this slimming plan. ALL the meals, from which you can choose freely, have been specially devised to contain a good percentage of those foods which supply a significant quantity of dietary fibre.

You should find it easy to consume 35g of fibre daily, and we suggest this as the lower limit in order to achieve the slimming benefits described in the previous chapters. Those keeping to a strict 1,000 calories a day allowance will usually find this to be a realistic target. Obviously, if you are eating more fibre-rich food you are likely to eat more grams of fibre. Those allowing themselves 1,500 calories daily might reach a fibre intake of 50g daily. We advise this as the higher limit.

If, after reading the advice in Chapter 9, you decide to keep to a very strict calorie intake of just 850 to 1,000 calories daily, you will find it very difficult to achieve the upper levels of the fibre recommendation and might even find it difficult to consume 35 grams of fibre daily. Don't worry. In these circumstances 30 grams daily will suffice. You are, you see, still consuming a very high *percentage* of dietary fibre. The average Briton who is not attempting to shed weight is consuming between 2,000 and 3,000 calories daily and only around 15 to 20 grams of fibre. So you will be taking in about twice as much dietary fibre in less than half as much food. You are on a high-fibre diet even on 30 grams a day. So the recommendations are a helpful guideline, not a biblical edict. No need to get too fussed about the odd gram.

All the meals on the F-Plan menu are fibre-counted for you. Don't worry about small day-to-day variations in intake, or aim for precise rounded figures – simply choose your menus to provide between 35g and 50g of dietary fibre each day.

11

What (and how much) to drink

On the F-Plan you are asked to drink a generous amount of calorie-free liquid, but only a very modest quantity of calorie-supplying liquid.

One liquid is obligatory. You must have half a pint of skimmed milk each day. This is to help ensure nutritional balance in your diet and, in particular, to supply calcium, because dietary fibre can hinder the absorption of calcium to some degree. There is no evidence of health problems arising from this particular factor, but on this healthy diet we want to take extra care to ensure all essential nutrients. You will also need to use at least part of this milk with your cereal breakfasts.

Doctors who prescribe high-fibre diets for health problems sometimes advocate a generous daily intake of fluid. One of the aims and functions of a high-fibre diet is to sustain a large bulk of semi-fluid matter in the stomach, and to produce more soft and bulky faeces. The fibre itself will ensure this but the extra fluid may help it a little – certainly the fluid has to come from somewhere, and it will do no harm if it is calorie-free. Calorie-free fluids do not add to body fat, hinder weight loss or cause fluid retention in those of normal health. The idea that they do so is one of the most persistent slimming myths of all.

Neither – to put another old fallacy to rest – is drinking with meals 'fattening', if the drinks are calorie-free. Drinking with meals the correct way can actually be 'slimming', in that it can helpfully add to the time it takes to consume high-fibre meals. The right way is to put down knife and fork in order to take a sip of water (or other calorie-free liquid) after a mouthful of food has been chewed and swallowed. The wrong, or 'fattening' way, to drink with meals is to use the drink to swill food down the throat before it has been swallowed, because then it will speed rather than slow the ingestion of food.

The reason why you are asked to be restrained in drinking calorific drinks is that these, even more than refined carbohydrate foods, have the opposite effect from fibre-rich foods in nearly all those steps in the consumption process which influence your degree of hunger. While fibre-rich foods are chewed slowly, calorific drinks require no chewing at all and go down the throat in a split second. While fibre-rich foods fill the stomach for lengthy periods, calories supplied in fluid alone pass through more quickly than any digested from solid foods.

Observers of eating behaviour have noted that people can take in very large numbers of calories in the form of liquids without noticeably diminishing their appetite for food at all.

Please read the following very important instructions about drinking while you are following the F-Plan.

Daily milk allowance

Your daily half pint of milk must be skimmed milk. This is essential. Half a pint of skimmed milk provides just 100 calories, while other kinds of milk can provide twice this number. Don't buy silver-top and skim off the cream yourself, because this doesn't provide an equivalent calorie saving. These days most dairies will deliver skimmed milk, so ask the milkman if he can supply it. Many supermarkets sell cartons of skimmed milk, sometimes sensibly labelled 'for slimmers'. You can also buy skimmed milk in powdered form; Marvel is one such product. So skimmed milk is now easily available, since people have become more aware of the dangerously fattening potential of full-cream milk.

Calorie-free drinks

All the following drinks are calorie-free, or negligible in calories, so they can be consumed freely on the F-Plan: water; tea and black coffee (without sugar, of course, though you can add milk from your daily half-pint allowance); all bottled drinks like bitter lemon, Diet Pepsi and Tab which are specially labelled 'low calorie'. These days most major manufacturers of non-alcoholic beverages produce special drinks of negligible calorie content for the weight-conscious. These include Canada Dry mixers, Energen one-calorie Drinks, Hunt's low-calorie mixers, Schweppes Slimline range, and Chekwate, Concorde, Safeway, Sunfresh, Tesco and Waitrose low-calorie drinks. But do check for that low-calorie label.

Of course the fashionable mineral waters – Perrier, Evian, Vichy, Malvern, and so on – are calorie-free, and are becoming increasingly popular in smart restaurants. So you can be chic as you get slim!

Bovril and Oxo do supply a few calories, but too few to be worth counting, and can provide a nice, hot, comforting drink on a dieting evening.

Real fruit juices

Fruit juices, other than lemon juice, are *not* allowed on the F-Plan. This is one of the ways in which this new method differs from diets of the past. The reason is that fruit juices are simply fruit stripped of its natural fibre content. When you drink orange juice you are getting all the calories which are present in the orange in the form of sugar, but with none of the fibre filling power. When you buy a small can of frozen concentrated orange juice you are getting the fibre-free contents of a large quantity of oranges, at a cost of more than 200 calories per can. Many people could easily consume a full can, diluted, during a thirsty summer day, and it would have little if any effect in reducing an appetite for solid food. To consume the same quantity of calories in the form of whole oranges you would have to eat about five of them. Obviously this would have some realistic effect in satisfying the appetite.

Manufacturers are doing the weight-prone no favour in removing fibre from fruits to make them into juices. Scientific tests recorded a great reduction in satiety level when subjects were fed apple juice (apples with their fibre removed) compared with the same quantity of apples eaten whole. The apple juice speeded the fibre-stripped apple through the mouth and stomach and also raised the blood-sugar level in a way which led to the rebound hunger factor described in a previous chapter. The apples produced all the weight-control benefits of low ingestion, high bulk and a lengthy period in the stomach – and they did not lead to rebound hunger.

By getting used to eating oranges rather than drinking orange juice, eating apples rather than drinking apple juice, and so on, you are establishing a good habit which will help to control your weight in the future.

Fruit-juice production is one of the 'refining' processes which can unfortunately help to increase our intake of calories on a modern Western diet. Lemon juice, however, unlike other fruit juices, is virtually calorie-free, as it lacks the sugar present in the juice of other fruit. Obviously you would need to sweeten this unless you have very eccentric taste buds – but saccharin sweeteners can do the job without calorie cost – making it an acceptable drink.

Alcohol

As far as health, fitness and fast weight loss are concerned, it is obviously better to avoid alcohol while following the F-Plan or any other slimming diet.

However, those are all physical factors. There are psychological factors to be taken into account, too. If you feel deprived and miserable by not being allowed an early evening drink, or a glass of wine with your evening meal, it is usually better to allow yourself a little alcohol while dieting. Otherwise it is unlikely that you are going to keep to the diet for very long. However, here is the vital F-Plan rule:

If you are allowing yourself a daily ration of alcohol, allow these calories in addition to a minimum calories' worth of food and milk from the F-Plan menus. First, allow 100 calories from the half pint of skimmed milk, and another 100 calories for your daily apple and orange. Then make up a minimum of 650 calories (more, if you are allowing yourself between 1,000 and 1,500 a day) from Fibre-Filler (see page 65) and the meals on the F-Plan menus. After that you can add the appropriate number of calories from alcohol.

Nearly everyone, female as well as male, can shed surplus fat at a good pace on 1,250 calories a day, and the vast majority of people will achieve a satisfactory weight loss on 1,500 calories a day. So nearly everyone can afford to drink a little alcohol while they are dieting, if they wish.

Alcohol does not provide any useful nutrients or fibre; hence the reason for consuming all your daily calories from food and milk, to ensure good nutrition, before adding any 'empty' alcoholic calories.

If preferred, calories can be averaged out on a weekly rather than a daily basis. For instance, as long as you average 8,750 calories a week you will shed weight just as quickly by having as many as 1,870 a day on Saturdays and Sundays, and only 1,000 each weekday, as you would by counting precisely 1,250 calories a day for all seven days of the week. This fact can be used to advantage by those who drink alcohol occasionally – perhaps only once or twice a week on social occasions, and not every day. Obviously, in terms of calories you can afford to drink a greater quantity of alcohol if it is an occasional rather than a daily indulgence.

You will find that the Drinks Calorie Guide (page 278) provides a very realistic way of measuring the calories consumed in the form of alcoholic drinks.

12

Fibre-Filler, the F-Plan's inbuilt slimming aid

While following the F-Plan you will be able to choose from a wide variety of meals to suit your own taste, in selecting daily menus. Nevertheless to make it really easy to reach your daily dietary fibre target of 30g plus, it is an excellent idea to have one regular, constant daily meal – breakfast is ideal because we tend not to vary our breakfasts – to supply about half the requirement. Add a couple of pieces of fruit each day as part of your menu, and after that it isn't at all difficult to include enough dietary fibre in your other two meals to succeed in your aims.

One of the great successes of the F-Plan method has been such a meal, a kind of home-made muesli, called Fibre-Filler. We think you will be surprised at the remarkable effect this relatively modest-looking quantity of food will have in satisfying your appetite for really long periods.

Your daily portion of Fibre-Filler provides 15g of dietary fibre, which is more than many Britons normally consume in a day. Most of this fibre is from cereal sources which are particularly recommended for their health value by some leading medical researchers. But fibre from fruit and nut sources is included too, which adds health and slimming value.

To make your daily quantity of Fibre-Filler, mix together the following ingredients:

For one day

½oz Bran Flakes
½oz bran
½oz All Bran or Bran Buds
¼oz almonds, chopped
¼oz dried prune (just one large fruit), stoned and chopped
¼oz dried apricots, chopped
½oz sultanas

Obviously you will find it easier to multiply the ingredients and make several daily servings at one time. But if you do, mix the ingredients well (the bran tends to filter down to the bottom, in its dry state), divide into daily quantities and store in separate plastic storage bags.

For eight days:

4oz Bran Flakes
4oz bran
4oz All Bran or Bran Buds
2oz almonds, chopped
2oz dried prunes, stoned and chopped
2oz dried apricots, chopped
4oz sultanas

Your daily quantity of Fibre-Filler tastes surprisingly good once you have mixed it with milk. If you like muesli-type cereals, you will find the taste pleasing. What is more, although the quantity for the day looks relatively modest in dry state, once it is mixed with milk you will find that it provides two good and satisfying servings.

We recommend that one serving (half the daily quantity) should be used to provide breakfast and a highly satisfying start to the day. This should keep you comfortably free of hunger right through to lunch.

The remaining half of the Fibre-Filler plays an equally helpful role in aiding willpower. Save this to be eaten at any time during the day (in addition to your other meals) when you begin to feel hungry and vulnerable to eating temptations. Many people will decide to save it until suppertime. Evenings represent maximum temptation for most slimmers, although around four o'clock in the afternoon, when the children come home from school, can be the worst time for many mothers who may be waiting until mid evening to dine with their husbands. In these circumstances, this might be the best time to eat the remaining portion.

Yet another way in which you might choose to use the second half of your daily Fibre-Filler is to divide it into two portions and eat one of these half an hour before each of the two main meals of the day. This way it will act rather like an appetite suppressant pill – or, rather, in the way pills should act if they contained sufficient cellulose. Fibre-Filler does contain a generous quantity of cellulose, so you will be feeling considerably less hungry when you start each meal; you will be able to eat more slowly and be very satisfied with a diet-restricted quantity of food.

The daily Fibre-Filler, made in the quantities given here, provides a total of 200 calories. These should be subtracted from your total allowance of 850 to 1,500 calories for the day.

Milk used with Fibre-Filler should be taken from the daily half pint of skimmed milk. You will find that only a small quantity of milk is necessary and that a quarter of a pint is quite sufficient to accompany the full daily Fibre-Filler allowance – an eighth of a pint with each portion. This will leave you a quarter of a pint of milk for tea and coffee through the day.

It is unlikely you will find Fibre-Filler unpalatable. It is a most important and valuable part of the F-Plan programme, so do include it. However, for occasional days when you might find yourself caught out with no time or ingredients (try to plan ahead to avoid this: you can easily carry Fibre-Filler with you in a plastic bag in your handbag!) we have listed a few alternative very high-fibre breakfasts in The F-Plan Meals.

Ideally, breakfast on half your daily portion of Fibre-Filler or have it mid morning if you dislike eating early in the day. Only when this is not possible should you have one of the alternative high-fibre breakfasts.

13

Eating out on the F-Plan

The F-Plan provides you with many easy-to-carry meals, like sand-wiches, and, hopefully, you will take your lunch to work with you while dieting.

However, business lunches may crop up from time to time – and also evening invitations which involve dining at restaurants. It is some-what unrealistic to expect to retire completely from social life. It is quite insane to imagine that you are going to sit in a restaurant adding up calories and grams of fibre. This is also quite impossible – nearly all restaurant meals are very low in fibre content and nearly every dish varies in calorie content from restaurant to restaurant.

So what are we to do?

The answer is simply to use the common-sense approach and avoid making the mistakes which cost the average slimmer so many un-suspected calories while eating out.

Forget about fibre while dining out. With your stomach nicely fibre-full from other meals you should not, at least, arrive at the restaurant table like a ravenous wolf. So this should help you in keeping the calorie intake low. To do so follow two simple guidelines.

1. Keep to the low-fat dishes.
2. Keep to the very simple dishes.

The first guideline is very important, not only for reducing your weight now but for controlling it in the future. The weight-conscious so often choose the most fattening dishes on the menu, in the mistaken idea that they were being virtuous. No, no ... they would not *dream* of having potatoes or a dessert. But they will select dishes absolutely swimming in butter or choose cheese instead of dessert. Fats are by far the most fattening foods of all. Even those tiny little protein-packed escargots or that leafy garden-of-Eden innocent aspar-agus or artichoke can be calorie-packed because of the luscious lure of all that horrifically high-calorie butter.

The old, and now much condemned, low-carbohydrate method of dieting had much to answer for in making social eaters fat. The idea that 'if it isn't sugary or starchy it can't be fattening' has accounted for the eating of many excess calories in restaurants.

Now, thanks to the publicity of the past year or two, people are beginning to realize that fats are dieters' enemy number one. Fats are more than twice as fattening as any other food. F-Plan dieters know that high-fibre carbohydrate foods are dieters' friend number one – they are the pioneers of a completely new and more effective attitude to food and weight control. But those old ideas do take a long time to die.

The reason for guideline number two, 'keep to the very simple dishes', is that fats can lurk in disguise in all kinds of sauce-covered dishes or recipe dishes. Did you know that taramasalata is crammed with fat? Or that avocado is the only fat-containing fruit – and that when you order it with an oily dressing, or with prawns in mayonnaise dressing, you are ordering one of the most fattening first courses of all? With that, or taramasalata, or pâté (also usually high in fat content), you could well be packing down more than 400 calories before you even start your main course.

That nasty shock should emphasize the importance of low-fat simplicity in restaurant meals while dieting.

All sauces, mayonnaise and salad dressings, creamed soups and cheese-containing concoctions should be considered highly suspect sources of excess calories. And Heaven knows the calorie mysteries of the East! Do you know how many calories are in Mr Singh's curry or Mr Wong's sweet-and-sour? Quite inscrutable, of course. Better give exotic Eastern eating a miss, if you are aiming at shedding weight fast.

Keep to the safest, simplest dishes when eating in restaurants while you follow the F-Plan slimming diet. Here is the regrettably modest list of best bets in each course.

Starters	Maximum calorie total per serving

These are the only really dependably low-calorie choices:

Consommé – any flavour (lovely and clear, so you can actually *see* that they have not sneaked in extra calories)	60

Oysters (for rich readers), each	5
Half a grapefruit (for poor readers)	20
A slice of melon, any kind	40
Any fresh fruit cocktail	60
Smoked salmon (if you can eat it 'neat' without *buttered* bread)	80
Parma ham with melon (a little more calorie-costly – but they are usually providentially mean with the ham), don't eat the ham fat	150

Main courses	Maximum calorie total per serving

Grilled Dover sole (not buttery), be assertive about any plain grilled white fish, tell the waiter that you do not want it served swimming with butter. Send it back if it is	350
Grilled liver (waiter's instructions as above)	250
Lobster, without one of those rich sauces (again, we give sensitive consideration to the problems of rich readers)	200
Plain grilled steak (6oz) with salad	300
Any seafood – crab, prawns, etc. – with salad (but be risqué! Insist that the salad is served totally undressed. If you add dressing, be very, very mean with it)	100
Omelettes (you cannot go too far wrong with an omelette, unless it is made with cheese, so no cheese, please)	350

Any vegetables can be ordered with these dishes, as long as you are sure they are not cooked or served with fat. A baked potato is very permissible, of course. But, without your low-calorie dressing to hand (you could smuggle it in a hip flask, perhaps), order a baked potato in restaurants only if you can resist that terribly high-calorie sour cream or butter. Be honest with yourself about this – rather than optimistic.

| **Desserts** | Maximum calorie total per serving |

The choice here is very simple. Ideally choose any fresh fruit – raspberries (fibre-high as well as calorie-low), strawberries, fresh figs, fresh fruit salad, but all without the cream, please. For those yearning for something just a little more sinful, the following are also dependably calorie-low:

Any fresh fruit sorbets	100
Crème caramel (when the waiter asks 'with cream, madame?' the answer is 'No')	200
Ice cream (but only if it is a simple, honest old-fashioned ice – not one of those staggeringly exotic multi-storey jobs, rising with layer upon layer of heaven-knows-what and terminating with a big blob of shaving cream)	150

Do not have cheese instead of a dessert. Most cheeses are crammed with fat and horribly high in calories.

14

The startling truth about US and THEM

Until very recently, the British, on the whole, were not all that keen on health. Of course, we worried about good health if we didn't enjoy it. But if we did appear to be reasonably well . . . well then, what is there to concern ourselves about? The national worry quota was already more than filled to overflowing by football hooligans and all those disturbing goings-on in the soap operas.

To be fair, there were two groups of Britons who were very concerned about health maintenance. The first, known as cranks, tended to swallow some extraordinary theories. The second, known as hypochondriacs, tended to swallow a large number of useless potions purchased from over the chemist's counter. But these were just two little subcultures, and in no way representative of Britain as a whole.

But *how* attitudes have changed, since the F-Plan diet was first published in 1982. This was the first occasion in which Britons in their millions had read, and begun to digest, the thought that all was not well with our eating habits in this relatively well-fed world of ours. The spate of major medical and nutritional reports published by governments and health authorities over the past few years has more than confirmed this suspicion.

Today, after a period of five short years, we are a health-conscious nation, exercising careful concern about our guests' cholesterol levels when we invite them round to supper, looking unconcerned as yet another jogger pounds us into the pavement as we take a stroll, and reacting with sheer open-eyed shock at the sight of a plate of bacon, eggs and bangers as we spoon down our own regular morning bran cereal – or dish of F-Plan Fibre-Filler.

Why has this major change in attitudes come about, and why all this concern about health in an affluent Western world where we can congratulate ourselves and count on our good fortune in having all the benefits of modern medicine to protect us – unlike the peoples of the developing world?

Many of us are old enough to remember the days when to contract tuberculosis – which many British people did – was to be given a virtual death sentence. This was still the situation as recently as the 1940s. Now, TB is practically non-existent in the Western world, and something we tend to forget all about, except on the odd cultural occasion when we hear Mimi coughing herself so touchingly and melodically to death in *La Bohème*, or read the life of a Lakeland poet, or dwell on the saga of the Lady of the Camellias. All the best people, it seemed, used to die of 'consumption' – as it was then called. And large numbers of ordinary people as well used to die of TB. Until recently it was one of the greatest of all killer diseases.

If you are in your forties you can also flash your mind back to those dramatic posters: 'Diphtheria is deadly – protect your child by immunization', and probably recall some child at your school who contracted polio and was crippled for life.

One of the most marvellous happenings of the past few decades is the way in which infective diseases have been brought under control and even virtually abolished by modern drugs and vaccines, better hygiene, safe water supplies, modern sewage systems.

IN THE WESTERN WORLD . . . that is. People in developing African and Asian countries do not have all our modern advantages and some infective diseases, which have become part of history here, remain rampant there. As the charity organizations keep reminding us, millions of people continue to die in Africa and Asia from diseases which are both preventable and curable. No wonder that poor people living in the traditional way in India and many African countries have a considerably shorter life expectancy than we – with our better living conditions and easily available medicine.

Or do they?

Prepare yourself for a major shock to your assumptions. It is true that a comparison of the generally accepted life-expectancy figures between the West and the Third World countries, or a comparison between ourselves and our grandparents' generation, would show that modern Western man has a great advantage in *average* expectation of life. But these figures are highly deceptive. Largely the difference is accounted for by a dramatic decrease in child mortality in the modern Western world, due to vast improvements in hygiene, protection against infective disease and plentiful food. In many Third World countries as many as three out of five children die before the age of five. Wander around any English country churchyard and you will see that here, too, child mortality was very common in the past, even at the start of the century. When life-expectancy figures are calculated, everyone who has been born and died is taken into account in arriving at the average life-expectancy figures. Obviously, the short lives of all those babies and children will have a great effect in bringing down the average figure – as even the least mathematical of us will be able to understand.

Those who are born in the Third World have a considerably smaller chance of surviving childhood than those born here – and the same was true of those born in the West a hundred years ago. There is an enormous difference in the child-mortality figures.

But what of the expectation of life of someone who has reached the age of forty?

It may surprise you to discover that the continued life expectancy of a forty-year-old man in Britain today has scarcely increased at all on that of a forty-year-old man living in Britain a century ago. Having conquered the killer epidemics of infectious diseases it seems strange that we do not have a greater life expectancy in this sense too.

Considering the rifeness of disease, the poverty and the malnutrition prevalent there, and all the medical aid available here, it is even more surprising to discover that the continued life expectancy of a forty-year-old British or US citizen is not considerably greater than that of an Indian who has survived childhood and reached the age of forty. This is true of the inhabitants of most of the developing Third World countries, in what might be described as 'normal' conditions, as opposed to the horrific periods of famine which have afflicted some African countries in recent years. In the West the general pattern is that we are rattling through merrily until our forties and fifties, and then . . .

The middle-aged are being afflicted by a great plague of modern Western illnesses, many of them fatal. These illnesses are not caught from germs and viruses. They seem to creep up on us gradually – for reasons that medical science is only now beginning to understand. They are known, collectively, as degenerative diseases.

Among the major degenerative diseases is coronary heart disease, the commonest cause of death in Western countries, killing about one man in four. The second great destroyer is cancer – cancer of the lung and cancer of the bowel being the most common fatal forms of cancer in Britain.

As well as the two 'big Cs', coronaries and cancer, there is a whole group of other degenerative diseases like diabetes, diverticulosis and other disorders of the bowel – and less serious but still troublesome problems like varicose veins, haemorrhoids and constipation.

The big factor that all these illnesses and health problems have in common is that they are virtually non-existent among Third World communities, living on what-grows-naturally in age-old traditional ways. However, when groups from such communities move to and settle in countries living and eating in Western style, and adopt Western habits, repeated surveys and studies have shown that, gradually, over the years, they too become equally prone to the 'big Cs' and all those other Western diseases.

It looks as if it must be something we are eating. Or not eating . . .

15

Thou shalt

Perhaps the main reason why we British have not in the past been particularly enthusiastic about positive health maintenance is that sensible medical advice on the subject is mainly concerned with telling us not to do things.

Not doing things is, in general, considerably more difficult than actually doing things. And much more dreary. We are wisely told not to smoke, not to drink much alcohol, not to eat all that sugar or salt or fat. All good advice, but all a matter of 'thou shalt not'.

Until recently, the only medically based 'thou shalt' advice was on the subject of exercise. Thou certainly shouldst do that. The benefits in weight control are obvious, the benefits in physical health undoubted, and the benefits even in mental health becoming increasingly apparent. Physical exercise is becoming known as a valuable tool in treating depression, and if you find that hard to believe just try forcing yourself into a vigorous half hour's sport, jogging or even just a brisk walk next time you feel low, and note the lift in your mood afterwards.

But, exercise apart, the medical profession has been mainly concerned with telling us not to do things, rather than to do things, and banning things rather than advocating them.

It takes a relatively modest amount of scientific evidence to have a substance banned. There are many people, for instance, leading experts among them, who would argue that cyclamates, a useful calorie-free substitute for sugar, were banned on somewhat flimsy evidence involving massive overdosing of animals. Many natural foods we have happily consumed for centuries would never be allowed to be sold in the shops today if they were subject to the same tests as modern drugs and edible substances. This caution obviously arises from the need to minimize the risk of long-term side-effects caused by seemingly innocent new substances.

Conversely, it takes a quite massive amount of scientific evidence to have a substance positively recommended for health. The general attitude of the medical profession is to be highly sceptical, question the benefits, divide into camps and argue bitterly among themselves, and continue scientific testing, surveying and debating for years before becoming convinced.

So when a large body of medical opinion is convinced of the positive benefits of any substance you too can be sure that the evidence must be pretty . . . well, convincing!

This is so of dietary fibre. Today, the medical establishment, in both Britain and America, is of the opinion that dietary fibre is of value in protecting us from the diseases of modern Western civilization. Any list of nutritional recommendations from any eminent medical organization in the Western world will consist of an 'Eat less of these' list (fats, sugar, salt, calories) and a single 'Eat more of this' item. The foods which we are advised to eat in greater quantities are those supplying dietary fibre.

It seems strange that this great surge of medical interest in dietary fibre should have occurred only in the past decade. For very much longer nutritionists have been delving into the values and virtues of vitamins, minerals and the proteins necessary for growth and repair of body tissue. But dietary fibre provides nothing of use in this way. It can be viewed simply as the packaging that encloses these goodies – and who gets excited about the packaging of anything, once it has performed its function of delivering and protecting the goods? Perhaps this was why its importance was overlooked.

When it became known that people in many developing countries remained free of the major killer diseases of Western civilization, it was obvious that medical research into these illnesses should start by delving into the question of what these people were doing, or not doing. One of the things they were doing, it transpires, involves one of man's most private functions – emptying the bowels. Medical friends have told us that one very eminent medical researcher grows so enthusiastic when he shows colour slides of stools excreted by rural Africans that comments like 'Look – aren't they beautiful' fly from his lips during his lecture. Beauty is in the eye of the beholder, of course, and what he is seeing in his mind's eye, after years of study into world-wide distribution of disease in relation to diet, is the stool of someone unlikely to die from cancer of the bowel.

Third World communities who remain free of our degenerative diseases have been found to live on diets which contain a much higher percentage of carbohydrate than ours – carbohydrate obtained from cereals which have not been stripped of their dietary fibre, fibre-rich vegetables (potatoes and other root vegetables), legumes and fruits. The rural African or Asian, living on a diet like this, moves his bowels in a way which can only fill the constipated Western world with envy. Effortlessly, and daily, he evacuates nearly one pound in weight of soft stool – the kind of stool which overwhelms our medical expert with its beauty. In striking contrast the Westerner passes only a quarter of that weight in much firmer, harder stool daily . . . and often not daily . . . and often only with difficulty.

The transit time – the time taken for the food we put into our mouths to pass along the whole of the intestinal tract until the residue is excreted as stools – has also been found to differ enormously between us and them.

In rural Third World communities the average transit time is one and a half days; in Western countries it is about three days in young healthy adults; among the elderly it is often over two weeks.

But does this matter? Only a few years ago, in their efforts to quell the excessive and unhealthy use of laxatives, many doctors were insisting that it did not matter. 'Go when the good Lord moves you,' was the general attitude. 'Some people will move their bowels every day, others only once a week . . . just do what comes naturally.'

We know, from personal experience, that the British nanny and school matron were never really convinced by this argument. It was their view, and that of many an old-fashioned Mum, that the good Lord required a regular daily bowel movement. Come back matron, all is forgiven. It seems that he does. But not by straining, or discipline, or the use of laxatives. When food is eaten in the way that the good Lord grew it, this daily task is accomplished effortlessly and even joyfully.

It is strange how attitudes have come the full circle. People used to have an instinctive feeling that all that waste matter hanging around inside them could not be doing them any good. Hence the popularity, at one time, of some strange practices like collonic irrigation – and the excessive use of laxatives, which was, and still is, condemned on medical grounds. Then, because of these questionable and unnatural methods, doctors began to insist that 'regularity' did not really matter.

Now modern research clearly indicates that a good speedy transit time and daily effortless evacuation of soft stool is indeed a vital protective factor in maintaining our health.

Dietary fibre is the substance which makes the waste matter from the food we eat pass through us and out of us at the desirable, speedy, natural rate. This is one of the main reasons why it is now considered to be such an important protective factor in saving us from diseases of the bowel, like cancer.

Before you continue to discard 'the packaging' with Christmas morning abandon, eating those refined carbohydrate foods, read in the next chapter about the links that are emerging between dietary fibre — or the lack of it — and so many of our Western degenerative diseases and complaints.

16

Major illnesses linked with lack of fibre

In this chapter you will read about the links between intake of dietary fibre and the major Western degenerative diseases – links which connect the factors prevalent in those who fall victim to those illnesses, and in those who do not.

Most people are aware, for instance, that a major link between those who suffer heart attacks is that they tend to have a high level of cholesterol in the blood. This does not necessarily mean that the cholesterol is the cause, or certainly not the sole cause, of heart attacks. But the established association would clearly indicate, at this stage of research, that it isn't a good idea to have too much in your blood.

A diet rich in fibre tends also to be low in fat content because carbohydrate foods provide many of the calories. So these two nutritional factors go together in societies free of our Western ailments – and also in the F-Plan diet.

The F-Plan is a low-fat, low-cholesterol diet, as well as being a high-fibre diet. So it is also the diet to choose if you have sensibly taken to heart the well-established benefits of reducing fat intake.

Dietary fibre and cancer of the colon

There is a vast variation in the incidence of cancer of the colon in different countries throughout the world. In America it is the most common fatal form of cancer, in Britain it is second only to cancer of the lung. In many developing countries it is virtually unknown. There is little doubt, in the view of even the most conservative members of the medical establishment, that the cause of large bowel cancer is environmental and that the factors involved are related to economic development. The greater the degree of economic development, the greater the incidence of cancer of the colon.

No other form of cancer has been found to be more closely related to the Western way of life – and the Western way of eating. Research is showing that diets which appear perfectly all right in other respects may lead to processes occurring within the gut that could increase the production or the concentration of cancer-inducing substances – carcinogens.

There are various ways in which fibre-depleted foods are now thought to be linked with cancer of the large bowel. Firstly, the small stools of Western man will have a higher concentration of these cancer-inducing substances than the large diluted stools of the fibre eater. The slow transit rate of fibre-depleted diets is also thought to encourage the formation of these potentially dangerous substances within the body – and to leave them in contact with the gut for too long.

In short, the basic instinct which seemed to tell many people that they needed a good 'clean out', and that nasty things could happen while waste matter lingered around in the body, seems to have been largely correct. It was only the unnatural methods they used in order to combat the problem which were wrong.

Bowel cancer is invariably rare in communities passing large stools, and stool volume is always small in communities with a high frequency of bowel cancer. It is dietary fibre, of course, which affects this stool volume. In rural Finns, for example, who consume a relatively high-fibre diet, cancer of the colon is rare. They have been found to eat about twice as much dietary fibre as New Yorkers, among whom this form of cancer is rife.

Perhaps the most compelling evidence of all comes from studies of people who have moved from one country to another – Japanese who have emigrated to California, for instance – and adopted Western diets. Large bowel cancer is uncommon among Japanese eating their traditional diet, but it was found that, within a generation, Japanese eating the American way had developed a risk of large bowel cancer equal to that of Americans. This strongly endorses the 'it-must-be-something-we-eat' theory as against the theory of the genetic susceptibility to certain diseases of different races.

The strong dietary links emerge from studies of communities with high and low incidence of this form of cancer. Those at high risk are eating a lot of fat and very little dietary fibre. Those at low risk are doing just the reverse. All the evidence available clearly suggests that excessive fat in the diet increases the risk of developing large bowel cancer and that fibre provides protection against it. The Royal College of Physicians has gone on record as stating that 'there are reasonable grounds for the statement that, in genetically susceptible persons, large bowel cancer could be favoured by a fibre-depleted diet'. Though they add, of course, that other explanations for the prevalence of this cancer in Westernized countries are possible.

This statement, from such a conservative and distinguished authority, certainly puts the idea that dietary fibre is beneficial well beyond the 'crank threshold'. For all sensible people it would clearly suggest that more thought should be given to the fibre content not only of their own diets, but of those of their children.

Dietary fibre and coronary heart disease

Coronary heart disease is essentially a modern Western disease and was rare, even in Western countries, until after the First World War. Today it is the commonest cause of death in the West. It remains almost unknown among rural Africans and is uncommon in most rural communities in Asia. The evidence suggests that a variety of factors in our modern Western environment – cigarette smoking, diet, sedentary living, soft water, stress – may be involved. In our diets, emphasis has for many years been laid on the intake of saturated fat as the major danger factor, but this is certainly not the whole explanation.

When a project researching into the cause of this disease carefully examined a group of men in London, recording their way of life and following their subsequent history for twenty years or until they died, the strongest risk factor for coronary heart disease was found to be smoking and the strongest protective factor the intake of cereal fibre.

The dietary fibre connection is not in any way as clear and direct as it is in the evidence concerning cancer of the colon. But what evidence has emerged about dietary fibre certainly puts it among the 'good guys', helping to protect us from heart disease, as opposed to the 'bad guys' like animal fats and smoking.

The 'good guys' so far seem to consist of a team of two.

Bad guys (factors which are thought possibly to increase risk of coronary heart disease)

Being overweight; smoking; suffering from stress; eating too much animal fat; eating too much cholesterol-containing food (like eggs); eating too much salt; eating too much refined sugar; sedentary living.

Good guys   (factors which are thought to help prevent coronary heart disease)
Taking sufficient prolonged exercise; consuming sufficient dietary fibre.

One of the reasons for the beneficial effect of dietary fibre is that it reduces the absorption of cholesterol – but there are other ways, too, in which it would appear to perform useful functions in keeping the heart healthy.

The evidence in favour of dietary fibre as a preventative measure in heart disease is not strong enough to be conclusive at this stage, but is certainly strong enough to be thought-provoking.

Diverticular disease of the colon

This is another of those modern Western diseases that seems to have mushroomed up from nowhere over the past fifty years. But only over here – not over there. It is almost unknown in Africa and Asia, while in the West, from being relatively rare as recently as the 1920s, it has now become the commonest disorder of the large intestine. It is said to be present, although usually without symptoms, in one in ten people over the age of forty, and in one in three over the age of sixty.

Constipation is now recognized as the underlying cause of this disease – and fibre-depleted diets are recognized as the major cause of constipation.

It is the effort and pressure which the bowel-wall muscle has to exert in propelling onward the firm faeces produced by a Western diet (rather than the soft and voluminous matter produced by fibre-rich diets) which has been found to be the cause of this illness.

In relation to diverticular disease the beneficial role of dietary fibre is very clear. Today a fibre-rich diet, often including bran, is not only advocated as a preventative measure: it is also widely used in the treatment of this disease. Since the advent of treatment with bran, fewer patients have required surgery for the complications of diverticular disease.

Dietary fibre and diabetes

Having read earlier about the 'rebound hunger' factor involved in diets consisting of large quantities of refined carbohydrate foods, you will already have gained some clue to the role that dietary fibre can play in the prevention and control of adult-onset diabetes, particularly common among overweight people.

In Western populations a fairly large proportion of people develop difficulty in utilizing carbohydrates in their diets during middle age. This difficulty is caused by a fault in the insulin production of the body. Insulin, as we have already explained, is necessary to control excess blood sugar. If blood-sugar level rises too high then sugar also appears in the urine and the person may be regarded as a diabetic.

As well as diabetics, there is a borderline group of people who are better classified as having 'impaired glucose tolerance' rather than being frank diabetics. Though only a small proportion go on to develop diabetes, these subjects have an increased risk of death from cardio-vascular disease.

As we have explained earlier in the book, insulin response to the carbohydrate foods we eat varies with the speed of absorption of the carbohydrate. Any dietary factor which delays the absorption of carbo-hydrate may be regarded as beneficial – and here, once again, is where dietary fibre appears in a valuable preventative and protective role. Carbohydrate foods rich in fibre are absorbed more slowly than those from which the fibre has been stripped.

It looks as if the adult-onset type of diabetes is most likely to appear among those who eat refined low-fibre foods. Again, it has been found to be uncommon among those living on traditional unprocessed foods. In the United States, it has been found that a diet very rich in unrefined high-fibre starch has caused remission of the disease in 85 per cent of the adult-onset diabetic patients on which it has been tested.

This change of diet should not, of course, be attempted by diabetics except under medical supervision, and so far no juvenile diabetics have been treated successfully using this type of diet. However, more doctors are beginning to recommend more unrefined high-fibre starch foods in diabetic diets and once again it seems as if fibre points the way to a healthier future.

17

Little things that mean a lot

It is not the purpose of this book to provide a complete medical directory of all the illnesses that are attributed, at least in some measure, to lack of natural fibre in the Western diet. We simply want to emphasize that the medical indications for the need of more of this substance in our diets are strong and impressive. This is not simply a passing fad.

If you have not been impressed by the very positive connection between a lack of dietary fibre and the incidence of cancer of the colon, and the possible connections between fibre and heart disease, you are unlikely to rush off for a wholemeal loaf in order to prevent appendicitis or gall stones, just two of the other ailments being associated with our fibre-depleted modern diets.

However, little things which affect our vanity often influence us more strongly than major things which could affect our health. Possibly because we don't take an 'oh, that couldn't possibly happen to me' attitude to the former.

In our view, the advertising award of the decade should go to the brain who thought up the series of anti-smoking television adverts which did not even mention lung cancer, but drew attention to the fact that smoking gives you bad breath. Well done, sir! Possibly an HM government warning about bad breath would be more effective than the present slogan.

Certainly, the enlightened medical-research award of the future should go to any researcher who has the wit to do further investigation into the connection between smoking and the complexion. So far, one survey has clearly suggested that smoking makes the skin wrinkle sooner, but research seems to have stopped there. How amazing. How remarkable that it doesn't seem to have occurred to the medical profession that earlier wrinkles would be a motivation without parallel in encouraging the female half of the population (at least) to abandon the nasty habit.

However, it has occurred to us that to mention some of the unglamorous little things that can happen to you if you don't might be highly effective in getting you to eat up your dietary fibre.

For starters – varicose veins

We all know what varicose veins look like. Those who haven't got them certainly don't want them, and those who have them already certainly don't want them to get worse.

Oddly enough, the initial cause of varicose veins is not fully understood, but there are some eminent medical researchers, like Dr Denis Burkitt, who believe that the major cause of varicose veins is increased abdominal pressure caused by straining to pass small, firm, Western-style stools. Hurry off for the bran.

For male readers – haemorrhoids

There is simply no sex appeal in a haemorrhoid. Surprisingly little sympathy too – considering the discomfort haemorrhoids can cause. Wary sufferers will have learned to suffer silently lest they raise stifled giggles rather than sympathy.

Considering the nature of the ailment it will come as no surprise that one of the major causes is thought to be constipation and, again, the straining involved in evacuating a hard faecal mass. In recent years it has been found that a high proportion of patients suffering from piles require no further treatment once they have switched to a high-fibre diet and as a result pass soft stools that can be evacuated with minimal straining.

For the kiddiwinks – bad teeth

Most children are probably sick of hearing about bad teeth, but the guardians of their dental health will be interested to note that the Royal College of Physicians quite firmly advocates a fibre-rich diet which 'encourages mastication' for the good of the teeth. Those teeth were made to chew with. If they are not used in the way nature intended they become more subject to dental disease and caries; chewing fibre-rich foods helps to keep the teeth cleaner and free of plaque in a variety of different ways.

After years of medical doubt it is at last safe to say with conviction that an apple a day – along with the other fibre-rich foods you will eat on the F-Plan – does indeed keep the doctor away. And also the dentist.

18

The ever-after fibre factor

Probably the most depressing words that have ever been pronounced about any slimming diet are those enthusiastic phrases from well-meaning medics on the lines of 'This is a diet that you can follow for the rest of your life.' Normal human beings will discard all thought of even starting any such diet – instantly! Who on earth wants to think of following a slimming diet for ever.

Do not throw this book away. We are most positively not going to say anything like that. What we are going to say is simply that the parts of this diet which are easy and effortless and even enjoyable to you will become part of your normal eating in the future.

Quite probably you simply didn't realize that peas and beans and sweetcorn are such valuable vegetables, and you will now continue to eat them rather more frequently because you like them anyway.

Having tried bran flakes you might well find that you like them just as much as ordinary cornflakes. There isn't much difference in the flavour. And if you find that sprinkling on just a little bran in no way detracts from your bowl of breakfast cereal, then you will be tempted to continue to do so.

Preferences between wholemeal bread and white bread are largely a matter of habit. Having become accustomed to wholemeal bread during your F-Plan slimming programme you might well find that, by the time you have got slim, you have actually grown to prefer it.

Once you have shed your surplus weight you will be able to increase your food intake, and on a normal quota of calories it isn't at all difficult to increase your dietary fibre intake to 40g a day just by becoming aware of the fibre-rich foods – as you will during the following weeks. It is considered that something in the region of 40g daily should be quite sufficient to protect your health in all the ways which have been described, and to make it much easier for you to control your weight in the future.

If you are a parent it is almost certain that your increased awareness of the value of dietary fibre will start to influence the foods you provide for the family – and thus their habits and preferences in the future.

The major Western degenerative diseases don't happen in an instant – like infective diseases – but appear to creep up on us slowly as a result of years and years of bad eating.

Although you will never know it, it could be that the slimming diet you are about to embark on will prevent your own children from suffering from cancer of the colon, forty years from now. Quite a bonus, when you think of it.

19

The F-Plan diet rules

Here are the essential rules to follow in order to shed your surplus weight on the F-Plan diet:

1. Determine your total daily calorie intake at a minimum figure of 850 and a maximum of 1,500. Read Chapter 9 for guidance on your ideal dieting calorie total.

2. Choose your foods from the charts to ensure a daily intake of more than 30g of dietary fibre. Between 35g and 50g is the F-Plan recommendation, but this could be lowered a little by those on very low-calorie, short-term slimming programmes.

3. Have half a pint of skimmed milk each day. This supplies 100 calories, which must be subtracted from your daily total.

4. Apart from milk, drink only those drinks which are negligible in calorie content. These are listed in Chapter 11. (If you find it difficult to diet without enjoying a moderate amount of alcohol, refer to Chapter 11 for advice and guidance on how this can be made possible.)

5. Have two whole fresh fruits each day, either an apple or a pear, and an orange. No need to weigh these fruits; day-to-day variations will tend to balance out the calorie and fibre content. Subtract another 100 calories from your daily total for this fruit and add 5g to your fibre total.

6. Eat the daily quantity of Fibre-Filler – the ingredients and amounts are given on page 65. Divide this into two portions, each mixed with milk from the daily half pint; have one of these for breakfast and the other at any time later in the day. To account for the Fibre-Filler, subtract 200 from your daily calorie total and add 15g to your daily fibre total. Have one of the breakfasts listed on the following pages *only* if you don't have Fibre-Filler.

7. To get maximum benefit in making your diet easy, speedy and healthy, obtain your dietary fibre from a wide range of cereal, fruit and vegetable foods – rather than seeking to make up the total from just one or two very fibre-rich foods.

8. Choose freely from the calorie- and fibre-counted meals on the

following pages to make up the remainder of your daily calorie and fibre total. As you get used to the F-Plan method you will probably want to plan your own high-fibre meals and can do so easily with the calorie and fibre charts in the middle of the book.

This is all much more simple than it might seem from the previous, necessarily precise, rules. It works out this way. Your daily milk, two pieces of fresh fruit and portion of Fibre-Filler add up to a total of 400 calories and 20g of fibre. Subtract these calories from your total for the day and make up the rest from other meals. Also, make up your additional 15g or more of dietary fibre from the meals – so that your total daily intake of dietary fibre is, ideally, between 35g and 50g.

If you are dieting on 850 calories a day, choose meals adding up to 450 calories a day.

If you are dieting on 1,000 calories a day, choose meals adding up to 600 calories a day.

If you are dieting on 1,250 calories a day, choose meals adding up to 850 calories a day.

If you are dieting on 1,500 calories a day, you can choose meals adding up to 1,100 calories a day.

When you eat and how often you eat is entirely up to you as long as you keep to the correct calorie total and aim for the right fibre total. Some people prefer to save a large proportion of their calories for a big evening meal, and others prefer to eat small meals more frequently. 'Do your own thing' is excellent advice in dieting – because 'your own thing' tends to be the easiest thing for you, and the diet method that is easy is the one you will succeed in keeping to.

The F-Plan recipes, meal suggestions and charts on the following pages give you plenty of scope both for doing your own thing and eating your own thing, whether it is something as simple as beans on toast or a sandwich, or something considerably more adventurous.

A word about your weight loss

From the day you start F-Plan dieting you will start shedding surplus fat. But, because you are eating fibre-rich food, it may be three or four days before the loss of that fat becomes apparent on the scales.

The reason is simply a minor fluctuation in the fluid content of your body. Remember, fibre-rich food holds extra water, so two or three extra pounds of liquid retained inside you can easily obscure the same quantity of lost fat. Be patient. By the end of the first week's dieting the scales will start to reveal the true story of your excellent rate of weight loss, and from then on it will be downhill all the way to your ideal weight!

One little 'running yourself in' problem may occur as you switch to this healthier pattern of eating. Those who have become used to low-fibre food may suffer from a little flatulence for the first week or two. This problem should soon resolve itself as you adjust to the diet. If you do find this a particular problem during the early stages of F-Plan dieting, concentrate on the meals which do not have a high content of peas and beans until you have become accustomed to high-fibre eating.

Important health note

If you are overweight but are otherwise in sound health, it would be unrealistic to ask you to get your doctor's permission to diet. However, if you suffer from any health complications it would be wise to tell your doctor that you are planning to follow a high-fibre, low-calorie diet, and to ask his advice. Happily, apart from patients with high-grade obstruction within the alimentary tract, or with coeliac disease, dietary fibre in its natural state in food has not been shown to cause or exacerbate any human disease in the Western population. Its effect, as you will have read earlier in the book, is to protect you from ill-health rather than cause it.

The F-Plan meals

THE F-PLAN MEALS

The quantities for most of the meals on the following pages are given for a single portion. Experience shows that dieters very often prefer to eat alone rather than at the family table – contrary to the exhortation 'make this for the family too' beloved by diet experts.

As you read of the great virtues of dietary fibre in the prevention of illness you will almost certainly want to introduce more fibre in the general family diet. But it is generally more helpful to give meals for slimmers in single portions – and it is very easy to multiply up the quantities, of course.

Where a fairly lengthy list of ingredients is involved, and a little more time, *and where the recipe will freeze*, we have given recipes for four portions. This is to save you time in the kitchen, which is a very hazard-filled area for slimmers. The less time spent there, the better.

When you make these dishes, or other obviously easily freezable recipes which you particularly like, it is a good idea to cook several portions at one time and then divide them into individual portions and store them in the freezer in bags. A freezer well stocked with little bags, each containing a prepared calorie-counted and fibre-counted meal, provides excellent protection against temptation to break your diet simply because you haven't had time to shop for the right foods.

All these meals are grouped into sections based on the fibre-rich food which forms the main ingredient of the meal. In each section the individual meals are listed in rising order of calorie value. You will find the lowest calorie meals at the start of the section, the highest at the end. Any four-portion recipes are listed at the end of the appropriate section.

We have rounded off calorie values of meals to make it easy for you to add together your 450–1,100 calories allowed for the day (in addition to your 400 from Fibre-Filler, fruit and milk); we have also rounded off metric ingredient figures for easy measuring. The amount of fibre provided by each meal is given (in grams) beside the calorie count. Again we have done a little rounding off of figures to avoid decimal points.

The meals themselves are designed to cater for all tastes. They include some very simple meals as well as some more imaginative dishes. We believe you will find it quite difficult not to find a large number of meals which appeal to you, because no less than six cookery experts have combined their various tastes and talents to provide this selection of low-calorie, high-fibre meals.

The desserts can be consumed with an utterly clear conscience when you have calories to spare in your daily allowance. They provide you with fibre and healthy nutrients in place of the usual surplus calories, tooth decay and guilt.

On pages 206–211 we give some sample ready-planned daily menus made up from these meals, to show you how easy it is to keep to your preferred eating pattern and daily dieting calorie allowance.

Note. Where quantities are measured in spoonfuls we mean a *level* spoonful unless otherwise indicated. We use the standard teaspoon of 5 ml, the standard tablespoon of 15 ml capacity.

BREAKFASTS

F-Plan dieters should ideally breakfast on a portion of their Fibre-Filler. These fibre-rich breakfasts are only for those who want an alternative. Milk should be used from the daily allowance. For this reason it is not included in the calorie total.

PUFFED WHEAT PLUS BRAN

Calories 100; Fibre 6g

½oz (15g) Puffed Wheat
¼oz (7g) bran
½oz (15g) sultanas

ALL BRAN AND SULTANAS

Calories 150; Fibre 12g

1½oz (40g) All Bran or Bran Buds
½oz (15g) sultanas

ALLINSON'S HONEY BRAN

Calories 150; Fibre 9g

1½oz (40g) Allinson's Honey Bran
½oz (15g) sultanas

PREWETT'S BRAN MUESLI

Calories 175; Fibre 12g

2oz (55g) serving

ENERGEN BRAN CRUNCH

Calories 200; Fibre 7g

1½oz (40g) Energen Bran Crunch
½oz (15g) sultanas

BRAN FLAKES PLUS BRAN

Calories 200; Fibre 8g

1½oz (40g) Bran Flakes
½oz (15g) sultanas
¼oz (7g) bran

BAKED JACKET POTATO MEALS

All the meals listed in this section begin with a 7oz (200g) raw-weight potato. The potato is first baked in its jacket and then it can be used in one of the variety of meals which follow, either as an accompaniment to other foods (for example, baked chicken joint and sweetcorn) or stuffed (for example, with cheese and pickle). The baked jacket potato, on its own, provides 175 calories and at least 5g fibre – remember to eat the jacket too, because this is a good source of dietary fibre.

Baked potato served on its own screams out for butter or soured cream to moisten it, but since these are high-calorie foods, two low-calorie dressings which will moisten and add flavour have been given with the basic recipe. If these do not appear in your baked jacket potato meal and you wish to use one of them on your potato, just add the calorie value to your daily calorie total. Where they are included in a meal, the calorie value has also been included.

To complete one of the stuffed baked jacket potato meals you might like to add a salad, so we have included two low-calorie salads after the basic recipe, on page 105; just add the calorie value and fibre content to your daily totals.

BAKED JACKET POTATO – BASIC RECIPE

Calories 175; Fibre 5g

7oz (200g) potato

Scrub the potato well, then bake by one of the following methods:
1. Place the potato in the centre of a moderately hot oven (400°F, 200°C, gas 6) for 45 minutes or until soft when pinched.
2. Place the potato in a pan of water, bring to the boil, then simmer gently for 20 minutes. Drain, then place the potato in a moderate oven (375°F, 190°C, gas 5) for 10–15 minutes to crisp the skin.
3. Prick well all over and cook in a microwave oven on full power for 4 minutes, turning over after 2 minutes.

Serve the baked potato as a vegetable accompaniment, with one of the dressings listed below to moisten, if preferred, or serve in one of the following meals.

TOMATO YOGURT DRESSING

Calories 25

2 tablespoons low-fat natural yogurt
1 teaspoon tomato purée
salt and pepper
a dash of Worcestershire sauce (optional)

Mix the yogurt with the tomato purée until evenly blended. Season to taste with salt and pepper and add Worcestershire sauce, if liked. Spoon over the cut surface of a baked jacket potato.

CHEESY POTATO DRESSING

Calories 25

1 tablespoon cottage cheese with chives
2 tablespoons Waistline Oil-Free French Dressing

Beat the cottage cheese and dressing together until well blended. Spoon over the cut surface of a baked jacket potato.

ITALIAN COD WITH BAKED JACKET POTATO

Calories 300; Fibre 9g

7oz (200g) potato
4oz (115g) frozen cod steak
8oz (225g) canned tomatoes
1oz (25g) chopped onion
1oz (25g) chopped green pepper
pinch dried oregano or ½ teaspoon chopped fresh oregano
1 tablespoon bran
salt and freshly ground black pepper

Scrub the potato and bake in a moderately hot oven for 15 minutes. Meanwhile place the frozen cod steak in a small ovenproof dish or casserole. Chop the canned tomatoes and mix with the juice, onion, green pepper, oregano, bran and seasoning to taste. Spoon over the fish. Cover and bake with the potato for another 30 minutes. Serve with the baked potato.

COTTAGE CHEESE SALAD WITH BAKED JACKET POTATO

Calories 350; Fibre 8g

7oz (200g) potato
4oz (115g) cottage cheese (natural or with chives or onion and peppers)
1 walnut half
a few lettuce leaves
a small bunch watercress (about 1oz, 25g)
1 small onion, cut into rings
1 small orange, segmented and membranes removed

Prepare and bake the potato (see p. 99). Serve with the cottage cheese garnished with the walnut half and with a salad prepared from the lettuce, watercress, onion rings and orange segments.

GRILLED BACON STEAK WITH BAKED JACKET POTATO AND BAKED BEANS

Calories 375; Fibre 8g

7oz (200g) potato
3½oz (100g) bacon steak
4oz (115g) baked beans

Prepare and bake the potato (see p. 99). Grill the bacon steak without added fat until cooked through. Heat the baked beans. Serve the baked potato with the grilled bacon steak and baked beans.

HAM AND COLESLAW SALAD WITH BAKED JACKET POTATO

Calories 375; Fibre 11g

7oz (200g) potato
2oz (55g) sliced lean boiled ham
3oz (85g) firm white cabbage, shredded
2oz (55g) carrot, grated
2 sticks celery, finely chopped
1 tablespoon chopped fresh parsley
1 tablespoon Waistline Oil-Free French Dressing
1 tablespoon low-fat natural yogurt
1 portion cheesy potato dressing (p. 100)
½ carton mustard and cress

Prepare and bake the potato (see p. 99). Trim off and discard any fat on the ham. Mix the cabbage, carrot, celery and parsley together in a bowl. Blend the French dressing and yogurt together and stir into the vegetable mixture. Divide the coleslaw between the two slices of ham and roll the ham around it. Serve the ham and coleslaw rolls with the baked jacket potato topped with cheesy potato dressing and garnish with the mustard and cress.

PILCHARD SALAD WITH BAKED JACKET POTATO

Calories 375; Fibre 13g

7oz (200g) potato
1 portion cheesy potato dressing (p. 100)
4oz (115g) canned pilchards
2 sticks celery, chopped
2oz (55g) carrot, grated
2oz (55g) fresh garden peas or thawed frozen peas
1 tablespoon Waistline Oil-Free French Dressing
a few lettuce leaves

Prepare and bake the potato (see p. 99). Mix the celery, carrot, peas and French dressing together. Place the lettuce leaves on the plate with the pilchards and baked potato and pile the celery salad on top. Serve with the cheesy dressing.

BAKED CHICKEN, JACKET POTATO AND SWEETCORN

Calories 400; Fibre 8g

7oz (200g) potato
8oz (225g) chicken joint
2oz (55g) frozen or canned sweetcorn kernels
1 portion tomato yogurt dressing (p. 100)
sprigs of watercress (optional)

Scrub the potato. Wrap the chicken joint in foil and bake with the potato in the oven at 400°F (200°C, gas 6) for 30 minutes. Open the foil so that the chicken can continue to cook uncovered. Bake for a further 10 minutes. Meanwhile cook the sweetcorn as directed on the packet and drain. Remove and discard the skin from the chicken. Split the baked potato in half lengthways, and top with the tomato yogurt dressing. Serve the chicken with the baked potato and sweetcorn, and a few sprigs of watercress, if liked.

GRILLED BEEFBURGERS WITH BAKED JACKET POTATO AND PEAS

Calories 400; Fibre 10g

7oz (200g) potato
2 × 2oz (55g) frozen beefburgers
2oz (55g) frozen peas
1 portion tomato yogurt dressing (p. 100)

Prepare and bake the potato (see p. 99). Grill the beefburgers well on both sides so that much of the fat drips away. Cook the peas as directed. Serve the jacket potato with the tomato yogurt dressing, beefburgers and peas.

GRILLED LAMB CHOP WITH BAKED JACKET POTATO, SPROUTS AND CARROTS

Calories 450; Fibre 10g

7oz (200g) potato
4oz (115g) lamb loin chop
3oz (85g) Brussels sprouts
2oz (55g) carrots, sliced
1 portion cheesy potato dressing (p. 100)
2 teaspoons mint sauce

Prepare and bake the potato (see p. 99). Grill the lamb chop without added fat until cooked through. Boil the Brussels sprouts and carrots until just tender, then drain. Split the baked potato and top with the cheesy dressing. Serve with the lamb chop, mint sauce, Brussels sprouts and carrots.

LIVER CASSEROLE WITH BAKED JACKET POTATO

Calories 450; Fibre 12g

7oz (200g) potato
4oz (115g) lamb's liver, sliced
salt and freshly ground pepper
2oz (55g) onion, sliced
1 stick celery, chopped
8oz (225g) canned tomatoes
1 teaspoon Worcestershire sauce
2oz (55g) Brussels sprouts

Scrub the potato. Arrange the lamb's liver in the bottom of an oven-proof dish and season to taste. Put the onion rings and celery on top. Chop the canned tomatoes and mix with the Worcestershire sauce. Spoon with the tomato juices over the liver and vegetables. Season with salt and pepper. Cover and cook with the potato in the oven at 375°F (190°C, gas 5) for 45 minutes or until the potato is soft and the liver cooked. Boil the Brussels sprouts and serve with the casserole and baked potato.

STUFFED BAKED JACKET POTATO MEALS – BASIC RECIPE

Calories 175; Fibre 5g

7oz (200g) baked jacket potato (p. 99)

Cut the potato in half lengthwise and scoop out some of the flesh. Mix with one of the fillings described in the meals below and pile back into the potato jacket. Heat through in the oven for 5–10 minutes, if necessary.

Salad vegetables make an ideal accompaniment to these stuffed baked potatoes. The following two simple salads may be added to any of the stuffed baked potato meals. (Remember to add the calories to your total.)

MIXED SALAD

Calories 25; Fibre 2g

a few lettuce leaves
a 1in (2·5cm) piece cucumber, sliced
1 medium tomato, sliced
2 spring onions, chopped, or ½oz (15g) onion rings
1oz (25g) green or red pepper, sliced and chopped
1 tablespoon Waistline Oil-Free French Dressing

Arrange the salad vegetables in a bowl and toss with the dressing.

COLESLAW

Calories 50; Fibre 4g

3oz (85g) white cabbage, shredded
2oz (55g) carrot, grated
1 tablespoon Heinz Slimway Low-Calorie Salad Dressing

Mix the cabbage, carrot and salad dressing together until thoroughly blended.

SCRAMBLED EGG AND TOMATO STUFFED JACKET POTATO

Calories 275; Fibre 6g

1 egg, size 3
2 tablespoons skimmed milk
salt and pepper
1 medium tomato, chopped
7oz (200g) baked jacket potato (p. 99)
sprigs of parsley

Scramble the egg with the skimmed milk and seasoning in a non-stick pan. Stir in the tomato. Mash the potato flesh and mix with the scrambled egg. Pile into the potato jacket and serve garnished with sprigs of parsley.

FISH AND SWEETCORN STUFFED JACKET POTATO

Calories 275; Fibre 7g

3¼oz (92g) pack frozen coley or cod steak
1oz (25g) canned sweetcorn kernels
7oz (200g) baked jacket potato (p. 99)
1 tablespoon tomato sauce

Poach the frozen fish steak in a little water until cooked through. Drain and flake the fish. Cook the sweetcorn and drain. Prepare the stuffed potato using the flaked fish, sweetcorn and tomato sauce. Heat through in the oven if necessary.

SAUSAGE AND MUSTARD PICKLE STUFFED JACKET POTATO

Calories 300; Fibre 5g

2 beef chipolata sausages
1 tablespoon mustard pickle
7oz (200g) baked jacket potato (p. 99)
2 sprigs watercress

Grill the sausages well. Slice into small pieces and mix with the mustard pickle and the flesh from the potato. Pile into the potato jacket and heat through if required. Serve garnished with watercress.

CHICKEN AND PEPPERS STUFFED JACKET POTATO

Calories 300; Fibre 6g

2oz (55g) roast chicken
1oz (25g) green pepper, chopped
1oz (25g) red pepper, chopped
1 tablespoon low-calorie salad dressing
7oz (200g) baked jacket potato (p. 99)
2 tablespoons skimmed milk
salt and pepper

Remove and discard any skin from the chicken; chop the meat. Mix with the chopped peppers and salad dressing. Mash the potato flesh with the skimmed milk and seasoning to taste, then mix with the chicken and peppers. Pile back into the potato jacket. Reheat in the oven.

CHEESE AND PICKLE STUFFED JACKET POTATO WITH SALAD

Calories 300; Fibre 8g

7oz (200g) baked jacket potato (p. 99)
2oz (55g) natural cottage cheese
1 rounded tablespoon sweet pickle

Mixed salad
a few lettuce leaves
2oz (55g) sliced green pepper
1 medium tomato, sliced
1oz (25g) watercress
2 spring onions, chopped
1 tablespoon Waistline Oil-Free French Dressing

Prepare the stuffed potato as described on p. 105 using the cottage cheese and pickle to fill. Serve with the mixed salad.

PRAWN, SWEETCORN AND SPRING ONION STUFFED JACKET POTATO

Calories 300; Fibre 9g

2oz (55g) fresh or frozen prawns
7oz (200g) baked jacket potato (p. 99)
1oz (25g) canned sweetcorn kernels
2 spring onions, chopped
1 tablespoon low-calorie salad dressing
2 medium or 1 large tomato, halved and sliced

Thaw the prawns if frozen. Mix the mashed potato flesh with the prawns, sweetcorn, spring onions and salad dressing. Pile back into the potato jacket. Serve garnished with the tomato.

CHEESE AND BAKED BEANS STUFFED JACKET POTATO

Calories 300; Fibre 10g

7oz (200g) baked jacket potato (p. 99)
2oz (55g) baked beans
1oz (25g) Edam cheese, grated
a small bunch of watercress, about 1oz (25g)

Prepare the stuffed potato as described above, using the baked beans and grated cheese to fill. Serve with the watercress.

CHEESY GRILLED JACKET POTATO

Calories 325; Fibre 6g

7oz (200g) baked jacket potato (p. 99)
2 tablespoons skimmed milk
1½oz (40g) Edam cheese, grated
1 medium tomato, chopped
salt and pepper
grated nutmeg

Mix the potato flesh with the remaining ingredients, reserving ½oz (15g) grated cheese. Pile the mixture back into the potato jacket, sprinkle the tops with the remaining grated cheese. Place under a hot grill until the cheese has melted.

HAM, SWEETCORN AND CELERY STUFFED JACKET POTATO

Calories 325; Fibre 8g

7oz (200g) baked jacket potato (p. 99)
2 tablespoons skimmed milk
salt and pepper
2oz (55g) lean cooked ham
1 tablespoon canned sweetcorn kernels
1 stick celery, finely chopped
a few sprigs of watercress

Scoop the flesh out of the potato and mash with the skimmed milk and seasoning to taste. Chop the ham, discarding any fat. Add the ham, sweetcorn and celery to the potato and mix together. Pile back into the jacket and heat through in the oven. Serve garnished with watercress.

CHICKEN LIVERS AND MUSHROOM STUFFED JACKET POTATO

Calories 350; Fibre 7g

4oz (115g) chicken livers, chopped
1oz (25g) mushrooms, sliced
1 tablespoon finely chopped onion
4 tablespoons chicken stock
salt and pepper
a dash of tabasco sauce
7oz (200g) baked jacket potato (p. 99)
2oz (55g) white cabbage, chopped

Place the chicken livers, mushrooms, onion and stock in a small pan. Add the salt and pepper and tabasco sauce. Heat to simmering point, cover and cook gently for 5 minutes. Prepare the stuffed potato as described on p. 105, using the chicken liver mixture to fill. Serve with the chopped cabbage either raw or lightly boiled.

MUSHROOM, EGG AND BACON STUFFED JACKET POTATO

Calories 350; Fibre 7g

1 rasher streaky bacon
3oz (85g) mushrooms
1 egg, size 3
salt and pepper
¼oz (7g) low-fat spread
7oz (200g) baked jacket potato (p. 99)
½ carton mustard and cress

Grill the bacon rasher until crisp, and crumble or chop it. Chop the mushrooms and simmer in a little salted water for 5 minutes, then drain. Beat the egg with salt and pepper and stir in the bacon and mushrooms. Melt the low-fat spread in a small pan and add the egg mixture. Cook over a low heat until the egg is just set. Stir in the potato flesh and pile into the potato jacket. Garnish with the mustard and cress.

SARDINE AND COTTAGE CHEESE STUFFED JACKET POTATO

Calories 350; Fibre 7g

2 sardines canned in tomato sauce
2oz (55g) cottage cheese
7oz (200g) baked jacket potato (p. 99)
1 teaspoon finely chopped onion or chives
1oz (25g) frozen peas, cooked
salt and pepper
sprigs of watercress

Mash the sardines with the cottage cheese and potato flesh. Add the onion or chives, peas and seasoning to taste. Pile into the potato jacket and heat through in the oven. Serve garnished with the watercress.

SAVOURY MINCED BEEF STUFFED JACKET POTATO

Calories 375; Fibre 6g

4oz (115g) raw minced beef
1oz (25g) chopped onion
1oz (25g) grated carrot
1 teaspoon concentrated curry sauce
7oz (200g) baked jacket potato (p. 99)
salt and pepper

Fry the minced beef in a heavy saucepan without added fat until well browned. Drain off and discard the fat. Add the onion, carrot, curry sauce and 4–5 tablespoons water. Heat until boiling, then simmer, covered, for 15 minutes. Cut the potato in two lengthwise, scoop out some of the flesh and mix with the hot minced beef mixture. Season to taste. Pile back into the jackets and serve at once.

PEANUTS AND TOMATO STUFFED JACKET POTATO

Calories 375; Fibre 11g

7oz (200g) baked jacket potato (p. 99)
1oz (25g) salted peanuts
1 large tomato, about 4 oz (115g), chopped
freshly ground pepper
a few sprigs of watercress
3oz (85g) Chinese leaves, shredded
1 tablespoon lemon juice

Mix the potato flesh with the peanuts and chopped tomato and pile into the potato jacket. Season with pepper. Reheat. Garnish with sprigs of watercress. Serve with the Chinese leaves tossed in lemon juice.

COD AND SAUCE STUFFED JACKET POTATO

Calories 400; Fibre 12g

7oz (200g) baked jacket potato (p. 99)
6oz (170g) pack frozen cod in parsley sauce
a sprig of parsley
3oz (85g) frozen peas

Cook the frozen cod in parsley sauce as directed on the packet. Flake the fish into the sauce. Mix the mashed potato flesh with the fish and sauce. Pile into the potato jacket and heat through in the oven. Cook the peas as directed and serve with the stuffed potato.

'SAVOURY CUT' CASSEROLE WITH BAKED JACKET POTATO – TWO SERVINGS

Two portions: 950 calories; 32g fibre
Individual portion: 475 calories; 16g fibre

7oz (200g) potato for jacket baking, per serving
4·97oz (141g) can Farrow Giant Marrowfat Processed Peas
1 small onion, chopped
7oz (198g) can Sainsbury's Sliced Young Carrots
7½oz (213g) can Granose Savoury Cuts

Scrub the potato and bake in a moderately hot oven for 45 minutes or until tender. Cut the savoury cuts into cubes and place in a casserole with all the sauce. Stir in the onion and drained carrots. Cover with a lid or foil and cook near the bottom of the oven with the potato. Add the drained peas 10 minutes before the end of cooking. Serve the casserole with the baked potato.

SPINACH MEALS

Spinach, as all Popeye fans know, is a good source of iron, but more important, it is a good source of dietary fibre and is very low in calories. A 4oz (115g) serving of cooked chopped spinach has only 35 calories and contains 7g dietary fibre.

It makes a good bed on which to serve other foods (for example, poached eggs) and so it can be turned into simple, quick meals. However, to add variety, one or two other methods of using spinach in meals have been included.

CHOPPED SPINACH – BASIC RECIPE

Calories 35; Fibre 7g

8oz (225g) fresh spinach, washed, *or* 4oz (115g) frozen chopped
   or cut-leaf spinach, thawed
salt and freshly ground pepper

If fresh spinach is used, cut out any coarse stalks, wash well and pack into a saucepan with only the water that clings to the leaves. Heat gently, turning the spinach occasionally, then bring to the boil and cook until soft, 10–15 minutes. Drain thoroughly and chop finely. Season to taste with salt and pepper.

If using thawed frozen spinach, do not add butter but heat very gently until simmering, adding 1 tablespoon water if necessary, and simmer for about 7 minutes, stirring frequently. Drain off any surplus liquid. Season to taste with salt and pepper. Use as a vegetable accompaniment or in one of the meals below.

SPINACH AND EGG BENEDICT WITH MUSHROOMS

Calories 150; Fibre 8g

1 portion chopped spinach (see above)
1 egg, size 3
2 tablespoons natural yogurt

1 teaspoon tomato purée
a dash of Worcestershire sauce
2oz (55g) button mushrooms
a sprig of parsley

Arrange the spinach on a hot serving plate. Poach the egg in water and place on top of the spinach. Mix the yogurt with the tomato purée and Worcestershire sauce and spoon over the egg. Poach the mushrooms in salted water or stock and serve with the spinach and egg, garnished with a sprig of parsley.

SPINACH WITH CREAMY HAM

Calories 175; Fibre 7g

2oz (55g) lean boiled ham
2 tablespoons low-fat natural yogurt
¼ teaspoon prepared mustard
1 portion chopped spinach (p. 114)

Trim off and discard any visible fat from the ham; chop the ham. Mix the yogurt with the mustard. Stir in the chopped ham. Arrange the hot spinach on a serving dish and spoon over the creamy ham topping. Serve at once.

SPINACH AND POACHED EGG ON TOAST

Calories 175; Fibre 9g

1oz (25g) slice wholemeal bread
1 portion chopped spinach (p. 114)
1 egg, size 3
paprika pepper
vinegar (optional)

Toast the bread on both sides. Pile the hot spinach on top of the toast. Poach the egg in water and place on the spinach. Garnish with a sprinkling of paprika pepper and serve with vinegar, if liked.

CHEESY SPINACH CRUMBLE

Calories 200; Fibre 8g

a pinch of grated nutmeg
1 portion chopped spinach (p. 114)
salt and pepper
4oz (115g) cottage cheese (natural or with onion and peppers)
½oz (15g) wholemeal breadcrumbs
1 tablespoon grated Parmesan cheese

Stir the grated nutmeg into the spinach, then arrange in a small oven-proof dish. Season the cottage cheese to taste and spoon over the spinach. Mix the breadcrumbs with the Parmesan cheese and sprinkle on top. Bake at 400°F, (200°C, gas 6) for 15 minutes or until the topping is crisp.

SPINACH OMELETTE WITH MUSHROOMS

Calories 225; Fibre 8g

2 eggs, size 3
1 portion chopped spinach (p. 114)
salt and pepper
¼oz (7g) low-fat spread
2oz (55g) button mushrooms

Separate the egg yolks from the whites. Mix the chopped spinach with the egg yolks, seasoning and 2 tablespoons water. Whisk the egg whites until stiff. Gently fold the egg whites into the spinach mixture. Grease a non-stick omelette pan with the low-fat spread and heat. Pour in the omelette mixture and cook over a moderate heat until the bottom is set. Place the pan under a grill to set and lightly brown the top of the omelette. Fold the omelette in half and turn out on to a warm serving dish. Poach the mushrooms in a little salted water or stock and serve with the omelette.

SPINACH WITH BEEFBURGERS AND TOMATO SAUCE

Calories 225; Fibre 8g

2 × 2oz (55g) frozen beefburgers
5oz (140g) canned tomatoes and juice
1 teaspoon dried onion flakes
salt and pepper
a dash of Worcestershire sauce
1 portion chopped spinach (p. 114)

Grill the beefburgers well on both sides so that much of the fat drips away. Mash the tomatoes with their juice and put in a small saucepan with the onion flakes, seasoning to taste and Worcestershire sauce. Bring to the boil and simmer gently for 5 minutes. Arrange the hot spinach on a serving plate. Place the beefburgers on top and pour the tomato sauce over them.

CHICKEN AND SPINACH WITH CARROTS

Calories 225; Fibre 10g

1 portion chopped spinach (p. 114)
4 tablespoons low-fat natural yogurt
1 teaspoon Worcestershire sauce
3oz (85g) cooked chicken
salt and pepper
paprika pepper
4oz (115g) carrots, sliced

Arrange the spinach in an ovenproof dish. Mix the yogurt with the Worcestershire sauce. Remove and discard any skin on the chicken, then cut into bite-size pieces. Mix the chicken with the yogurt and season to taste. Spoon the chicken mixture over the spinach, and heat through under a hot grill. Sprinkle over a little paprika. Boil the carrots and serve with the chicken and spinach dish.

FISH FLORENTINE LAYER

Calories 275; Fibre 10g

6oz (170g) haddock fillet or any white fish fillet, skinned
1 teaspoon lemon juice
salt and freshly ground pepper
1 portion chopped spinach (p. 114)
1oz (25g) fresh wholemeal breadcrumbs
½oz (15g) Cheddar cheese, finely grated
1 tablespoon chopped fresh parsley

Place the fish fillet in the bottom of a $1-1\frac{1}{2}$ pint (600–900ml) oven-proof dish. Pour lemon juice over fish and season. Cover fish with the spinach. Mix together the breadcrumbs, cheese, parsley and salt and pepper to taste. Spoon the mixture on top of the spinach. Bake at 400°F (200°C, gas 6) for 20–30 minutes until breadcrumb topping is golden brown. Serve hot.

SPINACH WITH MINCED BEEF TOPPING

Calories 300; Fibre 11g

4oz (115g) raw minced beef
1 fresh tomato *or* 2oz (55g) canned tomatoes
1oz (25g) chopped onion
1oz (25g) mushrooms, chopped
½oz (15g) brown rice
4 tablespoons beef stock or water
salt and pepper
¼ level teaspoon dried mixed herbs
1 portion chopped spinach (p. 114)
2oz (55g) carrots, sliced

Fry the minced beef, without added fat, until well browned. Drain off and discard any fat which has been cooked out of the meat. Chop the fresh or canned tomato and add, with the chopped onion and mush-rooms, rice and stock or water to the meat in the pan. Season to taste with salt and pepper and add the herbs. Stir well and heat to simmering point. Cover and simmer gently for 30 minutes. Meanwhile, boil the carrots in lightly salted water until tender; then drain. Arrange the hot spinach on a serving plate and spoon the minced beef mixture on top. Serve with the boiled carrots.

WHOLE-WHEAT PASTA MEALS

Whole-wheat pasta includes spaghetti, spaghetti rings, macaroni and lasagne, which gives plenty of scope for interesting meals as can be seen in this section. A 2oz (50g) dry-weight portion of any whole-wheat pasta, which when cooked gives a generous slimmer's portion, provides 5·7g fibre at a cost of 195 calories.

The fibre and calorie values of the pasta have been included in the total value for each meal in this section. However, should you want to add boiled whole-wheat pasta to any other meals, then use the figures above.

ITALIAN VEGETABLE SOUP

Calories 200; Fibre 8g

1 small onion (about 1oz, 25g), coarsely grated
1 carrot (about 2oz, 55g), coarsely grated
2oz (55g) parsnip, coarsely grated
½ chicken stock cube dissolved in ¼ pint (1·5dl) boiling water
¼ pint (1·5dl) tomato juice
1oz (25g) whole-wheat macaroni
2oz (55g) cabbage, finely shredded
salt and pepper
1 teaspoon chopped fresh parsley

Put the onion, carrot, parsnip, chicken stock, tomato juice and macaroni into a saucepan. Bring to the boil, cover and simmer gently for 15 minutes. Add the cabbage, bring back to the boil and cook gently, covered, for a further 5–10 minutes. Season to taste with salt and pepper and serve topped with the chopped parsley.

PASTA AND PRAWN SALAD

Calories 300; Fibre 7g

2oz (55g) whole-wheat macaroni or spaghetti rings
2oz (55g) peeled prawns
2oz (55g) button mushrooms, sliced

1 tablespoon low-calorie salad dressing
1 tablespoon low-fat natural yogurt
1 teaspoon lemon juice
salt and pepper
a few lettuce leaves
1 teaspoon chopped fresh parsley

Cook the macaroni or spaghetti rings in boiling salted water until just tender. Drain, rinse in cold water and drain again. Mix with the prawns and mushrooms. Blend together the salad dressing, yogurt and lemon juice. Add to the pasta mixture and stir until all the ingredients are thoroughly mixed. Season to taste. Arrange a bed of lettuce on a plate, spoon the salad on top and garnish with the chopped parsley.

PASTA WITH TUNA AND TOMATO SAUCE

Calories 325; Fibre 7g

2oz (55g) whole-wheat spaghetti or macaroni
5oz (140g) canned tomatoes
a pinch of dried basil or oregano
3½oz (100g) can tuna in brine, drained
a pinch of garlic salt
freshly ground pepper

Boil the pasta in salted water for about 12 minutes or until just tender. Meanwhile, purée the canned tomatoes in an electric blender or mash well with a fork. Place in a saucepan with the herbs. Flake the tuna and add to the tomato purée. Bring to the boil, reduce the heat and simmer for about 5 minutes. Add the garlic salt and pepper to taste. Drain the pasta. Serve the tuna and tomato sauce on the pasta.

MACARONI SCRAMBLE

Calories 350; Fibre 9g

2oz (55g) whole-wheat macaroni
2oz (55g) canned sweetcorn kernels mixed with red and green pepper
1 large egg (size 2)
2 tablespoons skimmed milk
salt and pepper

Boil the macaroni in salted water until tender, about 12 minutes. Drain
and place in a non-stick saucepan with the sweetcorn. Beat the egg
with the milk and seasoning to taste. Add to the saucepan. Heat gently,
stirring continuously until the egg begins to set and becomes creamy.
Turn out on to a serving dish and serve at once.

SPAGHETTI WITH CHILLI LENTIL SAUCE

Calories 375; Fibre 11g

1 teaspoon oil
1 small onion, peeled and chopped
½–1 teaspoon chilli powder
8oz (225g) canned tomatoes and juice
1oz (25g) lentils
1 level tablespoon tomato purée
salt and pepper
2oz (55g) whole-wheat spaghetti
1 level teaspoon chopped fresh parsley

Heat the oil in a small saucepan. Add the onion and fry gently until
softened. Stir in the chilli powder. Chop the tomatoes and add to the
pan with their juice; add the lentils, tomato purée and 2fl oz (55ml)
water. Bring to the boil, reduce the heat, cover and simmer gently for
about 30 minutes until the lentils have softened. Stir frequently and
add more water if the mixture becomes too thick. Season to taste with
salt and pepper. Boil the spaghetti in salted water until just tender,

about 12 minutes. Drain the spaghetti and pile in the centre of a plate. Spoon the chilli lentil sauce around the spaghetti and sprinkle with chopped parsley.

PASTA WITH CHICKEN LIVER SAUCE

Calories 400; Fibre 8g

2oz (55g) whole-wheat spaghetti, macaroni or spaghetti rings
4oz (115g) chicken livers
¼ pint (1·5dl) chicken stock
2oz (55g) mushrooms, sliced
1 tablespoon dry sherry, optional
1 teaspoon tomato purée
salt and pepper
2 teaspoons wholemeal flour

Boil the pasta in salted water until just tender. Meanwhile, chop the chicken livers and place in a saucepan with the stock, mushrooms, sherry (if used), tomato purée and seasoning to taste. Bring to the boil, cover and simmer for 10 minutes. Blend the wholemeal flour with a little water and stir into the chicken liver sauce. Continue to heat, stirring continuously until the sauce is thickened. Drain the pasta and arrange in a circle on a plate. Spoon the sauce into the centre.

SPAGHETTI WITH FISH SAUCE

Calories 400; Fibre 8g

2oz (55g) whole-wheat spaghetti
6oz (170g) packet frozen cod in mushroom sauce
1oz (25g) frozen peas, cooked

Boil the spaghetti in salted water for about 12 minutes or until just tender. Heat the cod in mushroom sauce as directed. Boil the peas. Drain the spaghetti and arrange on a serving plate. Flake the fish into the mushroom sauce and stir in the peas. Spoon on top of the spaghetti and serve.

SPAGHETTI BOLOGNESE

Calories 400; Fibre 9g

2oz (55g) whole-wheat spaghetti

Sauce
4oz (115g) lean minced beef
1 small onion, peeled and finely chopped
1 stick celery, finely chopped
¼ beef stock cube dissolved in 2½fl oz (70ml) boiling water
salt and freshly ground pepper
a pinch of mixed herbs
1 teaspoon tomato purée
1oz (25g) frozen peas

Fry the minced beef in a non-stick saucepan until well browned. Drain off all the fat which has cooked out of the meat. Add the onion, celery and stock to the meat in the pan and bring to the boil, stirring. Reduce the heat, season to taste with salt and pepper and add the herbs and tomato purée. Cover and simmer gently for 40 minutes, stirring occasionally and adding more water if it begins to boil dry. Boil the spaghetti in salted water for about 12 minutes or until just tender. Drain and arrange around the edge of a serving dish. Stir the peas into the sauce and heat through for 5 minutes, then pour into the centre of the pasta.

KIDNEY LASAGNE

Calories 425; Fibre 13g

2oz (55g) whole-wheat lasagne
2 lamb's kidneys
1 small onion, peeled and sliced
2oz (55g) mushrooms, sliced
⅓ beef stock cube
1 teaspoon tomato purée
1 tablespoon wholemeal flour
salt and pepper

2oz (55g) frozen peas
4 tablespoons low-fat natural yogurt
a squeeze of lemon juice

Boil the lasagne in salted water for 15–17 minutes, stirring occasionally. Drain and rinse under running water. Skin, halve and remove cores from the kidneys. Chop and place in a pan with the onion, mushrooms, stock cube, tomato purée and ¼ pint (1·5dl) boiling water. Bring to the boil, cover and simmer for 15 minutes. Blend the flour with a little cold water and stir into the kidney sauce. Bring to the boil, stirring. Season with salt and pepper to taste and stir in the peas. Place half the lasagne in the base of a lightly greased ovenproof dish. Spoon over the kidney sauce and top with the remaining lasagne. Mix the yogurt with the lemon juice and season to taste. Spread over the lasagne. Cook in the oven at 400°F (200°C, gas 6) for 15 minutes or until heated through. Serve hot.

CHEESY-TOPPED VEGETABLE AND PASTA PIE

Calories 425; Fibre 17g

2oz (55g) whole-wheat spaghetti rings
2oz (55g) peas
2oz (55g) sweetcorn kernels
1 canned red pepper, sliced
5oz (142g) can condensed Golden Vegetable Soup
a dash of Worcestershire sauce
½oz (15g) wholemeal breadcrumbs
1 tablespoon grated Parmesan cheese

Boil the spaghetti rings in salted water until just tender. Drain and mix with the peas, sweetcorn and pepper. Blend the condensed soup with 3fl oz (85ml) water and stir into the pasta and vegetables with the Worcestershire sauce. Turn into a baking dish. Mix the breadcrumbs and cheese together and spoon over the top. Cook in the oven at 400°F (200°C, gas 6) for 20 minutes or until heated through.

MACARONI CHEESE WITH VEGETABLES

Calories 475; Fibre 12g

2oz (55g) whole-wheat macaroni
4oz (115g) frozen mixed vegetables
½oz (15g) wholemeal flour
¼ pint (1·5dl) skimmed milk
¼oz (7g) low-fat spread
salt and pepper
¼ teaspoon made mustard
1oz (25g) Edam cheese, grated

Boil the macaroni in salted water for 12 minutes or until tender; drain.
Cook the vegetables as directed and drain. Put the flour, milk and low-fat spread into a saucepan and heat, whisking continuously until it boils and thickens. Season to taste with salt and pepper. Add the mustard and half the cheese. Stir the macaroni and vegetables into the sauce. Turn into an ovenproof dish. Sprinkle over the remaining cheese. Cook in the oven at 400°F (200°C, gas 6) for 20 minutes or until the cheese is melted and bubbling.

BEAN LASAGNE

Calories 475; Fibre 22g

2oz (55g) whole-wheat lasagne
1 teaspoon low-fat spread
1 small onion, peeled and chopped
8oz (225g) baked beans with tomato sauce
a dash of Worcestershire sauce
2oz (55g) cottage cheese
2 tablespoons low-fat natural yogurt
salt and pepper
1 tablespoon grated Parmesan cheese

Boil the lasagne in salted water for 15 minutes. Drain and rinse under the cold water tap. Heat the low-fat spread in a non-stick pan and fry the onion over gentle heat until soft. Add the baked beans and Worcestershire sauce and heat through. Place half the lasagne in the bottom of a lightly greased ovenproof dish. Spoon in the hot baked bean mixture and top with the remaining lasagne. Mix the cottage cheese and yogurt together and season to taste. Spread over the lasagne to cover. Sprinkle on the grated Parmesan cheese. Place under a hot grill for 5–10 minutes until the Parmesan cheese is browned or cook at 400°F (200°C, gas 6) until the top is browned.

PEASE PUDDING MEALS

Peas are an excellent source of dietary fibre, so it is time to revive that good old favourite, pease pudding.

The basic recipe here gives quantities for one serving, but if you like pease pudding it would be sensible to multiply the ingredients and make at least four portions. Divide this into individual amounts, put each in a freezer carton or bag, freeze and use as required for the selection of meals listed below. To use, remove from carton or bag and place, still frozen, in a small ovenproof container. Cover and heat through in a moderate oven (375°F, 190°C, gas 5) for 30 minutes.

PEASE PUDDING – BASIC RECIPE

Calories 200; Fibre 7g

2oz (55g) dried split peas
1oz (25g) chopped onion
1 bay leaf, optional
salt
$\frac{1}{2}$ beef or ham stock cube
freshly ground black pepper

Cover the peas with boiling water and soak overnight. Drain, then put into a pan with the onion and bay leaf. Cover with fresh water, add a pinch of salt and the stock cube. Bring to the boil, then cover and simmer slowly until tender, about 1–1$\frac{1}{2}$ hours. Remove the bay leaf. Drain the peas and either sieve or purée in an electric blender or food processor. Stir in freshly ground pepper and salt to taste. Use in the meals set out below.

PEASE PUDDING SOUFFLÉ WITH TOMATO, ONION AND WATERCRESS SALAD

Calories 300; Fibre 9g

1 portion pease pudding (see above)
1 egg, size 3

salt and pepper
$\frac{1}{4}$ teaspoon made mustard
1 tomato, sliced
1oz (25g) onion, sliced into rings
a small bunch of watercress

Place the pease pudding in a basin. Separate the egg yolk from the egg white and beat the yolk with seasoning to taste and the mustard into the pease pudding. Whisk the egg white until stiff, and gently fold in. Spoon the mixture into a $1\frac{1}{2}$ pint (2l) ovenproof dish or soufflé dish and bake at 400°F (200°C, gas 6) for 20 minutes. Serve hot with a salad made from the sliced tomato, onion rings and sprigs of watercress.

BACON STEAK WITH PEASE PUDDING

Calories 325; Fibre 8g

$3\frac{1}{2}$oz (100g) bacon steak
1 small tomato
1 portion pease pudding (p. 128)

Grill the bacon steak well on both sides without added fat. Halve the tomato and warm through under the grill. Serve the well-grilled bacon steak with the tomato and pease pudding.

PEASE PUDDING WITH LAMB'S LIVER

Calories 450; Fibre 10g

4oz (115g) lamb's liver, sliced thinly
1 tablespoon bran
salt and freshly ground pepper
16 squirts low-calorie cooking spray (Limmit's Spray & Fry)
2oz (55g) Brussels sprouts
1 portion pease pudding (p. 128)

Wash the liver, coat with the bran, season with salt and pepper, and spray one side with 8 squirts of the cooking spray. Cook under a hot grill for 3 minutes, turn, spray the second side and cook for a further 3 minutes, or until just cooked through. Boil the Brussels sprouts. Serve the grilled liver with the pease pudding and sprouts.

PEASE PUDDING WITH COTTAGE CHEESE AND TOMATO TOPPING

Calories 325; Fibre 9g

1 portion pease pudding (p. 128)
4oz (115g) cottage cheese (natural or with chives)
2oz (55g) chopped fresh green pepper
salt and freshly ground pepper
1 tomato, sliced
1 tablespoon chopped fresh parsley

Spoon the pease pudding into a 1½ pint (2l) ovenproof dish. Mix the cottage cheese with the chopped pepper and season to taste. Pile the cottage cheese mixture on to the pease pudding. Arrange the tomato slices over the cheese and season lightly. Bake at 400°F (200°C, gas 6) for 15–20 minutes or heat through under the grill. Serve hot, sprinkled with chopped parsley.

BAKED BEAN MEALS

In this section you will find many of the simplest no-nonsense sort of meals on the diet menus – and also many of those highest in dietary fibre content. Good old baked beans, canned in tomato sauce, are a splendid source of fibre at very moderate calorie cost. An 8oz (225g) can gives a generous serving for one, at a cost of only 160 calories.

Each meal gives quantities for one serving. At the end of this section, however, we have given recipes for a couple of baked bean meals which involve rather more ingredients and a little more time than you would want to spend on one meal. These are given in portions for four servings.

POACHED EGG WITH BAKED BEANS

Calories 250; Fibre 16g

1 large egg, size 2
8oz (225g) baked beans with tomato sauce

Poach the egg in water and serve on top of the heated baked beans.

BAKED BEANS ON TOAST

Calories 250; Fibre 19g

1 slice wholemeal bread (1¼oz, 35g)
1 teaspoon tomato purée
8oz (225g) baked beans with tomato sauce

Toast the bread and spread with the tomato purée. Spoon the heated beans over the toast.

BACON AND BAKED BEANS

Calories 275; Fibre 16g

2 rashers streaky bacon (¾oz, 20g each)
8oz (225g) baked beans with tomato sauce

Grill the bacon until crisp. Serve with the heated beans.

FISH FINGERS AND BAKED BEANS

Calories 275; Fibre 18g

2 cod fish fingers
1 large or 2 small tomatoes, halved
8oz (225g) baked beans with tomato sauce

Grill the fish fingers and tomatoes without added fat until the fish fingers are crisp on the outside and cooked through. Serve with the heated beans.

BAKED BEAN NEST

Calories 300; Fibre 13g

1 beefburger (2oz, 55g)
4oz (115g) baked beans with tomato sauce
1oz (25g) instant mashed potato, made up with boiling water as directed on packet

Grill the beefburger well and heat the beans. Pipe or spoon a ring of potato around the top edge of the cooked beefburger. Spoon the heated beans into the centre.

BAKED BEANS WITH CHEESE

Calories 300; Fibre 16g

6oz (170g) baked beans with tomato sauce
1oz (25g) Edam cheese, grated
1 canned red pepper, drained and chopped
½ teaspoon Worcestershire sauce
1 slice wholemeal bread (1¼oz, 35g), toasted

Heat the beans with the cheese, pepper and Worcestershire sauce over a gentle heat until hot and the cheese is melted. Serve the bean mixture on the hot toast.

BAKED BEANS AU GRATIN

Calories 300; Fibre 20g

2 tomatoes (2oz, 50g each)
8oz (225g) baked beans with tomato sauce
1oz (25g) wholemeal breadcrumbs
½oz (15g) Edam cheese, grated

Slice the tomatoes and place in a small gratin dish. Spoon over the heated beans. Mix the breadcrumbs with the cheese and sprinkle over beans. Grill until crisp and bubbly.

CHICKEN DRUMSTICKS WITH CURRIED BEANS

Calories 325; Fibre 16g

2 chicken drumsticks (3½oz, 100g each raw weight)
8oz (225g) baked beans with tomato sauce
1 teaspoon concentrated curry paste or curry powder

Grill the chicken drumsticks until cooked through. Heat the baked beans with the curry paste or powder. Remove and discard the skin from the chicken drumsticks and serve them with the curried beans.

WAGONS ROLL

Calories 325; Fibre 17g

1 wholemeal bread roll (2oz, 55g)
½oz (15g) low-fat spread
6oz (170g) baked beans with tomato sauce
salt and pepper
2 teaspoons sweet pickle
1 teaspoon slimmers' mayonnaise

Split the bread roll and spread with the low-fat spread. Mash the beans with seasoning to taste. Spread over the roll and top with the pickle and mayonnaise.

BAKED BEANS WITH MUSHROOMS

Calories 325; Fibre 23g

½oz (15g) low-fat spread
1 medium onion, peeled and chopped
4oz (115g) button mushrooms, trimmed
8oz (225g) baked beans with tomato sauce
1 teaspoon soy sauce
salt and pepper
1 slice wholemeal bread (1¼oz, 35g), toasted and cut in fingers

Melt the low-fat spread in a non-stick pan on a low heat. Add the onion and mushrooms and cook until soft. Add the beans, soy sauce and seasoning to taste. Serve with fingers of wholemeal toast.

CURRIED BEANS IN PITTA POCKET

Calories 325; Fibre 18g

8oz (225g) baked beans with tomato sauce
½oz (15g) sultanas
1 teaspoon curry powder
1 pitta bread (1⅝oz, 45g)

Heat the beans with the sultanas and curry powder until hot and bubbly. Halve the pitta bread and carefully cut again to make a pocket in each half. Fill the pockets with the bean mixture.

CHILLI BEEF AND BEANS

Calories 350; Fibre 13g

$\frac{1}{2}$ green pepper, seeds removed and chopped
3oz (85g) lean minced beef
1 small onion, peeled and chopped
4oz (115g) canned tomatoes
1 tablespoon tomato purée
$\frac{1}{2}$ teaspoon salt
1 teaspoon chilli powder
1 bay leaf
4oz (115g) baked beans with tomato sauce
2 crispbreads

Brown the green pepper, beef and onion in a non-stick saucepan. Drain off any fat which has cooked out of the meat. Add the tomatoes, tomato purée, salt, chilli powder and bay leaf. Cover and simmer for 40 minutes over a low heat. Add the beans and cook for a further 5 minutes. Serve with the crispbreads.

FRANKFURTER BEAN BAKE

Calories 350; Fibre 16g

8oz (225g) baked beans with tomato sauce
1 teaspoon tomato ketchup
$\frac{1}{2}$ teaspoon made mustard
1 teaspoon dried onion flakes
2oz (55g) frankfurters, sliced

Mix all the ingredients together, add 2 tablespoons water and spoon into a small ovenproof casserole. Cook, uncovered, in the oven at 350°F (180°C, gas 4) for 30 minutes.

CORNED BEEF WITH BAKED BEANS

Calories 350; Fibre 17g

3oz (85g) corned beef, sliced
8oz (225g) baked beans with tomato sauce
a few sprigs of watercress

Serve the corned beef with the heated baked beans. Garnish with the watercress.

QUICK AND EASY CASSOULET

Calories 375; Fibre 12g

1 rasher streaky bacon, rinds removed and diced
2oz (55g) garlic sausage, cubed
4oz (115g) canned tomatoes
4oz (115g) baked beans with tomato sauce
salt and pepper
¼ teaspoon mixed dried herbs
1oz (25g) fresh wholemeal breadcrumbs

Place the bacon and garlic sausage in a non-stick saucepan and cook over a low heat until the fat runs and the bacon turns a crisp brown. Drain off any surplus fat. Add the tomatoes, beans and seasoning to taste. Transfer to a heatproof dish. Mix the herbs with the breadcrumbs and sprinkle over the bean mixture. Brown under a low grill for 5–10 minutes until crisp and bubbly.

OMELETTE AND BAKED BEANS

Calories 375; Fibre 16g

½oz (15g) low-fat spread
2 eggs, size 3, beaten
salt and pepper
8oz (225g) baked beans with tomato sauce

Melt the spread in a non-stick frying pan. Add the seasoned eggs and
cook over a high heat until set. Fold the omelette in half and serve with
the heated beans.

BEANS, SAUSAGE AND MASH

Calories 375; Fibre 21g

2 pork chipolata sausages
8oz (225g) baked beans with tomato sauce
1oz (25g) instant mashed potato made up with boiling water as directed
  on the packet

Grill the sausages very thoroughly so that the maximum amount of fat
runs off. Serve with the heated beans and mashed potato.

BEAN BURGER

Calories 400; Fibre 20g

1 beefburger (2oz, 55g)
1 wholemeal bread roll (2oz, 55g)
8oz (225g) baked beans with tomato sauce

Grill the beefburger thoroughly and toast the split bread roll. Place the
burger on top of the bun and spoon over the heated beans.

SHEPHERDS' BEAN PIE

Calories 400; Fibre 21g

2oz (55g) lean minced beef
1 small onion (2oz, 55g), peeled and chopped
salt and pepper
8oz (225g) baked beans with tomato sauce
1oz (25g) instant mashed potato made up with boiling water as directed
  on the packet

Cook the beef and onion with seasoning to taste in a non-stick pan until cooked and browned. Drain off any fat which has cooked out of the meat. Add the beans and heat through. Spoon into a small dish. Top with the mashed potato and grill until golden.

EASY BEAN GRILL

Calories 450; Fibre 17g

salt and pepper
1 lamb chump chop (5oz, 150g raw weight)
2 tomatoes, halved
8oz (225g) baked beans with tomato sauce

Season the chop and tomatoes and grill until the chop is cooked very thoroughly. Serve with the heated beans.

LIVER, BACON AND BEANS

Calories 500; Fibre 16g

4oz (115g) lamb's liver, sliced
1 teaspoon oil
2 rashers streaky bacon ($\frac{3}{4}$oz, 20g each raw weight)
8oz (225g) baked beans with tomato sauce

Brush the liver with oil. Grill liver and bacon until the bacon is crisp. Serve with the heated beans.

HEARTY SAUSAGE AND BEAN SOUP – FOUR SERVINGS

Four portions: 900 calories; 40g fibre
Individual portion: 225 calories; 10g fibre

2 medium onions, peeled and chopped
6oz (170g) carrots, peeled and chopped
8oz (225g) canned tomatoes
2 chicken stock cubes

16oz (450g) baked beans with tomato sauce
4oz (115g) frankfurters, sliced
salt and pepper
4 tablespoons cornflour

Place the onions, carrots, tomatoes and stock cubes in a saucepan with
2¼ pints (1·25l) water and bring to the boil. Cover and simmer for 45
minutes. Add the baked beans, frankfurters and seasoning to taste.
Simmer for a further 10 minutes. Blend the cornflour with a little
water to make a smooth paste and blend into the hot soup. Cook for a
further 2–3 minutes, stirring constantly. Serve hot.

SAUCY BEAN RAREBIT – FOUR SERVINGS

Four portions: 1,100 calories; 80g fibre
Individual portion: 275 calories; 20g fibre

½oz (15g) low-fat spread
1 medium onion, peeled and chopped
1 garlic clove, crushed
1 green pepper, seeded and sliced
14oz (397g) can kidney beans, drained
16oz (450g) baked beans with tomato sauce
4 tablespoons tomato ketchup
1 tablespoon Worcestershire sauce
salt and pepper
4 slices (each 1¼oz, 35g) wholemeal bread, toasted

Melt the low-fat spread in a non-stick frying pan. Add the onion,
garlic and green pepper, and cook for 5 minutes until the onion is soft.
Stir in the kidney beans, baked beans, tomato ketchup, Worcestershire
sauce and seasoning to taste. Cook for a further 5 minutes, stirring
occasionally. Serve the bean rarebit on the slices of hot toast.

KIDNEY BEAN MEALS

The recipes in this section use fibre-rich kidney beans. These are mainly four-portion recipes so that you can store away the three remaining portions in freezer bags ready for future dieting meals.

To allow you a choice, here are the calorie and fibre contents of a variety of foods which you might serve with the kidney bean dishes. Add the figures of the food you choose as an accompaniment to that of the dish.

	Calories	Fibre (g)
Brown rice (2oz, 55g dry weight)	190	2
Energen Brancrisp crispbreads (2)	50	3
Lightly boiled cabbage (4oz, 115g)	20	3
Baked potato (6oz, 170g)	175	5

TUNA, TOMATO AND RED KIDNEY BEAN SAVOURY – TWO SERVINGS

Two portions: 400 calories; 16g fibre
Individual portion: 200 calories; 8g fibre

8oz (225g) can peeled tomatoes
1 tablespoon (15ml) tomato purée
7·9oz (223g) can Batchelor's Red Kidney Beans
freshly ground pepper
$\frac{1}{4}$ level teaspoon curry powder
7oz (198g) can Sainsbury's Tuna in Brine
4oz (115g) frozen whole green beans, per serving

Put the contents of the can of tomatoes into a pan and break down with a fork. Add the tomato purée, drained kidney beans, ground pepper and curry powder and heat through. Drain and flake the tuna, add to the tomatoes and beans and heat through. Cook the frozen green beans. Serve the tuna, tomato and red kidney bean savoury with the green beans.

PORK AND BEAN CASSEROLE – FOUR SERVINGS

Four portions: 900 calories; 30g fibre
Individual portion: 225 calories; 8g fibre

12oz (340g) pork fillet
1 large onion, peeled and chopped
1 canned red pepper, sliced
3oz (85g) dried red kidney beans, soaked overnight
1oz (25g) haricot beans, soaked overnight
7oz (200g) canned tomatoes
salt and pepper
½ pint (3dl) stock
¼ pint (1·5dl) cider

Cut the pork into small pieces. Put all ingredients into a large saucepan, bring to the boil. Boil for 10 minutes, then cover and simmer gently for 1–1½ hours until cooked. Remove the lid for the last 15 minutes to reduce the sauce.

BEAN AND BEEF STEW – FOUR SERVINGS

Four portions: 1,000 calories; 24g fibre
Individual portion: 250 calories; 11g fibre

1 tablespoon oil
12oz (340g) very lean stewing beef, diced
1 large onion, peeled and sliced
1 tablespoon flour
½ pint (3dl) brown stock
2 teaspoons tomato purée
salt and pepper
a pinch of mixed herbs
15oz (425g) can red kidney beans, drained

Put the oil, beef and onion into a large saucepan and heat until slightly browned. Sprinkle on the flour and stir in the stock. Bring to the boil, add the remaining ingredients, cover and simmer for about 1½–2 hours until the beef is cooked.

KIDNEY BEAN SALAD –
FOUR SERVINGS

Four portions: 1,000 calories; 42g fibre
Individual portion: 250 calories; 11g fibre

4oz (115g) dried red kidney beans, soaked overnight *or* 15oz (425g)
    can red kidney beans, drained
4oz (115g) frozen French beans
1 cauliflower (about 1lb, 450g)
1 small onion, peeled and finely chopped
4oz (115g) Edam cheese, cubed
juice of 1 lemon
2 tablespoons olive oil
3 tablespoons Waistline Oil-Free French Dressing
salt and pepper

Drain the soaked kidney beans, place in a saucepan and cover with
fresh water. Bring to the boil, add a little salt, cover and simmer for
about 1 hour until tender. Drain and rinse with cold water. If using
canned beans, drain and rinse. Cook the French beans in boiling salted
water for 2 minutes, then drain. Break the cauliflower into florets.
Mix the kidney beans, French beans, cauliflower florets, onion and
cheese together in a salad bowl. Mix the lemon juice, olive oil and
French dressing together. Pour over the salad and toss well. Leave to
stand for 30 minutes, then toss again and check seasoning before
serving.

CHILLI CON CARNE – FOUR SERVINGS

Four portions: 1,200 calories; 28g fibre
Individual portion: 300 calories; 7g fibre

1lb (450g) lean minced beef
28oz (795g) canned tomatoes
1 large onion, peeled and chopped
15oz (425g) can red kidney beans
salt and pepper
chilli powder to taste (about 2 teaspoons)

Brown the minced beef in a non-stick pan and drain off the fat. Heat the tomatoes in a large saucepan. Add the mince, onion, drained red kidney beans, and seasoning and chilli powder to taste. Bring to the boil, cover and simmer very gently for about 1 hour.

HI-FI OMELETTES

CORN OMELETTE

Calories 250; Fibre 6g

2 eggs, size 3
2 tablespoons milk
a dash of Worcestershire sauce
salt and pepper
2oz (55g) sweetcorn
1oz (25g) peas

Beat the eggs, milk, Worcestershire sauce and seasoning together. Pour into a non-stick omelette pan and cook gently until almost set. Add the sweetcorn and peas and heat under the grill for a few minutes. Fold the omelette and serve.

VEGETABLE OMELETTE

Calories 400; Fibre 12g

$\frac{1}{2}$oz (15g) butter
$\frac{1}{2}$ small onion, chopped
1oz (25g) green pepper, chopped
7$\frac{1}{2}$oz (213g) can red kidney beans, drained
2 eggs (size 3)
a pinch of dried mixed herbs
salt and pepper

Melt the butter in an omelette or frying pan and fry the onion and pepper until softened. Stir in the beans and heat through. Beat the eggs, herbs, seasoning and 2 tablespoons water together. Pour over the vegetables. Cook gently, forking up the cooked mixture frequently to let the raw egg mixture get to the bottom of the pan. When the egg is just set, fold in half and serve.

HI-FI SALADS

The average salad isn't necessarily as good a source of fibre (or anything else of much nutritional value) as people imagine. Professor Peter Van Soest – one of the top fibre experts in the USA – has commented that 'salad is little more than packaged water'.

Combine on your plate a generous quantity of lettuce and cucumber and radishes, a spring onion or two and some watercress and you are unlikely to be eating much more than one gram of dietary fibre.

The salads in this section are specially devised to make a realistic contribution to your daily fibre intake, and at modest calorie cost.

We haven't included the calorie cost of salad dressings, but we have indicated where they might be nice. Add the modest calorie cost to that of your hi-fi salad. Here is a list of commercial low-calorie salad dressings for you to choose from, followed by some recipes for home-made salad dressings.

Dietade Low-Calorie Salad Dressing without Oil	negligible calories per tablespoon
Waistline Oil-Free French Dressing	5 calories per tablespoon
Heinz Slimway Low Calorie Salad Dressing	20 calories per tablespoon
Waistline Vinegar and Oil Dressing	25 calories per tablespoon

HOME-MADE SALAD DRESSINGS

TANGY TOMATO DRESSING

Calories 5

1 tablespoon tomato juice
1 teaspoon Worcestershire sauce
1 teaspoon lemon juice or vinegar
salt and pepper

Blend all the dressing ingredients together.

YOGURT MINT DRESSING

Calories 10

1 tablespoon low-fat natural yogurt
1 teaspoon lemon juice
½ teaspoon chopped fresh mint or ¼ teaspoon concentrated
  mint sauce
salt and pepper

Blend all the dressing ingredients together.

TOMATO YOGURT SALAD DRESSING

Calories 15

1 tablespoon tomato juice
1 tablespoon low-fat natural yogurt
a pinch of sugar
a pinch of dry mustard
salt and pepper

Blend all the dressing ingredients together.

HI-FI SALADS

PRAWN AND PEPPER SALAD

Calories 100; Fibre 5g

4oz (115g) green pepper, cored, seeded and chopped
2oz (55g) beansprouts
4oz (115g) tomatoes, quartered
2oz (55g) prawns
1 tablespoon lemon juice

Combine all the ingredients and sprinkle with the lemon juice.
   Suggested dressing: tomato yogurt dressing (above).

List of Illustrations

Illustration Acknowledgements:

Every effort has been made to trace all copyright holders but if any has been inadvertently overlooked, the author and publishers will be pleased to make the necessary arrangement at the first opportunity.

Illustration nos 1, 5, 12, 13, 16, 18, 19, 24, 29 are reproduced by kind permission of the Houdini Historical Center, Appleton, Wisconsin

Nos 6, 9, 11, 22, 23, 26, 33, the Library of Congress

Nos 3, 7, 14, 15, 17, the Hoblitzelle Theater Arts Collection, Harry Ransom Humanities Research Collection, The University of Texas at Austin

Nos 27, 28, the Harry Price Library, University of London

Nos 4, 32, Morris Young

The Manacled Diver

On 30 June 1909, it was announced that Harry Houdini would jump, manacled, into the North Sea, just off Aberdeen in eastern Scotland. He would attempt, as he had done on many previous occasions, to free himself from his bonds and surface before his lungs burst. If he failed, he would of course drown.

The attempt was to be made from a point in the bay a little beyond the pierhead at one o'clock. But at midday the harbour authorities told Houdini that they could not permit it: conditions were too unsafe. No small boat could survive the seas that were coming in that squally day. By then, however, hundreds of people had already gathered to watch the jump, and more were arriving every minute.

> Houdini . . . arrived at the dock gates, from which the start in the boat was to be made, and on being informed of the conditions outside the pier, drove out to see what they were like for himself. Returning he expressed his determination to make the dive, and at once got into negotiations with Captain Forbes of the tug John McConnachie, which was lying at Poora Jetty. The captain told him he had no fear of going out into the bay, but with the sea that was on it would be impossible to launch a small boat from the tug for the purpose of picking him up after he came to the surface, as they would probably never get it alongside again. It was proposed that the dive might then be made in the channel, but this part of the water being under the jurisdiction of the harbour authorities, they would not allow of that. By this time thousands of people had arrived on the pier, and they lined the channel all the way from the Poora Jetty to the pierhead, while on the other side of the water there was also a vast crowd. Unwilling to disappoint the spectators who had assembled to see a spectacle, and confident of making the dive even in the stormy weather, Houdini determined to at least go into the bay and see how the sea actually was from

the tug. Accordingly the tug left Poora Jetty with Houdini and his attendants, Mr Gilbert of the Palace Theatre, and a few other passengers. As the pierhead was reached, it was seen that it was absolutely impossible to make the attempt there, the waves being so strong. The seas were coming washing over the prow of the tug, drenching those who were even standing on the bridge. The boat was turned about, and for a time it seemed settled that the dive would have to be completely postponed till some other time. When just about the head of the channel, however, Houdini expressed his determination to carry out his purpose there, if only the necessary permission could be obtained from the harbour authorities. [They] offered no objections. Houdini then at once prepared for action. Having divested himself of his clothes he was manacled by one of the attendants. A heavy chain was put round his neck, crossed on his breast, and each end fastened to his arms above the elbows. His hands were then carried behind his back and heavy handcuffs placed and hooked on his wrists. A small boat having been set down – the sea here was much calmer than out in the bay – to pick him up when he regained the surface, he dived off the bridge, over the right side of the vessel. A strong wind was blowing and it was cold. The pier was crowded with thousands who were all in tense excitement . . . The odds seemed great against the diver. After about 18 seconds he reappeared, his right hand and arm free, and the fetters in his left hand. A lifebuoy was at once thrown to him which he clutched. He was pulled to the side of the tug and hauled on board amid the loud cheers of the spectators on the pier and also from those on board the tug. He went underneath to the engine and got dried and by the time the tug had got alongside the jetty again he was on deck in a long dressing gown apparently none the worse.

He appeared, as always, calm and businesslike. But this was not because he was unaware of the dangers he ran. After a similar jump six months earlier he remarked: 'I expect the grim fiend is following me up in these tricks, and he may catch me some day yet.' The reporter characterised this remark as 'quaint' and 'curious'. But for Houdini the consciousness of a possibly imminent death was as much part of the day's work as the meticulous preparations that must be made before every show, every demonstration. Death was his constant companion. And it was that shadowy figure behind Houdini's compact and muscular frame that the crowd had really come to see.

Otherwise he was alone. How alone, photograph no. 1 shows more poignantly than any words. This picture is actually of a different jump, in Boston: but all the essentials are the same. There is the crowd, tense with concentration, packed into every available cranny. And there, between the bridge and the water, is the small figure of the manacled Houdini. His entourage – his assistants, his wife – followed him everywhere, but finally he was on his own.

Death always loomed: but not, on occasions such as this, too ominously. Houdini's aim in performing these jumps was publicity, not suicide. He had taken his precautions and he knew what he was doing. His team, of course, played a vital part. The reporter noted that it was 'one of his attendants' who fastened the handcuffs and chains. And both the items themselves and the way they were put on were of the utmost importance.

Handcuffs were Houdini's stock-in-trade. He liked to carry a good variety around with him – he listed fifteen different preferred types, light ones which he could easily open. As for how he opened them, the methods varied. Keys and picklocks were the most usual methods; but some, such as the English Regulation cuffs (used in most police stations) could be opened by tapping them sharply in the right place on some hard surface.

In an underwater escape, the cuffs themselves presented even less of a problem than usual. Onstage, it was Houdini's habit to ask for 'challenge' cuffs from the audience, into which he would be locked and from which he would escape. The escape was always done in the privacy of his curtained 'cabinet', with its range of conveniently concealed picklocks. But in an underwater jump there was no time to fiddle around with keys, and no need, either. In the excitement of the moment, with the craning crowds pressing in, the attendant boats filled with journalists and photographers, the sense of a momentous drama about to take place, no one was likely to insist on checking the handcuffs, especially if they looked massive enough – 'heavy', as the Aberdeen reporter noticed. In fact the cuffs on these occasions were almost certainly 'gaffed' – they could be opened without a key.

As for the heavy chain, that served several purposes. One was to add the weight that would pull Houdini quickly down to the bottom, so that he could make his escape in plenty of time without any danger of his methods being spied out. Another was psychological. A long, heavy chain is an impressive-looking thing. But in fact the longer the chain (or piece of rope) the harder it is to tie it so that no slack is left which will facilitate the beginning of an escape. And in Aberdeen (as on every such occasion – this was his invariable procedure), it will be noted that Houdini's hands were handcuffed behind his back *after* he was chained. The visual effect was formidable. But it meant that as soon as his hands were freed he had the use of them to detach himself from the chain.

The stripping down before he jumped, to bathing trunks or even less, was a regular feature of his appearances. He would strip not only for a dive such as this, where it was the natural thing, but under any circumstances and in any location: in a police station, a prison cell, onstage whenever the stunt permitted. Many of his publicity pictures are in the near-nude. One reason for this was to reinforce the sense that he had nothing to hide: where was he to hide it? But, as so often with Houdini, the overt reason concealed and justified more powerful, covert attractions. The publicity photographs, naked in his chains, a posing-pouch just to be made out behind the array of hardware, convey a powerful sexual rush – all the stronger for being completely innocent. Houdini was pre-Freudian. That was an essential element of his act. Its charge lay in his numbing lack of self-awareness.

The crowd naturally knew nothing of all this. As far as they were concerned, they were watching one man pit himself

4

against the elements, with the odds stacked fearfully against him. In their minds they jumped with him; they agonised as, second after second, he failed to reappear; and the tumult when, eventually, he surfaced spoke as much of their own relief as of his triumph. It seemed to them that they had witnessed a miracle. So that with every successful feat, the ambiguity of Houdini's reputation increased. What he did seemed impossible. Was he really nothing more than a mere illusionist?

Rabbits from a Hat

For my sixth birthday, my parents hired a magician. They believed in doing things properly: immigrants' children know about properly. So lots of uncomfortable little gold chairs were set out for us in rows. But we were so entranced that we forgot even to wriggle as the top-hatted, tail-coated conjurer performed his ancient tricks. Eggs and coins appeared from nowhere. Silk handkerchiefs were flourished, singly, before us and placed ceremoniously in the top hat whence they were immediately extracted knotted together in a string. The same hat was turned upside down, shaken, shown to be empty. The next moment, a quivering white rabbit was lifted out and offered to us all to stroke

We knew, of course, that these were tricks, not real magic. But they *seemed* like magic: could they not *be* magic? That was what we would have liked to believe. Harry Houdini once pointed out that 'all magicians are shy of working before children', because children have no preconceived notions of what is going to happen and so are more likely to spot what *is* happening. But there was not in our particular group of polite little girls one of those sophisticates who sits poised to call after every trick: 'I know how you did that, mister!' Our attention was easily beguiled. We looked obediently towards a gesturing right hand while substitutions were made with the left; we concentrated enviously upon a child called to the front to help, while the rabbit was pulled from its pocket inside the conjurer's tail-coat or behind that table whose velvet cloth so conveniently deadened sound, and upon which the top hat was so handily set. Misdirection, the fundamental technique of all illusion, had us in its thrall.

A large part of the enchantment was the very fact that we had no idea what to expect next. In a world where rabbits pop out of hats, anything may happen. We were given no indications. One of the first rules of conjuring is that you don't announce to your audience what it is you are trying to do. You may not achieve it; but if nobody knows what you were attempting, nobody knows you failed. And the more an audience remains in limbo, the more suggestible it becomes.

The parallel between the unpredictable and (to the audience) mysterious world of magic and that of the poor immigrant, set down in a strange country, is a striking one. Where he came from, he knew what to expect. The framework of his world, even if hostile, was familiar and explicable. In the new country, this is no longer the case. Everything is arbitrary. The language, the climate, the clothes, the customs – all are different. There is a more or less total disorientation: a state in which the immigrant is at the mercy of every shark or petty official who chooses to impose upon him. Luck is the only logic. My grandfather, a rabbinical student, told the authorities at Ellis Island that he was a locksmith. Perhaps he thought America was already oversupplied with rabbis. They gave him a lock to pick, and when (being no Houdini) he failed, they sent him back to Europe on the next boat.

No wonder people will put up with so much for so long in the home country. Anything – almost anything – is preferable to being cast adrift. The circumstances of emigrants at home must be extreme. Only famine, unrelenting prospectless poverty or intolerable persecution render life sufficiently unbearable to set off waves of mass migration.

'Mass migration': how the words trip off the tongue. The fleeing multitudes – jamming roads, crowding into transit camps, queuing for rations – are categorised in the mind's filing-system with earthquakes, floods, hurricanes: unavoidable natural phenomena which we may try to ameliorate or choose to ignore. But all these words cloak a million individual terrors. What did Cecilia Weiss imagine when, with her five boys, including Ehrich (the future Houdini), then aged two, she left Budapest, that most European of cities, for New York?

The Weisses were on the run from anti-Semitism. Accord-

ing to Ehrich's younger brother Theodore, who was himself
to become a magician under the stage name Hardeen:*

> Father insulted by prince Erik – challenged to dule – which
> was fought following morning and Father killing his
> opponent then fled to London and stayed there for a time after
> which he took sailing vessel to New York. After reaching
> New York kept going to Appleton Wis. where he had friends
> by the name of Hammel, one being Mayor of Appleton at
> that time. About 1874.
> A short time passed and as there were no syniogues in the
> town, the Mayor wanted to send to Milwaukee for one, but
> up spoke Mr. S. M. Weiss and said 'Why I am a Rabbi' and
> was given the job.
> He at once sent for Mrs. W. and soon after her arrival
> Houdini was born April 6th 1874. And he was named Ehrich
> Prach after Prince Ehrich.

A likely story! The notion that any nobleman of the Austro-
Hungarian Empire, let alone a prince, would sully his sword
by duelling with a lowly Jew is only slightly less implausible
than that (as Weiss family legend had it) a timid student of the
Torah might react to an insult by challenging the prince and
then killing him. Even less likely is it that the victorious rabbi
would, in his triumph, go on to name his newborn son after
his victim. But the bones are there. Budapest, that centre of
urbane civilisation, was not racked by pogroms in the way of
wilder lands further east. But the rigidly hierarchical Habsburg
domain – the Holy Roman Empire – was staunchly and intoler-
antly Catholic. Jews were permitted to live there, but they had
to know their place. Samuel Weiss stepped out of line. He had
to get out. So he made his way to Appleton, where some
compatriots were living; and his family followed him.

The adopted child who invents a romantic family history
for himself is a commonplace; and in the same way every
immigrant must reinvent himself, more or less drastically. The

---

* Neither Hardeen nor Houdini could spell. In all cases I have quoted
from manuscript sources exactly as written.

old rules by which one could place oneself within a society no longer apply. What possible connection was there between the culture of ancient Budapest and the recently-established farming community of Appleton, on the Fox River in the further reaches of the American north-west?

In this situation the facts of the old world lose all importance as facts. They become merely a background against which the reinvented immigrant chooses to set himself off. But of course the history he selects for himself tells us more about him – the reinvented man – than would the pedantic truth about a background now so completely irrelevant. This was particularly true in Houdini's case. His life, which he never ceased to invent, was a gothic fiction, and the beginning of the story had to fit its continuation. So he portrayed his parents as he would have wished them to be: as romantic participants in the cultural and noble life of Budapest.

Nevertheless, some facts are known. It is a fact that Samuel Weiss's first wife was the cousin of a well-known opera singer, Rosa Szillag. She died giving birth to a son, Armin (Herman), in 1863 when Samuel was thirty-four. He naturally wanted to remarry; and Houdini liked to tell how this came about. A bashful friend asked Samuel to propose on his behalf to pretty Miss Cecilia Steiner. Samuel (according to this tale) realised that it was his own feelings he was expressing, and, Miss Steiner preferring the active to the passive suitor, they were married despite the fact that he was thirteen years older than she was, had a small income and few prospects, and already had a child. Their first child died in 1865, but another, Nathan, arrived in 1868, and a third, William, in 1870. In 1874 Erik or Ehrich, the future Houdini, was born.

The family's circumstances in Budapest, like their reason for leaving the city, are obscured by webs of legend. Prince Erik, according to this myth, was not the only royal acquaintance of the Weiss family. Houdini's younger sister, Gladys, wrote to his wife Bess in 1938, twelve years after his death: 'You must remember how our blessed mother would swell with pride when she displayed the worn prayerrug, don't you?

9

I can still hear her boast in her gentle manner, that the Kaiserin Josaphine had walked on it many times when she visited some orphan asylum directly oppisite our home. On these occasions her Royal Highness looked in on our family to pay respect to our important and intellectual dad.' Maybe; then again, maybe not.

The mythologising does not stop there. According to a rumour circulating among American magicians just after Houdini's death, Samuel Weiss was Cecilia Steiner's second husband, and he was not Ehrich's father but his stepfather; Theodore was their first child together. Cecilia's first husband had killed a man in Austria and had been sent to prison.

One can see how this story may have evolved. There is the legend of the fatal duel, now transposed to the first husband; such a tale might also explain the physical dissimilarities between Ehrich and Theodore – the former was a very short man, the latter very tall and burly – and the lack of sympathy between Houdini and his father. But what, then, of William and Nathan? If Rabbi Weiss was no great catch for pretty Miss Steiner, it is hardly imaginable that any respectable man would have taken on the widow and three young sons of a convicted murderer. Houdini had little in common with Samuel Weiss, but that he was his son can hardly be doubted.

Houdini himself always gave his date of birth as 6 April 1874, and its place as Appleton. But there is no record of his having been born in Wisconsin, and in the 1880 census Erick, then aged six, is recorded as having been born in Hungary, as is Theodore, then aged four: only their youngest brother, Leopold, then ten months old, was, according to this document, born in America. Gladys, the youngest, and the only daughter, had yet to arrive. But if there is no record of Ehrich's birth in Wisconsin, there is a certificate attesting to his birth – or the birth of an Erik Weiss – in Budapest on 24 March, 1874; and, although Gladys put up some story of an infant Ehrich having died in Hungary, and Houdini having been named for this dead brother, we may take it that there was only one Ehrich Weiss and that he was born in Budapest.

Why *this* pretence? Could it possibly matter, in America, that land of immigrants, whether or not one was actually born stateside or arrived there at the age of two weeks, or two years? To Cecilia Weiss, apparently, it did matter – for it was she who bestowed the new birthday upon her son. 'Re the Birthdays,' Houdini wrote to Theodore in 1913, not long after she had died, 'I shall *celebrate mine*? always APRIL 6th. It hurts me to think I cant talk it over with Darling Mother and as SHE always wrote me on April 6th, that will be my adopted birthdate.'

Why should Cecilia have minded so much about such a seemingly trivial detail? Perhaps April 6 was the date she and the children arrived in Wisconsin, or at least in America; and perhaps, for her, this signalled the start of a new life, so that Ehrich's life, which was just beginning, started to all intents and purposes on that day. It began, then, as it was to continue: uneasy; opaque; defiantly American.

Metamorphosis

The very first trick ever performed by Houdini on the professional stage was a simple but effective illusion known generally as the Substitution Trunk, though he preferred to call it Metamorphosis. Houdini and his partner would bring a large trunk on to the stage. It was opened and a sack or bag produced from inside it. Houdini, bound and handcuffed, would get into the sack, which was then sealed or tied around the neck. The trunk was closed over the bag and its occupant. It was locked, strapped and chained. Then a screen was drawn around it. The partner (after they married, this was always Mrs Houdini) stepped behind the screen which, next moment, was thrown aside – by Houdini himself. The partner had meanwhile disappeared. A committee of the audience was called onstage to verify that the ties, straps, etc., around the trunk had not been tampered with. These were then laboriously loosened; the trunk was opened; and there, inside the securely fastened bag, was – Mrs Houdini!

Metamorphosis, like invisibility, is one of the great mythic powers. These powers (or the ability to mimic them) remain at the heart of the illusionist's art. When the lady vanishes, or Dr Jekyll turns into Mr Hyde before our very eyes, a delightful conspiracy to believe is enacted between the sceptical brain and the luxuriant, atavistic imagination. We *know* that the substitution was not done by magic; but we remember the princess's kiss releasing the prince from his frog's body, the fairy godmother turning pumpkins into carriages, mice into white horses. The ability to change one's form at will has always been an attribute of gods and fairies. When Danae was imprisoned by her father so that she would be inaccessible to all men – literally, impregnable – Zeus turned himself into a shower of rain and fell into her lap. And if this was the way

to insinuate oneself across barriers, it was also a way of escape.
When the witch Baba Yaga chases the little girl she has been
fattening for her supper, the girl bars her way by means of a
magic comb which turns into a forest when she throws it to
the ground, and a magic handkerchief which turns into a
river.

But offstage, and outside the realms of mythology, escape
and metamorphosis are not so easily achieved. The Weisses
had moved to America, but this did not turn them into Americans. The family settled in Appleton because they had friends
who were already there. This was the usual rule: amid the
uncharted seas of the new country, the greenhorn made for a
familiar rock, or for what is known in Yiddish as *landesleit* –
people from the same place. Thus the ambiguous nature of
the greenhorn's adventure was defined from the beginning.
He would recreate, as far as possible, the old life in the new
home.

Take the question of language. 'Polish,' wrote Eva Hoffman, now an editor of the *New York Times Book Review*, of her
thirteen-year-old self, newly arrived in Canada, 'is becoming a
dead language, the language of the untranslatable past . . .
[English] is beginning to invent another me.' But it is more
difficult for adults to reinvent themselves in this way. The
language of the Weiss household remained German. 'My
mother,' wrote Houdini, 'was educated on the continent and
proficient in five languages. When the family moved to Appleton, Wis., where I was born, she kept in retirement much of
the time and did not take up English studies.' Mrs Weiss never
did learn to speak or write English, and Dr Weiss only tried
to do so when he moved to New York at the age of fifty-nine
– with what little success may be imagined. (The one extant
recording of Houdini's voice shows that he spoke, to the very
end of his life, with a distinctly central European accent, with
very little of an American twang.) This meant not only that
the transactions of everyday life outside the ghetto (which
they thus brought with them) remained problematic, but that

psychologically the elder Weisses remained Hungarian and not American.

Appleton, at the time the Weisses arrived there, had been in existence for nearly thirty years. The first white settler had built his cabin in 1846; the first ten acres of wheat were sown two years later. By 1874 it was a flourishing agricultural community. 'Who that has seen Appleton rise up from the primeval forest within the last twenty years, with her railroads and bridges, her palaces, homes and stately churches, her public schools and noble college . . . can help prophesying for her a brilliant future?' mused the *Appleton Crescent* in 1874. The prophecy was not fulfilled. It is still hard to conceive of a place more totally unlike urbane, cosmopolitan Budapest than the sleepy little town of Appleton, Wis.

On the whole, the Weiss family preferred it. They lived over a store front on the main street; and, despite the differences and the difficulties in their being so adamantly foreign, they were happy there. 'My parents spent the happiest days of their life in that place,' Houdini told the popular novelist Edna Ferber, the second of Appleton's three most famous offspring. (The third was Senator Joe McCarthy.)' . . . It was a great pleasure to Mrs Houdini and myself to know that the "girl" who welcomed me in Appleton has like myself helped advertize that little berg amongst the other inhabitants of America.' He signed himself 'Harry Houdini (From Appleton Wisc.)'.

Some months after his mother's death (she died in the summer of 1913), Houdini wrote to his brother Theodore: 'I actually dreampt of Appleton Wisc a short time back and beheld Pa and Ma drinking coffee under the trees in that park. I ran for camera, as usual, and knew in my dream I had none in Appleton still I searched for it and stopped every once in a while to feats my eyes on both our Parents so calmy drinking and chatting as they did when you and I were romping kids . . . In my dream I feared they would note by my actions that I was excited, but you know how dreams are, only possiby visions of the brains efforts.'

A Freudian interpretation of this dream (by Dr Bernard

Meyer) sees it as an expression of 'the excitement and the fear of being detected' of a boy watching his parents engage in sex, as may well have happened in the various cramped living quarters of that numerous family: this is what the dream conveys when 'stripped of its censorship'. Meyer suggests that this may have been the origin of Houdini's lifelong inability to sleep, brought on by the consciousness that his parents were waiting for the children to go to sleep before they could indulge in sex. Certainly Houdini liked to recount how, as a baby, he had slept hardly at all, his 'eyes roaming around', taking only 'cat-like naps' after which he would be as wide awake as ever. (He used this story in his publicity: it was published in numerous 'souvenir programmes'.) Presumably, since he cannot have been aware of this himself at the time, he had it from his mother. The habit continued. Later in his life he had to wear a black silk blindfold if he was to get any sleep at all.

But to the ordinary reader the scene conjured up is far from sinister. On the contrary, it is a peaceful and pleasant one. In Appleton Dr and Mrs Weiss found what they had been seeking – a haven. Their children grew up ignorant of that anti-Semitism which had propelled them on their great journey. Houdini was deeply shocked when, twenty years later, he registered its existence while he was touring Germany on the crest of his first great wave of success. 'It may interest you to know that although a Jew must be a soldier, he cannot be an officer, as there is a secret feeling among the Europeans against Jews,' he wrote. 'In Bohemia and Austria they think as much of a nigger as a jew, and it has surprised me greatly to think that such things exist in this country.' (Houdini was an ardent Germanophile.) It would not have surprised his parents.

Other conclusions may also be drawn from these letters – as indeed from all the letters this compulsive correspondent ever wrote. The most obvious is that the writer was a man of great intelligence but unhappy with words. His head seethed with thoughts which he wished desperately to communicate: but the most straightforward means of communication – language – was not satisfactorily available to him. He could only express himself in the clumsiest way. His spelling was dreadful, his syntax barely existent. His handwriting was an illiterate scrawl, which is perhaps the reason he typed his letters whenever he could ('Managed to hire a writing machine at last,' he begins the letter describing his dream). In short, it is clear that he had little, if any, formal schooling.

On the face of it, this is surprising. Once they were settled in their new home, why should the Weiss children not have received an education? Appleton boasted not only schools but a college campus (Lawrence, which was progressive enough to admit women as well as men). But the sad fact was that they were *not* settled; and this was because they had failed to metamorphose into Americans.

Not only the language of the Weiss household, but its entire family structure, was that of Budapest rather than Appleton. In contrast with most Jewish immigrants to America, who arrived from muddy *shtetls* to the stony bewilderment of the big city, the Weisses moved from sophisticated Budapest to the backwoods. But in Budapest as in the *shtetl,* the centre of every European Jewish community, its most respected member, was the rabbi – a word which means, simply, 'my teacher'. Intellect was all; every man aspired to be a scholar. Even where he had to spend his working life in business, his spare time would be passed in prayer and disputation. Everything else, the altogether less lofty day-to-day business of coping, was the realm of his wife, who would labour at life's base necessities while her husband removed himself to the world of Torah or Talmud.

There is a special word in Yiddish for this breed of all-encompassing, all-competent homemaker: *balaboosteh.* A successful *balaboosteh* needs considerable drive, fortitude and organisational skills. She is the true adult of the family, the one to whom they all turn, the sheet-anchor.

But while these qualities are recognised, revered and, where possible, lavishly rewarded – as in the well-known figure of the Jewish American Princess – it is taken for granted that the *balaboosteh* will look to her husband for guidance, worldly or spiritual. She needs a strong character – but not so strong that she will not know her place. 'It's not a good thing,' mourned my grandfather when I went to university. 'She'll get a mind of her own. It's not a good thing in a woman.'

Cecilia Weiss was a *balaboosteh*. At home in Budapest she could have coped in spite of the least worldly of husbands. But what was appropriate for Budapest did not do in Wisconsin. What Rabbi Weiss had to teach was irrelevant to Wisconsin – even Jewish Wisconsin. What the Appleton community wanted was someone more like that David Hammel who had invited him there in the first place. Hammel had just the qualities necessary if one was to do well in a frontier town like this, where the Indians had not yet been wholly dispossessed of their lands. The first of these was adaptability. Hammel's name crops up constantly in the local paper, in a variety of capacities. He dealt in horses and lumber, and some years later went into wheat farming and milling. He was active in local politics, and was happy to give a deserving co-religionist a hand up: in 1871, Moses Kahn, who had been a clerk in his employ and had established himself in the town, set himself up in business as a storekeeper, and by 1876, when the Weiss family arrived, was flourishing. But Rabbi Weiss was not of this ilk, and never would be. In Appleton it soon became clear that he was an anomaly. And at his age, he was hardly likely to change. The community wanted somebody more forward-looking – in a word, more American. So in 1882, when the new Temple Zion was built, he was fired.

When Samuel Weiss died in 1892 Cecilia described their marriage as 'twenty-eight years of heaven'. But this heaven certainly bore little relation to their earthly surroundings. Without the rabbi's stipend life could not be sustained in Appleton. So they moved to Milwaukee, a large city with more Jews who might want what Rabbi Weiss had to offer. But his success, or lack of it, may be judged by the number of times they moved from one address to another in that city. They made at least five moves between 1883 and 1887; it is more likely that these were on account of needing to find somewhere cheaper, or having to keep one step ahead of the rent-collector, than because more commodious accommodation was on offer. Of this time Houdini said that 'Such hardships became our lot that the less said on the matter the better.' For the rest of his life, he disliked Milwaukee. In 1912, when he was thirty-eight, he returned there for a week in the course of a tour. 'I did not like it at all,' he told a friend. 'For many reasons, some which I do not care to put in writing.'

All this meant that he was deprived of any real education. The child of a family as poor as young Ehrich Weiss's had more pressing concerns than school. The fact that the son of a Jewish scholar should end up so completely untaught says something about the scale of the family's poverty, or his father's lack of control, or both. However, money had to be earned from somewhere. He recalled selling newspapers and shining shoes on Milwaukee street corners. At some point there seems to have been an interval of enforced study. A scrawled note survives which appears to have been written from some institution, presumably at this period when Ehrich was ten or eleven: 'darling mother at last the time has arrived when I am allowed to write you a few lines how slowly the time passes but still my term will soon be over and we shall be united in happiness again, your loving son Ehrichovitz'.

This is a fairly extraordinary outpouring for a boy to write to his mother, however homesick he may be. In fact Houdini never shrank from exposing the depths of his soul (in so far as he could make them out), often in terms of toe-curling sentimentality compared with which this note is a model of restraint. His mother was already the only one who counted for him. She was the one who kept things together in the pitiless world of America where his father had patently failed. Rabbi Weiss was tolerated with mild affection, a more or less useless appendage, while the boy, and, later, the man, was to spend his entire life yearning to be 'united in happiness' with his mother. These two ever-frustrated desires – to express his soul's contents to the world, to live an ideal life with his mother – were to shape and dominate his life.

In 1885, when he was eleven, Ehrich's elder half-brother Herman died of tuberculosis in New York. Death was to be the third of Houdini's chief preoccupations. This was the first death he encountered personally. A little later, on his twelfth birthday, his father finally admitted defeat. He was never going to be able to provide satisfactorily for his family. He made Ehrich promise to take care of his mother, as long as she lived. On the brink of puberty, adult life and responsibilities had begun.

What was Ehrich to do? Clearly, Milwaukee held few prospects. He decided that the best course would be to leave home and see if he could earn some money. Not long afterwards, a postcard arrived for Mrs C. Weiss (there is no mention of Mr Weiss) at 517 6th Street, Milwaukee: 'I am going to Galvaston, Texas, and will be home in about a year. My best regards to all. Did you get my picture if you didn't write to Mead Bros. Woodstock Ill. Your truant son, Ehrich Weiss.' Houdini later stuck this in a scrapbook and added: 'This postal card mailed by myself when I ran away from home to earn some money. I was on my way to Texas? got into wrong freight car and went to Kansas City Mo. This card was mailed in a place called Withers. I remember being in Hanibal Mo. The post mark on the card reads Hanibal and St Joseph RR. 1886.'

Ehrich did not return to Milwaukee, but worked his way over the next two years to New York. There he found his father, whom he had left in Milwaukee but who had decided to try his luck at running a Hebrew school in the city with the biggest Jewish population in America. Rabbi Weiss was living in Mrs Leffler's boarding house at 244 East 79th Street. He and Ehrich put their money together and found a flat on East 75th Street. The family was summoned from Milwaukee and 'We lived there, I mean starved there, several years.' Later, they moved to 305 East 69th Street, where they were to remain for many years more.

Their poverty was abject. There were certainly a lot of Jews in New York, but not many of them wanted what Samuel (and so many others) had to offer. Ehrich took odd jobs. He was working as a messenger boy one December when he heard his father pacing the floor and muttering in despairing tones, 'The Lord will provide. The Lord will provide.' The resourceful Ehrich lettered a card:

> Christmas is coming
> Turkeys are fat
> Please drop a quarter
> In the Messenger Boy's hat.

Before he came home that evening (or so he said: this story recalls others, and may have been yet another myth) after a successful day, he hid the coins everywhere about himself – up his sleeves, in his hair, in his jacket, behind his ears. When he got home he commanded his mother to 'Shake me! I'm magic!' She obeyed, with gusto: coins sprayed everywhere. There was almost enough to pay the overdue rent.

Once again, the essence, if not the detail, is probably true. But had the Weisses come to America in order to live off what a boy could get by begging?

Back in Hungary, the Weiss family was connected to one of the great conjuring dynasties of the nineteenth century. Samuel Weiss's first wife was a cousin of the opera singer Rosa Szillag or Czillig. She was married to Carl or (as he was usually known) Compars Herrmann, an extremely successful magician known throughout Europe and America in the mid-nineteenth century. ('Compars is the real name,' Houdini was to assure a friend. 'I have copies photographed of his marriage certificate and that is the name that appears and generally ? when a man gets married he usually gives his right name.') Compars was the first magician ever to be invited to perform at the White House, which he did before President Lincoln on 21 November 1861. He was not, however, as famous as his younger brother Alexander, whom he introduced as his legitimate successor at his farewell performance in New York City and who, with his mephistophelean appearance and the assistance of his clever wife Adelaide, became known throughout the world during the 1880s and 90s as Alexander 'The Great'. Compars meanwhile retired with a fortune to Vienna, where he died in 1887 at the age of seventy-two. This was no mere distant connection: 'My dear old Dad and Compars Herrmann were great companions,' Houdini told another magical friend, adding 'and for business reasons have never given out the facts, because they might think that at one time I was seeking publicity.' He never did use the Herrmann connection – possibly the only time in his life Houdini ever passed up the chance of publicity. Reflected glory was not for him.

Young Ehrich never met Compars Herrmann himself. But even when he was a very young child he was fascinated by magic. It spoke to him. 'You know how a fresh kid is,' he told an interviewer. ' "Oh, I see how he does that!" I used to exclaim. The difference between me and most youngsters was that I really did see.'

The abounding tales of his childhood magical exploits carry the mythic fuzz Houdini liked to generate. But there is little doubt as to the actual performance that awoke his obsessional interest in magic. A publicity pamphlet described how 'a circus coming to the town of Appleton, changed the entire world for this boy. He did not carry water to the elephants; instead, he stood amazed in front of the stand, for there he beheld the greatest, most wonderful human being he had ever seen. The man was dressed in a misfitting dress suit, had a goatee and mustache . . . and was taking rabbits out of a black-brown high hat. He cut off a man's arm, leg and head and brought him back to life. He took coins from the air. – The boy was hypnotized. Not coming home for his supper that night, a search was made and they found the boy still at the platform, but by now he was seated on it, the magician taking eggs from his mouth and cards and a spring snake from his coat . . .

By accident the magician dropped or had the misfortune to expose one of the tricks and to the astonishment of the young man, the worshipper of magic, he saw that there was no occult power vested in the performance . . . He gradually solved the problems that were presented, and from that day there was never a magical Santa Claus for the boy.'

Elsewhere, Houdini named this magician as Dr Lynn, and placed the performance in Milwaukee. Dr Lynn's famous trick was *Paligenesia*, in which a man is (apparently) chloroformed, cut up, his component parts tossed in the air, and is finally put back together again and produced whole and sound. The trick is in fact one of the 'Black Arts' family, in which black-clothed assistants moving against a black background can 'disappear' objects or parts of a body by masking them off. Dr Lynn's poster read ANOTHER MAN CUT UP TONIGHT. The performer appeared with a large, dangerous-looking knife and invited volunteers to be cut up. No one would volunteer. So Dr Lynn would usher in his own man, who was then securely tied to a door at the back of the stage. The framing of the stage was very brightly lit and the background to the trick matt black, so that the audience could only see objects that were brightly lit. In the course of the tying-up, the man's right arm and left leg were slipped behind the backcloth and a dummy arm and leg were hooked on, to be unhooked by an invisible black-clad assistant at the crucial moment. The man's head, when the time came to cut it off, would be thrust back into a trap door also covered in black material. When the head was 'severed', a cloth was dropped over it and the head (in fact a head-shaped dummy) was carried away under the cover.

The boy was indeed 'hypnotized' by this performance. The adult Houdini remained fascinated by mutilation: he possessed several grisly and much-thumbed photographs of Chinese executions, by beheading and by the death of a thousand cuts. These were images which spoke to his adult obsessions. But those may well have originated in Dr Lynn's terrifying show. 'I really believed that the man's arms, leg and head were cut off,' he noted in his diary years later. (In 1916, Houdini laid this particular ghost: he bought the illusion from Lynn's son and presented it himself.)

After this, young Ehrich's fascination with circus life knew no bounds. Various stories exist of his childhood exploits. According to one of these, his first public performance was at the age of nine, when he persuaded a visiting circus to pay him thirty-five cents to demonstrate his virtuosity at hanging upside-down and picking up needles with his eyelashes. In another version he began as a contortionist under the title 'Eric, Prince of the Air'. 'Thus, to any young man who has in mind a career similar to mine, I would say: "First try bending over backward and picking up a pin with your teeth from the floor, and work up from that into the more difficult exercises." '

It was at this time, too, that his fascination with locks began. Again the tale is wreathed in hyperbole. A publicity pamphlet tells how his mother locked up her larder so that her sons shouldn't raid it, whereupon Ehrich learned how to pick the lock, leaving Mrs Weiss mystified when she found the door still locked and the pie-plate empty. Or, his anxious parents plucked him away from the circus and apprenticed him to a locksmith. There, 'One day the son of a prominent banker came in with several of his friends to have a pair of handcuffs removed. For a joke, they had slipped the handcuffs on him, but were unable to release him, as they had no key. I found that they had broken off a bit of wire in the keyhole. By the merest accident I discovered the way in which I could unlock the handcuffs, without a key. I took them off and thought no more about it.' In another version, the local policeman had arrested the wrong man but was unable to release him and the locksmith left his apprentice to wrestle with the problem while he and the policeman went off for a drink.

The fascination with locks and magic was certainly genuine, and it persisted. When the family moved to New York in 1888, Theo got a job with a photographer who was an amateur magician and showed him a simple coin trick, which Theo in his turn showed Ehrich. Ehrich proved remarkably adept, and began to read everything about magic he could lay his hands on.

That same year he landed a steady job. Strolling down Broadway he saw a line outside H. Richter's Sons, neck-tie manufacturers. A board announced that an assistant cutter was wanted. He would never get the job if he waited in line – that was clear. So he walked to the front, took down the board, thanked the applicants for their interest and told them the position was filled. Then he walked in, holding the board, and got the job.

This cool and chutzpah were among the skills which would become the basis of his livelihood. He began to cultivate others. One of these was physical fitness. He was an excellent swimmer – good enough to try out for the American Olympic team. He joined the Pastime Athletic Club, whose field on 67th Street and the East River was not far from where he lived. Athletics provided the first outlet for that driving necessity to be first, to be the winner – to defeat all competition – which was to colour the rest of his life. 'I want to be first,' he told a newspaper reporter in 1910, when he was at the height of his fame. 'I vehemently want to be first. First in my profession, in my speciality in my profession. For that I give all the thought, all the power that is in me . . . When I can no longer, goodbye the joy of life for me! So I have struggled and fought. I have done and abstained; I have tortured my body and risked my life only for that – to have one plank on the stage where the imitators cannot come, and one spot where they all fall back and cry "Master!" ' This was the exact truth, then and always. He had not yet begun to push his body to those extremes which his later training involved. But he had begun his life-long abstention from alcohol or tobacco. His father disapproved of them on moral grounds, and the coach at Pastime told him they would undermine his athletic capabilities. He never touched either. He became a good runner; at the age of sixteen he won a prize in the American Amateur Athletic Union mile race but was disqualified for having pre-

viously competed in some unapproved games – 'Be very particular about this in future', admonished the Chairman of the
AAAU in a letter reinstating him.

Photographs taken at this time show a short, compact, well-
knit young man displaying his physique in athlete's strip. He
has the slightly bow-legged stance that was to become one of
his essential professional assets, since it ensured that, however
tightly he was tied up, he could always retain the essential
minimum of slack which would enable him to free one hand.
His grey eyes stare intently out of the picture. He looks very
innocent. An innocent, in many ways, he would remain.

He made friends – Joe Rinn at the Pastime Athletic Club,
Jake Hyman at Richter's tie store – who shared his interest in
magic and everything pertaining to it. Joe and he used to go
to the theatre on passes sent by a friend or on tickets bought
at a cut-price stall. Joe also went to seances from time to time,
and one day he agreed to take Ehrich along. They went to
see Mrs Minnie Williams, a very fat lady who specialised in
materialising the dead before the eyes of their loved ones. Mrs
Williams 'held forth in a house on Forty-sixth Street which
had been made over to her for one dollar by Mrs Anderson,
the widow of a tobacco dealer, who had been her devoted
follower'. Joe was a friend of Mrs Williams' daughter Gertrude. The boys watched as Gertrude collected a dollar each
from about forty people before the seance. They noticed that
each spirit, on leaving, said 'Gawd bless you!' in a hoarse
voice, and that the boards creaked as the spirits walked. Ehrich
was impressed – not by the performance, though he recognised
the bulky Mrs Williams' astuteness (particularly in not trying
to pass herself off as female ghosts, who might be expected
to be more ethereal), but by the easy pickings.

This was the year – 1891, when he was seventeen – that
Ehrich first read the memoirs of Robert-Houdin, the great
French magician of the mid-nineteenth century. The book
transfixed him. It is easy to see why. It is written with all the
panache and elegance which its author reputedly possessed.
But, more than that, Robert-Houdin's story might have been

specially designed to appeal to the seventeen-year-old Ehrich Weiss. It tells of a young man, about Ehrich's own age, who finds himself abandoned and alone. He falls ill and is rescued by an itinerant magician whose pupil and assistant he becomes. Finally he strikes out on his own and, after many hardships and tribulations, becomes the greatest magician of his age, hobnobbing with kings and living in elegance and luxury.

Ehrich's identification with this mythic version of himself was deep and immediate. 'My interest in conjuring and magic and my enthusiasm for Robert-Houdin came into existence simultaneously,' he wrote some years later. 'From the moment that I began to study the art, he became my guide and hero . . . What Blackstone is to the struggling lawyer . . . or Bismarck's life and writings to the coming statesman, Robert-Houdin's books were to me. To my unsophisticated mind, his "Memoirs" gave to the profession a dignity worth attaining at the cost of earnest, life-long effort. When it became necessary for me to take a stage-name, and a fellow-player, possessing a veneer of culture, told me that if I would add the letter "i" to Houdin's name, it would mean, in the French language, "like Houdin", I adopted the suggestion with enthusiasm.'

The 'fellow-player' was Jake Hyman, his friend at Richter's, who now became his ally and partner in magic. They gave, with some success, magical presentations at private parties. Until Jake came up with his momentous suggestion, Ehrich was variously known as 'Eric the Great' or (if he was doing card tricks, at which he was adept) 'Cardo'. 'Houdini' was an improvement on either of these. Quite apart from its reference to Ehrich's hero, it had a definite ring to it. It also sounded vaguely Italian, which was appropriate, since Robert-Houdin's own two mentors in magic both took Italian names, although both were Frenchmen: it was always vogueish for magicians to have Italian names. Ehrich had already been Americanised to Harry for most of his friends.

So Ehrich Weiss metamorphosed into Harry Houdini in the great substitution trunk that was America. He and Jake Hyman (who now became Jack Hayman) decided to take to the road and try their luck as The Houdini Brothers. Richter's wrote him a reference in case of future need:

H. RICHTER'S SONS
502 & 504 Broadway

New York, April 3, 1891.
To Whom It May Concern:

We hereby certify that Mr. Ehrich Weiss has been in our employ for two years and six months as assistant lining cutter and we cheerfully recommend him as an honest, industrious young man.

H. Richter's Sons.

Aaron's Rod

What rabbi would wish to see his brightest son throw up a steady job in the *shmatteh* trade, a business where Jewish boys traditionally make good (or at least make a living), in order to take up the uncertain life of a travelling conjurer? Rabbi Weiss had little time to brood: in 1892, almost as soon as the decision had been taken, he made the final abdication and died. Ehrich repeated to the dying man the promise that he had made on his twelfth birthday, about how he would always look after his mother. Then the Houdini Brothers (Jack Hayman was soon replaced by Theo as the subsidiary member of the duo) took to the road.

It appeared highly improbable that the promise would ever be fulfilled. No one was more keenly aware of this than Ehrich himself. When, many years later (in 1912), he finally achieved a salary of $1,000 a week in New York, he requested his first week's pay in gold, drove straight to his mother with the bag of coins and emptied them into her apron. (This melodramatic gesture is notably similar to the 'Shake me, I'm magic' incident of his poverty-stricken youth.) He always described this moment, when he finally and so spectacularly fulfilled his promise, as the greatest thrill of his life. In 1892, however, his did not seem a realistic choice. My son the doctor – yes (that was to be Leopold, the youngest Weiss boy); my son in neckties – possibly; but my son the conjurer?

Yet young Harry, as he was henceforth known, was only following in an ancient tradition – as Rabbi Weiss might have realised. Do not conjuring tricks of one sort and another lie at the very roots of Jewish history? What else facilitated the departure from Egypt of the children of Israel? It will be recalled that Pharaoh was at first most unwilling to let them go and had to be frightened into doing so by means of a series of wonders, beginning with Aaron's Rod. 'And Moses and Aaron went in unto Pharaoh, and they did so, as the Lord had commanded, and Aaron cast down his rod before Pharaoh and before his servants, and it became a serpent. Then Pharaoh also called for the wise men and the sorcerers; and they also, the magicians of Egypt, did in like manner with their secret arts. For they cast down every man his rod and they became serpents; but Aaron's rod swallowed up their rods.'

Even though Aaron's rod thus demonstrated its superiority, Pharaoh remained unimpressed, which was hardly surprising, since his own priests had showed that they knew the same trick. (It is still to be seen in Egypt today, where snake charmers paralyse snakes by applying pressure to a point on the neck, when the snake uncurls and looks like a stick.) More powerful magic was evidently called for; so God weighed in with the ten plagues (frogs, lice, murrain, rivers of blood, the slaying of the first-born, etc.) and climaxed this performance with the parting of the Red Sea.

The earthly impresario of all this was of course Moses, Aaron's elder brother and the founder of the Jewish religion. Moses is best known as the deliverer of the Ten Commandments. But in surviving fragments of ancient alchemical and magical literature, he figures as the author of secret magical texts. His activities while he was leading the Israelites through the wilderness suggest that he was familiar with, among other things, what became known as *natural magic* – the use of natural laws to apparently magical effect. With the help of his young assistant, Joshua, he arranged terrifying phenomena designed to strike awe into the hearts of the Israelite masses and make sure they kept well away from the scene of operations. When God dictated the Commandments, 'all the people perceived the thunderings, and the lightnings, and the voice of the horn, and the mountain smoking; and when the people saw it, they trembled, and stood afar off'. This allowed Moses the forty days and forty nights he needed to produce the tablets of stone inscribed with the Commandments. Similarly, when the Tent in which Moses was to receive God's word was pitched some way from the Israelites' camp, only Joshua was allowed inside. 'And it came to pass, when Moses entered into the Tent, the pillar of cloud descended and stood at the door of the Tent; and the Lord spoke unto Moses . . . face to face, as a man speaketh unto his friend.' Or so Moses assured them. The Israelites were naturally terrified, and maintained a respectful distance. Joshua, however, remained inside the Tent throughout, stage-managing the effects. He later became an impressive performer in his own right, bringing down the walls of Jericho by blowing his trumpet. Jesus continued the magical tradition, raising Lazarus, performing his trick with the loaves and fishes, having his friends walk on water and, finally, resurrecting.

So the evolution of Houdini from rabbi's son to vaudevillian in nineteenth-century America was less bizarre than it seems. And a good many other rabbis' sons were following much the same path. In 1918, Houdini was to form the Rabbis' Sons Theatrical Association. Houdini was President, Al Jolson First Vice-President, and Sergeant Irving Berlin Second Vice-President of this highly exclusive society. Its members had to be sons of rabbis or Jewish scholars. The original name of Jolson's family (it is tempting to say, their 'real name': but under these circumstances, is any one name more, or less, real than another?) was Joelson. They were immigrants from Russia, his father an orthodox rabbi and cantor who, like Rabbi Weiss, was appalled by his son's chosen career. Irving Berlin's father, Moses Baline, was also a cantor, also from Russia. Other big show-business names shared the same background. Louis B. Mayer's father, though an unsuccessful businessman rather than a rabbi, solaced himself with religion; as a very young boy, Louis was expected, as was Ehrich, to act as both an emotional and financial prop to his father. Adolph Zukor, from Hungary like the Weisses, was the son and brother of rabbis. The Warner Brothers, the Shuberts, George Gershwin, Fanny Brice, all shared the rabbinical heritage.

It was not as if these people were products of a particularly theatrical tradition. The cantor's role is a fairly operatic one, but no more so than that of, say, a Greek or Russian orthodox priest. And the traditional Jewish fields of excellence had been in the classical and intellectual arts – music, science, mathematics, philosophy – not those of popular entertainment. These were the acknowledged routes out of the ghetto. 'All the folk in our circle – brokers, shopkeepers, clerks in banks and steamship offices – used to have their children taught music,' wrote Isaac Babel. 'Our fathers, seeing no other escape from their lot, had thought up a lottery, building it on the bones of little children. . . . And in fact, in the course of ten years or so our town supplied the concert platforms of the world with infant prodigies. From Odessa came Mischa Elman, Zimbalist, Gabrilowitsch. Odessa witnessed the first steps of Jascha Heifetz.'

What, then, impelled this particular group of people so supremely to express the popular soul of everyday America? Perhaps it was their extraordinary devotion to America, their desire to proclaim their Americanness. In 1917, when America joined the first world war, Houdini wrote to a friend: 'I register tomorrow for enlisting. HURRAH, now I am one of the boys.' He was by then forty-three, and was rejected on grounds of age; but that did not stop him doing his bit. He cut down on his professional engagements in order to give free performances at war benefits and for the soldiers in training camps and canteens. For two years he more or less devoted himself to this work, responding to all requests and usually travelling at his own expense. If he could not go and suffocate in the mud with the young recruits, he could at least give them a little fun – and something more tangible: his favourite trick for the boys was an old standby, *Money for Nothing,* in which he produced an endless stream of coins out of thin air. Whenever he performed in front of men just about to sail for Europe, he would conjure up a succession of five-dollar gold pieces and present one to each of the soldiers. He managed to give away more than seven thousand dollars of his own money in this fashion; furthermore, by the time of the Armistice he had sold $1,000,000 worth of Liberty Bonds, singlehanded. Others were not to be outdone in their devotion to their homeland. Louis B. Mayer, like Houdini, adopted a symbolic American birthdate – in his case the most symbolic of all: his official birthday was July 4. So was George M. Cohan's (his real birthdate was July 3).

Although my own family's devotion to England, their adopted country, was and is exemplary, I can't imagine any of them expressing it in quite this way. It isn't the English style (and anyhow, what day would one choose? Shakespeare's birthday? The Queen's?). The gesture would seem ridiculous: *un*-British. It is hard for any Jew ever entirely to forget that he lives where he does usually because his family, in the recent or not-so-recent past, was thrown out of somewhere else. And in Europe, with its ancient and established national cultures, this does not make for a sense of belonging. Whenever a Jew – a politician, a businessman, a criminal – attracts too much attention, fellow-Jews shake their heads and exchange significant glances. It is generally agreed that this is not good policy. Jews should keep their heads down, practise good citizenship, and feel grateful for being allowed to live peaceful, unpersecuted lives.

But this attitude is essentially European, not American. If the Jews in America had been compelled into emigration by forces beyond their control, then so had almost everybody else. When the Weisses and Balines and all the others arrived at Castle Garden, they were only the latest in an endless stream – of Irish, Poles, Germans, Swedes – all there for similar reasons; all striving to make their way. When the Jewish immigrants arrived in America from the ghettos of eastern Europe, they found themselves *for the first time* in a society where they were merely members of the ruck of common humanity: nothing special.

Houdini's generation knew what their parents' experience had been. They could never forget it: it was their family history. However much it was dressed up with stories about princes and royal connections, the Weiss family legend was about being thrown out of Budapest because they were Jews. But where this had been the central fact of Mr and Mrs Weiss' lives, for the children it was just a story. First-generation Jewish parents were irretrievably locked into the ghetto they carried around with them. But the children, triumphantly, uniquely, could escape into being Americans. Shocked by his first encounters with German anti-Semitism, Houdini wrote: 'It may exist in America, but never that I have known. I never was ashamed to acknowledge that I was a Jew, and never will be, but it is awful what I hear from people that are Jew Haters, and do not know that I am a Sheeney.' He may have led a particularly sheltered existence. But the fact remained that anti-Semitism could never become a part of semi-official policy in America, as it was almost everywhere in Europe.

Of course, American Jews might not seem as wholly American to their fellow-Americans as they liked to think. When Ben Hecht asked David O. Selznick to sponsor an appeal for the formation of a Jewish army in Palestine to fight in World War II, Selznick refused: 'I don't want anything to do with your cause for the simple reason that it's a Jewish political cause. And I am not interested in Jewish political problems. I'm an American and not a Jew.' Hecht then challenged Selznick to name three people whom they would telephone and ask whether they considered him an American or a Jew. If one of them answered 'an American', Selznick would win. None did.

But, because this was America, not Europe, how others might view them was a secondary matter. Houdini's Americanism was something he was as entitled to as anyone else, and his life's work became an expression of this new sensation, unique to his generation: the knowledge that he was, first, an American, and only incidentally a Jew. This was a matter of especial pride and hope for him. And when Houdini, the archetypal little man, took on authority in its grimmest and most symbolic form and stepped magically free from the most savage restraint, all Americans and a good part of the rest of the world rejoiced with him.

Not that the dream was unmixed with disappointment or anger. E.Y. Harburg, who wrote the songs for *The Wizard of*

Oz, said: 'To be a Jew in New York at the turn of the century was a terrible adventure. From a very early age, I was aware of the power of the imagination to make people better, more peaceful and friendly. How to make people decent? How to soften them up so they'd know more compassion? These questions were very important to my life. It was part of my psyche which songwriting finally answered.' Indeed, anger was the propelling force behind a great many of these super-optimistic, super-American men. Louis B. Mayer, the Cohns, the Warner brothers, were known for their bouts of uncouth fury. Irving Berlin became a recluse. Houdini's whole act could be seen as an expression of anger – anger at having been held down; an anger he would later turn against himself.

Thus, far from starting at a disadvantage, Houdini's pedigree could not have been more apposite for his time and ambitions. Nor could his character. The Jews who made it big in show business in the early twentieth century were driven men. Their drive was not just the common American drive to make money (though they had that as well). But there were a thousand easier, surer ways to get rich. No: they were driven to share their compulsions with the public. They needed a stage, in the most literal sense, to work out their inner lives. And, in the most literal sense, they found it.

Houdini began in the smallest possible way: by scraping up engagements in dime museums such as Huber's, on 14th Street, which presented a series of acts – freaks, strong men – of the kind commonly associated with circus side shows. Then he ventured further afield. In Coney Island he worked with a strong man in a tent for 'throw money' – that is, they had no entry fee to rely on, but passed the hat round after the act.

After a while he saved enough to buy his first illusion. The magic press was filled with advertisements offering trick methods and equipment for small sums of money. Houdini himself, when he fell on hard times a few years later, produced his own catalogue of such offers. For the kind of money in question – amounts ranging from fifty cents to ten dollars – there would be no question of buying the exclusive use of a trick, although in the top echelons of the profession large sums changed hands and there was always a lot of bad blood about infringements of rights and revelations of secrets belonging to other people.

Houdini's illusion was the trunk and rope-tie trick he called Metamorphosis. This he presented, first with Jack Hayman, and later, when the two fell out, with his brother Theodore, or Dash – as he was generally known, possibly on account of his penchant for sharp dressing, but more probably because it was an anglicisation of his Hungarian name, Deszo. Harry and Dash travelled to Chicago, where Harry managed to get a booking at Kohl and Middleton's dime museum on the Midway at the 1892 World's Columbian Exposition. He gave twenty shows a day, for twelve dollars a week – sleight-of-hand, rope-ties of the kind used by spirit mediums and described in a number of books exposing the mediums' fraudulent ways, card tricks. By 1893 he had introduced a handcuff act: this marked the first appearance of 'Harry Houdini, Handcuff King and Escape Artist'. This personage, however, as yet held no interest for the public, any more than any of the other incarnations of Harry Houdini.

Still, he had made the great step out of the ghetto and into that other world he would henceforth inhabit. This was a world equally self-contained and removed from ordinary society: the nomadic world of the travelling entertainer whose home is a hotel room in whatever town he plays (once, that is, he has risen to the point where he can afford hotels). In a sense, Houdini had returned to his earliest roots. What was Moses but a travelling showman who, by sheer force of personality and skill of presentation, managed to lead his troupe forth from the unpleasant certainties of Egypt to a life on the road, replete with discomforts, uncertainties, and hope?

5

Two Ladies

Unquestionably the most important person in Houdini's life was his mother. If he could have cloned her, so that she need never leave his side, how delightful life would have been! Magic, as so often, provides a metaphorical solution. Among the notes Houdini left at his death was a charming variation on the old trick of sawing a woman in half. In this, a long rectangular box is shown standing on a large square platform. The box has two doors in front and two doors on top. These are opened, and the platform turns around showing the box from all sides. Then a large woman steps into the box and the doors are closed. Two sawhorses are carried in and set in front of the platform. Each front door of the box has a window with a small curtain. The illusionist raises one of these to speak to the woman: it turns out to be the foot end. So he raises the other: her head is duly in place. The assistants carry the box to the sawhorses and saw it in two. When this is done the two half-boxes are turned with their open ends towards the audience. The half-lids are raised: out of each steps a girl dressed just like the original woman.

Reality being less easily manipulated, mothers are not readily subdivided. So other steps must be taken. In 1894 Houdini had just turned twenty. He evidently concluded that the time had come when he ought to have a wife. So – abracadabra! – he found one. Traditionally, the magician sits his assistant on a chair, covers her with a cloth, waves a wand, and when he whips the cloth away – she has vanished. In Houdini's case it was the other way about. One moment, there was nobody; the next, there she was.

To say his marriage was sudden is an understatement. Houdini gave an account of it, emotionally true if factually inaccurate, in a magazine interview: 'One day I was hired to give an exhibition at a children's party in Brooklyn. At the close a little girl, about sixteen, said to me very bashfully, "I think you are awfully clever," and then, with a blush, "I like you." "How much do you like me?" I said, "enough to marry me?" We had never seen each other before. She nodded. And so, after talking the matter over, we were married.'

Mrs Houdini's own recollections are different, though scarcely less abrupt. According to her, Houdini had arranged to give a show at her high school. Wilhelmina Beatrice Rahner (usually known as Bessie or Bess) was just eighteen. She persuaded her mother, who thought all theatre wicked, to let her attend. Mrs Rahner and Bess sat in the front row. In the course of the show the young magician upset some acid on a table; it spilled over and, to Mrs Rahner's fury, spoiled Bess's dress. Houdini was devastated. But Bess was smitten. Some days later, he came to the house and asked if he could have the old dress, as he wanted to get a new one to replace it and needed to be sure the replacement would fit. Since he had no money to buy a dress, Mrs Weiss sat up nights for a week constructing one. When Houdini brought it round, Bess was thrilled, ran upstairs to put it on, then slipped out with Houdini while her mother was busy elsewhere. Houdini suggested they go to Coney Island. Bess, who had never been out on her own before, suddenly began to worry what her mother would say. 'If you were my wife they wouldn't dare punish you,' cried Houdini fiercely. Bess, not unnaturally, was startled at this sudden proposal – if that was what it was. No sooner said than done. They passed a second-hand jewellery store, and went in to try on wedding-rings. Having selected one, Houdini found he had hardly any money. Luckily, Bess had some, so they bought the ring together. They then went to visit the local ward boss, whose name was John Y. McKane. At first he refused to marry them. But, when he saw their determination, his heart softened. They acquired a licence and were 'properly married by the Boss of Coney Island, with two ward heelers as witnesses. The date was June 22, 1894.'

Thus Bess's account of the affair in the biography of Houdini she commissioned and oversaw in 1928, soon after his death. But a few pages later she reproduces a newspaper clipping which indicates that the truth was something else again. The *Coney Island Clipper* reports: 'The brothers Houdini, who for years have mystified the world by their mysterious box mystery, known as 'Metamorphosis', are no more and the team will hereafter be known as the Houdinis. The new partner is Miss Bessie Raymond, the petite soubrette, who was married to Mr Harry Houdini on July 22 by Rev. G. S. Loui, of Brooklyn. Harry has bought his brother's interest in the act, and he and Miss Bessie Raymond will hereafter perform it.'

'Miss Bessie Raymond, the petite soubrette'? Can this be the same demure schoolgirl whose mother thought all 'shows' were wicked? Yet another clipping gives yet another picture. The story was printed on the wedding date given by Mrs Houdini, and the one the Houdinis always celebrated as their anniversary: 22 June, 1894. 'Risey [a local wag who had been persecuting the "Hunyadi brothers", a misspelling of Houdini] ran afoul of one of the Hunyadi brothers who was taking one of the Floral Sisters, "neat song and dance artistes", for a stroll between turns. He had heard of Risey's boasts and he glared at him. Risey passed the word about "fakers and fake box tricks." . . . The Brothers Hunyadi offered Risey $100 if he could fathom the secret of their box . . .' The Floral Sister was Bess, who had run away from her severe and joyless mother. The Floral Sisters were on the same bill as the Houdini Brothers. Dash had arranged to meet the sisters on the beach. Harry saw Bess: the *coup de foudre* ensued. For the next two weeks they were inseparable. Then they disappeared, and reappeared announcing that they were married. The marriage did nothing to reconcile Bess with her mother, an implacable and rigidly Catholic German lady who had to cope with eight other daughters and a son besides. Here was a son-in-law who was not only a magician, but Jewish! For years, she would sprinkle the pictures in her house with purifying holy water every time he visited. Even a second wedding ceremony, a

Catholic one this time, could not mollify her. To cover all eventualities, they also got themselves married by a rabbi. 'I'm the most married woman I know,' Bess used to say. 'I've been married three times and all to the same man.' She and Mrs Rahner were not reconciled until twelve years later, when Bess fell dangerously ill and wanted to see her mother. Houdini, supported by one of his brothers, went round to his mother-in-law's and camped in her front room until she agreed to come back with him. After that, 'he was the same as a son to her'.

In the meantime, however, Bess would not lack for a mother. She could have Houdini's: indeed, she would have to. Mrs Weiss had not been present at the wedding. This was an omission so notable, given Houdini's emotional dependence on her, that it makes one wonder whether he would have been able to bring himself to marry at all if she – his first love – had actually been there with him. As it was, he had imperatively to obtain her immediate approval of this momentous step. Almost the first thing he did after the wedding was take his bride home to meet her.

Bess was afraid that Mrs Weiss would be as horrified by her son's having married a Roman Catholic as Mrs Rahner had been by her Jewish son-in-law. She need not have worried. She was welcomed with open arms into the Weiss household, poor and crowded though it was. 'I was perhaps fortunate in that the Weisses had several sons and only one daughter,' Bess commented. (The daughter, Houdini's little sister Gladys, was the youngest child.) The night they arrived, with so little room in the apartment, Harry had to sleep with one of his brothers, while Bess found a shakedown with some neighbours across the landing. They went on to find a furnished room. Mrs Weiss had to lend Bess a skirt, because in her own clothes the new Mrs Houdini looked so much like a little girl that lodging-house keepers became suspicious. She was tiny and slight with a sweet, childish face and curly hair, and looked about twelve years old.

'Two ladies,' sings the M.C. in the musical *Cabaret*,

Two ladies
And I'm the only man.
I like it
They like it
This two for one . . .

Did 'they' like it? A letter from Houdini to his wife, written years later, indicates that relations between the mother and the wife were not always so easy. 'My dear girl, where as I say you are mine, my mother claims me as her son. So the two loves do not conflict,' he wrote. But the fact that he felt it necessary to reassure her shows that, on the contrary, in Bess's view conflict they did. How could they fail to? And how could Bess, the newcomer, the interloper, fail to feel jealous?

Here, as throughout their relationship, Bess's view may only be obliquely made out. She hints at her frustrations, but never directly expresses them. There exist hundreds of letters, notes and postcards written by Houdini to his wife, but none from her to him. This says as much about the compulsive nature of Houdini's letter-writing as about Bess's mute acquiescence in the role he mapped out for her. The two were rarely apart: Houdini would frequently write to her from another room in the same house. But it may not be entirely coincidental that notes in Bess's hand begin to appear in the Houdini papers only after his death in 1926. It is as if she only then could begin to emerge as a person in her own right.

There are, however, clues to Bess's view of her life with Houdini. They emerge in the biography she commissioned soon after his death, which was written by Harold Kellock, a professional journalist, with her full co-operation and assistance. Houdini enthusiasts dismiss this book as over-romanticised, 'Bess's view of events'. But for this very reason it is sometimes revealing. And although it may be romanticised – for the period just after Houdini's death was, as might be expected, the period when Bess's view of her late husband was least critical – the fact remains that the events it describes are events in which she participated.

There is nothing in the Kellock book to indicate any tension between Mrs Weiss and Mrs Houdini. Although there must have been difficult moments, it seems clear that there existed a genuine affection between them. '[Mrs Weiss's] instant acceptance of me was the more beautiful because Houdini's love for his mother had dominated his life completely,' Bess remarks. 'After my coming there were of course two loves in his life, running parallel, so to speak. But never was there any sense of clashing or of division. As I look back at this, I realise that the perfect smoothness of our relationship was largely due to the mother's fine sense of human values and rare generosity of spirit. She kept her son's devotion and she made me feel that her life was enriched by my affection for her and by his happiness with me.' As to this happiness, husband and wife both described it in fulsome and rather similar terms. 'We were romantically in love to the end,' says Bess, while Houdini, on their thirtieth anniversary, described his marriage as 'still a Honeymoon'.

A honeymoon! There's a word to take you back. In the days when honeymoons still happened, their gruesome nature was a byword. The orgy was licensed to take place at last: but all rarely went as it should have done when the music stopped and the guests went home and the inexperienced young couple were left face to face. 'Honeymoon' is about moon and June and romance; the cold shock of reality is not catered for. Few married couples of thirty years' standing would describe themselves as 'romantically in love', nor their relationship as 'a honeymoon', and few would think that relationship diminished thereby. If they are still together, they have long since progressed to the pleasures of genuine intimacy. The Houdinis' descriptions of their marriage ring true, however. For the quality which most strongly characterised the emotional plane of this strange relationship was total unreality.

Adorable
Sunshine
of my Life,

> I have had my coffee, have washed out this glass, and am on
> my way to business.
> Houdini
> 'My darling I love you'

wrote Houdini to his wife in one of the countless notes he used to leave around the house for her to find; and the inverted commas around the expression of feeling perhaps convey more than was intended. Why should love exist only between inverted commas? It is as if he were suddenly struck dumb when it came to expressing his feelings – as if he could grope his way through the aphasia only by using someone else's clichés. Very often, in fact, he would literally do just that: he would clip some terrible piece of saccharine doggerel, the kind of thing you might find inside birthday cards or valentines, and paste it on to the end of his notes.

One might be tempted to conclude that the feelings thus expressed were as impersonal, as shallow and insubstantial, as the awful verses themselves. (*What is there in the Vale of Life/ Half as delightful as a wife* . . .) But this is not necessarily the case. Houdini did exactly the same thing when writing to or about his mother; and of the depth of his feelings for *her* there can be no shadow of doubt.

As strange as their expression is the fact that his love-letters to both his mother and his wife took exactly the same form. The quality of his love for his mother, in tune with the role imposed upon him at such an early age by his father, was more than what is generally associated with the filial. But, the feelings he so laboriously and literally tried to spell out in his letters to Bess were something less assured – something much more self-conscious – than those which usually exist between husband and wife. The role of son came naturally to him; but the role of husband was one which he was forever gingerly trying out. In language and sentiment he could not differentiate between the two.

★

Bess's account of her early married life is fairly fragmentary. The first emotion she records is disorientation and alarm as she takes in the strangeness of the universe she has entered. Houdini's world seemed normal, natural and inevitable to him. His family were of course used to him; and as for his friends, they were all very young (Houdini was only just twenty when he married) – and boys of that age tend to accept their peers without giving much thought to the springs of character and motivation. But for Bess, this was to be no superficial acquaintance, and her first glimpse of life with Houdini did not reassure her. 'Within a few days after my marriage,' she wrote, 'I began to realize that I had stepped into a world far different from my former well-ordered and sheltered life, a world of strange duties, strange contacts, and inexplicable happenings which my superstitious nature magnified into terrors.'

This world was characterised, both physically and emotionally, by a scene which took place after the Houdini Brothers' last performance together.

Houdini asked his brother and me to take a walk with him after the evening's work was over. He led us into the country on a dark, lonely bridge spanning some swiftly running black water. It was a weird-looking night, with a split moon that seemed to be dodging in and out behind heavy clouds. In the middle of the bridge he halted us, and there we waited for a time silently, I at least in growing trepidation.

Finally a distant bell tolled solemnly twelve times. As soon as the last beat ceased to reverberate, Houdini clasped his brother's hand and mine together, raised them aloft and cried: 'Beatrice, Dash, raise your hands to heaven and swear you will both be true to me. Never betray me in any way, so help you God.'

His brother and I repeated the vow after him. Then Houdini kissed me and shook Theodore's hand. 'I know you will keep that sacred oath,' he said.

This scene rings entirely true. Throughout his life Houdini was in the habit of demanding of his close associates that they swear undying loyalty on pain of death or worse. All his assistants had to sign such fealty oaths, couched in language as dramatic as Houdini could contrive. Through these scenes Houdini reassured himself that his interests would always come first, not only in his own mind but in the minds of all those who might be close to him. And in order to convince himself that this had been achieved he needed to stage a drama, to script the scene as he would script a play; as he scripted all the important moments of his life; as he scripted, indeed, his love-letters. This blurring of the boundaries of his private and his public life was to be one of the secrets of his charisma – that quality which ensured, from the moment of his first great success, that when he set foot upon a stage, audiences would be mesmerised by him. What the audiences were witnessing was the drama of the inner man. But the converse was also true: his closest friends, his brother, his wife, were faced with this curiously un-private figure, who was unable to see his intimate life other than in terms of the role he should be playing, and the roles *they* should be playing alongside him.

From the first, the marriage was conducted on this histrionic basis. Bess relates a couple of incidents which took place about a year after they were married. In one, she insisted upon going to see a show which Houdini, obsessively uncomfortable with any hint of the risqué, had forbidden. 'He said the show was unfit for me and if I disobeyed him he would spank me and send me home. Naturally after that warning I went to the show. He followed me, carried me out, spanked me thoroughly, divided all our poor savings, led me firmly to the railroad station, bought my ticket to Bridgeport where my sister lived, and put me on the train . . . At the last minute, lifting his hat courteously, he said: "I always keep my word. Good-bye, Mrs Houdini." My heart was breaking, and I was on the edge of hysteria, but the memory of the spanking rankled and enabled me to reply with a pretence of calm dignity: "Goodbye, Mr Houdini." . . . Six hours later, at 2 a.m., the bell rang and I heard Houdini's voice. I flew to the door, and we fell into each other's arms, weeping. "See, darling," said Houdini, "I told you I would send you away if you disobeyed, but I didn't say I wouldn't fly after you and bring you back." ' On another occasion, it was Bess who lost her temper. Whenever this happened, Houdini would walk round the block, return, open the door, and throw his hat into the room. If the hat flew out again, Bess was still angry. This time, the hat was promptly returned more than once. An hour passed; then a messenger appeared with a note 'To be delivered in a Hurry to Mrs Houdini, then Exit Rapidly'. It read: 'Mr Houdini wishes to inform Mrs Houdini that the globe fell out of his hands, but the second one slipped. He wishes to convey his sorrow, and promises that the one that fell will never fall again. Mr Houdini, Friend Husband.' Bess comments that 'It was impossible to be angry very long with a husband like that.' But the reader is left marvelling at the nature of this marriage in which, at the end as at the beginning, the protagonists addressed each other as 'Mr Houdini' or 'Mrs Houdini' – for this was still their habit right up until the day Houdini died thirty-two years later.

Bess was also struck early on by the double standards her husband applied in his dealings with the world. She gives an example: When a girl, Bess was deeply superstitious. 'My own entire family believed in ghosts, witches, and the power of the evil eye and lived in a constant dread of supernatural evils.' Houdini scolded her about this and set about teaching her the error of her ways. He did this by playing a trick which scared her half to death. Her father had died some years before; she had never told her husband his first name. Houdini told her to write that name on a slip of paper, crumple it up, and then burn it in the gas jet. After that, she was to rub the ashes onto his arm – and lo! the name, Gebhardt, appeared in letters of blood . . .

'I was paralyzed with fear. Then, slowly, a full realization of this diabolical thing dawned on me. In my early folk-lore, the devil, disguised as a handsome young man, lured girls to destruction. It was clear to me that I had married the devil . . .'

In fact this was nothing but a simple trick. If you write on your arm with a sharp instrument and then rub it hard, what you wrote will come up red. Houdini wanted to show Bess how it was done so that she would henceforth abandon her superstitions. He knew she was unaware he had found out her father's name (not hard to do, given all those sisters); and he knew, from his experiences of spiritualist seances, how effective such unexpected details can be.

But although he relentlessly attacked other peoples' superstitions, he was never a sceptic himself. Later in his life, he set about exposing false mediums, bringing all his habitual vehemence to that task; but the roots of his fury lay in thwarted hopes, not stony materialism. At the start of their life together, Bess realised that although he might denounce *her* superstitions, he cherished his own. For instance, he would not perform on Friday the thirteenth. Such inconsistencies never bothered him. He proceeded upon his sternly moralistic way as if his own lapses from the standards he imposed upon others simply did not occur. In his own mind, they did not: and that was all that mattered.

So Bess was expected to take her place as a member of Houdini's supporting cast – unquestioningly. Questioning was the one thing he would never put up with. It threw him into a fury. And yet in many ways their marriage was, more than most, a genuine partnership. Few married couples then worked literally side by side – indeed, few do so today. A magician, moreover, relies absolutely on his assistant. As a partner, Bess, small and lithe, was a considerable improvement on the large and lumbering Dash. There were those who thought that this was the principal reason for Houdini's wanting to marry her. Not only would she be a better performer, but half the takings would not have to be handed over to Dash. There may have been something in this; but it could never have been the whole story.

In Kellock's biography Bess recounts her shock when she first realised Houdini expected her to be his stage partner – though if she was already performing as a Floral Sister, this can hardly have been too overwhelming. True, the role of magician's assistant carried with it certain humiliations for a delicately-brought-up young lady. She would be expected to wear tights, and her figure would be the object of dispassionate appraisal. The fashion was for bosomy, well-built ladies: 'What the hell d'you think I'm running – a kindergarten?' demanded one burlesque-show manager when she presented herself. But on this level a true companionship developed between them. 'It was pleasant . . . to practice tricks with Harry and to be initiated into the secrecy of his mysteries,' she remembered.

Marriage is a bespoke garment: what fits one is unlikely to fit another. On its own terms, the Houdini marriage worked. Those terms were Houdini's. Within his world and according to his standards, Harry would do his very best to be a model husband. Those were the terms on which Bess either had to accept him or – what was totally unthinkable from his standpoint – not.

How he would have faced up to a rejection from Bess – whether he would have been able to survive it – we do not know because it never happened. If she did not find their marriage easy, she did not leave it. Often moody and bad-tempered, her one effective recourse was to upset or worry him. This was the only way she could make herself felt. And her moodiness did upset him, deeply and genuinely, as his diary records on numerous such occasions: 'Bess had a brain storm'; 'Raised hell because I kidded on the phone to the operator'; 'Bess very angry with me'; 'Bess has been very sweet lately; hope she keeps it up,' he noted once – but she did not, or not for long, for two weeks later he was lamenting again: 'When I get home she is sore, and is sore for the night.' Over the years, her discontent became more tangible. She increasingly took to drink. Towards the end of his life, while he was onstage performing, she would be in the dressing-room complaining: 'Listen to him! I, I, I! That's all I ever hear, I, I, I!' But Houdini's fulsome declarations of undying devotion would always coax her back into a good mood.

Children never came along to intrude their own peculiar

brand of reality into this laboriously constructed idyll. Both Houdini and Bess deeply regretted this. They kept a succession of dogs, most notably the little Charlie, who travelled with them everywhere: his cushion was stowed in Bess's trunk along with her linen and 'kitchen things'. They doted upon him, and were heartbroken when he died. But dogs were a lame substitute for the real thing. Bess revealed after his death that 'Houdini created a dream child, a son named after his own father, Mayer Samuel.' In their large New York house Harry occupied the fourth floor while Bess's quarters were on the third. He was in the habit of sending Bess daily letters via the maid about Mayer Samuel's progress. The letters stopped only when this 'son' became President of the United States. This was perhaps the best kind of son for Houdini. A dream child can never disappoint its parents. It is difficult to imagine how he would have coped with the obstinate realities of a flesh-and-blood child, especially a son. His view of fatherhood had been lop-sided; his relations with younger men were always strained and resentful. It seems improbable that this would have been an easy or satisfactory relationship in the flesh.

One can only conjecture as to the reason for this childlessness. Bess sometimes said her husband was sterilised as a result of over-exposure to X-rays. Houdini's youngest brother, Leopold, became a radiologist in the early days of that science, before it was realised how dangerous X-rays could be. He had his office and consulting-room in the house Houdini bought at 278 West 113th Street, and Houdini enjoyed playing with the X-ray machine. But the house was not bought until 1904, and by then the Houdinis had already been married ten X-ray-free – and child-free – years.

Infertility is not uncommon. But my own guess, based on his effusive daily – sometimes thrice-daily – outpouring of love-declarations – is that Houdini may have been impotent. Why all those protestations? What was so wrong that he had to keep proclaiming his devotion? Why this constant need to reassure both Bess and himself? The month before he died, when they had been married thirty-two years, he was signing himself 'your husband until and after the curtain rings down on our lives, e'en to the crack of Doom.'

It is not hard to imagine that the kind of attachment Harry felt for his mother may have led to difficulties in normal relations with other women. He was uneasy with any reference to physical sex. His own fantasy heroine, as he describes her, was far different from the usual heroine of the kind of he-man movies he later aspired to emulate: 'a girlish woman, or rather a womanly girl, one whose affections would spring from a mental attraction, rather than a physical or sex magnet'. Bess, the only woman with whom he ever had a romantic relationship, was scarcely more than a child when they met. As Houdini was forever saying, she represented his ideal of womanhood: an unthreatening girl with as little as possible of the woman about her.

His relations with women other than his wife were stilted to an abnormal degree. One of the big difficulties in Houdini's movie career was his complete inability to so much as kiss another woman, even – especially – before the camera. 'I'm afraid I'm not much of a ladies' man,' he told a Hollywood interviewer in the understatement of the century, adding, typically, 'I am so old-fashioned that I have been in love with the same wife for twenty-five years.'

How, then, did he ever bring himself to marry? Perhaps it was in the nature of a dive for freedom, away from the debilitating thrall of his mother (whose absence from the ceremony we have noted) and into adulthood. The headlong speed with which he did it suggests a man who shuts his eyes, holds his nose and plunges in without daring to pause for thought. If he had thought longer, he might never have nerved himself to it. 'I have uncanny feelings at times,' he wrote to a friend twenty-two years later. 'When I meet people [I] seem to know at once their whole pedigree . . . Never made a mistake. Saw a young girl passing down the board walk, she never gave me a "look" three days after she was my wife, and thank the Almighty we have had 22 years of connubial Felicity.' He had made his leap, and was absolved from having to think of such things again for the rest of his life. As for the notion of his wife looking at another man – the very possibility literally knocked him backwards. Once, at a party, Bess was invited to sit on the knee of one of their fellow guests, a colonel, and drink a glass of champagne with him. To tease her husband, she did so. But the idea that one might be able to joke about such sacred mysteries as sex, he found incomprehensible. Houdini completely lacked the detachment such jokes require. When he came in, he 'stopped sharply in the doorway with an expression of incredulous horror on his face that his wife never forgot. His knees sagged as if he had received a knockout blow . . . He could hardly speak. She helped him into a taxi and into their lodgings. None of her explanations could lift him from his utter prostration of spirit.' For weeks afterwards, the mere mention of the word 'colonel' would reduce him to the depths of gloom. Such a nervous effort as he had made in acquiring a wife would not bear repetition. The possibility that she might leave him – that she might find some other man more attractive – was so terrifying to him that it was wholly unbearable. If he indeed was impotent, he would naturally have been unsure of himself. All those over-emphatic reiterations of his love – that Niagara of cliché – could hardly have compensated either of them emotionally for what he could not supply physically. And if Bess were ever to leave him on that account, or have an affair with someone else, not only his fragile self-confidence but also his act, which depended so strongly on the image of Houdini as a virile superman, would have been destroyed. What sort of Tarzan is it who can't keep his Jane?

In time, he seems to have achieved his real dream. He had, in a sense, two mothers. Bess recounts how she had to clean his ears for him, make sure he changed his underwear, try to get him to wear clean shirts. The fact that they did not have children meant that Houdini could play the child within his marriage without competition.

In 1926, testifying before a Senate committee which was

looking into fortune-telling, the following extraordinary exchange took place:

> Houdini: Step this way, Mrs Houdini. One of the witnesses said that I was a brute and that I was vile and that I was crazy . . . I will have been married, on June 22, thirty-two years to this girl . . . Outside of my great mother, Mrs Houdini has been my greatest friend. Have I shown traces of being crazy, unless it was about you?
> Mrs H: No.
> Houdini: Am I a good boy?
> Mrs H: Yes.
> Houdini: Thank you, Mrs Houdini.

Evidently, after thirty years of marriage, Bess was still little more than an accessory to Houdini's self-image. Maybe, after all those years, she had lost any other perception of herself. She knew what was expected of her and she provided it. Those had always been the terms of the contract.

As for Houdini, it was all play-acting for him – and all deadly serious: so serious that he only dared approach it by play-acting. The only dialogues he could endure were predictable ones: those he had rehearsed with the other party, or which had been written for him by other people. Nor did he merely confine himself to reiterating romantic clichés: he acted them out. He would sometimes say to his wife, 'Mrs Houdini, you are a modern woman of liberal ideas. You will not be angry if I keep a date this evening. I expect to meet the most beautiful lady in the world at such and such a corner at six-thirty. I shall be home very late.' Bess would know this was her cue to dress up in her best and keep the assignation. Houdini would pick her up like a grand cavalier and sweep her off in a taxicab to 'some jazzy suburban roadhouse', where he would order a private dining-room and ply her with champagne (which he, of course, did not share). 'That wasn't no lady, that was my wife' – might have been written seriously about these romantic escapades of Houdini.

This was the man who took screen kisses so seriously that

he could not perform them. For Houdini, the world was the stage, the stage was the world. He did not differentiate. As he himself once said, 'All the world is a theater to me.' And within this theatre, his marriage was the most enduring of scenarios. They were both in thrall to it. For Houdini, it provided the base of support, both emotional and practical, which he needed in order to feel able to deal with the outside world. As for Bess, on the day she married, she had agreed to surrender her life to Houdini. She had joined his cast, and could conceive of no existence outside the play.

6

Freaks

Jack Flosso, whose father knew Houdini well, said to me: 'Never forget that Houdini was a product of his early professional years. He thought the freak world was normal and the straights were freaks.'

The freaks were among Houdini's earliest professional friends. 'I have often sat at the table with Unthan the legless wonder, who would pass me the sugar, and the fat lady, Big Alice, would obligingly sit at the edge of the table so as to give poor little Emma Shaller, the ossified girl, plenty of room. Jonathan Bass, who was announced as his own living headstone, did not become the cemetery ornament he threatened to be. Blue Eagle, the man who broke boards over his head to show the solidity of his cranium, is running an embroidery shop in New Jersey. Mexican Billy Wells, who had cobblestones broken on his head, is soliciting for a photograph gallery.' When the Houdinis worked dime museums, they appeared on what was known as the 'curio stage', where the freaks were exhibited. They were a 'working act', keeping the public amused until it was time for the freaks to appear.

The public, staring at a freak, senses something not quite of this world. Nature's aberrations inspire terror, and there is not much distance from terror to supersitious awe. But freaks do not *perform*, in the stage sense. They simply are. They exist: that is the extent of their performance.

Could Houdini, the performer *par excellence,* be called a freak? Certainly his world was the world of freaks. He never settled down in the conventional sense. He bought a house, but it was never much more than a *pied-à-terre* and a store for his vast collection of magical and theatrical memorabilia. He spent most of his life on the road, moving at first from rooming house to rooming house, later from hotel to hotel. His correspondence was conducted from his dressing-room on a selection of hotel stationery. He went on touring literally until the day he died. In the world where people stay in one place, raise a family, wash the car on Sundays, he was always walking on eggs, always on his guard because he felt at a disadvantage. The neck-tie factory was the extent of Houdini's adult acquaintance with the straight world, and that did not last long or amount to much. He grew up with the freaks. And he felt at home with them, because Houdini *was* a freak in all senses of the word. His performance was Houdini on display. His act was himself as much as was any fat lady's or ossified girl's.

That self, as he perceived it – or rather, as he enacted it, for he precisely did *not* perceive it – was as much an outsider as any physical freak. The story of Houdini's rise to fame is the story of his self-discovery. The closer he came to the core of his inner self, the greater the crowds he drew. The fantasies he acted out before them were in a sense everyman's fantasies – of invincibility, of immortality. But his starting-point was not everyman's. Most people feel themselves to a greater or lesser extent trapped by circumstance. But Houdini felt bound and gagged by it. He escaped from handcuffs, from strait-jackets, from police cells and the various shackles of authority; naturally, for they were part of his act, the *mise-en-scène* from which the climax would be developed. But for Houdini they were more than that, just as the act was more than just an act.

A question often asked in relation to Houdini is why all the fame accrued to *him*, and not to some of the other equally competent escapologists who worked the halls at the same time? Perhaps part of the answer lies here. For them the act was an act, a job, work; but for Houdini it was not an act at all. Once again, the boundaries between his public and his private selves were indistinct. His marriage was set up as a continual performance; his stage show continually invaded his private life. One of 'Monsieur and Mlle Houdini''s very first engagements was at Huber's, a famous dime museum on Four-teenth Street, New York. On their first day there, they arrived simultaneously with another exhibit – the original electric chair. Huber had acquired it from the Auburn prison, where it had been used to electrocute a murderer named Kemmler in 1890. Fascinated by it, Houdini returned to buy it when Huber's was sold up in 1910. Bess hated it, and kept moving it down to the basement intending to throw it out – but 'Houdini always missed it and had it brought upstairs again'.

Murderers particularly fascinated him. One of his most-vaunted escapes, performed in 1906, was from the condemned cell which had once housed Charles Guiteau, the assassin of President Garfield. This exploit – in the course of which he also freed all the other prisoners on Death Row and then locked them up again in the wrong cells – featured in countless publicity leaflets. But his interest in Guiteau did not end there. He collected Guiteau material – he owned, for example, the murderer's phrenological analysis. His drama collection included letters from Edwin Booth, the famous actor; but letters from John Wilkes Booth, Edwin's brother and (more importantly) the assassin of President Lincoln, also featured in the collection, and he was particularly proud of them. In his gaol breaks, he identified deeply with the prisoners who had languished, powerless, in those very places; and the worse the crime – the more it placed its perpetrator outside the bounds of society – the greater its fascination for Houdini.

The difference between him and the freaks he worked with, or the prisoners whose cells he temporarily occupied, was of course that he could do something about his condition. He could escape from it. But the condition itself remained – inescapably – in his mind. In 1901, in Germany, he was placed in a straitjacket from which it took him an hour and twenty-nine minutes to escape. 'The pain, torture, agony and misery of that struggle will forever live in my mind', he wrote. He knew better than most what it felt like to be ineluctably trapped: forever on the margin.

Harry and Bess needed, when they began, to get on stage – any stage. They lost no time in producing the first of a series of flyers extolling the virtues of 'Monsieur and Mlle Houdini' (or, on another occasion, 'Mysterious Harry' and 'La Petite Bessie') and their wonderful Metamorphosis act ('Exchange Made in 3 Seconds'). In the very first poster, the exchange took two minutes, and the poster concluded:

NOTICE TO MANAGERS
A STARTLING FEATURE
TIME OF ACT, 15 MINUTES
OUR ACT HAS BEEN FEATURED IN MASKELYNE
COOK'S EGYPTIAN HALL, LONDON
OXFORD, CAMBRIDGE AND ROBERT HOUDIN'S, PARIS
We will Forfeit $1000 if Any Detail of Our Act Given Herewith
is Misrepresented
Harry and Bessie Houdini

This was the first appearance of Houdini the publicist, a personage who never allowed mere fact to stand in the way of self-advertisement. Later, his stunts would rank him with Phineas T. Barnum: the two greatest publicists of their day. But no two men could have been more different. Barnum's achievement was essentially that of the successful tabloid editor. He knew how to catch the popular imagination, and exploited that knowledge cynically and shamelessly. Was he not the author of the immortal direction 'THIS WAY TO THE EGRESS' and the equally timeless aperçu 'There's a sucker born every minute'? Houdini, like Barnum, was obsessed with catching the crowds. But although he lured them with his tricks, he could never have spoken lines such as those. He was, like many freaks, an innocent. He always met any competition, real or imagined, in the most straight-forward way imaginable: he came out fighting, shouted louder, and hit his man harder. The same applied to his publicity. In publicity as in everything else, attack was the best form of defence. The bigger the lie, the more self-righteous he was in defending it.

Nobody took him up on this one, perhaps because nobody noticed it. The trunk trick might have figured in Paris and London, but not under the auspices of Monsieur and Mlle

Houdini, who had never set foot outside the United States. But despite their best efforts, work did not exactly pour in. They took what they could get, mostly in beer halls or dime museums. The beer-hall programme would generally begin with a melodrama performed by the ensemble: there was no rehearsal, but everyone knew the few stock pieces, such as the immortal *Ten Nights In A Bar-Room*. Then would come the various individual turns. Bessie did her song-and-dance act; Harry escaped from his handcuffs and did some sleight-of-hand; they performed the trunk trick. The dime museums were less rough and boozy than the beer halls, but still very hard work. At Huber's, the barker would shout, 'Your attention towards this end of the hall! Here you will find a clever young man; he will mystify you if he can, escapes from everything, makes no bluffs. Houdini, look at him, the king of handcuffs.' At Kohl and Middleton's, in Chicago, where they could usually find an engagement if all else failed, they were required to be on stage from ten in the morning until ten at night, giving ten to twenty shows a day. Speaking of those days 'when I was playing Dime Museums, and being classed a "freak" ', Houdini said: 'I generally kept very quiet, and tried to make a living, not knowing that I was developing my dexterity by working ten to fifteen times daily.' When the museum closed, Harry would visit gambling houses and buy used cards cheap, and Bess would make up special packs for card tricks and sell them between the acts. On their very best week they might make sixty dollars between them – but this was unusual.

It looked for a moment as if the Houdinis would make good quickly. They were playing in a concert hall in the south when a wire arrived announcing that they were booked to play Tony Pastor's Theatre next door to Tammany Hall in New York. This was real fame. Tony Pastor's was the leading vaudeville house. Irving Berlin and Al Jolson would get their first big breaks there. Captain West, who owned the concert hall, advanced them their fare to New York, and they set off in high excitement. When they arrived, however, they found that their names, in barely legible type, were (as might have been expected) at the bottom of the bill. They were to play three times a day, at the worst times: ten-thirty in the morning, when the cleaners were still clattering around; twelve-thirty-four p.m., in the middle of lunchtime; and six-thirty – dinner-time.

The management appeared not even to have noticed their presence. But just as they were getting ready for their third show one of the big stars, a singer named Maggie Cline, ran into them on the backstage stairs. She kindly showed Bess how to make up properly, then went round the front and watched the act, taking Tony Pastor with her. Afterwards she said, 'Say, you Great Houdinis, you are great!' Years later, in her last season, by which time Houdini topped every bill, they appeared together again, but however much they prodded her memory, she could not bring the evening at Tony Pastor's to mind. At the end of the week Mr Pastor wrote them a testimonial: 'The Houdinis' act as performed here I found satisfactory and interesting.' This, however, gained them no engagements; and the critics, not surprisingly, had failed to notice them at all.

So – since a living must be made – the Houdinis joined the circus: to be precise, the Welsh Brothers' Circus, 'a ten-twent'-thirt' show without animals which toured the smaller eastern towns during the open season'. Now they were really hitting the low spots. The circus, when they joined up with it, was in Lancaster, Pennsylvania, on a black, rainy night. They 'stumbled about through ankle-deep mud for miles in the dark, trying to find the tent', Bess remembered:

> At last a voice from out of the darkness hailed us. 'Is that the Houdinis?' Houdini shouted an affirmative, and the next instant we were pulled into what looked like a great black cave. It was the car – an old truck transformed into living quarters. In a minute a lantern flashed in our faces . . . [It] was Welsh, our boss.
> 'Well, what do you want?' he asked, looking us over.
> 'Anything,' was Houdini's prompt reply.

'The first thing you do with this outfit is to work in the sideshow,' said the boss. 'You do Punch and Judy; the wife, mind-reading. In the concert, Houdini to do magic, wife to sing and dance – then your trunk trick, and the handcuff act as the big feature. And of course, you are in the parade. Twenty-five a week and cakes.'

The rules and regulations governing the Welsh Bros.' All-United Golden Shows were down-to-earth. Number one stated that 'Artists asking exhorbitant prices that are not worth the salary agreed upon, must expect to be discharged after the first appearance . . . or receive a salary according to their worth.' Number ten laid down that 'Grumbling and growling will not be tolerated under any circumstances.' There was a handwritten addendum: 'All male members must go in daily street parades, if required.' The contract mentions only Metamorphosis and 'Miss Houdini's serio-comic specialties'. In addition to their twenty-five dollars the Houdinis would get their meals (the 'cakes') and accommodation in a cardboard cubicle in the 'car'. Bess was at first thoroughly disconcerted by all this, but after her first morning, when she awoke 'to find the sun streaming through a little hole in the side of our cupboard' and was kindly shown to the breakfast tent by one of the two other women in the company, she soon felt at home. The circus poster advertised a Wild Man who never appeared and was generally not missed; but one day he was called for, and Houdini volunteered to be him. 'The ringmaster, Clinton Newton, who could talk politely and sonorously about anything or nothing, made a preliminary address about the capture of the Wild Man in the depths of the Java jungle . . . and described how he lived on a diet of raw meat, cigarettes, and cigars. Then the cage was drawn in with Houdini growling and tearing at a bit of raw meat. The Wild Man was an immediate hit and became a permanent feature. He was a hit with the male performers as well as with the audiences, for the men showered him with cigars and cigarettes to hear him growl, and as Houdini did not use tobacco the rest of the men of the troupe enjoyed free smokes.'

Only the handcuffs did not do well. They aroused not a flicker of interest in the audience, who simply assumed that Houdini must be using prepared cuffs. However, even they were not without their uses. One Sunday in a small town in Rhode Island the whole troupe was suddenly arrested for breaking the Sunday law. Mr Welsh was in New York overnight, so they had no one to defend them and were summarily sent to spend the night in the lock-up. 'In the lock-up the Fat Woman wept bitterly. Her cell was too small, and she was wholly uncomfortable and miserable. So after the sheriff had gone and everything was quiet, Houdini picked the locks of the jail and the whole company stole quietly back to the big tent. The next day Mr Welsh arrived to fix matters with the sheriff, and we pulled up our stakes and went quietly away from there.'

At the end of the season, since all their living expenses were met, the Houdinis had managed to save up a certain amount of money even though twelve of their twenty-five weekly dollars were always sent back to Mrs Weiss. Houdini was persuaded to take a half-interest in a burlesque troupe called The American Gaiety Girls, the main feature of which turned out to be its debts. The show, possibly not helped by its new proprietor's loathing of anything resembling smut, sank into the mire, taking the Houdinis with it, until things got so bad they could scarcely afford to eat, let alone pay anyone's salary.

It was 1896, and they now joined up with a character named Marco. Marco, an erstwhile church organist, had put all his money into an elaborate travelling show, into which he incorporated the Houdinis. Their first trip took them to Nova Scotia. But this show, too, was a failure, and soon consisted only of Marco, the Houdinis and a man named Kearny, the 'manager, carpenter, stage crew, actor and confidential adviser to Marco'. Houdini decided to try a publicity stunt for the show: he would free himself from a running horse to which he had been roped. Unfortunately the horse turned out not to

be the docile old nag he needed, but a young and frisky colt
which dashed off with him into the fields, so that by the time
it was safe to free himself they were miles away from any
potential spectators. The show, like the horse, ran out of
control – downhill. Marco decided to go back to the States
and his church organ; Houdini took over. When they arrived
at the point where renting a church for eight dollars broke
them so that, unable to afford a room, they had to spend the
night in a hallway, where the two men gave Bessie their coats
to lie on, they decided the time had come for them to give
up, too.

A boat bound for Boston lay at the quayside. Bessie span a
sob-story to the captain and he agreed to give them their
passage in exchange for a show for the passengers. But this,
too, was doomed, for as soon as the boat began to move
Houdini was prostrated. It was his first experience of seasickness, from which he would always suffer appallingly – the
mere act of buying tickets for a passage made him nauseous.
Tricks were out of the question. Bess agreed to try her hand
at them, but with little success. She knew how they were
done, but that did not mean she could do them. A kind
passenger took pity on them and passed the hat round nevertheless. Bess was not sick but ravenous, and proposed to spend
the money on a meal, but Houdini flatly forbade her even to
mention food, let alone spend any money on it. The situation
was saved by the same kind woman who took pity on her and
treated her to a meal.

Then came more hard times. They travelled from one precarious engagement to another. In St Louis, in cold weather,
they found themselves stranded. Their baggage, including the
precious trunk which was their only key to a livelihood, was
held at the station with twenty dollars due on it. They had no
engagements, and without their props, would not find any.
They rented an unheated hall bedroom, containing only a cot
and a rickety stove, for $1.50 a week, and lived on pilfered
potatoes cooked on bits of old packing-case which they fed
into the stove. Just before rent day, Houdini wangled them an

engagement as 'The Rahners – Harry and Bess – America's Greatest Comedy Act' – at Escher's Music Hall, $30 a week. Unbelievably, this – mainly a compilation of old jokes cribbed from back numbers of comic magazines – went down well enough to secure them a second week 'at a cut' – $25. At the end of this, Harry revealed to the manager that they were really 'the Great Houdinis': the money had enabled them to redeem the trunk from the station. The manager agreed to book them for a third week, back on the original $30.

But three weeks' work was the exception, not the rule. In desperation, Harry set up 'Professor Harry Houdini's School of Magic'. 'DO YOU WANT TO LEARN AN ACT?' inquired the flyer. 'If you want to go on the Stage, travel with a Circus, play Variety theatres or Museums, you must first learn to do something to attract Attention.' He sold some magic apparatus on commission for a Chicago manufacturer called Roterberg (who was to become a lifelong friend), and also some tricks of his own. At this point, it would have been possible to buy, for $5, the 'Hindoo Needle Trick . . . taught to me by Hindoos at World's Fair in 1893. The trick is to have committee inspect hands and mouth; you then swallow 40 to 50 sewing needles, then a bunch of thread, and bring them up all threaded' and for a little more ('price on application') Metamorphosis Substitution, 'my original act'. Luckily for Houdini, nobody seems to have wanted these two: they were still acclaimed as his most spectacular tricks until the day he died.

This exhausting and uncertain life went on, not for months, but for years. A manager in Milwaukee (that least auspicious of towns) swindled them out of some earnings. Houdini lost more in a dice game trying to retrieve the situation: as with many Jews, gambling was his vice. Ruthless in his abhorrence of anything which might lead to bodily weakness – he was teetotal; he never smoked; his refusal to admit that he might ever be other than perfectly fit was one of the compulsions which ruled his life – this might have been his Achilles' heel. Bess's fury on this occasion, spectacular even by her standards, made him cautious. 'Even a small stake at cards is dangerous, for it cultivates the habit of gambling, which may soon become a passion,' he wrote. Passion – which implies letting go and loss of control – was something Houdini sought to eliminate from his life. That life increasingly depended upon his taking no chances. Bess made him promise never to gamble again, which he did not – or not very often.

Then, at the end of 1897, came an offer to join Dr Hill's California Concert Company, a travelling medicine show, at $25 a week.

The format was simple. The troupe would arrive in a small town (they all travelled in a decrepit victoria large enough to carry a small organ, and played a different town each day) and set themselves up on a street corner. Dr Pratt, Dr Hill's partner, would play the organ, Houdini would play the tambourine, and Mrs Houdini sang. A crowd would gather. When it was big enough Dr Hill would take the stage and tell everyone about his wonderful medicine, which he would sell to all and sundry. Then he would announce that the troupe would be giving a performance that evening in the local hall. The performance would open with a playlet. This would be followed by whatever acts the current ensemble could perform. Houdini gave a magic show: when Buster Keaton's parents, Joe and Myra Keaton, joined the show for a while, they did an Irish comedy routine. Bess liked the Keatons: she and Houdini claimed to have given Buster his name. He was just a toddler when they knew him, and Bess, in particular, seems to have been attached to him. When there was a fire in the hotel where they were all staying, she rushed up to the room where he was sleeping and rescued him. Perhaps she saw in him the baby she was still hoping for.

Medicine shows have a venerable history. In the sixteenth and seventeenth centuries they swarmed throughout Europe. They were little troupes of performers centred around a (supposedly) Italian doctor or *dottore* (Italian doctors were famous; *dottore* is still a polite Italian honorific). The purpose of the show was to attract a crowd which could then be persuaded to buy the doctor's miraculous medicine. In order to attract the crowd the troupe would stage a parade. The performers often included a monkey, a 'turk' or 'moroccan' to add even more exoticism, and a clown figure – the 'Zanni' or 'mountebank', or sometimes a harlequin. As time went on, the crowds became less interested in the medicine, and the show took on an increasing importance in its own right. Eventually, in the eighteenth century, it evolved into pantomime, the *Commedia dell'Arte*, with its stylised cast. The doctor, increasingly redundant in a medical sense, lingered on as the dominating, satanic Master of Ceremonies, or circus ringmaster.

In a sense, then, the American medicine show, like that which the Houdinis now joined, was a throwback. But its long history had earned it little status. In the world of vaudeville, there was a definite hierarchy. At the top were the established vaudeville theatres, such as Tony Pastor's, and the big theatre chains run by the Orpheum Circuit in the west and the Keith Circuit in the east. Then came the small music halls and dime museums like Huber's in New York and Kohl and Middleton's in Chicago. Below these were the beer halls. And at the very bottom were the travelling medicine shows.

There was a type of variety act at this time known as 'Hebe comedy' (in which, as it happens, Al Jolson started out with his brother Harry). It consisted of dialogue: 'You're a monkey.' 'Vot – you call me a monkey?' 'Sure. You know what a monkey is? A monkey is a very fine person.' 'I know dat. Mine father, mine mother and mine brothers and sisters are all monkeys, too.' Hebe comedy was to vaudeville acts as medicine shows were to vaudeville. So that to be a Jewish performer in a medicine show represented a theatrical depth below which it was virtually impossible to sink.

It was on Dr Hill's suggestion that, when business turned slack, the Houdinis became spirit mediums. After all, strange powers and exotic, supernatural connections were all part of the medicine-show tradition. They agreed readily enough. Houdini had no special bee in his bonnet regarding mediums at this stage – his medium-busting was to come much later.

They turned out remarkably successful in their new calling. This was partly because, being the good professionals they were, they did their preparation properly. Bess soon learned to go into trances and use the special medium's voice and language. They had already worked out a 'mind-reading' routine in which code-words represented numbers:

Pray = 1
Answer = 2
Say = 3
Now = 4
Tell = 5
Please = 6
Speak = 7
Quickly = 8
Look = 9
Be quick = 10

Thus, if the mind-reader needed to know the number on a dollar bill – say, 59321884778 – Bess, holding the bill, might speak as follows: 'Tell me, mind-reader. Look into your heart. Say, can you answer me, pray? Quickly, quickly! Now! Speak to us! Speak quickly!' The number code could also, of course, be used to represent letters of the alphabet and spell out a word or phrase.

There were other established procedures. There was a special mediums' 'Blue Book' giving relevant detail for a circuit of towns in the Midwest. When they arrived at a new town, they would go to the cemetery and memorise the names, which would be sure to make an impression upon the audience. They would listen hard to the gossip around the boarding-house dining-table. And they would often employ a 'tipster' who would relay points of interest about the audience as they filed in to the seance. Most impressive effects could be achieved using all these aids. So successful were they that, when the medicine show died early in 1898, they set up as mediums for a while on their own account.

Two coincidences finally frightened them off this line of

work. The first took place in a town over the Canadian border. Bess, in her trance, was reading and answering sealed messages from the people at the seance according to the usual system. One of the questions read: 'Where is my brother John? I have not heard from him in nineteen years. (signed) Mary Murphy.' Instead of the usual evasive, generalised answer, Bess, suddenly remembering a Mrs John Murphy who kept an ice-cream parlour near 69th Street where the Weisses lived in New York, replied, 'You will find your brother at – East 72nd Street, New York.' She reckoned that, by the time Mary Murphy had written and received a reply, they would be safely in another town.

But Mary Murphy fooled them. She wired – and received a reply from, yes indeed, her long-lost brother. 'There are an astonishing number of coincidences in life', mused Bess apropos this incident. The Houdinis suddenly found themselves celebrated as seers. They moved on, feeling shaken, but spiritualism was a much more certain living than vaudeville, so they persisted. The end came when Houdini noticed in one audience a mother whom he had recently seen scolding her little boy for riding his bicycle too recklessly. He told her he had a spirit message that her son would break his arm riding his bicycle. Soon after the woman returned home, the child was brought to the house with his arm broken. That was enough for Houdini. He gave up the medium business then and there.

After this followed a brief spell with a travelling theatre troupe specialising in melodramas, in which the Houdinis both played and did turns between the acts; followed in April 1898 by another six-month spell with the Welsh Brothers' Circus, where Houdini toyed with the idea of becoming an acrobat. He even went so far as to buy 'pink tights and uppers' on 3 September. But acrobatics was not what he wanted to do. On 8 October the Welsh Brothers closed. Success, even of the most modest kind, seemed as far away as ever.

What Houdini really wanted to do was not acrobatics, which

came so easily to him, nor supporting roles in melodrama, nor even card tricks, at which he was adept – but escapes.

The public was still resolutely uninterested in watching him free himself from handcuffs. But he already knew how this might be made more interesting. In 1895, while he and Bess were touring with the ill-starred Gaiety Girls, he conceived the notion of visiting police stations and challenging them to lock him into any handcuffs they cared to use: he would escape. He first tried this approach in Holyoke, Mass. He was manacled at the police station, walked into an adjoining room, shut the door, escaped in less than a minute, repeated the feat twice, and received a handsome notice in the local paper. He did the same thing in other towns: more press stories followed. But these were very small towns, and the stories escaped the attention of the circuit bookings managers. In the larger cities, police stations were too busy to give Houdini the time of day, and journalists had more pressing copy.

In Chicago at the end of 1898, he decided to improve on this stunt. A certain amount of preparation was required. First, he made friends with some newspapermen. Then there was the question of gaining access to the police. If any police force in the country was liable to be too busy to listen to him, it was Chicago's. So he wangled an introduction to Andy Rohan, a lieutenant of detectives, the right-hand man of the police chief, and a well-known Chicago character. He took Bess to the city gaol to visit Rohan: she kept him talking while Houdini wandered around studying the lock system of the cells. They were there a long time, but Houdini could not find what he wanted. The locks were too complicated. So next day, to Rohan's astonishment, they called again. Finally Rohan had had enough and threw them out. But by then Houdini had discovered what he needed. Next day, he told his reporter friends that he could escape from the city gaol after being handcuffed and locked in a cell. So they all returned to the gaol, where Andy Rohan was not averse to teaching Houdini a lesson in front of the newspapermen. He was locked up, and, a minute later, walked into the warden's office. But the reporters were unimpressed. They had heard about his previous visits, and assumed he had taken wax impressions of the locks and made his own keys. Houdini therefore offered to strip and be searched before he was locked up. They agreed; at his suggestion they even sealed his mouth with plaster. They left him handcuffed and naked; within ten minutes he was back in Rohan's office, dressed. A story! He even got his picture in the papers.

That was it! It was all he wanted. He spent everything he had on buying copies of the papers, cutting out the story and mailing it to everyone he could think of. The effort soon bore fruit. A few days later he received a visit from a representative of the Hopkins Theater, Chicago's top vaudeville house. The headliner had died: could the Houdinis fill in at short notice? They would have the star spot – the one before the finale.

It was manna from heaven. But Bess was ill in bed with flu. She was not particularly strong, and the hard life they were leading had taken its toll. Houdini's letters frequently mention that Bess is not well. But the Metamorphosis trick, the climax of their act, could not be done without her. Terrified of going on alone, but appalled at the prospect of having to turn down such an offer, Harry began to set impossible conditions. He wanted star billing; he wanted a hundred dollars a week; he wanted the star dressing-room with a large mirror. The representative agreed to everything – anything, if they would only come along at once. What were they to do? Bess solved the problem. 'Get me to the theatre,' she said. 'I'll work.'

The Hopkins engagement only lasted a couple of weeks; then they returned to the dime museums. But the Chicago publicity was still working, and Houdini persisted with the gaol-breaking stunts. One evening in Minneapolis, a stranger approached him after the show and invited him and Bess for a cup of coffee. During the show, evidently thinking that Houdini's handcuffs might be specially doctored, he had (Houdini later wrote) 'purchased a few pairs and sent them on stage'. The challenge had been dealt with in short order. Once they were seated, Houdini asked him what he thought of the act. He dismissed it all – except the handcuffs and the substitution trunk. Everything else, all the little magic – card tricks, sleight-of-hand, the production of pigeons, guinea-pigs and a multitude of other objects from a silk hat – only detracted from these two big stunts at which Houdini excelled. Why not exercise a little showmanship and cut the rest out? Then he introduced himself. He was Martin Beck, the booker for the Orpheum Circuit, the big western theatre chain. He would try them out at sixty dollars a week, and if they were a success, he would raise them.

'They are artists of the front line, and furthermore a lady and gentleman in all that the term implies and can always find room with any of our amusement enterprises,' ran the encomium they had received from the Welsh Brothers at the end of their last circus engagement. 'The Houdinis are truly great people.' Was it really possible that they had put the world of the Wild Man and the Fat Lady behind them for ever?

It was not. That was something they never could do, and never wanted to. Martin Beck had picked out the two items which were Houdini's own. They expressed, as nothing else expressed, the man himself. When he performed those two stunts, Harry Houdini, like the freaks, was putting his own oddities – his own psychological deformities – on show. He was a performing freak, but a freak nonetheless. He never lost his affinity with these companions of his early days; and at the time of his death, one of the many books he was preparing was a book about freaks.

7

Handcuff King

'I started in the show business when I was a youngster, but my mother took me out and apprenticed me to a locksmith,' Houdini told the Washington *Times* in 1906. 'That is where I got my first knowledge of the weakness of locks. I discovered a method of opening them which I kept to myself.' Elsewhere he retold the old story of how he was left by the locksmith to file a pair of recalcitrant cuffs off an unfortunate fellow marooned in them by a jammed lock. But he hadn't needed to use the file – there was an easier way: his 'secret'.

'Secret' was a word Houdini often used. There is something very attractive about it. Children have secrets. They huddle together over them and exclude everyone not privy to them. Exclusion, of course, is a large part of the attraction of any secret. It is also part of the attraction of the world of magic. Magicians, too, are clannish and exclusive. They have their societies and their publications – the Magic Circle, the *Linking Ring*, the *Sphinx*, *M.U.M.* – from which the general public are excluded. This is understandable: they want to guard their secrets. Exclusion, for them, affords more than simply pleasure: it affords a living. For magicians' secrets and children's secrets have this in common: revelation almost invariably means anticlimax. When you don't know how a trick is done, it seems magical. When you do, the pleasures of connoisseurship may remain, but the magic is gone for ever.

Naturally enough, Houdini made much of his 'secret'. Various people tried to guess what it might be. One ever-popular theory held that he was able to contract his hand by dislocating the bones, so that it became smaller than his wrist. Houdini himself asserted that this was how he escaped from the German convict chain (by which German prisoners were shackled together). In fact he could not have done so: the feat is physiologically impossible. Another (and likelier) method of escaping from the chain is the old strongman's trick of bursting one of the links. To do this, the chain is previously prepared: one of the links is held in a vice and the metal is pushed back and forth until it is 'fatigued' so that one more strain will break it. And here indeed is a 'secret' – or one of them. Houdini always made much of the strength and impregnability of his chosen restraint, whatever it might be – a specially-built packing-case into which he would be nailed, to emerge as if by magic, leaving it to all appearances miraculously untouched; a fearsome convict chain. But he always made sure he had a good look at it first, and took any opportunity to effect a little careful preparation.

The contents of his famous 'Trunk No. 8' reveal the full extent of that care and preparation. As Houdini became more successful, his baggage increased exponentially. But Trunk No. 8 was the secret of secrets. Only Houdini, Bess, and his closest assistants had access to it. After he died, it passed with the rest of his magical effects to his brother Dash, who was by then known as Hardeen. It remained in the basement of his house in Brooklyn; and there it was found, after Hardeen died, by a magic collector, Dr Morris Young. 'It was opened in a very ordinary manner exposing a canvas-covered tray; saws and other tools were attached inside the trunk lid . . .', he wrote.

Removal of the tray brought to light the large lower space that was crowded with what looked like a jumble of more tools. Straps attached to the bottom of the trunk served the purpose of holding some of the items . . . Two cigar boxes were labelled respectively 'Handcuff and leg iron keys' and 'Old Postcards Magicians, etc., Key Blanks.' There were a number of metal cash boxes. One contained many packages of sewing needles (needle trick) and a small leather pouch, a coin purse, corn kernels, jeweler's rouge, soldering supplies, keys, a *Wohnungs Waechter* key, sealing and other waxes, chalk, crayons, buttons and thread. Another box was filled with small tools such as pliers, dividers, calipers, drills, leather and canvas sewing tools, glass cutters and a few lock picks. When laid out on tables, the tools and other objects found in the trunk formed an impressive array. Carpenters, plumbers, leather and canvas workers, and mechanics would have felt quite at home. There were five planes, mallets, hammers (one double-claw), an axe, wood and metal saws, chisels, gouges, gages, a spirit level, plumbs, spool of marking twine, abrasive papers, a portable grindstone, many files, screw drivers, a spokeshave, wrenches, small reamers and threaders, a large and small blowtorch with soldering irons (some electric), caulking tools, sailors' palms, paint brushes, rulers and measuring tapes, pliers, putty knives, oil cans, nail pullers, crowbars, vises, a small candlestick, and a bench cleaning brush. From amidst all these, two small books startled me. They turned out to be a 14th edition copy of Henry T. Brown's *507 Mechanical Movements, Embracing All Those Which Are Most Important . . . and including Many Movements Never Before Published* (1884), and a copy of Fred T. Hodgson's *ABC of the Steel Square and Its Uses* (1908).

And these were by no means all the tools Houdini carried with him.

What mere challenge could withstand such an array? If the packing-case was displayed in the theatre foyer overnight as a 'draw', Houdini or his assistant would take the opportunity to replace a few long nails or bolts with short ones, easily removed, or make some other relevant adjustment. The convict chain, by the time it reached the stage, would not be the chain it was when first it left its maker.

The secret of the handcuffs was of course a simple one. It consisted of keys.

Sometimes not even keys were needed: just a sharp tap in the right place might be enough to open a spring-loaded cuff. Houdini wore a sheet of metal underneath one of his trouser-legs to knock catches of this type apart. Otherwise, he made sure that all eventualities were catered for. A letter to one of his assistants detailed the keys he needed and the handcuffs and leg-irons they would open. Twenty-eight varieties of handcuff are listed, beginning with a 'Double-lock twoer Ratchet', and ending with the Navey handcuff and leg-iron requiring two keys to open it. There are even more varieties of keys: sixty-one in all. Number 18 is a master key for ninety-five per cent of all regulation English cuffs. 'The key in this set being split, allows you to really unlock almost any cuff of this pattern, as you simply insert the key, give it sufficient turns to catch hold of thread and bolts, and pull. This split key, which is the invention of Harry Houdini, who patented it in England, is the best master ever used on any style cuff.' Not all obstacles are so simply overcome. Number 21, the 'Master English Plug, also known as the Slave Iron . . . will require two teeth on top to remove the plug, before it is possible to insert the key. Some of the plugs unscrew to the right, and some to the left. When the cuff is being locked on you, watch which way they turn the key.' The last key on this list, Number 61, opens the Nova Scotia Leg-iron, found by Houdini in Nova Scotia in 1895 (on the ill-starred Marco tour). 'Scarce,' he remarks laconically.

When it came to locks, he never stopped learning. 'In Berlin,' he wrote, 'I knew a locksmith, Mueller, who has a shop on Mittle Strasse, and he was more than willing that I should work for nothing, and I commenced repairing locks for him. He soon discovered that his 35 years of experience was nothing as compared to my trick in opening locks, and he soon had a thriving trade for his young man to open locks. In order that I should know the exact heights of the various locks used on the police chains, he ordered a great gross, and soon exchanged them for another great gross of other patterns, etc., In that way I would pass 6 to 10 hours daily picking locks and soon, with the assistance of the four marked picks, I could open any lock that contained the 5 or 6 Chubb levers. The "gate ways" were never made close, as is the case in the very fine lever locks, so it became a very simple matter for me to open each and every lock which was made on that principle.'

He acquired an ever-growing collection of special keys of his own design which were carried around in their own case.

But possessing the keys did not by itself ensure success. Just as important – perhaps even more so, as one commentator remarked – was the ability instantly to identify which key was required, 'for it is obvious that the audience cannot be kept waiting until the performer has tried all forty-five keys in every one of the locks'. Then it was necessary to know where to conceal them 'in spite of the searching which is sometimes insisted upon' – or, in Houdini's case, invited: this was one of the essentials of his routine. And even after all this, other skills were needed. Manipulating the key in the lock was no easy matter. 'The primary lesson is, to learn to use both hands with equal facility, as . . . one hand washes the other, but in this case one hand releases the other,' wrote Houdini, adding: 'The method adopted by me to acquire this end was, when at table I practiced to use the left hand persistently, until I could use it almost as easily as the right.' His toes were almost equally dexterous, although presumably he did not exercise them at table.

There were other important details, too. One of these he learned at the start of 1899, just after the Hopkins Theater engagement, when Sergeant Waldron of the Chicago Police Department locked his special cuffs around Houdini's wrists at Kohl and Middleton's Museum. Houdini was quite unable to extricate himself. He struggled with the cuffs for more than an hour. The audience began to jeer, and moved on to the next freak. He was still struggling when the museum closed at ten o'clock. Bess wept; Houdini stood disconsolately on his platform. Only Sergeant Waldron remained. He explained that he had dropped a lead slug into the cuffs, so that the lock was jammed. There was no way of opening it: Houdini would have to be sawed loose.

In future, clearly, he must never accept a challenge without first seeing the challenge cuffs locked and unlocked. That was the lesson. But would there be a future? Houdini, after this fiasco, was sure there would not. The world had ended for him when he failed to break free from Sergeant Waldron's doctored cuffs. The Chicago *Journal* carried the story: 'WAS AN

UNFAIR TEST: MAGICIAN HOUDINI SAYS SERGT.
WALDRON PLAYED A JOKE ON HIM.'

Marooned at the centre of his own universe, Houdini was
convinced that this was the end of his career. It did not occur
to him to wonder who was going to notice a small-time
mishap to a small-time performer in a dime museum. Next
morning he was suicidally dejected. Mr Hedges, Kohl and
Middleton's manager and a staunch friend of the Houdinis,
laughed and told him to get a move on or he'd be late for the
opening performance. But the dejection, which seemed so
extreme and exaggerated, was important. It was another poin-
ter to Houdini's *real* secret – the secret that would ensure his
name remains, after all these years, a byword; that, in his
prime, would pack the halls and sell out his every performance.
What, after all, was it that Martin Beck thought he had spotted? A man escaping from *handcuffs*?

There used to be an escapologist who performed on Tower
Hill, just outside the Tower of London. I saw him once when
I was a child. He stood in an open space struggling with
chains. The performance seemed rather pointless, although it
was evidently to some extent memorable. But even the child
I then was recognised that the escapologist was not an enviable
figure. He struggled on, isolated on his bleak hill. No tri-
umphal future beckoned. It just seemed a rather odd way to
make a living.

I remember the escapologist as a Laocoon-like figure, fighting with his chains as the prodigious statue fights with its
snakes. But Laocoon had no choice in the matter: his fate, his
fight, was ordained by the gods. By contrast, the escapologist's
occupation seemed somewhat arbitrarily chosen. Houdini,
however, had as little choice about what he did as Laocoon.
The struggle dominated his imagination.

In an extraordinary article written in 1908, he describes his
first view of a straitjacket. This took place in St John's, Nova
Scotia, just after Marco had skipped off back to Bridgeport
leaving the Houdinis to carry the show alone.

While in St Johns I met a Dr Steves, who then was in charge of a large insane asylum, and received an invitation from him to visit his institution, which I accepted. After showing me the various wards, he eventually showed me the padded cells, in one of which, through the small bars of the cell door, I saw a maniac struggling on the canvas padded floor, rolling about and straining each and every muscle in a vain attempt to get his hands over his head and striving in every conceivable manner to free himself from his canvas restraint, which I later on learned was called a strait-jacket. Entranced, I watched the efforts of this man, whose struggles caused the beads of perspiration to roll off him, and from where I stood, I noted that were he able to dislocate his arms at the shoulder joint, he would have been able to cause his restraint to become slack in certain parts, and so allow him to free his arms. But as it was that the straps were drawn tight, the more he struggled, the tighter his restraint encircled him, and eventually he lay exhausted . . .

Previous to this incident I had seen and used various restraints such as insane restraint muffs, belts, bedstraps, etc., but this was the first time I saw a strait-jacket and it left so vivid an impression on my mind that I hardly slept that night, and in such moments as I slept I saw nothing but strait-jackets, maniacs and padded cells!

Bewitched by this vision, Houdini could not wait to try out a straitjacket of his very own. What an impression that would make upon the public! 'The very next morning I obtained permission to try to escape from one and during one entire week I practised steadily and then presented it on the stage, and made my escape there from behind a curtain. I pursued this method for some time, but as it was so often repeated to me that people seeing me emerge from the cabinet after my release, with hair disheveled, countenance covered with perspiration, trousers covered with dust and ofttimes even my clothes being torn, remarked, "Oh, he is faking, it did not take all that effort to make his escape," that eventually I determined to show to the audience exactly what means I resorted to, to effect my release, and so did the strait-jacket release in full view of everybody.' (In fact it was Hardeen who first realised that this was the most effective way to present a straitjacket escape.)

The drama of Houdini's act lay not just in his skill and showmanship but in the figure he presented. In the challenges – to police departments, to handcuff enthusiasts, to constructors of impregnable packing-cases – he was that irresistible hero of a thousand fairytales, the little man who takes on all comers. Escaping from the straitjacket, he was psychodrama made visible. He very soon learned what he must do in order to be effective. Once he had realised the essentials – that the straitjacket escape must be presented in full view; that the handcuffs must not be allowed to seem too easy, or the act would be dismissed; that he must take on, not just inanimate restraints, but living authority – he was launched. The sheer suspense – would he do it? Would he be defeated this time? – could hold an audience spellbound while nothing, or virtually nothing, was happening on stage. And of course the reason the audience cared was that Houdini himself cared so enormously. For him, the question of whether he freed himself or not really was a matter of life and death.

One of Houdini's more improbable aficionados was Edmund Wilson, America's most distinguished man of letters. Wilson was a keen amateur magician; but he observed and admired Houdini as a phenomenon who transcended his calling. Writing about him in the *New Republic,* Wilson observed, 'He lived his own drama and had otherwise little of the actor about him – so little that . . . one has the feeling that, in his role of public entertainer, he was always a little out of his orbit.' When the apparently trivial is endowed with the weight of emotion Houdini brought to his act, it is no longer trivial; and nor, therefore, is the performer.

Beck started them with a booking in Omaha in April, at sixty dollars a week. The routine consisted of escapes. On the stage were some chairs, a table loaded with chains and manacles, the substitution trunk in a corner, and a cabinet of steel tubing, curtained on all four sides and over the top (Houdini had learned this lesson from a circus giant who had been able to peek over the top of a previous cabinet.) A committee was invited onto the stage from the audience, to inspect the cabinet for hidden aids and check over all the cuffs and irons to see that they really did lock. Houdini's skill as a magician, which meant that he could palm, misdirect attention, and hide his picks in unlikely places, came in useful here. A favoured hiding-place was his thick, wiry hair. When he had to strip naked, he sometimes hid a small pick in the thick skin on the sole of a foot – not a spot that would ordinarily be searched by even the most rigorous police surgeon.

A feature was made of challenges from the audience, such as Martin Beck had sent up on the night he had booked them. In Omaha, Houdini freed himself from five pairs of regulation handcuffs and a set of official leg-irons supplied from the police. 'MANACLES DO NOT HOLD HIM', gasped the Omaha *World-Herald*. 'The entire handcuffs and leg-irons of the police department were on exhibition and all of them were used that could be worn conveniently, or rather inconveniently . . . In less time considerably than it took to adjust this array of jail "jewelry" he returned from an adjoining room, where it was impossible to conceal a confederate, relieved from the entire paraphernalia and having the same linked together, forming a chain'. He also performed the needle act (which had not sold when Professor Houdini had attempted to lure the public to buy it). He made a hit. The Nebraska Clothing Co. ran a series of ads featuring him: 'The ad man put a pair of handcuffs on Houdini and locked them. Houdini got out of them in less than two minutes and had them interlocked without the aid of a key and without leaving the office. The ad man sent out and bought a deck of cards, having loaned his last deck to a missionary who was going to the Philippines and wanted to go as a deck hand. Houdini opened that deck and counted out 52 cards; he turned them over and showed that there were 52 queens of hearts in it, and next moment counted out 52 aces of spades . . . He unlocked a fine door lock without a key, using a wooden toothpick to pick it, and finally picked up a cigar off the ad man's desk, where there wasn't any cigar, and picked a match out of a black ink well . . . As Houdini is out at Fairmount park this week the ad man invites him to come in and find a few more cigars on his desk, for he can't. Give Houdini a few more years and he'll have cigars to burn and money to burn as well.'

That was what Martin Beck thought, too. He raised the Houdinis to ninety dollars and sent them off to begin a tour of the west coast Orpheum circuit, starting in San Francisco. This time they took a room at six dollars a week, with running water and a gas stove. Unfortunately it also had fleas; and, on their first morning, there was an earthquake. Houdini was not to be put off. He successfully challenged the San Francisco police department. The usual routine followed: he was strip-searched, weighed down with fetters, and left to do his worst – only to walk into the office hot on the heels of the complacent police sergeant and all the pressmen. There followed a week's successful run at the San Francisco Orpheum, followed by an article by one Professor Benzon in the *Examiner*. The Professor pooh-poohed the act and explained that the secret lay in a key which Houdini concealed in his mouth. Professor Benzon, given the same facilities, could replicate all Houdini's handcuff feats. Houdini did not let this heaven-sent opportunity pass. He offered to let Professor Benzon strip him, seal his mouth and lock him in a cuff. If he could not escape he would forfeit a hundred dollars. Then he would lock the Professor in a cuff and give him the key. If he could not escape, he must give Houdini a hundred dollars, and must also let him shave off the Professor's long black beard. This challenge was not taken up: but the public flocked in. A fellow performer advised the Houdinis to ask for a raise. They were worth at least two hundred dollars. Two hundred dollars! A week! Finally they plucked up courage to ask Beck to raise them to a hundred and fifty. He did so at once. Houdini went straight out and bought Bess a fur neckpiece for thirty-five dollars. It was, as

Winston Churchill remarked in other circumstances, the end of the beginning.

The Orpheum tour ended in the autumn of 1899. It had been hard work: every week a new location with vast distances to be covered between houses in the huge spaces of the American West. Bess and Harry were undaunted: they asked nothing more than to carry on indefinitely with this terrifying schedule. But if they hoped to repeat their triumph in the east, they were disappointed. The new century found them picking up a week here and a week there. They played the first week of February at the New York Theater, Manhattan, but suffered a débâcle when Houdini mislaid the key that released Bess from the Metamorphosis trunk at the end of the act. Bess, inside in the dark, was terrified and began to shout. The theatre manager arrived with a fire axe with which he was about to attack the trunk when, in the nick of time, the keys were found. When the mishap was not repeated, New York lost interest. 'Re-engaged for next week Keith's, Phila', recorded Houdini triumphantly on 9 February from Boston; but the Keith's circuit would not send him on a regular tour as had the Orpheum circuit. From Philadelphia they moved to Toronto, where they were so broke that Houdini had to write to a friend excusing himself for not sending some handcuffs – he had forgotten to do so in Philadelphia, and to send them from Toronto would involve paying duty, 'so I trust you will not be angry if I wait until we leave Canada and send the cuffs to you from the States'.

The engagements continued to come in steadily, but after their triumphs in the West the previous year, there was a definite air of anticlimax about it all.

What was to be done?

Early in 1898, Houdini had written to the famous London magician J. N. Maskelyne to ask if he could join his show at the Egyptian Hall. Maskelyne sent a curt refusal: 'I have no room for any addition to my company. I seldom change my artists.' But things had changed in the two years since then. They were proven crowd-pullers. 'Who created the biggest

Sensation in California since the Discovery of Gold in 1849? WHY! HARRY HOUDINI! The ONLY recognised and Undisputed King of Handcuffs and Monarch of Leg Shackles,' blared a publicity broadside. The time had come for the Handcuff King to conquer some fresh fields. Some time towards the end of April or beginning of May, Bess and Harry decided to try their luck in Europe. On 21 May they still did not know exactly when they would leave – 'Possibly we may sail in the early part of June as I have just landed in N.Y. and am rushed fixing things.' On 30 May 1900, with no engagements arranged, the Houdinis set sail for London.

8

With One Bound He Was Free

The most famous Bound Man in history was Prometheus. (There were of course countless Bound Maidens, chained to rocks and guarded by dragons. But that is a very different kettle of symbolic fish.) Prometheus annoyed Zeus, King of the Gods, by suggesting that if men had the gift of fire this would be of immense value to them. Zeus, mean-spirited as usual, demurred. He thought that once they had fire men would become conceited and would begin to consider themselves the equals of the gods. Prometheus, regardless, took a reed, lit it on the sun, and returned to earth with the flame. Zeus, looking down, saw the earth studded with thousands of flickering stars. In his fury he sent Pandora to punish mankind with her box of miseries and diseases. As for Prometheus, he was chained to a rock, where every morning a great eagle came and pecked open his body and ate his liver. Every night the wound healed and the liver grew again. Prometheus suffered inexpressible agonies. But, not possessing Houdini's skills (even though he was a demigod), he was unable to free himself. He had to wait hundreds of years until finally he was unchained by Hercules.

Houdini, though a mere mortal, needed no Hercules. In him (this would undoubtedly have been his own view) Zeus would have found an altogether worthier opponent. The reception he received in Europe confirmed his uttermost hopes and expectations.

The Houdinis did not sail for Europe entirely unprepared. They had no bookings, but they knew there were possibilities. In 1899 T. Nelson Downs, the King of Koins, who came from Iowa and was an old friend of Houdini's (they first met in Chicago at the Great Columbian Exposition seven years earlier), had secured an engagement at the Palace Theatre just by mailing some reviews to the management. His coin manipulation act had gone down well. He became a 'headliner', made a star-billed tour of Britain, and went on to triumph on the continent 'at the salary of an ambassador'. Other American magicians had also done well in London: Howard Thurston the card manipulator; Billy Robinson, who had been Herrmann's old stage manager and who had now set himself up as a 'Chinese Mandarin Magician' under the name Chung Ling Soo; Horace Goldin (another old acquaintance from Chicago days), who specialised in 'rapid-fire' stage illusions. Houdini, too, sent his reviews – but to no effect. So he decided to see what he could achieve in person.

They arrived in London after a crossing during which Houdini was so seasick that Bess had to tie him to his bunk during the brief periods when she left him, for fear he would try to throw himself overboard. They reached dry land, recovered, found lodgings and set out to assault theatrical agents and managements. At first they had no success. Downs had hit the right moment; the Houdinis had not. Another escape act, Cirnoc, had disappointed the management of the Oxford Music Hall. And some recently-billed challenge acts had also bombed. The Bullet-Proof Man had lost all appeal, together with his life, when a marksman shot him in the groin and it transpired that his bullet-proof vest (padded with powdered glass) did not reach down that far. Annie Abbott, the 'Georgia Magnet', had faded overnight when a newspaper disclosed that the failure of five men to lift her was attributable to the laws of physics rather than supernatural powers. Faced with Houdini, agents were polite but unforthcoming.

The Houdinis' break came when an agent they were supposed to see was called away. Instead, they met his assistant, Harry Day, a young man just starting out in theatrical management. The two Harrys immediately took to one another – so much so that Harry Day was to represent Houdini for the rest of his life. Day persuaded the manager of the Alhambra, C. Dundas Slater, to give the Houdinis an audition. Slater was impressed with the substitution trunk act, but dubious about the handcuffs. He could not really believe that Houdini could get out of any handcuffs presented to him. Cirnoc, for example, had insisted on using his own. If Houdini could get out of Scotland Yard's handcuffs, then he might consider him.

This was what Houdini had been waiting for. An appointment was made with Superintendent Melville for 14 June. The usual routine followed. Melville was altogether dismissive of Houdini's claims. He took a pair of regulation cuffs, locked Houdini's arms around a pillar and led Day and Slater off to his office. They would leave him to cool his heels for a couple of hours. Houdini had freed himself before they had so much as opened the door. On the strength of this, Slater booked him for two weeks at the Alhambra at sixty pounds a week.

A special press performance was arranged before the opening night, during which Houdini was surprised to see a total stranger walk down the auditorium, climb on to the stage and denounce him. Not only was Houdini a fraud, said this person; he was not even an American. *He*, on the other hand, was the Great Cirnoc, and he was the original Handcuff King.

At this point a man in the audience stood up and said, 'That is not true. I know that young man is an American. I also am an American and I saw him several years ago doing his handcuff act.' He identified himself as Chauncey M. Depew, a distinguished lawyer and politician. Houdini was saved. He whispered to Bess, 'Get me the Bean Giant.'

The Bean Giant was his showpiece. Its inventor, Captain Bean of Boston, had offered five hundred dollars to anyone who could release himself from it. Houdini had won the bet but forfeited the cash, as he would not reveal his method. The lock of the Bean Giant was so placed that, even given a key, it was impossible to release oneself. 'Properly presented this is a good trick for exhibition purposes,' Houdini explained some years later to an assistant, 'that is to carry a cuff of your own, and show to the public how difficult this handcuff is by locking it on one of your committee's wrists, giving him the original key and asking him to unlock the cuff.' In this case, Cirnoc was the 'committee.' He insisted that, first, Houdini

The lone figure of Houdini leaps, manacled, from the Charles River Bridge, Boston.

(TOP) Houdini's father, Rabbi Weiss.

(MIDDLE) Mrs Weiss, Harry and Bess in perfect harmony.

(BOTTOM L TO R) The Weiss Brothers: Leopold, Nat, Dash, Wilhelm, Ehrich.

An early beefcake shot.
He already prefers to strip
to be photographed.

The budding athlete, aged 16 or 17.

Houdini the collector
annotates his first book 25 years
after it was published.

The earliest professional pictures of Harry and Bess. He was 20, she was 18. She is wearing the tights that caused so much heart-searching.

Mysterious Harry and La Petite Bessie try to take their act on tour.

The Welsh Bros. Circus, c. 1895. The Houdinis are at the right of the front row.

Houdini's first flight, Hufaren, Germany, November 1909.

A publicity procession marches through town.

Houdini caged. The bars of
the cage are actually drawn on,
as are the trunks.

Another pose for the same
pre-Freudian series.

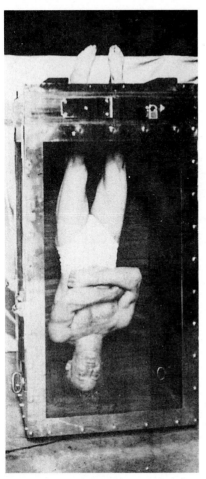

The 'old upside down': Houdini in his Chinese Water Torture Cell.

Jim Collins awaits the signal that Houdini is ready to be lowered.

The crowd roared, but the newspapers sided with
'because he is a *native* and I am a foreigner'.

, however, the vogue for escape artists was such that
t would easily support more than one – so long as
vays beyond question who was in control. Why not
the family? Harry sent a wire to Dash in New York:
OVER THE APPLES ARE RIPE'.

st no time in acting on this suggestion. He had been
s a nightclub bouncer, and rumour had it that he had
far one night, and someone had died. He arranged to
Germany on the first available ship, the *Deutschland*.
t him at the Friedrichstrasse station. He had set up
nent for a duplicate act, including a trunk, handcuffs,
t and musical score. But what was Dash to be called?
ld only be one Houdini – and yet there needed to
cho . . . He played his first theatre as 'Harden' (this
osed to sound English to German ears), then added
' to become 'Hardeen', which he remained. 'Hardeen
a wonderful reputation in Europe,' reported the
agazine *Mahatma* some time later. '[He has] made
nsation coming right after his brother, and is ack-
d as the best copy of Houdini in the profession

the key word here. A sense of uniqueness was
o Houdini's equilibrium. His immediate destruction
nn and Cirnoc was not merely professional – it was
ve. It was never enough for Houdini merely to defeat
e had to stamp on him, jump up and down on his
leave him for dead. He even felt equivocal about
who after all had been entirely his own creation. In
ning letter to another magician whom he thought
trespassing on his territory, he wrote, 'Why, you
worse than my brother. He calls himself Hardeen,
arry Hardeen.'
rman newspaper dated 9 December, 1900, Hardeen
to as 'Theo Hardeen . . . genannt HOUDINI der
with HOUDINI in huge letters while 'der Zweite'

free himself from the cuff. Houdini promptly did so – inside
his cabinet and using his own key, 'a long one, as it is impossible to reach the handcuff with the regular key and with the
aid of the extension you are enabled to reach the keyhole with
ease and facility'. Then he locked Cirnoc into the cuff and
presented him with the regulation key, which, of course, was
useless to him. Finally he had to ask Houdini to release him.
Next day, the papers were full of the story.

Cirnoc, far from destroying Houdini, had done the
opposite. Houdini, however, felt no gratitude for this involuntary assistance. He could never forgive intending competitors.
A little less than three years later, while he was playing at the
Pavilion, Leicester Square, he received a telegram from his
brother Dash: 'Cirnoc is dead.' Houdini noted: 'My most
unscrupulous imitator. He died on his way to Australia on my
opening night at Alhambra. He tried to ruin my show but
only succeeded in making my opening night a sensation.'

After this welcome publicity, the Alhambra engagement
was a smash hit. It began in early July and was extended to
the last week in August. Every night, sceptics brought along
their various unbeatable manacles; every night, Houdini beat
them. Suspicion grew that he had an assistant hidden inside
the cabinet. One night he agreed to do his escape outside it.
Police challengers chained and fettered him and fastened the
various restraints together behind his back with another handcuff so that he was forced into a kneeling position. He stipulated only that he be allowed to keep his hands out of sight;
he escaped within five minutes. He became so famous that
Lord Northcliffe, the famous newspaper proprietor, came to
his dressing-room to ask if he might consult Houdini upon a
number of subjects of American interest. Houdini's views
would be published in his paper. 'It appears he must have
thought it over, for they never appeared', Houdini noted.

His engagement would have been extended even further
were it not that he had agreed to take his act to Germany.

He was to open at the Central Theatre, Dresden, where he
was supposedly booked for the month of September. The Herr

Direktor, Gustav Kammsetzer, was, however, still sceptical about the real potential of the act, even though it had gone down so well in London. He explained to Houdini before he went on that when German audiences didn't like something they whistled. If the public whistled, he was to come off at once. 'You can well imagine my feelings,' Houdini wrote later. 'This manager had brought me to the continent with a contract which enabled him to close me right after my first performance if I was not a success, and I was not aware of that fact until just before going on . . . I had never addressed an audience in German before. I must have said some of the most awful things to make them believe I was good.'

There were no whistles. The audience rose and cheered after his very first handcuff release. 'When that audience rose in a solid mass . . . I knew I was going to stay my full engagement. And above all the din and noise and shouts and screams of the public, I heard Herr Direktor Kammsetzer's voice shouting like a madman. He ran to the middle of the stage and applauded. He took off his hat and cheered. In fact, I have no fear of saying that I recorded with him the greatest triumph of any artiste he had engaged.' He went on to escape from leg-irons and manacles from the Mathilda Gasse Prison, held by heavy locks forty pounds in weight. The house was sold out for the entire month: the takings broke all records. Herr Kammsetzer wanted to keep Houdini for another month, but the Wintergarten, Berlin, where he was to play October, refused categorically. They had already covered Berlin with flyers reading simply:

Wintergarten
HOUDINI
im
OKTOBER

His success in Berlin was even greater, if that were possible, than in Dresden. Everyone wanted to see Houdini. Tickets to the Wintergarten were sold out days ahead: the police inter-

vened to prevent more being sol[d]
on alert in case of some catastrop[h]
ahead to Ronacher's, Vienna, whic[h]
ember, to ask if the opening cou[ld]
The Ronacher manager replied th[at]
had secured a return booking in D[...]
to a delay, he was willing: but [...]
Wintergarten management, despe[rate]
ordinary new draw, agreed to pa[y]
of Houdini's salary for a month [...]
order to keep him. Triumphantly [...]
'THEATRICAL NEWS FROM G[...]
all this, topped with an elaborate [...]
graphs, signed 'Kindest regards an[...]
yours, Harry Houdini' – which he [...]
think of.

Meanwhile, imitation handcuff[...]
mushrooms. Cirnoc had opened a [...]
in Dresden, but had failed. In Berli[n]
to pay Houdini's fine if he wou[ld]
having failed to secure him, Herr [...]
brecher named Hermann. Houdini i[...]
ing this rival. He attended one of [...]
rushed into the ring when Herma[nn]
from the audience, ascertained tha[t]
regulation police ones, and made h[im]
give Hermann five thousand mark[s]
set of Houdini's cuffs, another five [...]
to escape from the ones Hermann [...]
five thousand more if the Germa[n]
latest feat – an escape he had mad[e]
in Berlin police headquarters. Her[r]
abuse and xenophobia. He accu[sed]
deceive the audience. He was not [...]
a 'low-life Hungarian'.

Not an American! Houdini flou[...]
ship papers and his passport and [...]

us a liar [...]
Herman[n]
Clearl[y]
the mark[...]
it was al[...]
keep it i[n]
'COME [...]
Dash [...]
working [...]
gone too [...]
leave for [...]
Harry m[...]
the equip[...]
straitjack[et]
There co[...]
be some [...]
was sup[...]
another [...]
has mad[e]
magic n[...]
quite a s[...]
nowledg[e]
today.'
Copy [...]
essential [...]
of Herm[...]
compuls[...]
a rival. [...]
head, an[...]
Hardeen [...]
a compla[...]
had bee[n]
have act[ed]
but not [...]
In a G[...]
is referre[d]
Zweite' [...]

free himself from the cuff. Houdini promptly did so – inside his cabinet and using his own key, 'a long one, as it is impossible to reach the handcuff with the regular key and with the aid of the extension you are enabled to reach the keyhole with ease and facility'. Then he locked Cirnoc into the cuff and presented him with the regulation key, which, of course, was useless to him. Finally he had to ask Houdini to release him. Next day, the papers were full of the story.

Cirnoc, far from destroying Houdini, had done the opposite. Houdini, however, felt no gratitude for this involuntary assistance. He could never forgive intending competitors. A little less than three years later, while he was playing at the Pavilion, Leicester Square, he received a telegram from his brother Dash: 'Cirnoc is dead.' Houdini noted: 'My most unscrupulous imitator. He died on his way to Australia on my opening night at Alhambra. He tried to ruin my show but only succeeded in making my opening night a sensation.'

After this welcome publicity, the Alhambra engagement was a smash hit. It began in early July and was extended to the last week in August. Every night, sceptics brought along their various unbeatable manacles; every night, Houdini beat them. Suspicion grew that he had an assistant hidden inside the cabinet. One night he agreed to do his escape outside it. Police challengers chained and fettered him and fastened the various restraints together behind his back with another handcuff so that he was forced into a kneeling position. He stipulated only that he be allowed to keep his hands out of sight; he escaped within five minutes. He became so famous that Lord Northcliffe, the famous newspaper proprietor, came to his dressing-room to ask if he might consult Houdini upon a number of subjects of American interest. Houdini's views would be published in his paper. 'It appears he must have thought it over, for they never appeared', Houdini noted.

His engagement would have been extended even further were it not that he had agreed to take his act to Germany.

He was to open at the Central Theatre, Dresden, where he was supposedly booked for the month of September. The Herr

Direktor, Gustav Kammsetzer, was, however, still sceptical about the real potential of the act, even though it had gone down so well in London. He explained to Houdini before he went on that when German audiences didn't like something they whistled. If the public whistled, he was to come off at once. 'You can well imagine my feelings,' Houdini wrote later. 'This manager had brought me to the continent with a contract which enabled him to close me right after my first performance if I was not a success, and I was not aware of that fact until just before going on . . . I had never addressed an audience in German before. I must have said some of the most awful things to make them believe I was good.'

There were no whistles. The audience rose and cheered after his very first handcuff release. 'When that audience rose in a solid mass . . . I knew I was going to stay my full engagement. And above all the din and noise and shouts and screams of the public, I heard Herr Direktor Kammsetzer's voice shouting like a madman. He ran to the middle of the stage and applauded. He took off his hat and cheered. In fact, I have no fear of saying that I recorded with him the greatest triumph of any artiste he had engaged.' He went on to escape from leg-irons and manacles from the Mathilda Gasse Prison, held by heavy locks forty pounds in weight. The house was sold out for the entire month: the takings broke all records. Herr Kammsetzer wanted to keep Houdini for another month, but the Wintergarten, Berlin, where he was to play October, refused categorically. They had already covered Berlin with flyers reading simply:

Wintergarten
HOUDINI
im
OKTOBER

His success in Berlin was even greater, if that were possible, than in Dresden. Everyone wanted to see Houdini. Tickets to the Wintergarten were sold out days ahead: the police intervened to prevent more being sold. The fire department was on alert in case of some catastrophe. The management wired ahead to Ronacher's, Vienna, which had booked him for November, to ask if the opening could be delayed for a month. The Ronacher manager replied that if the Alhambra, which had secured a return booking in December, would also agree to a delay, he was willing: but Dundas Slater refused. The Wintergarten management, desperate not to lose this extraordinary new draw, agreed to pay Ronacher's the equivalent of Houdini's salary for a month – DM4,000 or $1,000 – in order to keep him. Triumphantly, Houdini printed a flier – 'THEATRICAL NEWS FROM GERMANY 1900' – detailing all this, topped with an elaborate triptych of posed photographs, signed 'Kindest regards and well wishes, Respectfully yours, Harry Houdini' – which he sent to everyone he could think of.

Meanwhile, imitation handcuff acts were sprouting like mushrooms. Cirnoc had opened at the same time as Houdini in Dresden, but had failed. In Berlin, the Circus Busch offered to pay Houdini's fine if he would leave the Wintergarten: having failed to secure him, Herr Busch engaged a rival *ausbrecher* named Hermann. Houdini immediately set about undoing this rival. He attended one of Hermann's performances, rushed into the ring when Hermann called for a committee from the audience, ascertained that Hermann's cuffs were not regulation police ones, and made his own challenge. He would give Hermann five thousand marks if he could escape from a set of Houdini's cuffs, another five thousand if Houdini failed to escape from the ones Hermann was about to use, and yet five thousand more if the German could replicate Houdini's latest feat – an escape he had made while stripped stark naked in Berlin police headquarters. Hermann, in a fury, resorted to abuse and xenophobia. He accused Houdini of trying to deceive the audience. He was not even an American, he was a 'low-life Hungarian'.

Not an American! Houdini flourished his American citizenship papers and his passport and yelled, 'This brands one of

us a liar!' The crowd roared, but the newspapers sided with
Hermann, 'because he is a *native* and I am a foreigner'.

Clearly, however, the vogue for escape artists was such that
the market would easily support more than one – so long as
it was always beyond question who was in control. Why not
keep it in the family? Harry sent a wire to Dash in New York:
'COME OVER THE APPLES ARE RIPE'.

Dash lost no time in acting on this suggestion. He had been
working as a nightclub bouncer, and rumour had it that he had
gone too far one night, and someone had died. He arranged to
leave for Germany on the first available ship, the *Deutschland*.
Harry met him at the Friedrichstrasse station. He had set up
the equipment for a duplicate act, including a trunk, handcuffs,
straitjacket and musical score. But what was Dash to be called?
There could only be one Houdini – and yet there needed to
be some echo . . . He played his first theatre as 'Harden' (this
was supposed to sound English to German ears), then added
another 'e' to become 'Hardeen', which he remained. 'Hardeen
has made a wonderful reputation in Europe,' reported the
magic magazine *Mahatma* some time later. '[He has] made
quite a sensation coming right after his brother, and is acknowledged as the best copy of Houdini in the profession
today.'

Copy is the key word here. A sense of uniqueness was
essential to Houdini's equilibrium. His immediate destruction
of Hermann and Cirnoc was not merely professional – it was
compulsive. It was never enough for Houdini merely to defeat
a rival. He had to stamp on him, jump up and down on his
head, and leave him for dead. He even felt equivocal about
Hardeen, who after all had been entirely his own creation. In
a complaining letter to another magician whom he thought
had been trespassing on his territory, he wrote, 'Why, you
have acted worse than my brother. He calls himself Hardeen,
but not Harry Hardeen.'

In a German newspaper dated 9 December, 1900, Hardeen
is referred to as 'Theo Hardeen . . . genannt HOUDINI der
Zweite' – with HOUDINI in huge letters while 'der Zweite'

can hardly be seen. If Houdini was – just – able to accept Hardeen, it was because he never had been and never would be known as anything but an acknowledged copy. This was true even when in fact it was Houdini who was copying Hardeen. It was Hardeen who found out how the straitjacket escape should be presented. It takes quite a time to wriggle out of a straitjacket, and if it is done inside a cabinet there is nothing to prove that there was no assistance. A bored and hostile audience once let Hardeen know this is no uncertain manner. So he promised to repeat the challenge two nights later in full view. The theatre was sold out, and when Hardeen finally accomplished his feat, the crowd went wild. Hardeen sent Houdini the press clippings, and from then on Houdini's straitjacket escapes were all performed on the open stage, to much greater acclaim than Hardeen's. Even so, Houdini's fear that Hardeen would forget himself and step out of his agreed role always loomed edgily between them. In 1907 they were booked to appear in the same cities by rival American circuits. 'I don't think that I have anything to fear,' Houdini noted, 'as I am the originator, and he is like the rest of my imitators, with the exception that he is my brother (and a dam good brother at that.)' But as late as 1911, when he had been world-famous for years, Houdini was transported with fury when he arrived in England to find that Hardeen had just completed a tour of his own which appeared to have gone down only too well. Bess had to play the secret peacemaker: 'My Dear Bro. Dash . . . Just heard that you are not coming over here *and the reason why,* now Dash please do come over and if Harry does not pay the difference I will. Harry does not know that I am writing this. Now I want to tell you why he is sore, you know we are playing all the towns that you played, and of course there are plenty of guys always ready to tell Harry about your challenges and what you did, and Harry told me you had promised not to do the challenges, etc. Of course he is sore now but I am sure if he sees you he will forget all about it . . . I am as ever your loving sister Bess.'

Sir Arthur Conan Doyle, who was to become a good friend

of Houdini's, remembered with appalled astonishment his introduction to Hardeen. 'He did it by saying, "This is the brother of the great Houdini." This without any twinkle of humour and in a perfectly natural manner.' It was a revelation to Conan Doyle, that ultra-English gentleman, that such a sentence could be uttered without irony. But irony requires self-consciousness, detachment, self-awareness, and Houdini was sensationally free from any of these qualities. He was merely informing Conan Doyle of Hardeen's role in Houdini's world. An old family friend wrote, equally without irony, that 'When Harry passed on, Hardeen really came into his own.' The fact was that *until* Harry passed on, there was not the slightest possibility of his doing any such thing.

Leaving Hardeen in Berlin, Houdini filled in a free ten days with the now-customary triumphant sell-out at Magdeburg, and then returned to London where Dundas Slater was impatiently waiting. This time he was actually featured above the costly ballets for which the Alhambra was famous, '*which is something unheard of.*' 'It would be boastful to tell you how big a hit we are over here,' he wrote disarmingly to an old friend in Boston (thus telling him nevertheless). From there he moved to the north of England and played a week in Bradford, where on one evening, 8 February 1901, standing room was sold for ten shillings, seats were sold on the stage, and hundreds were turned away. Then they returned to Germany. 'We closed a *20* weeks engagement at Alhambra London and jumped here to Germany and stay here at least 6 more months, and at an excellent salary no not an excellent salary but an "*exhorbitant*" or newspaper salary,' he wrote triumphantly from Leipzig.

For any performer, such a progress would be astonishing. The only contemporary capable of generating comparable hysteria was Sarah Bernhardt. But Bernhardt was a great actress with many obvious attractions – beauty, spectacular presentations, a scandalous reputation. Houdini, on the other hand, escaped from handcuffs.

It was not as if, at this point, his act was in any way as slick and spectacular as it was later to become. An act such as Houdini's is routinely a team effort. In magic and illusion, part of the essential misdirection lies in the assumption that the performer's assistants are innocent stooges when, on the contrary, they are vital collaborators. As he himself put it: 'To avert suspicion from our assistants we make them seem as awkward and clumsy as possible. We have them drop things, stumble over chairs, and make mistakes of a minor nature. We want you to get the idea that these men play no real part in the performance of our tricks; whereas, of course, they are most important cogs in our work. Once I was sitting next to a woman who kept exclaiming at the clumsiness of one of the cleverest assistants I have ever seen. Instead of the magician doing the work, the assistant was really doing nine-tenths of the tricks. Yet he acted his part so well that this woman finally said, "My! how clumsy that man is! I wonder why the magician keeps him?" ' The essential jobs performed by Houdini's assistants and never suspected by the public included dealing with awkward customers who showed up obstreperously in the wings and would not be dissuaded (they were knocked out and woke up some time later elsewhere) and dealing with difficult challenge cuffs by substituting a more tractable set *en route* from challenger to performer.

Later on, Harry Day had a form letter printed which set out all the elaborate requirements for the Houdini show. These ranged from 'Bill Matter (The World-Famous HOUDINI, the original HANDCUFF KING & JAIL-BREAKER – The only living being who ever escaped from the SIBERIAN TRANS-PORT VAN in Russia . . . **Everybody Invited to bring their own Padlocks**)' to an elaborate plan of the 'STAGE PLOT for HOUDINI'S Death Defying Mystery, the dressing-room requirements and property list (**DO NOT get anything that is to be Charged to me**).' And Houdini had a form printed up which would enable him to keep track of his reception and working conditions in the different towns he visited, with such headings as OPPOSITION: WEATHER: COMPLAINTS:

RECOMMENDATIONS: REMARKS REGARDING BIL-
LING: WORKING OF SPECIAL NIGHTS.

But at this stage there was only Bess, the trunk, the handcuffs and the straitjacket. And the strain was beginning to tell.
In 1901 Houdini was only twenty-seven; but although he was
emotionally still almost childlike, in point of knocking about
the world, he was already a weary veteran. 'I am not well',
he wrote in March 1901, 'as the *prepetual* worry and excitement
are beginning to tell on me and I am afraid that if I dont take
a rest soon Ill be all done up. You know for the last 11 years
Ive had the same strain over & over day in & day out & before
this luck streak I had to do 8 to 12 shows a day.'

Life on the road in England was eased by the network of
'digs' available in every town. Years later, Houdini would
ruminate nostalgically on the virtues of British theatrical land-
ladies: 'The "digs" for my wife . . . and myself never cost
more than £6 per week, including tips, often considerably less,
and the table and service was in some ways superior to the
best hotels, including, as it did, pheasants, cream, and all
the "fixins" . . . To my mind no more comfortable form of
housing for the itinerant has ever been devised.' But conditions
in Germany were a good deal less luxurious. 'It was the custom
for acrobats to travel fourth class. This class of cars then had
no cross seats, but were furnished with benches along the sides
and during night runs the thrifty tumblers would spread their
tumbling pads on the floor and sell sleeping privileges at so
much per.' In Germany, Houdini was forced to hire a type-
writer for the first time: a challenger from Krupps, the arma-
ment manufacturers, had hurt his right hand screwing a cuff
sadistically tight and he was unable to hold a pen. 'To tell the
truth I had to get it to attend to my Correspondence, as I do
all of my own booking.'

He also arranged his own publicity. Houdini was passionate
about publicity. In Paris on this first trip to Europe, he had
seven men sit in a line along a café terrace on the pavement.
Every so often all these men would remove their hats and bow
their heads, which were revealed to be quite bald and each

inscribed with a letter – together spelling HOUDINI. From the very beginning, his career may be followed in a trail of posters, flyers, publicity hand-outs and every kind of stunt imaginable. The smallest details fascinated him. When he began distributing his own films, he sent out meticulous publicity hints. He instanced as a possible advance stunt 'Letters starting with I am droping this out of the window, am hemmed in by fire, must die and hope this will reach etc. The next line states that this is the way letters might come if the city was not protected with such an efficient fire department.' He added approvingly, 'Boasberg took the letters placed them in an airtight box, burnt the corners and smoked them, so they smelt firey.' The letters were then sent to all the local Chiefs of Police.

His detractors point to this avalanche of self-promotion as part of the reason for his enormous fame. This is true in so far as the urge to self-advertisement was a part of his compulsive nature. Just as he had to do what he did, so he had to tell the world about it. But no publicity stunt could in itself account for his success. Publicity was no use without the goods to back it up. And it is at this point, before there were any elaborations to obscure it, that one of the most fundamental aspects of Houdini's appeal is clear to see. It lay in the posters which plastered every town he played inviting people to 'BRING YOUR OWN PADLOCKS'. Houdini's act did not merely involve Houdini. The audience was in it with him.

There was an occasion in Blackburn in 1902 when audience involvement threatened to get seriously out of hand. Houdini had made his usual offer of twenty-five pounds to anyone who could lock him up successfully. It was taken up on this occasion by one Ralph Hodgson, who had been a soldier, had left the army, and was now trying to get a Physical Culture School going in Blackburn. Hodgson stipulated that he was to use his own irons and was to fix them himself. Houdini agreed, and deposited the money with the local paper, the Blackburn *Star*, as was his habit (it ensured capacity news coverage).

The two met at ten in the evening of 24 October. The hall was packed. Hodgson, a very big, strong man, towered over the diminutive Houdini. Hodgson was carrying six pairs of heavy irons with clanking chains and padlocks. Houdini examined them. He stated, to a buzz of disappointment, that his claim was that he could escape from 'regulation' irons. These, he said, had been tampered with – the iron had been wrapped round with string, the locks altered, and various other steps taken to impede escape. But nevertheless (cheers) he was prepared to try. Hodgson riposted that challengers were to bring their own irons, which was what he had done. Houdini agreed to take him on: but he would need a little extra time. There were more cheers.

Hodgson, with the help of a friend, began by fixing a pair of irons over Houdini's upper arm and pulling his arms tight behind his back with the chain. Then he took a pair of cuffs, pulled Houdini's hands forward and fastened them in front of his body. Such was the pulling and tugging that Houdini reminded Hodgson that he was to fix the irons himself – the challenge did not mention any assistance – and that it was no part of the bargain that his arms should be broken. The assistant stepped down. More cuffs were fastened and padlocked; Houdini's arms were trussed to his sides; and, to finish, a pair of leg-irons was passed through the chains binding his arms together at the back, and then fixed round his ankles. Another pair of leg-irons was added. Then the cabinet was placed over Houdini, and the waiting began. Strict watch was meanwhile kept over Bess and Hardeen, who were at the side of the stage.

After about fifteen minutes, the cabinet was lifted to reveal Houdini lying on his side, still securely bound. He indicated that he wanted to be lifted up. Hodgson refused; the audience hissed and booed; Hardeen lifted his brother to his knees. The cabinet was replaced.

After another twenty minutes the curtain was lifted again. This time Houdini said his arms were numb from the pressure of the irons and asked to have them unlocked for a minute to restore his circulation. Hodgson refused. 'This is a contest, not a love match,' he said, amid howls from the audience. 'If you are beaten, give in.' A doctor, examining Houdini, said that his arms were blue, and it was cruelty to keep him chained up in that way any longer. Still, he would not give in, and asked for more time.

Fifteen minutes later he reappeared and announced that one hand was free. There was terrific cheering. The curtain was dropped again. Houdini reappeared at intervals to let the audience know how things were going, and shortly before midnight, he emerged with torn clothes and bleeding arms to throw the last of the shackles on the stage. The huge audience, which had been sitting watching the cabinet for almost two hours, 'stood up and cheered and cheered, and yelled themselves hoarse to give vent to their overwrought feelings. Men and women hugged each other in mad excitement. Hats, coats and umbrellas were thrown into the air, and pandemonium reigned supreme for fifteen minutes.'

Houdini could never have allowed himself to fail a challenge of this kind. He would have seen it as the end of his career. He had to be invincible. And the more he was in the public eye, the more failures mattered. He was no longer a mere dime-museum freak-show performer; neither was he so well-established that he could have passed a failure off. Failure, moreover, would have broken him not just professionally, but personally. As much as any gladiator, he was fighting, each time he appeared, for his life. This was the terrible tension that held the audience during those long intervals when he was invisible in his cabinet. Houdini's actual appearances onstage constituted an astonishingly small proportion of his performance time.

The peculiar intensity of the Blackburn occasion lay in the fact that he was here confronting another desperate man. Ralph Hodgson was a bright lad who had never done very well since he had left the army. The physical training school was his last throw. If he could defeat Houdini, what a boost that would give him! So he, too, was fighting for his life – something of which the local audience must have been well aware. After this failure, his school came to nothing. He faded away.

Both men were drained by the encounter. But Houdini was not so exhausted that he could not learn the important lessons it held for him. One was that (as when Sergeant Waldron had trapped him with the immovable cuffs in Chicago) he must never again lay himself so open to defeat. The second was that nothing generated the intense emotions upon which his act relied so much as suspense. If he could really get people biting their nails then they would sit and wait happily for hours. But for this to happen the suspense must be – at least in the public's mind – real. The merest notion of a put-up job would destroy him as surely as a defeat. What he gradually learned was to generate the suspense without really facing the defeat.

In 1904, two years after the Blackburn contest, there was a very similar happening at the London Hippodrome. This time the challenger was the *Daily Illustrated Mirror*. A reporter from this paper produced a pair of handcuffs which it had taken a Birmingham blacksmith five years to make and whose lock could reputedly never be picked. Houdini accepted the challenge for the following Thursday afternoon.

Four thousand people crowded into the Hippodrome to watch the contest. At three-fifteen Houdini entered his cabinet, his wrists fastened. Twelve minutes later he reappeared. The crowd cheered: but he was still secured, and said he just wanted to look at the lock in the light. He disappeared; the orchestra continued to play. Twelve minutes later he appeared again, still bound. His knees hurt: could he have a cushion to kneel on? This was granted.

At ten past four, almost an hour after he had begun, he appeared again. He was crumpled and perspiring. Could he be unlocked in order to take his coat off? The reporter, like Hodgson, refused, saying that Houdini only wanted to see how the lock worked. The cuffs would only be unlocked if he declared himself beaten. The crowd, as in Blackburn, jeered. Houdini, with difficulty, extracted a penknife from his pocket and, bringing the coat over his head, ripped it to pieces while the audience cheered. Then he re-entered the cabinet. Ten minutes later he reappeared, free. The audience went wild and carried him shoulder-high round the arena.

What really happened on this occasion? One version has it that Houdini really was beaten and that, after he had cut his coat, he called for a drink of water which was brought to him by Bess. In the glass was a key; Houdini, while drinking, let this slide into his mouth. But the *Mirror*'s own report states that 'Mrs Houdini was present, but was so overcome that she had to leave the Hippodrome just before Houdini ripped the coat.'

Had Houdini, as it seemed, nearly been caught out again? After his previous experiences, it seems improbable. A third commentator, who claimed that he had evidence to prove his statement, said he believed that the whole challenge was Houdini's idea. He knew the blacksmith, knew there would be no problem with the cuffs, and paid him to offer them to the reporter. After that, he paced the show in just the way that had been so effective in Blackburn – frustrated appearances, begging for mercy, the cruel opponent, the dramatic gesture – and it worked again.

There is no way to be sure. A correspondent who has examined the *Mirror* cuff asseverates that 'there was no gaff built into [it]. It contains two genuine Bramah rotary locks which operate in sequence and which contain fourteen active tumblers between them. It's one snazzy piece of hardware.' In any event, there could be no more outings for this particular format, or things would start to look suspicious. But it is well-known that later in his career, after he had made a successful escape in three minutes, Houdini would sit behind his screen for half an hour more, calmly playing cards or reading the paper while the band played and the audience on the other side bit its lips, sat on the edge of its seat, and wondered whether this time, at last, Houdini had been unable to break free. And when the tension had just become unbearable there he would be, dripping with what looked like sweat but was really water with which he had just doused himself.

But if the difficulty was faked, the anguish was genuine. Houdini's audiences suffered with him because they sensed that they were witnessing not just his body, but his soul. Perhaps this spiritual nakedness – the absence, between performer and audience, of those walls of reserve generally imposed by detachment and professionalism, that sense that the performing and the private selves are separate entities – is the essence of charisma. Houdini, for the same reasons that he lacked all irony, was entirely lacking in reserve. His every peculiarity tended towards this essential confusion and conflation of what was public and what private. If he was detached, it was from what should have been his private life. Conversely, everything that went on in the theatre was terrifyingly personal. It was a revelation of that inner self which escaped him at all other moments. He could reach it nowhere else; there was nowhere else it could express its yearnings. The true charismatic, whether actor, politician, or escapologist, is acting under compulsion – not because he is mad but, on the contrary, *to preserve his equilibrium*. This is the nature of the psychodrama sensed by the audience. The script, naturally, varies.

But it was not just his own drama that Houdini was acting out in his escapes from gaols and handcuffs. It was also the drama of his audience.

Houdini's was a time when relations between performer and audience in the theatre had become very formalised. In earlier days there had been no such hard-and-fast separation. In the circular theatres of Elizabethan England, the actors were surrounded by the audience. In the theatres of eighteenth-century Europe, members of the audience not only sat on the stage but reacted noisily to the play and characters. The gap between theatre and life was rather narrow: while the theatre was relatively *informal*, role-playing in everyday life was, on the contrary, so formalised as to be almost theatrical. A person's dress, demeanour, language, were an infallible guide to his place in the world. Moreover, within this hierarchy the actor's place was as a subordinate, a kind of higher servant. In a very real sense, the actors were at the beck and call of their audience. For its part, the audience felt free to express its views of what was going on onstage – and of what ought to be going on – at any time during the performance.

All this was possible because the urban playgoing public was very small. Audiences were drawn from a narrow band of the well-to-do. They met frequently, attended all the plays, caught all the references. Performances – even public performances – were intimate affairs; and many performances were not public but private, financed by a patron and given for a select aristocratic audience in a private theatre. But by the nineteenth century this was a vanished world. Shop-bought clothes meant that the lady and her maid, the lord and the bank-clerk were not immediately distinguishable on the street. Huge masses of people moving from the country to the city, from the old world to the new, further softened hitherto sharp distinctions. They also vastly increased the potential size of audiences.

The old intimacy, possible only amongst a small and cohesive society, began to disintegrate. The stage presented an increasingly stylised view of life which, more and more, played out not the life of the audience but its fantasies. Actors and actresses were no longer varieties of upper servant, there to do a job to the satisfaction of their masters, but foci for these fantasies. So the spotlight turned increasingly upon individual performers, giving rise to a new breed: the star, who could successfully embody countless individual fantasies.

The first of these superstars was Sarah Bernhardt: Madonna as Phèdre. The fact that she was mobbed by thousands of people wherever she went made her an object of suspicion to the theatrical establishment. But what was proved beyond a shadow of doubt was that there were tens of thousands of people out there who desperately needed someone to adulate – someone like Sarah.

As time went on, Sarah took to appearing, not in full-length plays in a straight theatre, but in excerpts in music halls. This was seen as a humiliation by the world of classical theatre. But it was an entirely logical progression. For Sarah spoke to an audience classical theatre could never satisfy. They came to see her, not the play. Her appeal went beyond culture and education. Her dazzled audiences, for whom she was a kind of deity, were largely drawn from the new urban masses all over the world. They were the kind of people who in an earlier era would have found their entertainment in fairgrounds and travelling shows of all kinds. They were too numerous now to be satisfied with that. So the fairground was brought into the theatre, as vaudeville; and in the few years of its heyday – before it was swamped by the rise of the cinema – it had all the vibrancy, all the assurance of a genuinely popular art-form – which the theatre lacked. It was no accident that, in Sarah's view, the greatest English theatrical figure of her time was Marie Lloyd.

Mass communications (ensuring not only national but international publicity) had created Sarah: and the stage was set for the creation of other idols of popular culture. Harry Houdini, who could have flourished in no other milieu than vaudeville – for was his not the archetypal fairground act? – had, in the space of a few months, taken his place in this select band. He was one of those little men – physically small, metaphorically powerless – who were to dominate popular entertainment in the early years of the century. Charlie Chaplin and Mickey Mouse had their distinctive ways of triumphing over authority. Houdini did so in the most direct way it is possible to imagine – by literally breaking free of its shackles.

The fact that this was a large element of his popular appeal is clear from the pattern of his success during this part of his career – the part that was dominated by handcuff and gaol escapes. His popularity was greatest where authority was harshest. In the United States, where most people did not feel particularly oppressed, he did not manage to establish himself until some years later, when his act and its resonances were rather different. In paternalist industrial Britain he did well. But in the two most authoritarian states in the world – Germany and Russia – his success was phenomenal.

This was deeply resented by those who were responsible for keeping the hatches battened down – even though they could not help being fascinated by him. In Germany, where he made frequent appearances, Houdini found himself often at odds with the police. Germany was full of petty regulations which forbade, if they were strictly enforced, almost anything one might wish to do. Houdini ignored them. 'It does seem strange,' he wrote in 1901, 'that the people over here especially Germany, France, Saxony, and Bohemia fear the police so much, In fact the Police are all Mighty, and I am the first man that has ever dared them, that is my success.'

The first brush with authority had occurred soon after he arrived in Dresden, in 1900. Houdini wanted to try a new stunt: to be thrown from a boat handcuffed and free himself under water. The police refused to permit this on any account. Houdini did it anyway, and emerged to find a furious policeman on the scene. He was brought before the magistrate, who decided that the only chargeable offence he had committed was walking on the grass, for which he was fined a few pfennigs. The incident (to say nothing of his continuing practice of challenging the police to lock him up wherever he went, invariably to escape) did not endear him to them, and in the following year (1901) there was a more serious difficulty. This time they pursued him with regard to the very strict regulations which then obtained relating to misrepresentation. These had been used before to prosecute entertainers who were not what they set themselves up to be. Now Schutzmann Werner Graff of the Cologne Police denounced Houdini as a swindler and published a story to this effect in the *Rheinischer Zeitung* which put Houdini in a very bad light.

Houdini demanded an apology, but was simply laughed at. So he engaged the best lawyer in Cologne and went to court. There were three trials. In the first, Houdini charged Graff with slander. Graff told the judge and jury that he could easily prove his case: he would chain Houdini up so that he could not release himself. Houdini was chained: and to demonstrate just how easy escape was, he agreed to show the judge and jury (but nobody else) exactly how he opened the lock. He won his case, the police were fined, and Graff had publicly to apologise to Houdini 'in the name of the Kaiser'. He declined to comply, however, and took the case to a higher court. Here he produced a lock which had been specially made by a master mechanic so that, once it was locked, nothing, not even the key, would open it.

The case came to court in July, 1902. Houdini escaped from the restraint in four minutes; Graff was ordered to pay all costs (which were heavy, since the case had now been running more than a year) and insert an advertisement in all the Cologne papers proclaiming his punishment 'in the name of the Kaiser' and apologising to Houdini for slandering him. Once again he could not bring himself to comply, and took the case to the *Oberlandesgericht*, the highest court, from which there was no appeal. His argument now was that Houdini said he could open safes, and, although he had opened handcuffs and cell doors, he had never opened a safe in Germany. The judge decreed that Houdini should try the safe in his office. He was taken there, shown the safe and left alone with it. He was nervous, never having tried a German safe lock before. He gave it a good pull, just to see – and the door swung open: it had not been locked. After 'a decent interval' he presented his feat to the judge, who found in favour of Houdini. Graff was fined thirty marks and had to pay the costs of the three trials, as well as the rest of the punishment. Houdini, triumphant, published long descriptions of all this in his publicity releases.

Meanwhile, he was invited to Moscow, to appear at the Establishment Yard cabaret. This was not easy, as he was a Jew and Moscow did not welcome Jews. Bess filled in the papers for both of them, stating that she was a Roman Catholic. They arrived, and Houdini rehearsed his opening speech. He always liked to address audiences in their own language. So before leaving Berlin, where he had been playing at the Wintergarten, he had got an interpreter to teach him a Russian speech, which he had learned by heart. The manager in Moscow, however, was appalled. 'My God, we should be ruined!' he yelled at Houdini in German. 'That isn't Russian. You are speaking in Polish, which is forbidden, and with a strong Yiddish accent, which makes the offence much worse!' He wrote the speech out again, with the correct phonetics. Houdini went to say it over to himself in a nearby park. When he finally had it ready and turned to go, some policemen leaped from the bushes and frogmarched him to a cell. They were taking no chances with this suspicious, muttering stranger. Houdini was not rescued until the manager, mystified by his non-appearance, got in touch with the police himself.

However, he had used his time to make friends with the police, and now issued one of his usual challenges. He had noticed the Russian prisoners herded through the streets, 'carrying their black bread and a pot to cook their beloved *chey*, or what is known in English-speaking countries as common tea'. They were transported to Siberia in travelling gaols known as *carettes*. Houdini persuaded Lebedeoff the chief of the Moscow police to let him try to escape from a *carette*.

The attempt was set for 11 May 1903. It was a cold day. Houdini was stripped naked and searched – more thoroughly than he had ever been searched before. He was laid on a table, and one man worked upwards from feet to head while another worked in the other direction. Then he was turned over and searched again. He was led into the prison yard, and the *carette* was searched in its turn. Two iron bands joined by a short metal bar were padlocked around Houdini's wrists, and his ankles were fettered. Then he was locked inside the transport cell. Only after this was he informed that the only key that would open the door was in Siberia. If he failed, he faced a long, cold journey. The *carette* was then, at Houdini's request, turned so that its back, containing the door with its one small, barred window, was against the prison wall.

According to one account it took him forty-five minutes to get free; another gives the time as twenty-eight minutes. But free himself he did. The door of the *carette* was still locked; his shackles were on the floor. Lebedoeff was furious. Houdini was searched again, and so was his assistant, Franz Kukol, who had been held at some distance from the proceedings. (Houdini had engaged Kukol, an excellent mechanic and musician, in Germany: the beginning of that team which was to become ever more essential to him.) Nothing was found. Lebedoeff had promised Houdini a certificate if he succeeded in this escape, but now refused to give it to him. Needless to say, no newspapermen had been permitted in the prison yard. Nevertheless the story got about, and Houdini became a popular hero, because everyone hated the secret police. His engagement at the Establishment Yard was extended from four to eight weeks.

How was this escape effected? Harold Kellock, presumably on Bess's authority, says he worked through the window aperture. 'On the inside the door was merely a smooth sheet of steel, without any sign of a lock, but with a little high window six inches square, crossed by four bars. The lock was on the outside of the door, about thirty inches below the window.' But J. C. Cannell, in his *The Secrets of Houdini,* says Houdini pierced the metal floor of the *carette* with a 'cutter', folded back the metal, removed the wooden planking beneath, and slipped out. The magician Milbourne Christopher inclines to the window theory. 'The lithograph which he had made to publicize the feat in other countries, shows the window smaller than it was and higher above the lock. A showman would not give a clue to his method in his advertising.' Certainly he used the door-hatch in various of his gaol escapes. In Salford in 1904 the trap-door through which food was passed to prisoners was left open at his request, to enable him to reach the lock outside the door. And once he could reach the lock, the only tool he needed was a tiny pick or piece of wire.

Houdini remained in Russia, playing various engagements, until September 1903. In that seething and ironbound dictatorship, he was sensationally successful. 'The superstitious court went mad about me', he told a journalist years later. 'The Empress with her love of mysticism refused to believe that there was a scientific and mechanical explanation for my magic. The Empress begged me to stay and give her the benefit of my gifts, but I refused. I attended a court function where wine was served. It so happens I am a teetotaller. I did not know the elaborate court ceremony. It seems that a refusal to touch the wine served by the emperor is an insult to Russia. I promptly lost my standing at court.' During one week in Moscow he earned $1,750. 'Have managed to send home a small ship-load of Russian Roubles, so there is no complaint on this side of the question,' he wrote from Nijni-Novgorod in August. 'Things are still booming with us, and we have never been in such demand as at the present moment. It may be a long time ere we will work America, as I am actually asking for $1000 weekly salary, and to tell you the truth, I am not even anxious to accept that work at that salary. Over here I stay one, two and even 6 months in one City, and have a GREAT reputation, and in America it means every week jump to another city!! So I will nures Europe as long as it will accept HOUDINI, and then come home to America, and retire.' But he was glad to leave Russia, in spite of the money. 'After you leave Russia, you feel as if you had yourself come out of some sort of mild prison.' He never went back.

Houdini was now established as one of the world's leading performers. By the end of his first year in Europe, he was able to fulfil every immigrant's dream, which is to return in triumph to the place he left in ignominy.

In January 1901, he saw in a London shop window a gown which had originally been designed for Queen Victoria, who had just died. He was by then missing his mother dreadfully, and the sight of the gown made him miss her even more, since the two ladies were very much of a size – small and dumpy, although Queen Victoria was fatter than Mrs Weiss. So Houdini marched into the shop and offered to buy the gown. The shopkeeper was reluctant to let it go, but relented when Harry offered him fifty pounds for it and explained that it was for his mother. Then he wrote to his mother inviting her over for a visit: he had a fine surprise in store for her.

She arrived while he was playing in Hamburg, in time to watch a special benefit performance at which he was presented with a silver bowl. At the close of the engagement, the party entrained for Budapest. Despite his success Houdini had not much money. He was never good at business, and was not yet demanding the salaries he could have commanded. He had not learned the lesson of that occasion when Martin Beck had been so happy to raise his salary – but only when he was asked. So the Houdinis and Mrs Weiss had to sit up all night in a second-class compartment. But once they had arrived, all that changed. The finest hotel in Budapest was the Royal Hotel: this was where Houdini was determined to give a party for his mother. He wanted to book the palm-garden salon for it, but the management refused to let him have it. It was not let out for private parties. Houdini took the manager aside. 'After listening patiently to his remonstrances, I revealed to him my plot to crown my little mother and allow her to be Queen Victoria for a few fleeting hours. He immediately consented to become my confederate, for my scheme appealed to his sportsmanship, and he said, "My boy, for so worthy a cause you may have the room for nothing." Accordingly the stage was set.'

The party was a magnificent one. All the families on both sides were invited, including the most snobbish of his mother's relatives, her Uncle Heller, who had sternly disapproved of her imprudent marriage, and all his parents' friends. The manager entered into the spirit of the game by putting on the clothes he wore only to receive royalty, and bowing all the guests into the salon personally. 'How my heart warmed to see the various friends and relatives kneel and pay homage to my mother, every inch a queen, as she sat enthroned in her heavily carved and gilded chair', continues this extraordinary account of rococo wish-fulfilment. 'That night, Mother and I were awake all night talking over the affair, and if happiness ever entered my life to its fullest, it was in sharing Mother's wonderful enjoyment at playing a queen for a day. The next morning, after having lived two ecstatically happy days, I escorted the Fairy Queen Mother en route to America.' Then he borrowed the car-fare back to Germany.

With one bound he was free – from poverty, from humiliation, from entrapment. And, unlike Prometheus, he had loosened his own shackles. But his spirit was not assuaged.

9

The Disappearing Fathers Trick

One of the wittiest and most beautiful tricks in the history of magic was presented by Houdini's literary mentor Robert-Houdin in November 1846, for Louis-Philippe at the château of St-Cloud. It was called the Disappearing Handkerchiefs. Here is his description of it:

> I borrowed from my noble spectators several handkerchiefs which I made into a parcel and laid on the table. Then, at my request, different persons wrote on the cards the names of places whither they desired their handkerchiefs to be invisibly transported.
>
> When this had been done, I begged the king to take three of the cards at hazard, and choose from them the place he might consider most suitable.
>
> 'Let us see,' Louis Philippe said, 'what this one says: "I desire the handkerchiefs to be found beneath one of the candelabra on the mantelpiece." That is too easy for a sorcerer, so we will pass to the next card: "The handkerchiefs are to be transported to the dome of the Invalides." That would suit me, but it is much too far – not for the handkerchiefs, but for us. Ah, ah!' the king added, looking at the last card, 'I am afraid, M. Robert-Houdin, that I am about to embarrass you. Do you know what this card proposes? . . . It is desired that you should send the handkerchiefs into the chest of the last orange-tree on the right of the avenue.'
>
> 'Only that, sire? Deign to order, and I will obey.'
>
> 'Very good, then. I should like to see such a magic act. I, therefore, choose the orange-tree chest.'
>
> The king gave some orders in a low voice, and I directly saw several persons run to the orange-tree, in order to watch it and prevent any fraud. I was delighted at this precaution, which must add to the effect of my experiment, for the trick was already arranged, and the precaution was too late.
>
> I had now to send the handkerchiefs on their travels, so I placed them beneath a bell of opaque glass, and taking my

wand, I ordered my invisible travellers to proceed to the spot the king had chosen.

I raised the bell: the little parcel was no longer there, and a white turtle-dove had taken its place.

The king then walked quickly to the door, whence he looked in the direction of the orange tree, to assure himself that the guards were at their post. When this was done he began to smile and shrug his shoulders. 'Ah! M. Robert-Houdin,' he said somewhat ironically, 'I much fear for the virtue of your magic staff.' Then he added . . . 'Tell William to open immediately the last chest at the end of the avenue, and bring me carefully what he finds there – if he *does* find anything.'

William soon proceeded to the orange-tree . . . He carefully removed one of the sides of the chest, thrust his hand in, and almost touched the roots of the tree before he found anything. All at once he uttered a cry of surprise, as he drew out a small iron coffer eaten by rust.

This curious 'find', after having been cleaned from the mould, was brought in and placed on a small ottoman by the king's side.

'Well, M. Robert-Houdin . . . here is a box; am I to conclude it contains the handkerchiefs?'

'Yes, sire,' I replied with assurance, 'and they have been there, too, for a long period.'

'How can that be? The handkerchiefs were lent you scarce a quarter of an hour ago.'

'I cannot deny it, sire, but what would my magic power avail me if I could not perform incomprehensible tricks? Your Majesty will doubtless be still more surprised when I prove to your satisfaction that this coffer, as well as its contents, was deposited in the chest of the orange-tree sixty years ago.'

'I should like to believe your statement,' the king replied with a smile, 'but that is impossible, and I must therefore ask for proofs of your assertion.'

. . . Louis-Philippe unfastened a ribbon [from the neck of a turtle-dove] that held a small, rusty key with which he hastened to unlock the coffer. The first thing that caught the king's eye was a parchment on which he read the following statement: 'THIS DAY, THE 6TH JUNE, 1786, THIS IRON BOX, CONTAINING SIX HANDKERCHIEFS, WAS PLACED AMONG THE ROOTS OF AN ORANGE TREE

BY ME, BALSAMO, COUNT OF CAGLIOSTRO, TO
SERVE IN THE PERFORMANCE OF AN ACT OF
MAGIC, WHICH WILL BE EXECUTED ON THE
SAME DAY SIXTY YEARS HENCE BEFORE LOUIS
PHILIPPE OF ORLEANS AND HIS FAMILY.'

'There is decidedly witchcraft about this,' the king said . . .
'Nothing is wanting, for the seal and signature of the
celebrated sorcerer are placed at the foot of the statement,
which Heaven pardon, smells strongly of sulphur . . . But,'
the king added, taking out of the box a carefully sealed packet,
'can the handkerchiefs by possibility be in this?'

'Indeed, sire, they are; but before opening the parcel, I
would request Your Majesty to notice that it also bears the
impression of Cagliostro's seal.'

'It is certainly the same,' my royal spectator answered after
comparing the two seals. Still, in his impatience to learn the
contents of the parcel, the king quickly tore open the envelope,
and soon displayed before the astonished spectators the six
handkerchiefs which, a few moments before, were still on my
table.

As a famous magician put it, 'Any unprejudiced person will
agree that the effect of this trick was as close an approach to
real magic as it is humanly possible to achieve.' The main
principle upon which it is based – that of predicting which
hiding-place the king was likely to choose from a selection
forced upon him, so that all preparations might be made in
advance – is clear. But the skill and artistry of the presentation,
down to the key hung round the dove's neck and the smell of
sulphur emanating from the box of the devilish Cagliostro, go
far beyond such elementary principles. They make it easy to
see why Robert-Houdin achieved the success he did in his
lifetime – and why his memoirs so enchanted, among others,
young Ehrich Weiss. 'My interest in conjuring and magic
and my enthusiasm for Robert-Houdin came into existence
simultaneously,' he wrote. 'From the moment that I began to
study the art, he became my guide and hero . . . I . . . re-
read his works until I could recite passage after passage from
memory. Then, when Fate turned kind . . . I determined that

my first tour abroad should be dedicated to adding new laurels to the fate of Robert-Houdin.'

But alas! Things did not turn out as Houdini had hoped. 'My investigations brought forth only bitterest disappointment and saddest of disillusionment. Stripped of his self-woven veil of romance, Robert-Houdin stood forth, in the uncompromising light of cold historical facts, a mere pretender, a man who waxed great on the brainwork of others, a mechanician who had boldly filched the inventions of the master craftsmen among his predecessors.'

Thus the erstwhile disciple vilified the man he had so revered. He did so in a book published in 1909 after several years of preparation: *The Unmasking of Robert-Houdin.*

What had happened to occasion this startling reversal? The sequence of events is – I use the word advisedly – childish.

When Houdini, in London, was first struck by the thunderclap of instant celebrity, the effect upon both his character and his circumstances was profound. Materially he had, for the first time in his life, the means to indulge his predilections. Fame's other gift – at least in his own mind – was a universal entrée. If he wanted to meet somebody he had only to introduce himself and they would – he assumed – feel themselves honoured.

He was still very young – only twenty-six. Events were moving at an extraordinary, a truly magical, pace. In little more than a year he had been transformed from medicine-show barker to the most potent vaudeville draw in Europe. Is it surprising if he saw himself as his own publicity depicted him?

Others were less impressed. In London, during his first heady success there, he decided to visit Charles Bertram, then the most popular magician in London. He got himself up in the height of fashion as he conceived it – top hat, morning coat, striped trousers, spats and stick – and announced himself to Bertram: 'I am the Great Houdini.' Bertram replied crushingly, 'Well, and what of it?' Years later he confided, 'You know, Bertram did not like me. In fact, at that time, I was just a swell-headed kid.' When it happened, however, he was less philosophical; and even in later years the slight rankled, so that he could not resist denigrating Bertram and his book *Isn't It Wonderful?* – even though Houdini was by then world-famous and Bertram all but forgotten.

By the time Houdini reached Paris in 1902, Robert-Houdin was long dead (he died in 1871, before Ehrich Weiss was born or thought of). But this fact had not registered with the majority of Parisians, who told the inquiring American that he was running a small theatre on the Boulevard des Italiens. This was indeed the Théâtre Robert-Houdin, but it was now occupied by Georges Méliès, the pioneer of film. Méliès was a noted magician, and many of his brief movies feature tricks facilitated by the camera and performed by himself. 'At that time,' Houdini recalled, '[it] was on the style of a Fair Ground show. They gave performances with moving pictures every time they had a crowd. On Saturdays, at the Theatre Robert-Houdin, they gave Magical entertainments, and I saw Mons. Méliès, who was very interesting to me, and he managed to make quite a hit with the Harlequin the afternoon I was there.' Méliès, evidently, was sticking to the traditions of his location. The Théâtre des Italiens, just down the road, had housed the original *Commedia dell'Arte*, that theatrical development of the magical medicine show, with its Dottore and Arlecchino – the ancestor of all theatrical magic shows.

From Méliès, Houdini learned that Houdin's daughter-in-law was living in the Paris suburbs. Houdini had a little time on his hands. He had been booked to appear at the Folies-Bergère; but on the day of his arrival its owner had been committed to an asylum and his wife had sold the theatre. The owners of the Olympia were anxious to book him, but the contract would take a few days to work out. He therefore decided to seek out Mme Emile Houdin. He began his campaign with a letter, sent by messenger, with instructions to deliver only to the lady herself and await a reply. The letter ran: 'I, as a representative of American Magicians, do hereby kindly ask your consent to permit me . . . to place a wreath on the tomb of Robert-Houdin, also to grant me a few moments, so that I may have the pleasure of thanking you in person for your extreme kindness. Thanking you in advance for your awaited for letter, I do hereby sign myself *Harry Houdini.*'

All this flowery language, however, was unavailing. The letter was delivered, but the lady declined to reply. Later she let it be known that she was ill and did not wish to be disturbed.

Houdini was hurt by this rebuff, but he persevered. Robert-Houdin's tomb was in Blois, his home town, where his daughter Rosalie and her husband still lived. Houdini set off for Blois. Rosalie, a sculptress, was busy when he arrived and did not want to be interrupted; but her husband, Henri, welcomed the young magician. 'What a great difference to the reception, or attempted reception, of Mme Emile Houdin', he commented, (the word 'reception' here being used in an unusual transitive mode: *to reception*). 'I was soon placed at my ease and shown a great many "Grandfather Clocks" . . . Although at the time I thoroughly believed he had made them, I would not now be at all surprised if Robert Houdin had bought them and had his name engraved on the various articles.'

Henri pointed out that there was nothing to stop Houdini visiting his father-in-law's tomb with or without the family's permission. So Houdini went there, stood for half an hour, returned to Blois to order a wreath inscribed 'Honor and Respect to Robert-Houdin from the Magicians of America', collected a photographer, and had himself photographed at the tomb. He sent himself a postcard from Blois to his Paris address, 32 rue Bellefond: 'Visited the grave of Robert-Houdin this date. Photographed same. I mailed this P.C. to myself to remember the date.' It was 28 June 1902.

But although he had succeeded in his mission, his treatment at the hands of the Robert-Houdin family rankled. When he visited Russia the following year, he met a Frenchman living in Moscow, a M. Bolin, who specialised in building stage illusions. Bolin knew a great deal about magical history, and told Houdini that Robert-Houdin, whom he had met, was by no means the great magical innovator he had made himself out to be in his memoirs. Houdini latched on to this information, and set about expanding it. He was himself obsessively interested in the history of magic. From the moment he was able to do so – that is to say, from the moment of his arrival in London – he spent all his spare time and cash fossicking around curio shops and second-hand book stalls in every city he visited. This was the beginning of his great library of magic.

He now set about combining these two obsessions. He would avenge himself for his shabby reception at the hands of the Robert-Houdin family by finding out the history of all the great magician's principal illusions, thus exposing his claim to be a great original for the lie it was.

The task proved uncommonly absorbing. It led Houdini into the byways of magical history, where he was henceforth to find his greatest happiness. Magical illusions generally have venerable pedigrees. Originality lies more often in adaptation and presentation than in pure invention *ab initio*. In this sense, Robert-Houdin was a real innovator. He was the first to see the possibility of using electric current to produce apparently magical effects. And, as the handkerchiefs trick shows, his presentation was exquisite. He, like many magicians, presented a levitation act which he called *suspension etheréenne*. Who but Robert-Houdin would have thought of pouring ether onto a hot shovel behind the scenes as the levitation began, so that its smell permeated the theatre?

Houdini's diligent searches gave him great satisfaction. He began publishing his findings in 1906, as one of the features in a new enterprise: the *Conjurer's Monthly Magazine,* his first literary venture.

The *Conjurer's Magazine,* whose first issue appeared in September 1906, kept going for two years. In its pages, that cast of persons and obsessions which were to remain with Houdini for the rest of his life are already apparent. Here they all are, waiting to be moved to the foreground and magnified as circumstance dictates. Here is his great collection, choice selections from which are used to illustrate the magazine. Here are the veteran adversaries, unfortunates whose slights (real or imagined) were noted years before, never to be forgotten. An early occupant of this role was Horace Goldin, first met at Kohl and Middleton's on the Midway in Chicago when the Houdinis were trying to supplement their income by selling card tricks and Goldin was already earning seventy dollars a week. He was not helpful to the newcomers and Houdini never forgave him. 'Horace Goldin has arrived with his 9,000 assistants and 4,000 pieces of luggage, and the railroad companies are happy. So are all magical apparatus manufacturers, as Goldin is buying all the tricks in the world, as fast as they are turned out.' Here are the spirit exposés, railing at the inclination of prominent persons to see the supernatural in every conjurer's repertoire: 'W.T. STEAD FOOLED AGAIN . . . Credit certainly must be given to the Zancigs for so completely fooling and pulling the wool over the eyes of this well-educated, worldly man.' Here are the old friends, as tenaciously remembered as the old enemies: the magazine's London correspondent was Joe Hayman, whose brother Jack had been Houdini's first partner.

And here are the joys of authorship, which Houdini was now discovering for the first time. The year 1906 also saw the publication of his first book, *The Right Way to Do Wrong*. And the *Conjurer's Magazine* was the vehicle in which he organised the materials for his next two publications: 'Handcuff Secrets Exposed' and that excursion into magical history and paranoia, *The Unmasking of Robert-Houdin*, whose publication marked the end of the magazine.

The *Unmasking*'s language is so violent that the unbalanced nature of the whole project is immediately evident. 'The master-magician, unmasked, stands forth in all the nakedness of historical proof, the prince of pilferers. That he might bask for a few hours in public adulation, he purloined the ideas of magicians long dead and buried . . . That he might be known to posterity as the king of conjurers, he sold his birthright of manhood and honor for a mere mess of pottage, his

"Memoirs," written by the hand of another man, who at his instigation belittled his contemporaries, and juggled facts and truth to further his egotistical, jealous ambitions. But the day of reckoning is come . . .'

What has all this ranting to do with the graceful, genial performer who gave only pleasure to those people fortunate enough to witness him? The answer, of course, is – nothing. *The Unmasking of Robert-Houdin* is not about Robert-Houdin. It is about Houdini. He *had* to write it, just as he *had* to perform in the way he did. On 19 July 1907, just before he finished it, he noted in his diary: 'Wrote until 2.30 a.m. on Houdin book. This is a labour of love. I shall be happy when it is finished as it will take a lot of worry off my mind.'

The first clue as to what was going on is the dedication. The book is *'affectionately dedicated to the memory of my father, Rev. M. S. Weiss, Ph.D., LL.D., who instilled in me love of study and patience in research'*.

The overt intention of this is clear and simple. Houdini is presenting himself, as always when he speaks about his father, as a scholar and the son of a scholar. That was the defunct rabbi's role in the Houdini cast-list. To this end, he endows Rabbi Weiss with distinctions he never possessed (far from holding any higher degrees, he turned to religion because he could not make the grade as a lawyer). But the underlying meaning is equally clear. Houdini's father had failed him – failed to educate him, failed to support his beloved mother. Worse, perhaps – that mother had never ceased to be in love with him: their marriage had been 'heaven'. In this dedication he is associated with a book whose purpose is the destruction of another father-figure: Houdini's father in magic, Robert-Houdin, whose name he adopted. Samuel Weiss had failed in his responsibilities towards his son. Robert-Houdin, through his family, had rejected his magical ward. So now Houdini was rejecting *him*. The shrill tone of the book is that of the aggrieved child determined to get his revenge.

Part of the failure of Houdini's real father lay in the fact that the land of his ancestors, in both the physical and the intellectual sense, was closed to his son. Ehrich, who was this father's son, could return to Hungary as a visitor, but the rooted life he might have led there was not available to him, because his father had fled from it. And the intellectual territory of Jewish tradition, which his father inhabited, was also barred to him, because of his lack of education and because there was no place for it in the life the Weisses were forced to lead in America. So he chose his own territory – the land of magic – which he peopled with its own lore and ancestors: the history of magic and the old magicians who had practised it. In this land, he was Harry Houdini.

These two – Ehrich and Houdini – can be seen battling it out in his correspondence. His most personal letters to Bess in the early days are still signed 'Ehrich': 'Darling Kadaria Wilhelmina Weiss, In the train I woke up – looked for you and our love – Yours till *Death* – Ehrich,' reads one written from Dresden in 1903 in a moment of loneliness. Even at the very end, Ehrich still survived – just. In September 1926, a month before he died, he was 'your husband until and after the curtain rings down on our times, e'en to the crack of Doom – Harry Houdini (Ehrich)'. But the Ehrich signature became increasingly rare. Why inhabit an insignificant and unsuccessful persona rather than a famous and successful one? It was not long before Houdini was Houdini even to his wife. This was not entirely unselfconscious. After one particularly elaborate Houdini signature in a note left for Bess he added, 'The rare signature only found on his cheek and in his heart letters to his *wife.*' On legal or quasi-legal documents, such as the numerous directions he left for the disposition of his assets after his death, he appended both signatures. But before long, Ehrich Weiss was more or less obliterated. 'My legal name is Houdini, not my real name as you say it. That name was the name under which I was born', he explained to a friend in 1917, leaving the position as obscure as ever.

One of the many advantages Houdini had over Ehrich was that, if one father failed him, others were there for the taking.

If Robert-Houdin had feet of clay, there remained all the other old magicians. There they all were, just waiting for him.

Where?

In their graves, of course!

Q: What kind of magicians did Houdini like best?

A: Dead ones!

This was in every sense the literal truth. He could never abide competition, and his relations with his compeers were always uneasy. But once they were dead, he loved them. For Houdini, life and death were always seamlessly elided. Death was a vivid presence – increasingly so as time went on, but always there even at this period, when he was still in his twenties. His letters to Bess allude to it constantly – 'yours till Death', 'yours till the crack of Doom'. As soon as he had any worldly goods, his concern was their disposition in the event of his death. The first will I am aware of was made in September 1901, when he was twenty-seven: it divides all the monies in his German bank account between Theo and Bess ('The money mentioned here shall apply only to that deposited in the Deutsche Bank in Berlin'). And even while his friends were living, the prospect of their funeral was always pleasantly before him. Harry Kellar was a famous magician who had taken a paternal interest in Houdini (but with whom he did not fall out). At Kellar's retirement party, Houdini, presenting a bouquet, said: 'We have decided not to wait until he has passed to the GREAT BEYOND for his flowers, may he be with us for a long time, but we will give him his flowers whilst he is with us, for you cannot appreciate flowers when you are at rest in the cemetery.'

No, indeed.

Henry Ridgely Evans in *The Old and the New Magic* describes Houdini, whom he knew well, as the 'Old Mortality of Magic' after the old covenanter in Sir Walter Scott's novel who 'went about the country, from one churchyard to another, refurbishing and cleaning up the tombstones of the Puritan martyrs who were killed during the persecutions in Scotland in the reign of Charles II. On account of his pious labors, he was denominated "Old Mortality" by the peasantry. Now Houdini has a similar penchant, but for the graves of his predecessors in conjuring. He hunts them out; often employs people to fix up the time-stained tombstones, and enacts the part of an Old Mortality of Magic.' He invariably had himself photographed by the laboriously sought-out tombs. Robert-Houdin's was only the first of many. There are photographs of Houdini standing in some reverent posture by the graves of Heller, Bosco (which he discovered in Dresden in a state of disrepair, and, the lease on the plot having expired, about to be exhumed: Houdini bought the plot, and deeded it to the Society of American Magicians), John Henry Anderson, the wizard of the North, Lafayette, William Davenport, and countless others.

What do people see in cemeteries?

This has always puzzled me. I can see that such a fascination exists, but I am unable to share it. My parents, whom I loved, are dead: it would never cross my mind to visit their graves. For me, those graves and my parents are entirely unconnected. I could not even bring myself to go back to the cemetery and erect headstones there, as Jewish custom requires, a year after the death. Yet I cannot be so very different from all those people who draw comfort from these actions. On the contrary, the distress I feel at the thought of that meaningless place where my parents lie buried would seem to indicate that one ought to be able to feel something in cemeteries: that the absence of feeling is, in some sense, a deep insult.

The essence of cemeteries is surely that they are, or should be, in some sense *thresholds*. Here, if anywhere, is the point of contact between ourselves and other worlds: the world of the dead, centred upon the recent grave; the world of our ancestors, in the graves all around. Spiritualists sometimes speak of the 'borderland', where we may speak to the dead. If ' borderland' has a location, it is surely in cemeteries.

But if cemeteries are about roots and ancestors, they are also rude reminders of their absence. Nothing tells me that my roots are *not* here more pointedly than cemeteries. Every poetic country churchyard cries out that my ancestors are nothing to do with this. Would I feel more amid *their* graves – wherever those might be? In that cemetery described by Babel, perhaps? 'The cemetery of a little Jewish town. Assyria and all the mysterious stagnation of the East . . . Carved grey stones with inscriptions three centuries old. Crude high-reliefs hewn out in the granite. Lambs and fishes depicted above a skull, and Rabbis in fur caps – Rabbis girt round their narrow loins with leather belts . . . The memorial stone, all overgrown with green, sings of them with the eloquence of a Bedouin's prayer.'

It might equally have been Houdini's ancestral cemetery: and he had no more contact with it than I have. Nevertheless, he loved cemeteries – and loved them precisely because they are about ancestors. These cemeteries he everywhere visited *did* contain his ancestors – not his Hungarian ancestors, but his ancestors in magic. Beside these graves, he was able to orient himself spiritually: to place himself where he belonged. Standing by the grave of some old and all-but-forgotten magician he felt . . .

What did he feel? It was not something he was ever able to express in words. The words that seem to crop up among cemetery-lovers are *serene* and *peaceful*. (They are, as it happens, the words Bess used about the comfort she found in visiting cemeteries after Houdini's death.) Perhaps there was something there of that timeless peace which he otherwise sought in his library. Indeed, one collector drew the comparison directly. 'It's a bit like collecting,' he said. 'There they all are, with their granite.'

But for Houdini, there was more to it than that. The clue is in his life: that paradoxical conjunction of compulsive vitality and an obsession with death. It was as if he sucked his life from the jaws of death: and this, in cemeteries, was especially the case. He danced on the graves of those old magicians, and their power passed into him. 'Cemeteries,' says Elias Canetti, 'induce the triumphant feeling that, uniquely among the dead, one is still alive – the moment of exhilaration because of survival.' In that sense, Houdini was a sort of anti-vampire, the least sinister of figures. The stake through the heart, in his hands, blossomed and flourished.

This search for ancestors was not confined to the dead. He set out, throughout his life, to contact as many old magicians as he could. Old is the operative word here. Houdini was able to relax only with older men. *He* was supplanting *them,* which was as it should be. He was always edgy with his contemporaries, and saw younger magicians only as rivals, ready to push him into obscurity and the grave. He had potential threats such as Blackstone and Dunninger expelled from the Society of American Magicians, which he ruled with a rod of iron from the moment he was elected President in 1914.

Some of these older men, like Harry Kellar, became fast friends, even though they were still celebrated. Others had been celebrated in their day but now languished in obscurity: Henry Evans Evanion, whom he met in London and who helped him start his magical collection; Ira Davenport, the old spiritualist performer, in New York State. Houdini took a particular pleasure in seeking them out. He treasured the memory of the time he spent with them just as, later, he saw to it that their graves were not forgotten. Here were living father-figures who could replace Robert-Houdin.

Perhaps the most bizarre of these encounters was with Wiljalba Frikell, who had been a very famous magician in the nineteenth century, but who had long since retired. 'I have had an argument with FATE,' Houdini wrote Dash from Dresden in October 1903; and, for once, he was not exaggerating. Here is his account more or less in full, complete with his habitual misspellings:

Last Feb. just before I left for Russia, I discovered to my astonishment that the old time and well known magician, Dr. Wiljalba Frikell was alive and well. And living in Kotschenbroda. Well – I took the long ride from Berlin to Kotschenbroda which is about six hours, and arrived early in the morning. [He arrived in fact at 3 a.m. and spent the rest of the night on a park bench, since the station was all closed.]

I waited until ten, found the house and rang the bell. Herr
Frikell refused to see me. He refused even to come to the
window, so that I could have a look at him. Informing me
through his wife, that he had made enough bad experiences
through his life, and that he wanted to be left alone. Mrs.
Frikell said he was not well, and under no circumstances
would he allow me to even have a glance at him. I begged
and pleaded all day, but in vain. I searched the town for
assistance, and even his relatives refused to speak for me.
That is I mean an adopted daughter that he has. At any rate
I went to a photographer, engaged him to come along with
me to Frikell's house, to take a photo . . . Greatly disheartened
I left Kotschenbroda, went to Berlin and wrote him a long
letter. I sent him (to look at) some of the old time lithos that
he used to make use of when he was active. One being
spelled wrong, that is his name on it, he corrected same and
returned it to me. In this way I managed to open up a
correspondence with him, sent him some Russian tea from
Moscow, in fact really became very frienly with him through
our letters.

We corresponded regularry, and after my trip to Russia, I
returned and brough him another lot of tea. Eventually while
I was in Dodrecht Holland playing an engagement with Circus
Carre, I was greatly surprised to receive a letter from him
to the effect, that he is pleased and honored at the interest I
have taken in his welfare, and would like very much for me
to pay him a visit. This was in the middle of September, so
having a contract with the Central Theatre in Dresden, I
made all arrangements to visit him during my stay in
Dresden.

I wrote to him whilst in Dresden and invited him to come
and see me, as I would not be able to get to Kotschenbroda
until Thursday. My Lithographer Zier from Leipzig having
journeyed to Dresden to show me some new samples of
lithos that I was desirous of having for England. Well
Thursday came, and found that we gave no performance that
evening, so took the opportunity to go to Berlin.

But again wrote him that I would positively call Saturday.
In the mean time he came to Dresden, monday looking for
me but failed to locate me. He is 87 years of age and rarely
leaves his home. At the Theatre they refusesd to tell him
where I was stopping and he went to the Konig Kaffe, and
waited several hours, but finally being unable to see me, he

went back home. Yesterday morning Sat. I took the 1.14 train for Kotschenbroda, as that place is only 20 minutes' journey from Dresden.

Arrived about 1.35 and as my appointment was for two o'clock I walked very slowly towards his Villa. I did not wish to arrive too soon. (and I did not)

I slowly reached the house, I rang the bell, it seemed to ring with a peculiar shrillness, I felt a something in the air which I atributed to the fact of being able to see Frikell when a lady came to the door and said 'You are being waited for.'

I entered, and found to my great and unspeakable astonishment that Wiljalba Frikell had died two and a half hours – while waiting for me!!!!!!

I saw the man – but he was dead.!!! He was not cold yet. he had died of heart failure. Mrs. and Mr. Frikell had dressed up especially to greet me, but Death forestalled my visit . . . Well my dear brother – can you imagine my feelings.

There lie the man who had sworn he would not see any stranger as long as he lived – and Fate compelled him to keep his word.

His wife informed me that he was all worked up on my expected visit and the day before (Friday) had cleaned up everything and had written down a lot of dates for me . . . There lay the old man lifeless and not even stiff or cold. His well groomed form lay on the lounge, where his goodwife had placed him when he grasped at his heart crying 'My heart, what is the matter with my heart, O –' that was all he said. His face was still wet from the Cologne that his wife had thrown into his face, trying to revive him, and the wet sheets were still on the floor, . . . I never was so completely defeated in all my life. This had an awful effect on me, and I remained about two hours, then left meditatingly for Dresden. He will be buried tuesday and I shall attend his funeral. Will send a wreath for the S.A.M. [Society of American Magicians] and one for myself.

. . . last Monday he went to the photographers, and had his photo taken, something that he had not done in years. The proof he had taken was crooked, and thursday Oct 8th he had another sitting, saying that he wanted to give Houdini a good photo, in return for his . . . Madame Frikell will let me have it as soon as it is finished.

Characteristically, Houdini mailed two postcards back to himself in Berlin so that he should not forget the date.

Later, Mrs Frikell told Houdini why her husband so obstinately refused to see him on his first visit. 'It appears that he once had an assistant, a lady for the suspension, and they had a natural son. He was under the impression that I was a grandson, and wanted money.'

Still, the supply of father-figures did not run dry. The next year, 1904, Houdini was in London. He caught a severe cold which threatened to turn into pneumonia, and for the first time in his life was forced to cancel some performances and stay in bed. A newspaperman who called on him printed a piece about a number of old programmes and playbills which he had picked up and which were scattered around the bedroom. The day the article appeared, Houdini received a note on a stained piece of paper from Henry Evans Evanion. Evanion said he had some articles which might interest Houdini; Houdini, always a prompt correspondent in a case of this sort, replied at once asking him to call at one the next day.

One o'clock came and went: there was no sign of Evanion. At about four in the afternoon the doctor told Houdini he was allowed to walk once around the block in the mild sunshine. As he left the hotel, the porter told him that an old man had been waiting to see him since one o'clock, but that he was such a disreputable-looking character that they had not allowed him to go up. He was still there, huddled in a corner, a bent figure clutching an enormous portfolio. They sat down on a sofa to examine it. Inside was a treasure-trove of materials – original programmes of all the great magicians of the last century, engravings, lithographs . . . Next morning, without his doctor's permission, Houdini took a cab to Methley Street, where Evanion lived in a dark basement. There they spent the day over a succession of cups of tea poring over Evanion's collection, until Dash and Houdini's disgusted doctor tracked them down at midnight and dragged Houdini away.

Over the next few months, Houdini bought the bulk of Evanion's collection, which somewhat eased the latter's financial situation. A year later, while he was playing in Wigan, he heard from Mrs Evanion that her husband was dying of cancer of the throat. Houdini dashed back to be with his friend during his last days, and to see that he had every comfort. A fortnight later, Evanion's funeral took place. 'Poor Evanion,' Houdini noted in his diary that day. 'He certainly was the greatest collector of magical material in the world. Although I advertised the funeral in the papers, no one was there but four old women and two nieces, with Mrs Evanion. Paid funeral expenses.' He also went on helping Mrs Evanion – the first of a long string of pensioners he was to amass as his life went on.

For Houdini was always keenly aware of the transitory nature of luck. Things might suddenly change for the better, as they had with him: but all that good fortune might as suddenly vanish. 'For every conjurer who died well off,' he wrote a few years later, 'we can name many that died in actual want . . . the magician who is enjoying a little meed of success should take warning from those who have gone before. Tomorrow may bring a better trick – by another man – but today is the time to save against the morrow when popularity wanes.' Poor old Evanion might be a vision of his own future. Perhaps he saw his pensioners as a sort of amulet, a bargain with Providence: if I do this, I shall be spared that. (As he was.)

These good deeds went unremarked; sometimes even he was unaware of his commitments. He was once joyfully greeted by a man who, when Houdini pushed him aside and said he didn't know him, protested, 'But you have been paying my rent for the past eleven years!'

As the years passed, stories began to circulate to the effect that Houdini regretted the tone he had taken in *The Unmasking of Robert-Houdin*. Not everyone thought this. One friend commented, 'In my many conversations with Houdini on magical history, I never knew him to depart one whit from his statements regarding Robert-Houdin.' Nevertheless, it seems clear that his sense of outrage had somewhat abated, and he saw that he had made a fool of himself. But his retreat was to self-justification, more than regret. 'When a magician advertizes a trick as his version like you do the coin ladder that is *permissible*,' he wrote to a magician friend. 'But Robert-Houdin announced them all as his own tricks, and that is where the imposition came in . . . The older I get the more I know Houdin never invented his feats. The only mistake I made was in calling my book Houdin Unmasked. It ought to have been History of Magic from 1800 to 1850. In this way it would have shown Magic as it ought to have been known.' But in that case, Houdini would still have felt compelled to unmask Robert-Houdin.

10

All In the Mind

Perhaps Houdini's single most famous exploit was the Detroit Bridge Jump. This took place on 27 November 1906, when he jumped, manacled with two sets of handcuffs, from the Belle Isle Bridge into the Detroit River. What happened next was told and retold a thousand times. The river, ran the story, was frozen. A hole had been cut in the ice for Houdini. He freed himself successfully from the handcuffs, but when he surfaced, he found that the current had carried him away from the hole.

Among the spectators, panic mounted. His team knew that Houdini could not hold his breath for more than three and a half minutes underwater. The arrangement was that, if he did not appear after three minutes, a roped man would jump in after him. But the assistant was understandably chary of committing himself to the icebound river. Instead, he threw a rope down through the hole. Bess, who had not been able to bring herself to watch the jump and was in her hotel room, heard the newsboys below her window shouting, 'Houdini drowned! Houdini drowned!'

Houdini, meanwhile, had realised that he could survive, while he swam round looking for the hole, by breathing the air which was trapped between the water and the ice. Then he saw the end of the rope. He swam towards it and clambered out. Cheers resounded. Bess welcomed him with tears. He spent the next several hours thawing out, and, that night, played to a packed house.

So runs the tale. But there have always been difficulties with it. One of these is that on that day, 27 November, the temperature, although cold, was above freezing. So Houdini's publicists moved the date of the jump to 2 December, when the temperature did not rise above 30°F. But in order for thick ice to form on a big river, the temperature would have to be much colder for much longer.

Was the jump, then, simply a figment of Houdini's publicists' imagination? James Randi, the magician and Houdini enthusiast, assured me that this was the case. He met Gladys Weiss, Houdini's little sister, at a party on Long Island in 1953, when Gladys had with her a huge pile of postcards sent her by her brother while she was still a schoolgirl. After she told him how the girls at her school collected postcards, especially foreign ones, he sent her a postcard every day for two years while he was on tour. On the date in question, said Gladys, Harry and Theo were both in Europe, and she had the postcards to prove it. Houdini's publicists had put the story about in order to keep his name before the American public. Houdini was furious with them, because he reckoned that the truth, if it got out, could be severely damaging to him. But in those days long-distance communications were not what they are today. Nobody thought to check, and the story just passed into legend, as had been intended.

In fact the question of whether he did or did not actually make the jump, whether he did or did not actually fight his way through the ice, is of little consequence. The myth has its own reality, more solid than that of any mere happening. Houdini himself adapted the story freely in his lifetime. In a piece written for the *Strand Magazine* in 1919 he places the exploit in Pittsburgh, has himself shut in a trunk as well as handcuffed, and specifies that the ice was seven inches thick. Perhaps someone pointed out to him that the Detroit River, which is very fast-moving, never entirely freezes over.

As it happens he did make that jump – or a jump – from the Belle Isle Bridge that November day. Despite the evidence of Gladys' postcard collection (perhaps it was Theo who was sending them – he remained in Europe while his brother returned to the States) Houdini certainly was in Detroit at that time. He was booked for two weeks at the Temple Theater. And on 27 November 1906, the story appeared on the front page of the Detroit *News:*

'HANDCUFF KING' JUMPS MANACLED
FROM BRIDGE

Handcuff King Houdini Performs Remarkable
Feat and Comes Out Safely

Had a Rope Tied Around his Waist and Tied
to Bridge to Safeguard against Accidents

Tied by a lifeline a hundred and thirteen feet long, handcuffed with two of the best and latest model handcuffs in the possession of the Detroit police department, nerved by the confidence of a lion in his own powers . . . Houdini, the wonder worker at the Temple theater, leaped from the draw span of the Belle Isle Bridge at 1 o'clock this afternoon, freed himself from the handcuffs while under water, then swam to a waiting lifeboat, passed over the unlocked and open cuffs and clambered aboard.

Such is prosaic reality.

The bridge jump was part of a desperate campaign he was then conducting to bring his name to America's attention. It worked, or something did: that week broke all attendance records at the theatre. But Houdini, at this time, was by no means the draw in America that he was in Europe. From Europe in 1902 he wrote to a friend: 'If I don't come to America this summer, it will be at least three years before I will again land my small feet on the land of the free and the home of the dollars. I am booked up so far that it seems to me that I am booked for life . . . by the time I have my work all played, I think I can sit back and look at the world from my chair . . . I talk German or French, as well as Hungarian or English, but you ought to hear my pronunciation, that is the whole secret of my success in foreign countries. It makes them all friendly with me ere I have performed a single trick.' In 1904, it was still the same story. 'There is no possible chance of me working America, until season of 1905–6, and if I dont work America then, will N E V E R play at all,' he observed.

He was engaged for months ahead and could, if he so wished, engage himself for several years.

But he missed his mother, and the number of flying visits that could be made across the Atlantic was necessarily limited (especially given his terrible seasickness). Besides, he was American, not European. He would have to try his luck at home sometime. In 1904, on a quick visit, he acquired a home base in New York. It was a twenty-six-room mansion at 278 West 113th Street, in the respectable 'German section' of Harlem. It had been built ten years earlier, but Harry and Bess were its first occupants. Harry's bathroom, with its eight-foot square mirror before which he could practise and its outsize tub in which he could rehearse underwater escape techniques, was worked with a mosaic H; Bess's, on the floor below, with a B. There was also a basement laboratory-workshop where he could build his equipment. Into this house Harry moved his mother, who was thus finally able to quit the flat on 69th Street, and the already enormous collection of theatrical memorabilia which he had acquired from Evanion and countless others, and which had been following him around Europe, expanding all the while.

He also made time, during this visit, to plan for the future and revisit the past. He acquired a burial plot in the Machpelah Cemetery, Cypress Hills, to which he moved the bodies of his father and brother Herman. He took the opportunity to inspect the corpses: 'Saw all that was left of poor father and Herman; nothing but skull and bones,' he noted in his diary. 'Herman's teeth were in excellent condition.' And he paid a flying visit to Appleton, where he had been happy. He was interviewed there by the young Edna Ferber, who was to become known as the blockbusting author of *Cimarron* and *Showboat*, but who was then a cub reporter on the *Appleton Crescent*. She failed to find him at his hotel or the theatre, but ran into him by chance outside a drugstore opposite her office. 'He is a quick nervous chap, inclined to jump when an unexpected noise is heard and to shut his eyes until they are almost closed, when speaking under excitement,' she noted. She found him 'pleasantly and very interestingly dressed in the conventional light grey summer suit, oxfords, flowing tie and sailor hat. One would never think him of the "profesh" unless, maybe, his diamond shirt stud might speak. But then, Armour wears diamond shirt studs too . . . The reporter was allowed to feel his forearm, which is amazing, as massive and hard as a granite pillar. His neck, too, is large, and corded.' He confided to her his future plans. 'I think that in a year I may retire. I cannot take my money with me when I die and I wish to enjoy it, with my family, while I live. I should prefer living in Germany to any other country, though I am an American, and am loyal to my country. I like the German people and customs. Why don't I go then? Why it is too far away from my mother, who lives in New York City with a couple of my young brothers.' Miss Ferber asked him about the secret of his wonderful escapes. 'My secret? Well, certainly it is a trick of my own', he replied enigmatically. He confided that, while he was in England, he had been offered 'an enormous sum of money' if he would consent to establish a school of burglary. But he had declined. At the end of the interview, he dropped a metal object into Miss Ferber's hand. It was the padlock to the vending machine full of chocolate and chewing-gum against which he had been carelessly leaning. 'Better give this to the drugstore man', he said. 'Somebody'll steal all his chewing-gum.' The reporter left to write up her story, 'tottering with admiration'.

Then it was back to Europe, where Harry Day was now insisting that he be paid on a percentage basis, which, as he almost invariably played to capacity audiences, substantially increased his earnings. His much-vaunted retirement was postponed again (as it would be until he died): an American tour was arranged for the following year. 'Then I will return to Europe for my last trip, as I will be well pleased to retire on what I have managed to collect.'

While he had been unknown, Houdini's outstanding characteristic had been his unwavering, almost absurd certainty that he was unique and would be famous. Now that this, as if by magic, had actually happened, he was plagued by insecurity. 'A rich man,' says Canetti, 'collects cattle and hoards of grain, or the money which stands for them. A ruler collects men . . . whom he can make die before him, or take with him when he dies. A celebrity collects a chorus of voices. All he wants is to hear them repeat his name.'

In the American-Jewish showbusiness community, insecurity such as Houdini's was the rule rather than the exception. George Burns said of Al Jolson, 'It was easy enough to make Jolson happy at home. You just had to cheer him for breakfast, applaud wildly for lunch and give him a standing ovation for dinner.' The movie kings demanded constant flattery and unquestioning kowtowing. One of the many reasons for this was that their success had a mirage-like feel to it. At any moment the whole thing might melt away and they would be returned to the dismal realities of the ghetto. Both Adolph Zukor and Louis B. Mayer were plagued by nervous skin rashes. When Mayer met important people he was often terrified. He would stand with tears in his eyes until his secretary calmed him. And spending his now-plentiful dollars did not come easily to Mayer. He did not build a home of his own until 1925, seven years after his arrival in California; and when he did, it was not in Beverly Hills among the stars but in Santa Monica, because then he would be near the ocean and would not have to spend money on a second vacation home.

Houdini, the essence of whose public persona was boundless courage, was debarred from showing any of the fears he may have felt. But those fears were nonetheless real. He never made any secret of his insecurities regarding money. The prospect that he might wake up one morning and find himself returned to poverty never ceased to plague him. It was one of the recurring themes of the *Conjurer's Magazine*. Ten years later, in 1916, addressing Rotarians in Cincinnati, the same refrain was still running through his mind. They should not think that a high-priced artist might take things easy. 'You should rather say he has a temporary spurt of prosperity . . . The moment an artist loses his personality and magnetism, the moment his secret leaks out, the curtain comes down on his prosperity. He is not like a businessman who can bequeath his business to his son – for the artist cannot fasten his personality and powers upon another.'

The poverty terror, it will be noticed, is inextricably linked with another: that of his 'secret leaking out'. Just as Houdini sucked in strength and power from his contact with those old magicians whom he visited so assiduously both before and after their deaths, so he lived in constant terror that others, rivals and imitators, would purloin his methods – his 'secret' – and debase his currency. They would drain his powers – his magical powers, and hence the most magical power of all, the power to earn money – away from him. He was always on the alert for this, and when he spotted some sign of it, the blackguard in question had to be compulsively and comprehensively destroyed.

A scene of this kind took place in Glasgow, where he was booked to perform at the Zoo on his return from New York in 1904.

It might have seemed improbable, to judge from the reception he received there, that he should be worried about imitators. 'The Northern District of the city was in a state of uproar last night,' reported the *Glasgow Herald*.

. . . You might have walked on the heads of the surging, struggling, swaying mass of people almost from George's Cross to the Normal School. A stranger within the city gates might well have wondered what strange happenings were abroad to bring out such a curious congregation. And yet the explanation was simple. Houdini, the Handcuff King and Prison Breaker, was announced to have accepted a most unique challenge which he would try in front of the spectators in the Zoo . . . It was evident that only a small proportion of the huge crowd could gain admission. There was no turning back, however, and the mass pressed on, obstructing the car traffic, and giving the police who endeavoured to preserve order a rough time of it . . . Inside the crush was as great as the regulations of the Police Act allow. When 'The Manacle Manipulator' appeared, with his small stature, coal-black hair and eyes, and his deliberate articulation, with only a tinge of the American accent in it to give it flavor, there was an ovation. Excitement was rife, and for the distinction of securing a seat on the stage something like 50 people paid five shillings each.

Houdini does not boast too much to the audience. He told them simply that he meant to get out of the box which Messrs. J. & G. Findlay had specially made in order to test his ability to do so. Of course, he said, he could not say he would, but he would try . . . When he had asked for volunteers to come on the stage and 'put a nail in his coffin' without receiving any response, eight carpenters set to work. They nailed and roped the box. With the driving of each separate nail the excitement increased . . . Afterwards the casket was placed inside the curtain on top of the raised platform to show that there was no trap-door trickery.

Houdini was left to his thoughts – and his trappings; the audience were left to their curiosity and conjectures. For an interval of about 15 minutes the spectators, consumed with curiosity, waited for something to eventuate. The 'man who knows and doesn't care who knows that he does know' was just beginning to throw out hints that 'Houdini's fairly boxed this time' when – Houdini himself appeared before him to disprove his statement. Covered with smiles and sweat, the mystifier was minus his hat and boots, while his clothes and collar were crumpled. Houdini had all evidence of a stern struggle, safely negotiated, but the box was left as if untouched. Not a nail was loosed, nor was one of the three binding ropes tampered with. It was all very mystifying. If the cheering of the audience can be taken as an indication, they certainly obtained full value for money and the fancy prices many of them paid for admission; prices being doubled and trebled.

That performance took place on 22 September. A greater triumph can hardly be imagined. But a week later, Houdini found that a rival – evidently hoping to capitalise on his extraordinary success – was advertising an escape from 'an unprepared coffin'. He could not let this pass. On 30 September, in front of a house jam-packed as always, he had a coffin brought on stage and demonstrated just how his rival had lied and cheated. The coffin was far from being 'unprepared'. It had been tampered with between the time it was left in the lobby for inspection and the time it appeared on stage. In the intervening period, the long screws holding the ends in place had been removed and short screws substituted. Houdini lay down in this coffin, had the lid secured, and showed how he could get out by pushing the ends out. Then he prepared the coffin on his own account. All the screws were replaced and tightened. He got in, had the lid clasped down, and invited a committee to add screws of their own anywhere they chose, and then to seal them so that any tampering would show. Some pasted stamps over the screwheads and inscribed their initials; others pasted stamps across the crack between the coffin lid and the sides. Then the cabinet was lowered over the coffin. In a few minutes Houdini emerged: behind him was the coffin, apparently untouched.

The psychology of such a performance is rather subtle. It turns on the inherently absurd notion that there is such a thing as an honest trickster. Houdini always presented himself as the one perfectly straight man in a crooked world. In a typical example, he talks about P. T. Barnum and his motto that 'The American people want to be humbugged'. He comments: 'In my own particular work I find there is so much that is marvellous and wonderful that can be accomplished by perfectly natural means that I have no need to find recourse to humbugging the public.'

Houdini was always at great pains to emphasise his absolute freedom from dishonesty. His frequent recourse to nakedness was a sort of metaphor for this. The impression of straightforwardness was reinforced by the straitjacket escapes, which he performed in full view and which were demonstrably not tricks, but feats of strength and suppleness. His incorruptibility was something he continually stressed. In 1906 he published his first book, *The Right Way to Do Wrong: An Exposé*. It discussed the methods and motives of a variety of thieves and tricksters, as revealed to him by police chiefs he had met in the course of business. In it, he takes a sternly moral line: 'Disgraced, they are ruined for life, often ruining all their family. It is a terrible thing to have the finger of fate point at you with the remark, "His father is serving time for doing so-and-so" . . . To those who read this book, although it will inform them "The Right Way to Do Wrong", all I have to say is one word and that is "DON'T".' And this impression of straightforwardness was no mere mask, cynically assumed. Houdini himself was entirely convinced by it. In Bradford a challenger had suggested that Houdini let himself be tied up so that he could not escape. The challenger would bet a large sum on the outcome, and they would divide the winnings. Houdini rejected this out of hand. He wrote contemptuously in his diary: 'Guess he didn't know how I was brought up.'

Because he was himself convinced he was able to convince others. He presented himself as an exemplar of straight dealing because that was how he saw himself. His self-righteousness was an essential part of his armoury. Yet how was he able so shamelessly to ignore his own deceptions?

'A despot,' observes Canetti, 'is always aware of his inner malevolence and therefore must dissimulate. But he cannot deceive everyone in this way. There are always others who desire power and who do not acknowledge his claims, but regard themselves as his rivals . . . He waits for the right moment to "tear the mask from their faces"; behind it he finds the malevolence that he knows so well in himself. Once they are unmasked he can render them harmless.' But Houdini was never aware of his own despotism. He was too much of a solipsist for that. In his world, all rivals were unconscionable villains, and he did not hesitate to destroy them by breaking the first rule of showbusiness solidarity – the very act for which he himself condemned so many of his compeers to the outer reaches of his displeasure: he betrayed their techniques. In *his* case, however, that was all right. 'I am induced to take this step for the manifest reason that the public of both hemispheres may, through ignorance of the truth, give credence to the mendacious boasts and braggadocios of the horde of imitators who have sprung into existence with mushroom rapidity of growth, and equal flimsiness of vital fibre, and who, with amazing effrontery and pernicious falsity, seek to claim and hold the credit and honor, such as they may be, that belong to me,' he fumed.

How did he know about those techniques which he revealed with such relish? Because, of course, he used them himself, time and again. Those techniques belonged to him, so he was free to reveal them if he chose. In the case of the coffin exposé, replacing long screws with short before a performance was one of the standard methods by which he himself had escaped from a variety of containers. On the Glasgow occasion, however, that method was ruled out. Houdini had to find some other way. The implication was that he did not (like his rival) use trickery. How, then, was it done? By magic? This, indeed, was the impression given by his performance.

So he sowed the seeds of a confusion which underlay that extraordinary power he exerted over the public imagination. Houdini always insisted in stentorian tones that he had no magic or supernatural powers. He had his 'secrets' – that word he so often used – and naturally he was not telling anyone what those might be. They certainly had nothing to do with the puny secrets of his dastardly rivals. These 'secrets' of Houdini's acquired a public life of their own. There is a rumour that, like Pandora or Joanna Southcott, he left them locked in a box, not to be opened until a certain number of years had elapsed after his death. My dentist mentioned this story to me the other day and wanted to know if it was true.

The kind of secrets my dentist had in mind are mostly pretty well-known among magicians by now. Most of them were in fact known in Houdini's lifetime. He tended to make them public when they began to leak out, or when he had replaced them with something better – which had the added advantage of making things more difficult for hopeful competitors. They had, as he always said, nothing to do with magic. In the case of the Glasgow coffin, the secret was in the screws attaching the *bottom* of the coffin to the sides. These were good, long screws. They attached the coffin bottom to lengths of dowel inserted into the thickness of the sides. When Houdini wanted to get out, he turned over on to his front, crouched on his knees and levered the top away from the bottom by bodily force. Then he carefully stood the coffin on the dowel pillars and forced it down by jumping on it while the band played to cover any noise he made. His real advantage over his rivals lay in his prodigious capacity for misdirection, for controlling his audience, for devising new techniques – that, and the terrible innocence with which he exposed himself, body and soul.

Such secrets as he did possess were not the sort which could be bought, sold and finally 'revealed'. They were the kind of thing he discussed with an Australian reporter a few years later (in 1910): 'I am strong, as you see; strong in flesh, but my will has been stronger than my flesh . . . I have done things which, rightly, I could not do, because I said to myself, You must; and now I am old at 36 . . . If the thought is intense enough, the pain goes – for a time. It is good for me that I am not a tall man. Why? Because I must be quick! quick! and a tall man is always slow. It is so through all professions. The best men are not too high . . . All the mean, cunning men that I have known – short! All the keen, eager, ambitious men – short! And for work – the tall man has too much to carry, he is too far from the ground, he cannot lose and recover balance as is necessary – in a flash.'

In the fall of 1905 he opened in the Colonial Theater, New York, as a top-liner, the start of a six-week tour for which he was to receive $5,000. This was the tour which would make or break his American reputation.

Never had he tried harder. He devised spectacular feat after spectacular feat with which to catch the headlines.

In New York he performed Robert-Houdin's beautiful trick with the vanishing handkerchiefs. In Houdini's version the handkerchiefs were sent to the foot of the Statue of Liberty. He did not pretend to have originated this trick, but – perhaps ashamed of acknowledging its true provenance, since he was at that very moment writing *The Unmasking of Robert-Houdin* – said he had learned it from old Henry Evanion.

In Washington, D.C., he performed an exploit which especially appealed to him and which featured in all his publicity thereafter. This was the Guiteau escape. The Warden of the Tenth Precinct gaol challenged him to defeat his new lock system. Houdini was particularly interested in Murderers' Row, which comprised seventeen cells, then containing eight prisoners awaiting judgment or execution. He asked to be locked into Cell No. 2, which had once housed Charles Guiteau, the assassin of President Warren Harding. Notorious assassins always fascinated him: he was particularly gratified to step, if not into Guiteau's shoes, into the cell which had seen his last days. This was now the home of one Hamilton, who was alleged to have smothered his wife and then sat up all night beside the body celebrating. Houdini, naked as always, was locked inside while Hamilton cowered in a corner.

Can any more bizarre scene be imagined? The small, naked man is locked inside the cell. The warden stomps away. From their hiding-places – in his bushy hair, between his prehensile toes, stuck with a blob of chewing-gum to the underside of a ledge – Houdini retrieves his miniature picklocks and the pieces of wire which serve as handles and levers. He frees himself. Then, still naked, he runs to the cells housing the other inmates. Quickly he lets them out of their cells – too astonished by this strange vision to protest, too alarmed to take advantage of the situation – and locks them up again in cells not their own. 'As I was stripped . . . the prisoners thought the devil, or someone akin to him, was in their presence, and, trembling with fear, they obeyed my command.' Then he finds his clothes, dresses, lets himself out of the wing and rejoins Warden Harris. E. L. Doctorow, in *Ragtime*, transposes this scene to the New York Tombs and gives it a distinctly sexual flavour. In his version, the society convict, Harry Thaw, in prison for murdering his wife's lover, undresses as Houdini dresses, and waggles his penis at him through the bars: a scene which acknowledges the sexual agenda underlying Houdini's insistent professional nudity.

Naked gaol escapes were one constant feature of his publicity. So were bridge leaps. There were escapes from safes. There were straitjacket escapes. There were escapes from special challenge containers: in Washington, D.C., September 1906, from a zinc-lined piano box; in Boston, early 1907, from – yes – a coffin whose lid was nailed down by members of the audience; from a paper box (razors and glue were his tools for working with paper); from a ladder to which he was locked; from an iron boiler; from a glass box. Another boiler, in Toledo, Ohio, nearly defeated him; in San Francisco, a government mail-pouch held him for twenty-five minutes. In Detroit the river was not frozen; in Rochester, in his first bridge-leap the following year (after a series of conditioning baths in cold water) a drunk jumped in after him, and waded safely ashore; in Passaic, New Jersey, the pollution was nearly too much for him; in Pittsburgh, forty thousand people watched him leap, handcuffed, from the Seventh Street bridge.

But despite all this, Houdini was not prospering as he had in Europe. His very success meant that he had to face increasing numbers of rivals. In Detroit, a young Canadian handcuff artist opened at a rival house on the same night and was adjudged by the Detroit *Times* critic 'unquestionably better' than Houdini (who pointed out that the Temple Theater, where he was playing, never advertised in the *Times*). Houdini destroyed him in characteristic fashion. In San Francisco he had to face an erstwhile friend, Brindamour, who now called himself 'King of all the Handcuff Artists'. He, too, was successfully destroyed. But each imitator detracted from Houdini's novelty. In January 1908, he was in St Louis and noted in his diary: 'Manager Tate informs me, "You are not worth a five-dollar bill to me." I told him, "I hope you are mistaken." We shall see.' A few weeks later things were even worse. 'Arrived in Cleveland seven o'clock. Am not featured. Is this week the first step towards oblivion? No attention paid to me.' The spectre of what might happen if he failed was, as always, solidly before him. 'Downs has retired, and is land-lording in Marshaltown, Ia. He could not change his act and so died theatrically', he noted (T. Nelson Downs, the King of Koins, had preceded him to London in 1900). He had his pension-roll of once-great vaudevillians, a constant reminder, an offering to fortune, an amulet to protect himself from their fate. But lucky charms do not always work.

Something new was needed: and on 27 January 1908, it appeared. It was a galvanised-iron can shaped like an extremely large milk can – large enough to hold a man: Houdini.

The can was filled with twenty-two pails of water. While this was going on, Houdini left the stage to change into a bathing-suit. On his return, he announced that a man can only live a certain time 'deprived of life-sustaining air'. He then entered the can, and before disappearing under water, chal-lenged the spectators to try to hold their breaths as long as they could. Then the can was topped up and he vanished from view. Houdini, who had been practising this kind of thing for years, was naturally able to outlast the fittest spectator. By the time he finally reappeared, they were awestruck and long since breathless. (Later he would challenge swimming champions to test out the can and see how long they could last in it. Houdini could hold his breath for three minutes underwater; few pro-fessional swimmers were able to match this.)

Having made his point, Houdini had himself handcuffed. He bobbed under the water; the can was filled to the brim; then the lid was screwed on and padlocked down with six padlocks. The curtain was drawn. The orchestra played 'Sailor, Beware'. Half a minute, a minute, a minute and a half went by. At this point Franz Kukol appeared, wielding a fire axe. He went up to the curtain, put his ear to it and listened intently. At the end of three minutes, by which time the audience's lungs were bursting, he raised the axe. And at this point, Houdini appeared, dripping but triumphant. The can was revealed, filled to the brim, all its locks intact.

The new act was a sensation. It brought in the crowds, and it defeated the increasing army of handcuff kings. From now on, handcuffs were merely an accessory to Houdini's other tricks rather than a draw in themselves. 'I never do handcuffs, always something ELSE. I . . . change my show on the month about 12 to 15 times,' he wrote a little later. By 1911 his baggage included no fewer than four cans – one '1910 New York Can', one 'Duston Challenge Can', one 'Gamage Can' and one 'Can 1910 unprepared'.

Much was made of the Milk Can's uniqueness and its dangers. 'This stunt was a bit too dangerous to attract imitators', wrote Harold Kellock, Houdini's first biographer. 'It required rare agility combined with under-water endurance, and complete equanimity of spirit. Houdini had to practise it for months before he dared risk it on the stage.'

This was certainly true, since any illusion requires painstaking practice before it can be successfully presented. But the Milk Can was just that – an illusion. The committee Houdini invariably invited on stage checked out everything except the real escape mechanism. The seams of the can were all riveted and soldered in order to be watertight. It was shaped like a normal milk can, with a shoulder, a lid and two handles, except that it was much bigger – it stood forty-two inches high. The can sloped in about an inch towards the floor, which seemed to kill the possibility that it was simply a double vessel, constructed so that, once Houdini was inside, he had simply to stand up to lift off the outer covering.

As it happens this was precisely the principle on which the can was built (it had been made, to Houdini's own design, in Chicago). Only the shoulder, however, was doubled. It was apparently riveted to the body – and the handles attached to it, by which the can was carried on to the stage, cunningly reinforced the impression that it was solidly attached. The rivets, however, were fakes. Inside were dummy ends of rivets which the examining committee could feel with their fingers. But in fact the top of the can was attached to the body only by two trick rivets. The can was filled with water; Houdini stepped inside, unscrewed the two rivets, scrambled out and replaced the top without ever touching the padlocks. There were tiny airholes in the lid so that he would not suffocate if something should go wrong.

The danger with any illusion of this sort is that it can be replicated. There were, inevitably, a few imitators. August Roterberg, his old magical supplier from the days when Professor Houdini was trying to make a few cents selling his tricks, wrote from Hamburg, where he was on holiday, describing one. Naturally it could not hold a candle to Houdini's: 'His act is indeed compared with yours a schwindel.' And Houdini's was never the only Milk Can in existence. At the time when he was making such a hit with it in America, the British magic dealer Will Goldston had in stock a Milk Can which he had bought from a French mechanic. He was an old friend of Houdini's, and refrained from advertising the effect. Nevertheless, a potential rival found out about it and made an offer for it. Goldston refused, mentioned the matter to Houdini, and let him have the apparatus at cost price in order to forestall other imitators. In 1909, however, Houdini was much perturbed to find that Horace Goldin, that voracious consumer of illusions, had just bought a Milk Can. He wrote to his old rival in typically aggressive mode. Goldin wrote a mollifying reply: 'To ease your mind, I once more tell you that my intentions were not to ever perform it or let anyone else do it, when I bought it, it was bought merely for curiosity. I have never copied anyone else's tricks, and I appreciate an original one.'

But Houdini was not appeased. He took it for granted that, if he performed an illusion, or even took an interest in it, it was his by right. Will Goldston told a story about how Houdini admired a picture Goldston had just acquired. He would certainly have bought it himself if he had seen it. But he had *not* seen it, and Goldston had bought it. However, at the end of the evening Houdini simply picked the picture off the wall and walked off with it. Such was his assumption of right that Goldston let him get away with it.

Houdini's power, which was something more than a mere show-business creation, depended absolutely upon what went on in people's minds. It was of no account that, when he did the bridge jump in Detroit, the water wasn't frozen and he had a rope tied round his waist; or that he used picklocks and, sometimes, dollar bills applied in the right place, to make his gaol escapes; or that he got the better of his imitators simply because he was more ruthless and better at showmanship and deception than they were. However much he protested the contrary – *the more* he protested the contrary – in people's minds he was becoming a magical figure endowed with super-human powers. And now – in people's minds – when he lowered himself into the Milk Can he was confronting the most terrifying adversary of all. He had brought Death to share the stage with him.

11

The Death and Resurrection Show

Death had never been far from Houdini's thoughts. He was only twelve when his eldest half-brother, Herman, died of consumption in New York. Bernard Meyer, the Freudian analyst, points out that it was only a few weeks later that he ran away from home. The ostensible reason for this was in order to make some money, since his father had charged him with the care of his mother. Was this simply the last straw, yet another emotional burden at a time of life which is anyway difficult enough? At any rate, Houdini never forgot the anniversary of Herman's death, any more than that of any other death that mattered to him. Wherever he might be, he sought out a synagogue to say Kaddish on the anniversary of his father's death – the only Jewish ceremony he kept. He noted other anniversaries in his diary much as you or I might remind ourselves of birthdays:

February 24, 1914: Brother Herman died twenty-nine years ago.
February 25, 1915: Aunt Sally passed away. Only outlived my beloved mother one year, seven months and nine days.
May 30, 1915: Trip to cemetery with Dash, Sam and Fanny G., etc. Sam's father died eighteen years ago today.

As his act developed, so this preoccupation became increasingly apparent. He had haunted cemeteries for years. Now he seemed set upon finding out personally what it felt like under there. Specially-built coffins were frequent accessories. He gave careful thought to the special problems a 'buried alive' act would present. Getting out of the box would be only the beginning, for earth, unlike water, is not easily displaced. In some notes written in 1911 on board a steamer near Cherbourg (he often made use of time on board ship to work out new methods, when he was not too seasick) he suggested a special type of end trap in the box. Two loose boards are held by a catch in the top of the box: the release of the catch allows them to drop inward, leaving a large opening for escape.

He finally accepted a challenge in California in which he was to be buried alive, manacled, under six feet of earth. A spot near Santa Ana was chosen where the earth was light and sandy and the vegetation scarce. They began by burying him one foot deep, then two: gradually progressing to six feet. The first two tries were easy enough, but by four and five feet he was experiencing some difficulty. The challengers were for leaving it there. Houdini, however, insisted on going for the full six feet.

But when he realised that he was in a real grave, he was overcome by panic – he, who knew better than anyone that panic was the one thing to be avoided at all costs. Among the most important of his training exercises were those ensuring mental control under stress. In life and death situations, only keeping calm conserves air and allows the body to function efficiently. Mechanically he began to dig himself out, but felt his strength failing. He tried to shout, but his mouth filled with earth. Finally he managed to burrow his way out. He never tried this stunt again. He had typed some notes for a buried packing-case escape. Underneath them he added in pencil: 'I tried out "Buried Alive" in Hollywood, and nearly(?) did it. Very dangerous; the weight of the earth is killing.'

He thus enacted, and very nearly succumbed to, the nightmare which prompted, in the nineteenth century – that era of body-snatchers and Gothick imaginings – the creation of a Society for the Prevention of Premature Burial, whose members were promised the reassurance of a stab through the heart before the coffin was closed. Indeed, the nineteenth century, both Gothick and Decadent, was rife with such fantasies. Pictorially they are most notoriously represented by Millais' Ophelia and the famous photograph of the young Sarah Bernhardt elaborately laid out in her coffin; in literature, by

Dracula and the stories of Edgar Allan Poe. Bernhardt with her infinite variety of death-scenes, Bram Stoker's story of the Undead, Poe's imaginations of what it feels like to be dying – to be at the moment of death; to be dead – all explore that threshold, that point of elision between life and death, which was Houdini's overriding preoccupation. Houdini recognised this affinity. Not only did he know Poe's tales: one of his prized possessions was Poe's writing-desk.

Poe, inevitably, himself imagined a Premature Burial. His protagonist, who is prone to cataleptic fits, has taken all possible precautions against such an eventuality – but it seems nonetheless to have arrived:

Despair – such as no other species of wretchedness ever calls into being – despair alone urged me, after long irresolution, to uplift the heavy lids of my eyes. I uplifted them. It was dark – all dark . . . the intense and utter raylessness of the Night that endureth for evermore.

I endeavoured to shriek; and my lips and my parched tongue moved convulsively together in the attempt – but no voice issued from the cavernous lungs, which, oppressed as if by the weight of some incumbent mountain, gasped and palpitated . . . The movement of the jaws, in this effort to cry aloud, showed me that they were bound up, as is usual with the dead. I felt, too, that I lay upon some hard substance; and by something similar my sides were, also, closely compressed . . . I could no longer doubt that I reposed within a coffin at last.

The therapeutic qualities of sublimation – of being able to order one's terrifying imaginings then to express them as art – are a psychological commonplace. In the process, such fantasies are often transmuted. But both Poe and Houdini expressed theirs with remarkable directness. And those fantasies are very similar. They are claustrophobic; they are about the myriad guises of approaching death; they pursue the theme of consciousness after death. But in the end Poe and Houdini are not alike – indeed, they are almost opposites. Poe embodies horror and hopelessness. His stories express the tortures of the damned: they are written by *one of* the damned. The fact of Poe's death in destitution and despair comes as no surprise: overwhelmed by such horrors as he recounts, how could he fail to succumb? But this is not the case with Houdini. Despite all the morbid imagery, his is essentially a hopeful figure. Houdini had no intention of succumbing. On the contrary. He was single-mindedly dedicated to winning the daily battles which constituted his life. Diving into the maelstrom, he knew exactly how he was going to emerge from it: under the same circumstances, Poe's concern was with what, precisely, it feels like to face certain death. The same set of symbols may signify very different things. The act of drinking blood, in Count Dracula's hands – or fangs – is murderous. He sucks life out of his victim. But the Christian communicant, drinking Christ's blood in the sacramental wine, feels nothing sinister in his beverage. For him, this is the pathway to salvation. Both are imbibing immortality, but to very different effect.

It is clear from his career between the years 1908 (the first Milk Can escape) and 1913, when everything changed yet again, that what Houdini was pursuing was proof of his own immortality. He showed, time after time and in increasingly hair-raising ways, that death had no more power over him than the mere shackles which he regularly threw off within minutes if not seconds. Not that he did not fear death. The opposite was true. He was so haunted by it, the consciousness of it filled his thoughts so entirely, that his life was tolerable only if he could assure himself, time after time, that he could defeat it. If he was not to lapse into breakdown, he had to force himself to confront this terror. This is the essential Gothick situation: one in which the protagonist is faced by some nameless terror, which is in fact death, and which may be overcome by confronting it. The bonds with which he began his career had been, like all those gloomy castles and dark labyrinths, a mere symbol, a precursor, of the real, underlying thing.

He demonstrated his immortality in a variety of water-, milk- and beer-filled containers: nothing could hold him. In 1908, he saw an irresistible new possibility. Five years earlier, in 1903, the Wright Brothers had made the first powered flight. In 1908 he offered $5,000 for the use of a Wright Brothers plane. He planned to be flown over the West End of London where, handcuffed, he would parachute down, escaping from his manacles on the way, to land in Piccadilly Circus. This sensation, however, was not to be: 'technical difficulties' intervened. But he did not forget about flying.

His opportunity came the next year, in Germany. He was playing at the Hansa Theatre in Hamburg when it was announced that an aviator named Grade would be demonstrating a new French biplane, the Voisin, at a nearby field. The Voisin was the latest thing in aviation technology. A similar machine had stayed in the air for an hour and twenty minutes near Rheims. Houdini watched the flight and was enthralled. He cornered the aviator and demanded to know where he could get such a plane and what it cost. There were at that time only about two dozen aviators in the entire world: there were certainly no flying schools. This did not deter Houdini. A week later, for five thousand dollars, he owned a Voisin and had hired a French mechanic, Brassac, to teach him how to fly it. If Brassac's name has not survived along with those of the pioneers of flying machines, this shows merely how arbitrary is fame. He taught Bleriot to fly, and actually built the monoplane which first crossed the English Channel. But for the next year he devoted himself entirely to Houdini.

Houdini persuaded German Army officials to let him do his learning at the nearby Hufaren exercise field, and they agreed on condition that he teach their officers how to fly. (When World War I came, he characteristically berated himself for having been the means of putting countless enemy aviators into the air for the first time – 'I taught those fellows to fly and they may have killed Americans!' he mourned to Bess.) Every night he made his escapes at the Hansa; every morning before the cold November dawn, he and Brassac made their way to Hufaren. The weather was freezing cold, windy and snowy, so that, more often than not, flying was out of the question. Every morning he sat with Brassac in the cockpit learning what he would have to do when, finally, he could fly.

At length the weather cleared. Houdini took his place at the controls: Brassac swung the propeller. He was airborne – but not for long. 'I smashed the machine. Broke propeller all to hell,' he noted in his diary. The damage, however, was not fatal, and Brassac soon got new parts and repaired it. On 26 November 1909, Houdini made his first successful flight at Hufaren. After that he went flying every day.

Was it what he had hoped for? The ultimate escape, the genuine assumption – for real, at last – of superhuman power? If anyone could approach the sensations of Superman, that man was surely the pilot of one of the early flying machines. So light, so flimsy, constructed of wooden struts and sized canvas: a powered box kite. The pilot sat at the front; behind him was the engine – an 80hp Enfield – and behind that the wooden propeller. There was literally nothing between him and the empty air. But he could not stay aloft for ever. Ten or twelve minutes was the maximum the engine's fuel capacity would allow. After that there was always the bumpy return to earth.

The Hamburg engagement finished at the end of December, and Houdini's next engagement was at the other side of the world. He was booked to go to Melbourne, Australia. Still obsessed by flying, he arranged to take Brassac and the Voisin on the trip with him. He would be the first person to make a flight on the Australian continent. He was not, however, the only one with this idea. Ralph C. Banks, the owner of the Melbourne Motor Garage, was importing a Wright aircraft with the same purpose in mind. When the ship finally reached Melbourne, the crated plane caused a certain amount of trouble with Customs. 'They charge you 35% duty or you can bring it in . . . in bond. The Wright machine that is here is under 800 pounds bond. My machine is not quite that much, but by the time I am ready to leave Australia, it will cost that much.' In fact he decided to bring the Voisin through, and ended up paying only £154 deposit.

The voyage had been a trying one for Houdini, who had lost twenty-eight pounds on account of seasickness. (The pain was slightly alleviated by the consciousness that the eager Australian management was paying him his weekly salary for the three-week duration of the voyage.) In the interviews he gave on his arrival at Melbourne he talked about his fear of sharks interfering with his dives, his impending retirement (after he had completed the eighteen months' work for which he was already contracted) and his superhuman toughness. He did not, however, mention his main concern, which was his aeroplane.

The airfield was at Digger's Rest, about twenty miles from Melbourne. He learned to drive a motor-car in order to get there early in the morning, but he was an impossibly distracted driver and nobody except Brassac (for whom, one can only assume, anything actually in contact with the ground seemed safe) would drive with him. Once again Houdini and Brassac began the apparently endless business of waiting upon the weather. It remained stubbornly unsuitable. Houdini fretted. He saw the precious days passing and the record passing with them, out of his reach. Finally, on 18 March, he made his attempt. It was a success, and he was able to claim his trophy and a certificate signed by Brassac, his frustrated rival Banks, Franz Kukol and several others to the effect that 'We, the undersigned, do hereby testify to the fact that on the above date, about 8 o'clock a.m., we witnessed Harry Houdini in a Voisin Biplane (a French heavier-than-air machine) make three successful flights of from one minute to three and a half minutes. The last flight being of the last mentioned duration. In his various flights he reached an altitude of 100 feet, and in his longest flight traversed a distance of over two miles.' Houdini noted in his diary: 'Never in any fear and never in any danger. It is a wonderful thing.'

In fact it had not been quite as uncomplicated as that. During his longest flight Houdini had risen to two hundred feet at forty miles per hour, then turned and met the wind full on. The engines stalled and the machine fell towards the ground.

'But when only a few feet from the ground the plucky aviator managed to start his engine again, and the plane rose once more.' He was always very keyed up before a flight, as well he might have been considering the real dangers and the absence of possible precautions. But, he told the *Sydney Herald*, 'As soon as I was aloft all the tension and strain left me. When I was rolling every muscle of me was taut. When she cants over at the turns – you know how she goes when she's rolling – I'm always afraid the wing will break in the air. It was different as soon as I was up. All my muscles relaxed, and I sat back feeling a sense of ease, freedom and exhilaration. That's what it is. Oh, she's great. I know what it is to fly in real earnest. She's like a swan. She's dandy. I can fly now.' He wrote to a friend: 'I have been very bisy trying to win the Australian Prize, and I'm pleased to inform you the trophy is MINE!!! But it was hard work, my engine seemed to go wrong, and though I had five men working on it for seven days and nights it refused to pull the amount required, and I almost gave up in despair. Finally last Sunday it awoke to the fact that I had no more days left, and I made the flight of my life. The wind was very strong, but though it carried me about like a feather, I managed to make a grand flight.' He added: 'I have had the Grave of Wm. H. H. Davenport all fixed up, and will send you a picture of it as it looks today.'

His challenge to the air was over. He had won. Flying held no more interest for him. 'It is time I had the biplane packed, or it would have given me nervous prostration,' he noted. 'Have not had much sleep for two months and now I seem to have lost the habit.' The following year he read that an aviator named Moisant had crashed his Voisin, and sent a letter by wire, reply pre-paid, 'in which I offered you GRATIS my entire Bi-plane, propeller, and any spare parts you might have been able to make use of'. This act of conspicuous generosity did not go unpublicised – why pass up a good opportunity? The letter was sent via the *Daily Mirror*. But to Houdini's indignation Moisant, possibly unable to believe that this princely offer was really what it seemed, failed to reply.

Houdini recognised the important part death played in his act – to a certain extent. He said: 'I knew, as everyone knows, that the easiest way to attract a crowd is to let it be known that at a given time and a given place some one is going to attempt something that in the event of failure will mean sudden death. That's what attracts us to the man who paints the flagstaff on the tall building, or to the "human fly" who scales the walls of the same building.' His friend of later life, Sir Arthur Conan Doyle, said of him: 'He had the essential masculine quality of courage to a supreme degree. Nobody has ever done, and nobody in all human probability will ever do, such reckless feats of daring. His whole life was one long succession of them.'

In fact no man was ever less reckless. He had by now acquired a specialist team who travelled with him and helped with the preparations. Franz Kukol dealt with bureaucrats and arranged the music. Bess was in charge of the wardrobe and maintained sanity. Houdini thought out the stunts; and, in 1908, the year of the Milk Can, he hired someone who was able to embody his wildest ideas in solid form. This was Jim Collins, a Londoner, a master mechanic and cabinet-maker, who had the advantage of being utterly inconspicuous – the man you would not pick out in a crowd: an almost invisible accomplice. Houdini always insisted that he had picked Collins at sight and on instinct, much as he had picked Bess. There were also two other assistants, Jim Vickery and (in Europe) George Brooks. All these, and anyone who sold Houdini an illusion, had to sign an oath which inducted them into the dark melodrama of Houdiniland:

I the *undersigned* do solemnly swear on my sacred honor as a man that as long as I live I shall never divulge the secret or secrets of Harry Houdini, or any thing I may make for him and the secret of the can I further swear never to betray Houdini

. . .

So help me God almighty and may he keep me steadfast

In those spacious times, they travelled in two railroad cars, one for the personnel, the other for baggage, props and Houdini's travelling library (built for him by Jim Collins) which would hold a hundred books. 'I carry 40 pieces of baggage,' he wrote in 1912. 'And my chief assistant wears a uniform costs over $1000 in GOLD.' The act occupied three dressing-rooms – one for Houdini, one for the team, one for the apparatus, 'the shop'. Here new parts were constructed, keys cut, and any special tools needed to escape from challenges kept in readiness. While the act was on, the stage was always blocked off with special screens, so that no curious stagehands could penetrate Houdini's secrets. At the end of the week, to show that this was simply a professional requirement and not a sign of stand-offishness, trestles would be laid across the stage and all the other acts, the orchestra and the stagehands would be treated to beer and sandwiches. Meanwhile, at home in 113th Street, John W. Sargent, a veteran magician, looked after the collection. Houdini had been in the habit of giving Sargent, an old friend, various secretarial tasks as his magical career thinned out and money got scarce. Finally Sargent moved full-time into Houdini's employ.

To be a member of Houdini's team was to have your life entirely subsumed in his. This was the return he demanded for what was, for him, the hardest thing in the world: the bestowing of his entire confidence. The team alone were privy to his 'secrets'. Only Bess was as intimate with him. In a way she was simply the longest-serving team member, the only difference being that he couldn't sack her. He would frequently lose his temper and dismiss the others: they learned to disregard these outbursts, which would be forgotten the next day. No one would have been more shocked than Houdini had they been acted upon.

The team supported Houdini in all aspects of his life. 'Laying off to have Bess celebrate her birthday,' reads one diary entry. 'Came from Philadelphia. Even had fine menu cards printed, though at first she didn't wish them. Bess originally invited thirty-six guests, but lo and behold, sixty-five arrived. Bess was equal to the occasion, though somewhat flurried, and my assistants, Franz, Collins and Jim Vickery, helped in the kitchen.' When Houdini died and left his act to Hardeen, Collins and Vickery went with it. They were part of the act.

Of course jumping off the Golden Gate Bridge while wearing leg-irons must always remain a dangerous activity. But it was possible to minimise the danger. 'In the first place,' Houdini advised, 'it is absolutely necessary that the aspirant be a good swimmer, well versed in treading water, floating, and all methods of keeping afloat without the use of hands. This is not as difficult as it at first appears . . . It is also necessary to acquire the art of swimming with a forward and back motion of the feet, in place of the old scissors stroke, and once having mastered this method the body can be kept afloat as easily as by the old style. The necessity for the above is apparent when we consider that the hands must be used on the knots continuously. Bear in mind that the release must be accomplished rapidly, not only on account of the necessity of breathing, but because the ropes shrink when they become watersoaked, although this is not rapid enough to seriously interfere with your work . . . Deep breathing in order to strengthen the lungs and increase their capacity must also be practised, for it will be necessary to hold the breath for a considerable time, and as the escape is bound to require rather violent struggles, this is no child's play . . . This is dangerous business at best, and two of my imitators have been drowned when thrown overboard in manacles. If you are not an absolutely fearless swimmer, I warn you to keep away from ropes under water, and unless you are an expert of the highest order, never substitute handcuffs unless you resort to fixed cuffs, which require only a pull to open, and even these might go wrong with disastrous results. I have never used fixed manacles in any of my stunts, always allowing stage cuffs to be affixed. When I did use my own it was only to lend extra weight, so that I might sink quickly to the bottom and out of sight of my audience, so that they might not inspect my method of releasing myself.' To this end, holes were bored in his boxes and extra weights were attached to them. And as he supervised the immersion of the box, Jim Collins invariably waited for the signal from within telling him that Houdini was free of his bonds and shackles before he gave the signal to lower away. To the watching crowd, of course, Collins was effectively invisible, and Houdini remained a lone hero.

But out of doors, even with the most careful preparations, something might always go wrong since the environment could never be wholly predictable. The most spectacular stage stunt was, by comparison, relatively safe – though nothing was entirely foolproof. The world of magic was shocked when William Robinson, a.k.a. Chung Ling Soo, an old acquaintance of Houdini's, was killed during his famous bullet-catching act – an act which he had performed countless times. All sorts of rumours about murder and suicide floated about. In fact what happened was that the thread of the breech-block in Soo's gun had worn loose from being constantly unscrewed, and the very fine powder he used worked its way down so that on the fatal occasion not only the blank charge in the ramrod tube but the real charge in the barrel was ignited. Houdini would never do this trick. His friend Harry Kellar, the doyen of American magicians and the one father-figure with whom Houdini never fell out, had advised him not to in the most emphatic terms: 'No matter what precautions are taken with the bullet-catching trick, it's a damn-fool trick, and the chances for an accident or a "job" are always present. Now, my dear boy, this is advice from the heart. *Don't try the bullet-catching trick*. There is always the biggest kind of risk that some dog will "job" you . . . Harry, listen to your friend Kellar, who loves you as his own son. DON'T DO IT!' Houdini needed no telling: he had himself warned of the act's dangers in the *Conjurer's Magazine*.

His own most famous stage stunt was far less risky. It was built for him by Collins, and known as the Chinese Water-Torture Cell. Houdini always referred to it as 'the old Upside-Down' or 'U.S.D.' In it, a glass-fronted tank was brought on stage and filled with water. Houdini, his ankles clamped in stout wooden stocks, was lowered into it head-first, and the top was secured by a metal grille. Kukol, armed with his fire-axe, was always ostentatiously to hand in case the escape could not be effected. The inside of the tank was fitted with horizontal iron bars, ostensibly so that no injury would result should the glass need to be broken. The function of the bars was actually to allow Houdini to 'walk' his head and shoulders to the top of the tank, where, doubled up, he released the catch holding the stocks. The back of these then pulled out like a drawer, allowing enough space for Houdini to scramble out. In a later design there were no bars: the catch was probably activated when the water in the tank reached a certain level after Houdini's immersion.

The persona Houdini now presented was no longer that of a mere escape king, but of an invulnerable hero. Invulnerability may be judged in absolute terms; but also in comparative ones. 'The moment of *survival* is the moment of power,' writes Canetti, and adds: 'The moment of confronting the man he has killed fills the survivor with a special kind of strength. There is nothing that can be compared with it.' In the cemeteries, the knowledge that he was alive when all the great names he revered were underground had strengthened Houdini's hold on life. Now, however, there were keener pleasures to be had. He was not in the business of killing his rivals. But he took an unmistakable delight in recording the details of how they killed themselves. A swimmer in Pittsburg jumped, bound, from a bridge: his body was retrieved ten minutes later, when it was found that his knots had failed to slip as intended. A Human Fly fell to his death. Houdini noted these happenings with some satisfaction. Everyone who died in this way contributed not only to his legend, but to his immortality.

Invulnerability was both a psychological and a physical affair. From his earliest youth, Houdini had been preparing himself not merely to remain calm but to meet any physical eventuality. He cultivated his body fanatically. Absolute fitness was essential to his job. The knowledge that he could always rely on his body was essential to the control of his mind.

But there was more to it than that. Which came first, the chicken or the egg? The mind or the body, or the body or the mind?

Yukio Mishima, the Japanese novelist, shared many of Houdini's preoccupations with death and the cult of the body. Mishima, who ended his life with a public ritual suicide, wrote a novel, *Kyoko's House,* in which one of the main characters is an actor-body-builder. The question he asks himself is, 'Do I really exist or not?'

'On the one hand,' says Robert Jay Lifton, discussing Mishima as he speaks through the actor, 'in rendering his body beautiful, agile, and capable of disciplined violence, he could find in it a constant source of transcendence – of what he called the " 'ultimate sensation' that lies a hairsbreadth beyond the reach of the senses." And . . . he goes on to say, "My solace lay more than anywhere – indeed lay solely – in the small rebirths that occurred immediately after exercise . . . By now . . . it was not words that endorsed my existence . . . but something different. That 'something different' was muscle." '

Mishima's addiction existed, as addictions do, on two levels. One was psychological. Like Houdini, who was always inviting people to feel his iron-hard body, he conceived of himself narcissistically in terms of muscle and what he was able to do with it. For Mishima as for Houdini this narcissism was to play a part in his death – in Mishima's case directly, in Houdini's, indirectly. But the addiction was also physiological, in those 'small rebirths'.

In one way this may have been fairly straightforward. It is well-known that intensive exercise stimulates the production of endorphins and produces a high, so that stopping the regime may bring on withdrawal symptoms. It is very probable that this was true of Mishima and also of Houdini: he had to get his fix of urgent struggle. 'Sometimes I think that these stunts hold far greater thrills for me than they have even for the spectators,' he wrote revealingly.

But there was more than a simple high to these extreme occasions, so often repeated. Mishima's 'ultimate sensation' recalls that state of mental transcendence achieved by masters of zen and some of the martial arts. Such a state may of course be attained in many other ways. 'The list,' says Lifton, 'suggests a continuum from extraordinary Dionysian "excess" (sexual orgy or absolute union with God) to relatively "ordinary excess" (sexual intercourse, athletics) to much quieter, indeed, Apollonian moments (contemplation of the past or any kind of beauty.) The crucial requirement for feeling ecstatic – "outside of oneself" – would seem to be not so much excess per se as the breakout from prosaic psychic complexities into a state of pure focus, of inner unity and harmony.'

There are probably as many routes to ecstasy as there are people. Some people take drugs to attain it. A great many religious rituals – the whirling of dervishes, yoga, speaking in tongues – are designed to induce it. But religion has no monopoly of it. It seems to me almost certain that Houdini experienced transcendence in the course of his exploits. He said to Conan Doyle: 'It all comes as easy as stepping off a log, but I have to wait for the voice. You stand there before a jump, swallowing the yellow stuff that every man has in him. Then at last you hear the voice and you jump. Once I jumped on my own and I nearly broke my neck.' Conan Doyle took this to mean that Houdini had to admit, in spite of himself, to having had 'psychic experiences' – i.e. having been in touch with another world. But I think he was simply explaining how, like a kendo master, he had to attain a 'pure state' permitting effortless concentration before he embarked on action. He was certainly aware of the effects of concentration. In 1922 he wrote, apropos crystal-gazing: 'The practice induces calmness which is very helpful for people of nervous temperament, and of great assistance in the practice of collecting one's thoughts at a crucial moment . . . Concentration constitutes a powerful magnet that enthralls an audience spontaneously.' He thought that sufficient concentration would induce self-hypnotism and trance, leading (in this case) to hallucinating images in the crystal. 'Keep on trying and eventually you WILL SUCCEED', he added with the certainty of personal experience. Action, at that point, was exquisite in its perfect control.

There were other possible delights. It seems probable that Houdini took a sexual pleasure in bondage. And near-asphyxiation can reputedly induce exquisite pleasure. Did he also experience it in the state of surrendering himself to danger? In French, those moments at the extreme boundaries of consciousness which include drunkenness, vertigos, fits and also orgasms are given the generic name of *petites morts*. One might add to the list the instant of complete absorption in mass violence. All these routes lead to the same point: the overwhelming present, when conscious thought ceases.

Picture the scene as Houdini performs one of his bridge jumps, so often described with such unvarying excitement. The excited crowd, several thousand strong, jostles around. Houdini and his team arrive. A silence falls. Houdini strips to his bathing suit and climbs on to the parapet. The attention of all these thousands of people is focused upon him – a small man, slightly bow-legged, very muscular. The local chief of police comes forward carrying handcuffs, often two sets; leg-irons. Houdini allows himself to be manacled. He stands there, waiting until he 'hears the voice'. Then he jumps. The crowd surges forward. It is waiting for – what? What it sees, in a minute or so, is Houdini, swimming strongly for the bank or the boat, brandishing the irons in one hand. It is slightly disappointed, but also satisfied. Death has been defeated once more.

Occasionally, circumstance interrupted the lone dignity of the performer. In Australia, a jump into the muddy Yarra River dislodged a corpse which floated to the surface alongside an appalled Houdini. He was so shocked that he was unable to swim away and had to be hauled aboard a boat. But generally the ritual was undisturbed. For ritual it surely was. What does the scene recall so much as an ancient ceremony of human sacrifice, death and rebirth? The old year's king killed in the sacred grove, the living hearts offered to the Aztec gods, the sacrificial figure central to all mythologies in which death is followed by resurrection, as spring follows winter? '*Come forth, Lazarus! And he came fifth and lost the job.*'

The specific functions of these sacrificial figures vary according to mythology. But one role is common to them all. They are the surrogates detailed to investigate, experience, and if possible exorcise on behalf of the rest of us, the great mystery: Death, the consciousness of which differentiates man from other animals. We may refuse to think about it. Dr Johnson considered that 'it matters not how a man dies, but how he lives. The act of dying is not of importance, it lasts so short a time.' But even Dr Johnson could not escape the reluctant consciousness that life is finite. And *what happens then?*

That, as they say, is the question. It dominates many lives: it dominated Houdini's. People yearn for an answer. And the disadvantages of a sacrificial victim when it comes to supplying one are evident. He is dead, and communicating with the dead is problematical.

So another way of probing the great mystery evolved. People came forward who would, so to speak, dip their toe in the water; who would take on death in the hope of coming out the other side imbued with wisdom.

These people, *shamans,* are a feature of most primitive societies. They are figures of great power. They can intercede with the powers of darkness because their life-experience has been in some way extreme. Everyone has to cope with life's crises, starting with the separation of birth. The potential shaman has for some reason experienced these more intensely, and has had to evolve special ways of dealing with the intensity of his or her experience. All Houdini's brothers had to cope with the same difficult circumstances; only he had to work out a special route to survival.

Shamans derive from the extremity of their experience a

knowledge which is denied to most other people. They have journeyed from horror and madness through countless dangers to rebirth and joy. They are healers, psychologists, repositories of ancient wisdom; they are feared and honoured; they are outside society. They operate through performance – elaborate dramatic ceremonies during which they not only speak with spirits in their own languages but become them. A shaman performs miraculous feats. In his own body, he descends to the underworld and returns unharmed. Siberian shamans enact this by diving through a hole in the ice and then resurfacing through it: a scene with which Houdini enthusiasts will be familiar. The shaman may ascend to the sky as a bird or travel to the depths as a marine creature: he (or she) is a master of transformation. In short, the shaman is a *magician*. Or rather, he is *magic: a mage*. The connotations of magic have always been religious. It is a very ancient word. In Akkadian, *imga* meant priest; this was transposed by the Assyrians to *maga* and Latinised to *magus* – a man of power. For some, even in the modern west, magic is still a religion: and the knowledge and mastery of death is still the centre of its mysteries.

The most common term for the art of magic – conjuring – was in its earlier meanings associated with devils, spirits and the unholy powers. In his performance, the shaman's body is inhabited by these powers, and they are defeated by him. He acts out the innermost fears of his society – fears of madness, sorcery, disease: above all, the fear of death. He undergoes these experiences on behalf of the assembled watchers. He is a mythic figure. Myths, in Freud's view, are public dreams. The dream expresses a private neurosis, within which the dreamer is alone. Myth, or religion, expresses the shared neurosis of society. So the shaman, when he acts out and defeats these neuroses, helps his society to come to terms with its great fears, just as, ideally, the psychoanalyst helps the patient come to terms with his or hers.

The shaman, with his appeal to atavistic fears and beliefs, has never been a popular figure with the propagators of civilisation. His potent appeal runs counter to everything that civilisation is about: the defeat of superstition, the imposition of rationality, education, the rule of law. No shaman can be too civilised. The effect of education is to induce self-consciousness, and self-consciousness is a quality from which a shaman and his adherents must be wholly free. If Houdini had been aware of what he was doing – if he had been able to formulate his needs in words – it is unthinkable that he could have acted them out with the compulsive abandon of one who blindly does what he must. For a shaman's is not a voluntary calling: 'When I was twenty years old I became very ill and began "to see with my eyes and hear with my ears" that which others did not see or hear; nine years I struggled with myself, and did not tell anyone what was happening to me, as I was afraid people would not believe me and make fun of me. At last I became so seriously ill that I was on the verge of death; but when I started to shamanise, I grew better; and even now, when I do not shamanise for a long time, I am liable to be ill.'

Thus a Siberian shaman on his vocation. It is doubtful whether Houdini would have been capable of so cogent a piece of self-analysis. That was not how his mind worked. But the circumstances were very similar. Each had to 'shamanise' if he was to retain his sanity. For Houdini, his performance was as grave an affair as any religious ritual. Any attempt to introduce a light-hearted note was met with a fury few could comprehend. When the comedian Loney Haskell, during a benefit performance, cracked some jokes about how Houdini, who lay tied in a straitjacket on the other side of the stage, could not escape from the traffic jam at Forty-Second Street and Broadway, he was stopped by a tremendous kick in the shins. Houdini, still tied, had wriggled right across the stage to administer it. He was red with anger. 'No, no,' he whispered. 'No comedy, Lon. I just can't stand comedy.' In this ritual and symbolic role, all his peculiarities and obsessions fell into place: the lack of detachment and irony, the absolute seriousness, the compulsion to perform, in public and in private, the ceremonies of his personal drama, which was at the same time so absolutely universal.

It was perhaps at this moment, when he assumed the symbolic role for which his whole life had been an unconscious preparation, that Houdini stepped over the boundary between magical performance and real magic. The relations between the two have always been close; but they are not the same thing. When Hero of Alexandria used newly-discovered physical laws relating to water vapour and air pressure to make temple idols move and pour libations, the awe this inspired was occasioned very largely by its setting. In a fairground booth, the effect would have been quite different. Magic is not contained in conjuring tricks, although these may enhance it. Real magic is what goes on in people's minds when, for instance, they receive the sacraments. The wine does not have to change physically into blood for that to occur.

Houdini's performance differed from that of the Siberian shaman on two counts. One was that he was not conscious of the resonances of his performance. He did not, for example, know *why* comedy was so inappropriate to it, only that he couldn't bear it. The second was that his performance was an essentially egotistical affair. He was doing what he did in order to save himself. So was the Siberian shaman, but he, unlike Houdini, also recognised and accepted his role vis-à-vis society. The shaman's role is always a lonely one. When its social context is not recognised, it becomes uniquely narcissistic.

The remains of shamanism in western society can be traced to various groups which operate essentially outside that society, on its boundaries and outskirts. It is an appropriate place for them, since the shaman deals essentially with those transitional moments for which civilisation has little to offer: the moves from childhood to adulthood, from life to death; the occasions for rites of passage. The shaman is essentially a liminal figure, on the threshold between this world and the next; sometimes, between one sex and another. His performance is a drama, and includes tricks and miracles. Where he is still truly a powerful figure, these are peripheral to the main religious and healing purpose of the performance. As that power wanes they assume a greater importance in attracting and holding the audience. Finally, as with the *Commedia dell'Arte*, they constitute the whole show, a tradition handed down from player to player in those groups whose existence is barely tolerated by the authorities but which – because of their popular appeal – have never really been suppressed, popping up in fairs, on holidays, wherever a crowd gathers. They are the travelling players, the fairground magicians and fortune tellers, the medicine shows, the freaks, the dime-museum players . . . They are the actors and singers who, once again today, wield huge popular power because they speak to those dimly-perceived needs which society has attempted to rationalise and educate out of existence.

This is not the high-art performance favoured by authority where the approved text is played upon a stage and watched with respect in a theatre, a concert-hall, a church. On the contrary: here the audience is a part of the show: it makes a vital contribution. Engagement is total. If a ritual may be seen as an 'organization of mythological symbols' the participation enables the audience to experience the living myth: arguably, the true religious experience. So the screaming, fainting audience is as much an essential part of the show as the rock star. And the crowd tensely waiting to see if he would emerge once more from the jaws of death, the invulnerable hero, the quasi-supernatural figure, was as important to Houdini's performance as the feat itself.

The performer's needs speak to those of the audience. Together, they experience catharsis. In this sense, charisma is the antithesis of civilisation. Civilisation is about control, of both the individual and the crowd; cathartic release is about the abandonment of that control. The shaman's crowd is uncivilised. So civilisation views the charismatic figure, rightly, as its enemy.

The year 1912 was the high point of Houdini's vaudeville career. That summer he was offered eight weeks at Hammerstein's Roof Garden at $1,000 a week. He determined that, this time, he would conquer the New York press, which alone still resisted him. Hitherto, the bridge jumps and the container escapes had been two quite separate acts. The handcuffs and leg-irons were now no more than an accessory – an essential accessory, but an accessory nonetheless. They magnified the drama; they were no longer the drama itself.

Now, early in the morning at the Municipal Swimming Pool on 80th Street and the East River, Houdini and his team began to practise a new stunt. He would be lowered into the river, manacled, in a formidable iron-weighted box specially constructed by Jim Collins. The box would defy the closest inspection. It was solid in every respect; only the team knew that one of its boards was attached by those short screws which Houdini had so bitterly denounced in his rival's coffin.

The stunt was announced for the day he was due to open at Hammerstein's. The press was notified and turned out in force at the East River pier. Mrs Weiss was present to watch her son in his supreme moment. Crowds filled the docks. Then at the last moment the police showed up and forbade the stunt. Jumping off piers in New York was forbidden. But by prescience or good fortune, a tugboat just happened to be on hand. Houdini jumped in, his packing case was loaded aboard, and the pressmen followed. Once out in the harbour he had them inspect the handcuffs and leg-irons and lock them in position. The he was helped into the box, the top was nailed in place, and Jim Collins supervised its lowering into the water. The pressmen took out their watches.

They waited, counting, for fifty-seven long seconds. Then Houdini appeared. The most cynical news corps in the world burst into cheers. The box was hauled up. It was tight closed: inside were the cuffs and irons. The evening's headlines were secure. That evening he repeated the stunt in the large pool which was one of the features of Hammerstein's Roof Garden. Houdini had conquered New York.

It was at the end of this week that he demanded his first thousand dollars' salary in gold, so that he could pour it into his mother's lap. This scene is of course familiar to us all from fairytales. The poor boy leaves home and accomplishes the ten impossible tasks that will make him rich, marry him to the beautiful princess and give his parents a secure old age. In the fairytale, however, all is rarely what it seems. As often as not the gold turns back into dead leaves or stones. But in this case that did not happen. Mrs Weiss held out her apron and it really was filled with real gold: an archetypal fulfilment, as was only fitting for an archetypal personage.

12

The Lady Vanishes

The power to vanish – or to make someone else vanish – is one of the classic magical attributes. Invisibility, in the old tales, is a gift from the gods or the fairies. It is a protective device bestowed upon their favourites to render them invincible and untouchable. Vanishing other people is an altogether different matter. It is often an aggressive measure, the prerogative of witches and wizards, who are also apt to materialise suddenly out of nowhere, usually with the worst of intentions.

Where do they come from, where do they go to, all these invisible people?

If you are merely protected by the cloak or ring of invisibility, the answer is simple. You don't go anywhere: you are there all the time. You can't be seen, but you can be felt, and you can make yourself felt: a circumstance upon which more than one story has pivoted. But the matter is more complicated if you are vanished (or if you materialise). The understanding under those circumstances appears to be that the invisible one arrives from a kind of limbo, an incorporeal state symbolised by the traditional puff of green smoke which marks the appearances and disappearances of the Demon King in the pantomime.

The puff of smoke fulfils not merely a dramatic but a practical purpose: it distracts attention from the mechanics of what is going on. For it is not only wizards in fairytales who can make people vanish at will.

As with most famous illusions, there are many different ways in which the effect may be achieved. For example, the vanishing lady may assume the cloak of invisibility. This happened in an illusion called 'Gone!' which was invented by W.E. Robinson, who later performed as Chung Ling Soo (and died, it will be recalled, when his bullet-catching act went wrong). In this illusion a girl sits on a chair and is hoisted six or seven feet into the air. The magician fires a pistol at her, she screams, the pieces of the chair fall to the ground, and she is – gone!

'Gone!' is performed against a black backcloth. The chair is hoisted by a winch mounted on a scaffold framework. In the top bar of the frame are two pulleys through which the ropes pass to the winch. In the middle of the frame is another bar, apparently to strengthen the framework, but important to the trick. Behind this bar is a kind of roller blind, connected to the top bar by powerful springs. When the catch is released, the blind – black to match the backcloth – shoots up to the top bar. The girl is sitting on a loose seat hooked to the ropes. By pressing a catch on this she disengages the collapsible chair, which falls on to the stage in pieces.

Or it may all be done with mirrors. An angled mirror will reflect the backcloth in such a way that the mirror itself is invisible to the audience, although it is of course opaque and will conceal whatever needs to be hidden. This property is the basis of a great many illusions (for instance, disembodied talking heads) and may be used in a variety of ways to effect a successful vanish.

A third method is to use a collapsible framework. This is the secret of those illusions where the magician throws a cover over the lady, claps his hands or waves his wand or fires a pistol, and whips off the cover (and the framework) to reveal – nothing at all. What has happened is that the lady has been lowered off the stage through a trapdoor while the framework holds the cover in place. This was the method used in some very famous illusions, notably David Devant's 'Mascot Moth' and Buatier de Kolta's 'Vanishing Lady' (which was later acquired by Houdini).

One thing all these tricks have in common is, of course, that the lady later reappears. Here magic has it over reality. For in the final disappearing act of all, there is no return.

After his triumph at Hammerstein's Roof Garden in 1912, Houdini returned to Europe. But he agreed to return to

Hammerstein's in 1913 for a two-week engagement in spite of the fact that the round trip would last almost as long as the engagement. His mother was by now seventy-two; she was getting frail, and he would not have another chance to see her that year. She sat in the front row and beamed while he escaped from straitjackets and the Water Torture Cell, which was here presented for the first time. 'It is his act and practically his act alone, which gives the present bill its one gleam of intense interest and originality,' noted the *New York Times*. 'Owing to this man's wonderful flubdub and personality, one follows his entrances and exits as breath-batedly as if he were pushing himself through the small and hindermost entrance of a Yale lock. And he would get himself out of there – that's the wonder of the man.'

On 7 July Houdini had dinner with some magician friends, including Ching Ling Foo, who (unlike Chung Ling Soo) was genuinely Chinese and who was taking over his spot at the Hippodrome. Next day he sailed for Europe and an engagement in Copenhagen. Hardeen, meanwhile, was engaged to perform in Asbury Park, New Jersey, from 14 July, and invited Mrs Weiss to take a holiday and accompany him down there. She was to stay at the Imperial Hotel while he leaped, manacled, from the end of the pier, and performed straitjacket releases, handcuff escapes, the Milk Can act and other items from the old Houdini repertory at the Lyric Theater. On the night of the 14th Mrs Weiss suffered a stroke which left her paralysed. Theo called his sister Gladys in New York: she arrived next day. Mrs Weiss's condition was critical. On 16 July Hardeen performed his act as usual, then rushed to his mother's bedside. She seemed to be trying to say something. Then she fell asleep, never to wake again.

Houdini, meanwhile, had opened at the Cirkus Beketow in Copenhagen. Two members of the Danish royal family, Prince Aage and Prince Axel, were in the audience. He had memorised his patter in Danish, according to his principle of addressing audiences in their own language. ('I am doing my entire act in Danish,' he told Nelson Downs as early as 1901.

'It is 100 percent better than my German, I mean worse, but it is very funny and I make a hit with my introduction.')

This trick, along with all the others, worked like a charm. The audience went wild with enthusiasm. Next day at noon, Houdini joyfully met the press in the circus vestibule. He wanted to thank everyone for his wonderful reception the previous evening. As he talked, he was handed a cable. He opened it, read it, and fell unconscious to the floor. When he came to he was sobbing, 'Mama – my dear little mother – poor little mama.' The pressmen quietly left.

Houdini did not perform that night. Next day a Danish doctor diagnosed shock followed by a recurrence of chronic kidney trouble. In 1911 he had suffered a ruptured blood-vessel in his kidney brought on by too many strenuous strait-jacket escapes. The doctor then had prescribed three months' rest and no more straitjacket escapes or other such exhausting stunts. Houdini was unable to contemplate such a thing. His aura of invincibility was as essential to his self-image as to his public image. Not only could nothing contain him, not only was he immune to deathly dangers, but disease could not be allowed to touch him as it might any ordinary mortal. He went on playing for the next three nights in great pain, then rested for a fortnight. 'Think I started work too soon', he confided to his diary. 'Wish I had laid off another week.' The kidney never really healed. It gave him intermittent trouble from then on. He had to sleep with a cushion under the affected side; it was after this that he took to wearing a black silk eye-mask in bed, since the least ray of light would wake him from his troubled sleep. Now mortality was reaching out: it had claimed his mother; he could feel its fingers on his own body.

Distraught, he cabled Hardeen to delay the funeral. He was coming home at once. He and Bess managed to get berths on the same ship that had brought them to Hamburg. Bizarrely, or appropriately, it was named the *Kronprinzessin Cecilie*. They landed in New York on 29 July, in time for Houdini to see his mother in her coffin. On 30 July the funeral took place.

'This day Cecilia Weiss, *geboren* Steiner, my darling Mother, was laid to rest alongside of her husband and my father. (As we stood on the deck, July 8, Mother asked me to bring back a pair of the warm woollen house slippers and she said, "*Nicht vergess' nummer 6.*" In Bremen I bought the slippers on our return journey and they were placed with her when she was laid to rest.)'

For a month afterwards he could think about nothing but the freshly-dug grave. He visited it every day, throwing himself upon the mound of earth as if physical proximity might restore contact with his mother. Bess said that a certain youthful joyousness disappeared from him then, never to return.

Why was Houdini so obsessed by his mother? Why just him, and none of his several brothers? That he was so can hardly be in doubt. Erich Fromm's description of the mother-fixated man might have been written with Houdini in mind:

> Mother-fixated men . . . are usually quite affectionate and in a qualified sense 'loving,' but they are also quite narcissistic. The feeling that they are more important to mother than father is makes them feel that they are 'wonderful,' and since they are already 'father,' they are already grown up and need not do anything in reality to establish their greatness; they are great because – and as long as – mother (or her substitute) loves them exclusively and unconditionally. As a result they tend to be extremely jealous – they must keep their unique position – and they are simultaneously insecure and anxious whenever they have to perform a real task; while they might not fail, their actual performance can never really equal their narcissistic conviction of superiority over any man (while having at the same time a nagging, unconscious feeling of inferiority to all).

Clearly Mrs Weiss's Ehrich could not offer her or receive from her the sexual and emotional fulfilment which she had enjoyed with his father, and to which their numerous children and her sadness at Rabbi Weiss's death bore testimony. So he looked elsewhere – to the world of make-believe. The happiest moments of Houdini's life had been those when, together, he and his mother had shared the fulfilment of some fairytale fantasy. There was the time when he had dressed her in the Queen's dress and thrown a royal reception for her in Budapest. There was the occasion when, as a young boy, he had brought home the rent ('Shake me, I'm magic!'); and the not dissimilar occasion when he had emptied his shower of gold into her apron: both characterised as 'the happiest day of my life'.

Now it was as if that life had lost its mainspring. Houdini's real life was in his act. And that act and the fascinating power which lay behind it were intimately related to his mother fixation.

There is general agreement among the many psychologists who have discussed Houdini that inside this conspicuously brave man was a conspicuously frightened man. In order to face life at all he had to prove to himself again and again that he could overcome his deepest fear: the fear of being separated from his mother, as he had been so brutally when he was born. This fear must, logically, have been the background to his entire life. At least one school of psychoanalytic thought sees birth, that earliest of all separations, as the causation of all the neuroses.

Houdini, characteristically, was especially direct in the expression of his neuroses. His dearest wish was to return to the safety and security of life with his mother, and above all, to the safest and securest place of all: right inside her. He always particularly enjoyed laying his head upon her breast 'in order to hear her heart beat. Just [one of the] little peculiarities that mean so much to a mother and son when they love one another as we did.' The mother's heartbeat is of course the pervading sound heard by the foetus in the womb: recordings of it have a soothing effect upon young babies.

His act was a constant evocation of this ideal spot. Womb-like containers filled with water were at its centre. Shut inside them, with no exit apparent, he re-enacted again and again the moment of his birth. The trauma of his entry into life consti-tuted, paradoxically, his drama of death. He clipped a report about three American murderers 'Sealed up for Life in a Mexican dungeon . . . A bottle-shaped cell, about ten feet in diameter at the bottom and twenty feet high, has been cleared of the accumulated rubbish of years for [their] reception.' What was that but some enormous womb, the prison of his dreams?

Birth is just the first of many separations which must be endured and accommodated on the path to adult life. Houdini, in this sense, fell at the first fence. His precarious equilibrium needed constant reinforcement. The repeated re-enactment and overcoming of his besetting fear – that he would not survive separation from his mother; the almost daily demonstrations that he was literally a superman, immune to all the bonds and physical limitations which generally beset mere humans – barely sufficed to reassure him. Everyone who lived or worked with him knew how easily he was upset. He was always certain that any joke, even the mildest, was part of some plot to make him look a fool. Towards the end of his life, when his position was unassailable, when he was rich, famous, and on visiting terms with the President of the United States, he agreed to edit a weekly supplement to a Brooklyn paper which would be called *Red Magic* (it was soon abandoned). Since he was extremely busy it was clear that he would do little more than lend his name to this: the real work would have to be done by others. There happened at that time to be a young man working for the paper by the name of Hugh Deeny. The editor, thinking Houdini might appreciate the joke, sent young Deeny along to offer what help he could. But when he arrived at the Houdini house and announced himself, the great man's first reaction was to throw him out and shut the door in his face. It was only after repeated and prolonged pleadings that he accepted that this was the young man's real name, not some malicious practical joke, and agreed to let him do the work he had been assigned to. But he could never bear to call him anything but Murphy.

His team knew that his angry outbursts must be ignored, for their sake and for his, since next day they would be forgotten. But in other circumstances his anger was not so quick to vanish. He was always ready to pick a quarrel with anyone he saw as infringing upon his copyright. He saw insults everywhere and remembered them indefinitely. For years he nursed a bitter grudge against Dr Archie Wilson, editor of *The Sphinx*, a magical magazine. Acquaintances had to choose between them. 'Some time ago I wrote you that a certain Dr Wilson was a bitter enemey of mine and that if you wished to take your choice, as to which one you wanted as friend, you had that right,' he informed a fellow magician, Ottakar Fischer. 'As you have seen fit to accept his friendship by writing for his paper, which it still is, although you try to tell me different, you can consider our years of friendship at an end and I trust you will have the good sense NEVER TO WRITE TO ME OR APPROACH ME IN CASE I PLAY YOUR CITY NEXT SEASON.' Fischer was an old friend who had been 'the very able Viennese correspondent' of the *Conjurer's Magazine*. But he was a friend no longer. In 1915 Houdini and Dr Wilson were reconciled (by Martinka, who engineered a meeting in his famous New York magic shop, a point of call for all magicians). They liked each other enormously and much regretted the lost years of what could have been friendship. The origin of the quarrel was lost in the mists of time. Nevertheless, Houdini continued to bear his grudge against Ottakar Fischer: it lasted for the rest of his life. In 1925, he was still seeing slights in every mention Fischer made of him. 'Have no desire to write to him, he having elected to slight me years ago and an explanation in order from him for that incident,' he wrote indignantly to Harry Price. These things, for Houdini, were not open to reason. They came from somewhere much deeper and darker than that.

For several months following her death, Houdini could think of nothing but his mother. It was now that he adopted the birthday she had preferred for him – April 6th – rather than his real birthday, March 24th: 'It hurts me to think I cant talk it over with Darling Mother and as SHE always wrote me on April 6th, that will be my adopted birthdate.' He visited her grave daily. He had her letters, which he had saved since

1900, transcribed into good German and typed up so that he could read them more easily. He had the clock which he had given her stopped at the hour of her death. He had cards printed with her photo and the legend 'If God ever permitted an Angel to walk the earth in human form, it was my Mother.' He referred to these as his 'mother cards', and sent them to friends whose own mothers were unwell or had died. He ordered new writing-paper, thickly bordered with black – 'This is my new letterhead, and it was not with gladness that I ordered same.'

He became apathetic about everything unconnected with his mother. For the first time in his life he, who had always been such a compulsive worker, lost interest in his act. 'I never knew what it was to shirk work, until one morning I awoke July 17th and (1913) found that my Mother had departed . . . since then I "loaf" in some of my work.' To Dash he wrote: 'Dash, I knew that I loved Mother, but that my very existence seems to have expired with HER, is simply writing my innermost thoughts . . . With all my efforts, I try and still my lounging, as I know positively that Mother would not like the way she Passing Away has effected me, but what can I do.' He brooded endlessly upon her last moments – those last moments which he had not been there to witness. She had tried to say something at the end. What could it have been? Dash seemed to think that it had been 'Forgive . . .'. What or who was there that needed forgiving? Houdini himself, perhaps: he had been far away performing when his mother needed him most. But this was not a thought it was possible to entertain.

'Time heals all Wounds, but a long time will have to pass before it will heal the terrible blow which MOTHER tried to save me from knowing,' he wrote Dash that November. The nature of this blow remains unclear. But it seems to have to do with a marital muddle which enabled Houdini finally to assign elsewhere the unbearable burden of responsibility for his mother's death.

This was eventually saddled upon his youngest brother Leopold, who was always known as 'Dr Weiss' but who was in fact a radiologist. Leopold was living with Sadie Weiss, the estranged wife of his brother Nathan, the second eldest of Cecilia's children. Nat was a rather unsuccessful businessman. If his diary is anything to go by, Houdini never had much time for him, although he had been fond of Sadie, while he and Leopold were very good friends. Leopold's consulting rooms were located, at least until 1913, in Houdini's house at 278 W. 113th Street. And in fact it seems that for some considerable time after 1913 they remained good friends. On 16 July 1915, two years after Cecilia's death, Leopold joined Houdini and Dash on a trip to Asbury Park to visit the scene of the tragedy. Nor did Houdini apparently disapprove of Sadie's behaviour: Nat had found another girlfriend, and, writing about the situation to Dash, Houdini remarked (in January 1914), 'I hope [Nat] gets divorced'. Eventually he did; and Sadie and Leopold took advantage of the event to marry.

It was at this point, in 1917, that Houdini's wrath descended upon Leopold. Apparently arbitrarily – for their behaviour was no worse, and arguably more acceptable than it had been hitherto – both Sadie and Leopold were dismissed to outer darkness. There was an old family photograph, taken in 1909, commemorating a trip Mrs Weiss and Bess's mother Mrs Rahner had made together to Europe, to visit Bess and Houdini who were playing there. Leopold was also in London at that time, and the photo showed all five of them. Now Houdini took the photograph and, with a pair of scissors, cut off his brother's head. On the back he wrote: 'This is the picture from which Houdini later cut off his brother's picture, because he thot that an act of the brother had hastened his mother's death.' The picture has been frequently reproduced: the mutilated figure of Leopold is invariably airbrushed out.

Like Ottakar Fischer, Leopold was never forgiven. But blood was thicker than water, or at any rate family blood was thicker than the unrelated product. In his will (dated 20 July 1924) Houdini made his feelings quite clear: 'It is my express desire, intention and direction that no part of either the principal or income of my Estate shall ever directly or indirectly go to Sadie Glantz Weiss, the divorced wife of my brother Nathan Joseph Weiss and the present wife of my brother Doctor Leopold David Weiss.' Nor was Leopold to receive anything 'unless his present wife, the divorced wife of my brother Nathan . . . shall have died'. Even should that occur, Leopold was excluded from the ultimate benefit in Houdini's gift. His name did not appear upon the list of those entitled to be buried in the family plot at Machpelah Cemetery. As to the nature of the original crime, that was lost in the mists of Houdini's fantasy – where it had originally taken shape. Perhaps the crime was Sadie's, in preferring Leopold to Harry when she left the disreputable Nat. It seems improbable that it was ever formulated with any distinctness.

Life, however, had to go on. As Houdini was constantly aware, his income depended on his continuing to work. By September 1913 he was back in Germany. Early in 1914 he wrote: 'From what I can find out we will with the Will of God return to America June 17th possibly on the Imperator. Hope to be able to get a few contracts so that I can work America though it does not seem so important to me now as it did before God called for Ma.'

The *Imperator* trip in fact provided one of the few highlights of this period of his life. Among the other passengers was Theodore Roosevelt, whose acquaintance Houdini determined to make. He succeeded in doing so by a spectacular coup which delighted and mystified the great man. On the second day out Houdini was asked to act as spirit medium and answer questions from the passengers. His 'control' was W. T. Stead, the famous journalist and enthusiast for spiritualism, who had recently been lost on the *Titanic*. Colonel Roosevelt, who was returning from an exploring trip to South America, asked 'Stead' to trace on a sheet of paper the path of his journey – about which nothing had as yet been published. Using a slate, 'Stead' reproduced the exact map of the travels in question.

Roosevelt was understandably astounded. He told Houdini it was the most amazing thing he had ever seen. They were photographed together on deck, together with several other passengers. Houdini later had the photograph reproduced with the other passengers airbrushed out.

In an article, Houdini revealed how he had done this trick, which he described as 'really nothing more or less than a case of practical forehandedness on my part'.

> I was about to sail from London for America, and learned at the ticket office that Colonel Roosevelt was to be a fellow-passenger, although no public announcement had been made of the fact. Figuring things out in advance, I foresaw the customary request from an entertainment committee of passengers for a performance from me on board ship, and I also realized that Colonel Roosevelt would be the dominating presence in the audience. I therefore resolved to work up something which would involve some recent activity of his.
>
> It so happened that he was returning at that time from his trip of exploration in South America with the announcement of the discovery of the River of Doubt. He had given – privately – a map of his explorations to a famous London newspaper and it was to be published three days after the steamer had sailed. No one, with the exception of Colonel Roosevelt and one or two others, knew the details of the map. I, therefore, determined to get a copy.
>
> I will not tell you how I managed to secure this copy, but I can say that it is always easy to get people to assist one in a trick. They feel that they are being 'let in on the ground floor,' and will practice all kinds of deceits to which they are unaccustomed by nature, simply for the sake of being one of the few in a large crowd who are 'in' on the thing. It is a human failing which I have seldom been unable to make use of . . . So it was that I got a copy of Colonel Roosevelt's map.

It remained to manoeuvre Roosevelt into asking his question. This again was a matter of psychology. All that was really needed was to engineer a situation where the audience put up questions for Houdini to answer. Roosevelt would certainly be one of those who did so; and this, or something related to it, would almost certainly be the question he would ask.

Back in New York, Houdini found it impossible to take up the threads of his old life. He could not bear to live in West 113th Street, where everything was associated with his mother. On 25 August he announced that he and Bess were moving to Dash's house in Flatbush. It is not known what Dash thought of this arrangement. He had a wife and two children of his own, and, even allowing for Houdini's frequent absences, the move can hardly have been very convenient for them. But Dash had always been ruled by Houdini – not surprisingly, since his livelihood consisted of imitating him slavishly. No doubt Houdini did not hesitate to remind Dash of this if the need ever arose. So the Houdinis and their voluminous baggage stayed in Flatbush for three and a half years, until in February 1918, he moved back: it was reported that Harry Houdini had bought a Manhattan home at 278 West 113th Street and that the move from Flatbush had required two vans to transport his magic curios, automata and other conjuring paraphernalia, plus four more for his library and collection of rare manuscripts.

This Flatbush interlude was for Houdini a period of half-life. It was as if he considered himself in all important respects already dead. He knew exactly what his grave – or its tombstone – would be like, because he was busy having it made. The plot at the Machpelah Cemetery which now housed the bones of his mother, father and brother Herman was intended for the whole family, but – literally above all – himself. Jewish tradition dictates that a tombstone is erected on the grave a year after the funeral. I do not know what memorial if any had been erected to Rabbi Weiss or his son, but once Cecilia had joined them, Houdini commissioned a design which exceeded the statutory year as greatly as it exceeded the average family tomb. In 1916 it was reported that a sculptor had been toiling for a year to produce 'last resting places for Houdini's father and mother . . . It has taken over two years of constant work to construct and place the Exedra in position and there is yet six months to a year's work ahead to complete it. The Exedra weighs more than 50,000 pounds and 1,000 tons of Berry Vermont granite were used in the setting and building. Each piece is cut from solid stone. Of the original block of fifteen tons required for the seat only eight remain in the finished product. The check stones each were ten tons in the block but only five remain. So a great deal of granite was hewn away to make this odd Exedra.'

The Exedra is a sort of semicircular granite wall with a step or bench against which (in strict defiance of the Jewish custom forbidding statuary) kneels a weeping stone female figure. In the centre is a block reading WEISS in large letters. This was finally unveiled in October 1916. After Houdini's death a central pillar was added, completing the design, topped with a large portrait bust with HOUDINI inscribed on its base in even larger letters.

Houdini took a good deal of pleasure in controlling the dispositions of this final home in which he so vividly pictured himself. He ruthlessly dictated who was and who was not to be buried there. Leopold and Sadie, the guilty couple, were out. The rest of his brothers and sisters would be welcome, but none of their husbands, wives or offspring. The only exception was made for Bess.

It is clear that this extraordinary construction and the arrangements concerning it were a form of therapy for Houdini in his desperation. One function of any tomb is to comfort survivors. Elaborate tombs help them bear their loss by letting them make various expenditures and symbolic substitutions which compensate for that loss. Nothing less than this palace among tombs would have sufficed for Houdini's mother. Moreover, its design and construction placed him in the delightful situation of being able to preside over his own obsequies even though he was still nominally alive. He could thus ensure that his own tomb would be grandiose enough to satisfy even himself.

*

The death of his mother, not surprisingly, raised tricky questions regarding his relations with Bess. Still with his mind firmly ensconced in the grave beside his mother, he set out elaborate arrangements regarding Bess's conduct in the event of his death, evidently determined to control her life as firmly after his decease as he did in the flesh:

> January First 1916
> First letter this year
>
> My Darling Sweetheart,
>   Just a few important instructions, after our conversation, in case I die first.
>   If it enters your mind to once again enter the 'bonds' of wedlock, I want you to be able to protect yourself from any one who may marry you simply for the money that is left to you.
>   Make whoever it is **sign away his marriage right in everything, otherwise do not marry him.**
>   If he will give you as an argument that you do not trust him, it is evident that he does not deserve to be trusted.
>   Under no circumstances what so ever, marry any one who will not sign away the marriage potion, as they will have half of everything I worked and slaved for, suffered and went hungry and sleepless nights to earn.
>   . . . I ask you from my tomb **to protect yourself**, then I will be able to sleep easy and know that I have succeeded in helping you to a restful and happy old age. I know you will miss me, but sweetheart never grieve for me, for I am through, my ascent is settled, and if you will only enjoy life that is my request.
>   Save this letter and read it when anyone comes to you for any of the above motives.
>   I am wishing you a Happy New Year, for I am herewith in a position to do so.

Who was this letter intended to benefit? A Houdini enthusiast I discussed it with feels it shows a tender regard for Bess and her welfare. But it doesn't strike me that way. Houdini is the only person whose interests are consulted here. He wants to make quite sure that 'everything I worked and slaved for' doesn't end up in the hands of some unworthy fellow. He wants to be certain that Bess, after his death, will continue to play the role he has allotted her in the strange drama she entered when she married him. He evidently regarded this letter as particularly important and satisfactory. He frequently re-read it and countersigned it: 'Have re-read this June 2 1918 and found it to my desire. Re-read Feb 26 1921. Re-read May 1926.'

But he was not yet dead; and his mother's death meant he had to rethink his relations with those living women who were close to him. These were the kinds of question he had tried to pre-empt with that abrupt marriage twenty years before. He tried to work out his feelings in a curious letter centred, like almost everything he did or wrote at this time, upon two deaths – his mother's and his own:

Monday Feb 15 1915   11.30 a.m.

It is my wish that all of my Darling Beloved Mothers letters also the 2 enclosed letters, shall be placed in a sort of black bag, and used as a pillow for my head in my coffin, and all to be buried with me.

The two letters, one that I wrote to Ma before my marriage and the love letter from my dearest wife, all can be buried with me, and they are of no use to anyone. My wife may read the letters if she desires, and then let her place them under my head.

I have loved two women in my time, my MOTHER God bless her memory and my wife.

My sister I love, so when I mention two women she need not think think that I do not love her [added later:] I love her as very darling sister. My actions in the past has proven that I hope.

With the jewelry found Bess should keep it a year and then do what she likes with same [added:] the big jewel I bot in England, give to my sister Gladys. June 13 1915 (All attended to re this as you Bess gave it to Gladys. HH)

Harry Houdini
Ehrich Weiss
also Sept 27 1916
OK HH Feb 26 1921

Bess herself was merely a bit player in this welter of brood-
ing and grieving. How can she have felt? Presumably she was
by now used to Houdini's curiously impersonal style when he
was supposedly addressing her on the most intimate matters.
Had he ever achieved anything more relaxed in the course of
day-to-day communication over twenty years?

Mrs Weiss's death had removed Bess's chief rival for Houdini's affections – although there must have been moments,
during his violent and prolonged mourning, when she felt that
it had also claimed her husband, totally and irretrievably. Who
can compete with a memory? Nevertheless, it was at this point
that he began writing Bess daily love-letters, a practice he kept
up until his own death. He would leave them around the house
for her to find: 'Good morning, my *handsome* sweet wife –
Houdini [this was a very ornate signature] – the rare signature
only found on his cheek and his heart letters to his *wife*'.

As usual, these notes, with their curiously public style (as
if they had been written to be read aloud in his defence, perhaps
on the occasion of the Last Judgment), catered to Houdini's
needs rather than Bess's. What they conveyed was Houdini's
total emotional dependence upon Bess now that his mother
had gone. He had to be sure that she would always be there
to supply the uncritical support he craved – a need which
extended to the grave and beyond.

These letters from the dead – these notes, as it were, from
underground – resemble nothing so much as the kind of letters
which are often written by intending suicides. In November
1913 he noted in his diary (he was then playing the Alhambra,
Paris): 'Am doing needle trick and U.S.D. Doing very big.
Am very melancholy.' Suicide was much on his mind. In

December he took Bess to Monte Carlo. He needed a rest, and gambling had always diverted him. He felt like losing some money. Instead, he won: five hundred francs on his first visit to the casino, fifteen hundred the second time. So he abandoned the casino and spent most of the rest of his time in the place that most answered his mood – the suicides' graveyard. It was the only part of the trip he described in detail. He took his usual lively technical interest in details relating to death and burial:

> Dismal day. Visited graveyard where all suicides are buried. Persons who had lost their money and then committed suicide. A terrible feeling pervades the first time one sees the graves, and thinks of the human beings who finish their lives in this manner.
>
> More suicides in winter than in summer. Casino now pays return fares to losers, makes them sign papers, etc., and even ships bodies to their home towns to keep things quiet. When a body is found, money is stuffed in the pockets to cause the belief that money affairs did not cause the deed.
>
> Suicides are buried for seven years, then dug up, placed in boxes and saved in this manner for future reference in case relatives wish to take bodies away . . . Saw grave of man and wife who committed suicide together.

The first crisis passed, but two years later, death and his mother were still uppermost in his mind. 'When you say your Mother's word is sacred, I envy you still having your Mother, for I lost mine 23 months ago, and Time has NOT healed the terrible wound, in fact it has caused my hair to turn white . . . I take the liberty of enclosing one of my Mother cards. Never forget her birthday or the holidays, for Time will call some time when you least expect it . . . I only work six months a year since I lost my Mother, and that is all I ever expect to do for some time to come.'

Why, feeling like this, did Houdini not actually commit suicide? Death was an old prepossession, almost an old acquaintance. The temptation – given his opportunities – must have been very great.

Sublimation is one partial answer. Artists are able to deal with destructive and self-destructive feelings by diverting them into their art; and Houdini was an artist of death. But this does not prevent them from eventually committing suicide just the same. Edgar Allan Poe and Yukio Mishima both shared Houdini's imaginative preoccupations, and both expressed them through their art to overwhelming effect. But this successful sublimation of their terrors did not prevent them from killing themselves in reality as well as the imagination. Poe drank himself to death, which may be seen as a particularly protracted and painful form of self-destruction. For Mishima, his suicide was – or was intended to be, for it was terribly botched – the culmination of his life and art.

But their dramas were centred only upon death. Resurrection had no place in them. For Houdini, however, it had always been the central thing. He could not kill himself because he was too used to saving himself. The reflex had become so strong that it was in the end impossible to resist. In a sense, he committed suicide thousands of times. Louis J. Bragman, one of the earliest of Houdini's psychological devotees, remarks that 'almost every stunt staged by Houdini represented a form of pseudo-suicide'. But the whole point was that Houdini's suicides did not end in his death, but in his miraculous survival.

Nevertheless, after his mother's death, his stunt-dramas, which had always been fairly dangerous, became truly terrifying. The last limits seemed to have been kicked away. It appeared that there was nothing he would not risk, nominally in order to get publicity, but in fact to act out his own despair. It was now that he began to do straitjacket escapes while hung by his ankles from the top of skyscrapers. Although this position facilitated the escape, the stunt held a number of dangers apart from that of falling head-first to the ground. 'A number of times his body, held taut by the strait-jacket, was swung towards the building by the wind, while a murmur of fear arose from the crowd,' ran one account. 'A minute, two minutes passed, and the crowd roared. Houdini's body, held rigid by the strait-jacket, was beginning to move. Slowly, but surely, the man who has startled the entire world by his feats and by his magic, began to work himself free from the instrument of torture. The wind continued to swing his body back and forth as it hung suspended by the feet in mid-air. Again the wind swung him towards the building, but once more he narrowly escaped being dashed against the brick wall. A roar from the crowd and the strait-jacket slowly floated to the ground!! He was free!!! Houdini waved his hands to the cheering crowd as he was lowered to the street again. Although the temperature was rather low, he was perspiring freely when he was released from the ropes that bound his ankles.'

The routine was that he would seek out the leading newspaper of whatever city he happened to be playing and arrange to do the dive from their building. This ensured that his picture would make the front pages and his name would be on the lips of the entire population, a large proportion of which would flock to his show.

In Pittsburg, the crowd 'not only packed the streets but filled every window and rooftop within view of the scene', reported the *Sun*.

> . . . Urbane, smiling, the elusive Houdini appeared in the office . . . at 12 o'clock. The two attendants from Mayview [insane hospital] awaited him, and with them the strait-jacket, in a satchel. Houdini shook hands with both men, speaking humorously of his position as substitute for the deranged persons the two Attendants ordinarily handle . . . 'Treat me,' he advised, smiling, 'as you would the most dangerous of the criminal insane.'
>
> . . . It was almost 12.30 o'clock. Houdini glanced out of the window, and again his characteristic, quiet smile came to his face as he saw Wood street and Liberty avenue congested from wall to wall . . .
>
> Then, a white-clad attendant on each side, he went downstairs to the street to be bound. A suppressed shout came from the crowd as he appeared in the doorway of the Sun building . . . Above him, like a gallows, a single beam projected from a window at the top story of the building, and

a rope swung clear, coiling in sinister fashion at his feet. Houdini had removed the outer clothing from the upper part of his body. 'Ready,' he said.

The two attendants pressed close. His arms were inserted in the long, closed sleeves of the straitjacket. One of the attendants clasped him about the body, as if fearing he would make some mad effort to escape. The other standing behind him, fastened strap after strap . . . 'Make it tight,' came the quiet word from the prisoner.

The man's knees went up for purchase in the small of Houdini's back. Using apparently every ounce of strength in his broad-shouldered six-foot body, the attendant drew the big strap through the buckle until it would not yield even a sixteenth of an inch more. He caught it there and made it fast.

Then the arms of the prisoner were crossed over his body, and the ends of those closed sleeves were brought around in back. Again the knee was brought into use. Again the strap was pulled to its highest tension . . . Then Houdini's ankles were fastened to the rope, by a special appliance that prevented injury, but insured safety.

A word was spoken. The two attendants seized the bound man's body. Workmen drew the rope steadily through the pulleys. Houdini's feet went up, and as his body cleared the platform it was released. The handcuff king dangled head downward. Each moment he was drawn higher, swaying slightly, spinning dizzily . . . Then he hung still.

Only for a second. While watchers gleamed in the crowd below, the handcuff king was seen to struggle, not frantically, but with a steady systematic swelling and contracting of muscles, and almost imperceptible lithe wrigglings of the torso. The struggle went on. One minute – two – then three –

Would he do it? . . . From above came an inarticulate shout. The muffled arms writhed one after another over Houdini's head. His hand, still encased in the sleeves of the straitjacket, fumbled quickly and effectively with the buckles at his back. Another contortion and the straitjacket slipped down over his chest, over his head and was flung from his arms to the street, in a crumpled heap.

Once again he had succeeded. Once again he had failed. That was November 1916. It was the culmination of a long tour. In September 1915, 'the greatest street throng in the history of Los Angeles' – 20–25,000 people – had seen him swing from the Los Angeles *Tribune* building. The same month, 5,000 saw him in Kansas City, where the tie-in was with the Kansas City *Post*. The following April 50,000 watched him in Baltimore; the same month, he repeated the stunt in Washington, D.C. In San Antonio, Texas, 12,000 gathered to see him plunge from the San Antonio *Express* building. He gave an interview there in his dressing-room in the Majestic Theater. 'I don't know how long this thing can last,' he said. 'I have given myself from one to eight years, and that's a liberal estimate. I am now forty-two years of age. I feel like I am fifty-two years, and some of the time much older – just as I do this afternoon. I have been told that it is hardening of the arteries. Perhaps it is. Whatever it is I am getting old and yet I have no particular regrets. Some time or another we all grow tired. I have been tired for a long time.'

13

Film Star

Houdini knew exactly how he would go over Niagara Falls in a barrel. Or rather: how he would 'go over Niagara Falls in a barrel' – a very different thing. People *have* gone over Niagara Falls in a barrel and lived – the first, incredibly enough, was a schoolmistress in her forties – but that was not what Houdini was proposing. 'The idea,' he wrote, 'is to be nailed in a packing case, thrown over Niagara Falls, and eventually make an escape!'

> So that the crowd can see I am being nailed into the packing case, the nailing is done on a platform, into which I can slide after the box is nailed up.
> The best way would be to have the platform on a large wagon, which is drawn down to the landing place, where I get into the water according to opportunity.
> Or else get back into the box when placed on wagon, and be found there, having failed to escape (being 'knocked out' coming over falls.)
> This can be worked into an extra good idea and needs doing some time.

The nearest he actually came to realising this 'extra good idea' was on film. In *The Man From Beyond* the heroine, who is unwisely canoeing in the Niagara River, finds herself drifting helplessly towards the falls. She is rescued in the nick of time by Houdini, the eponymous Man from Beyond. This is one of the more effective scenes in the Houdini movies. As *Variety* put it, 'It has a whale of a punch.' In *The World*, Quincy Martin 'quivered at the views of the couple battling in the rapids on the verge of the cataract and almost cheered when they made the crawl to safety'. The *Tribune* asserted that: 'There is no fake about this: Houdini actually does it.'

Really? Movies are not about *live* suspense. Film suspense, as every Hitchcock devotee knows, is created in the cutting-room. Cary Grant was never in any real danger from that aeroplane in *North By North-West*. What would have been the point? What use to a film is a dead film-star, or even a disabled one?

Nevertheless, 'It was said later,' Milbourne Christopher reports in the tone of one who reveals a shameful secret, 'that dummies had been used for some shots.' And why ever not? Houdini and his director would have been out of their minds if they had not used dummies, or safety-lines, for this scene. But of course the answer is obvious. The Houdini legend was founded upon live risk. To acknowledge anything else would fatally undermine it. And the Houdini legend was what was going to sell the movies. In other words, everything Houdini was about was in direct opposition to everything movie-making was about. It was a fatal contradiction, and he never resolved it.

Houdini went into movies because it was clear that something new had to be pulled out of the bag. He was getting older. He could not spend the rest of his life hanging off tall buildings in straitjackets. No stunt has eternal drawing-power. The public quickly gets blasé and demands something even more spectacular. Imitators spring up. And although he still missed his mother terribly, time dulls the edge of even the keenest grief. He no longer felt so suicidal. By 1918 he could bear to move back into his own house. He had by now a large staff to support, as well as an ever-growing library to house and feed. All this cost money. Houdini was always one for the coming thing: and movies were the coming thing, just as vaudeville was quite obviously on its way out. In 1908, the Kinetograph, showing 'Interesting and Humorous Motion Pictures' – an international cross-country run in England and a melodrama, 'And the Villain Still Pursued Her', with musical accompaniment – had followed Houdini, who had the next-to-last star spot, as just another vaudeville attraction in the Keith Theater circuit. In 1927, following the overwhelming success of Al Jolson in *The Jazz Singer,* the Keith-Orpheum circuit wound up its theatre interests and joined with the Radio Corporation to form the RKO film company.

The fact that films were potentially a far greater draw than vaudeville had been obvious to the future Hollywood moguls for years. Many of them had started in show business by opening vaudeville arcades 'filled', as Jesse Lasky remembered, 'with automatic fortune tellers, strength testers and other fascinating gadgets'. The gadgets also included movie peep-shows. And 'a row of movie peep-box dispensers of thirty-second dramas was collecting the steadiest stream of coins'. William Fox had a similar experience with the burlesque theatre he acquired in Williamsburg, Brooklyn, in 1906. Fox's theatre combined movies and vaudeville at popular prices – fifty cents for the most expensive seats, ten cents for the cheapest. In 1911 he decided to do some audience research, and sent out ten thousand cards requesting his customers to say what part of the performance they liked best. 'Fifty-five percent of the answers were in favor of moving pictures,' he told an interviewer. 'Interest in "comedy scenes" and "heart interest" photoplays seems to be about equally divided. Instructive pictures showing countries and their manufacturing industries are appreciated most in the poorer districts. But everywhere it is the pictures, more than the vaudeville acts, that hold the audiences. The only explanation I can find is that motion pictures, perhaps, realize the American idea of speed and activity.'

The Jews were able to take over the moving picture industry because it was not respectable. Movies were 'toys' or 'peephole sensations', and old money, gentile money, would have nothing to do with them. At best they were a fad, at worst, a moral embarrassment. Respectable finance refused to touch them or to recognise that this was where new money was to be made. First-generation Jewish immigrants, however, suffered from no such inhibitions. They were alert to any new business opportunities. As a rule, the route led from the Lower East Side to the garment trade. Marcus Loew was in velveteen capes; Adolph Zukor made his pile in furs; Carl Laemmle was a clothing salesman in Oshkosh. The garment trade made them prosperous. They were looking for new outlets for their energies, and they saw that vaudeville arcades, moving picture theatres and burlesque theatres had enormous business potential. They quickly realised that the movie business was far more interesting than garments. Of his first venture into the new field, an arcade called Automatic Vaudeville which was never meant to be more than a sideline to the fur business, Zukor wrote: 'Our fur offices were nearby in Twelfth Street and, though handling the main end there, I couldn't keep away from the arcade.' They began by smartening up the theatres, in order to change the movies' sleazy image into something respectable the whole family could enjoy. Laemmle called his first theatre the White Front – the cleanest image he could conjure up. They financed all this themselves, bringing in friends and family when they wanted to expand. (Hence the famous Hollywood rhyme: *Uncle Carl Laemmle/Has a very big faemmle*.) Then they went into distribution, supplying their own chains of movie theatres. Production was the last, logical link in the chain.

It was Zukor who realised that the barrier movies had to overcome was not artistic, but psychological. By 1908 he had perceived 'that these short films, one-reelers or less, didn't give me the feeling that this was something that was going to be permanent'. For something permanent, he needed to be able to attract a middle-class as well as a working-class audience: films would have to be weightier – longer, and better. 'You couldn't head him', recalled his associate at the time, William Brady. 'Presently he was in my office bubbling over with grandiose ideas about the future of the movie racket. Some sixth sense had convinced him that the day of mere shorts was drawing to a close and full-length features, like *The Great Train Robbery*, only far longer and far better, could be the coming thing . . . It didn't make sense to me then . . . Zukor was about the only living human being who could guess what would happen.'

And soon it was happening. In 1913 F. E. Powell, a well-known magician and a good friend of Houdini's, reported from Cuba to the magical magazine *M.U.M.* regarding the writing plainly visible to him on the wall. The 'movies', he said, 'now almost monopolize the best houses to the exclusion of the legitimate. The moving picture business has extended to an amazing degree, and the increase of theatres in all parts of the island is marvelous.'

And yet it did not seem that Houdini was finished as a stage star. The years of World War I, which were also his years of despair at Flatbush, saw him at the height of his fame. Never had he received more publicity.

Not all of it showed him in a good light. In 1915, in Los Angeles, he had a set-to with the world heavyweight champion, Jess Willard. Hearing that Willard was in the audience at the Los Angeles Orpheum, he invited the boxer to come up onstage as one of the audience committee. Willard declined. Houdini would not take no for an answer. He turned the occasion into a contest of wills between himself and Willard. Willard, who was famously sulky and aggressive, was on a hiding to nothing. Houdini knew all about controlling his audience and getting it on his side. And in a public contest of this sort, it was never enough merely to make his point. He would never rest until his opponent was entirely destroyed.

This destruction was accomplished by means of a bludgeon, not a rapier. That was Houdini's mode; and that is the reason Houdini was and is not universally admired among connoisseurs of magic. 'I don't like his style', is the way one of them puts it. 'I don't like the way he rapes the audience.' Hearing the recording of his patter for the Water-Torture act, one is struck by this quality. There is nothing here of the silky charm or wit that is many magicians' stock-in-trade. Each phrase is punched out with shattering force.

But Willard, who was not a bright man (nor a particularly popular champion) was used to trading physical, not verbal blows. He continued to refuse Houdini's entreaties, and soon became insulting. The audience cheered Houdini's sallies and hissed Willard's furious replies. Houdini won. Willard finally slunk out of the theatre amid hisses from the audience. Next day the headlines were Houdini's: '2,000 HISS J. WILLARD, CHAMPION DRIVEN FROM THEATER BY HOOTS AND CALLS', reported the *Los Angeles Times*; and the next day it followed this up: 'WILLARD LEAVES TOWN, SNEAKS OUT OF TOWN AS INDIGNANT FANS ROAST HIS CONDUCT'. Houdini was jubilant. 'My Dear Sister Gladys', he wrote,

> Well, at last I manage to sit down and relate to you how I defeated the World Champion Heavyweight Pugilist Mr Jess Willard, and why the newspapers gave me the decision over him, which makes me the Newspaper Champion of the World.
>
> As usual I called for my committee during the course of my performance, and only seven men responded, so I stepped to the footlights and made a neat little speech, which you know is one of my favourite pastimes. I said that I would be highly honoured, and I thought the audience would likewise, if instead of three men, one who was equal to three would come up. 'I refer to Mr Jess Willard, our champion, who is here in the house.' . . . Willard glowered down upon me . . . 'Hey, you, go on wid the show – but if you pay me what youn pay those seven men who are on the stage, I'll come down.'
>
> The audience started to hiss and boo him.
>
> 'All right,' I said. 'I accept your challenge. Come right down and I'll pay you what I pay these seven men. Don't crawfish. Kindly step right downstairs and come on stage.'
>
> Audience applauds.
>
> Mr Jess Willard half arose and was going to crush me forever, blurting out in his guttural voice, 'Go on wid the show, you faker, you four-flusher. Everyone knows you're a four-flusher.'
>
> Hisses from the audience, and I walked right down to the footlights nearest his side . . . 'Look here, you. I don't care how big you are or who you are. I paid you a compliment when I asked you to be one of the committee. You have the

right to refuse, but you have no right to slur my reputation. Now that you have thrown down the gauntlet, I have the right to answer, and let me tell you one thing, and don't forget this, that I WILL BE HARRY HOUDINI WHEN YOU ARE NOT THE HEAVYWEIGHT CHAMPION OF THE WORLD.'

. . . Nothing like this howling mob of refined ladies and gentlemen ever crossed my vision of success . . .

The next night Willard was to referee a boxing match, but he was not allowed to appear.

Honest, Gladys, I have received at least a million dollars' advertising space from this fray.

(Willard had the last laugh, however. When he appeared at Hammerstein's Victoria Vaudeville Theater he was paid $4,000 a week to Houdini's $2,000. Evelyn Nesbit Thaw, presumably performing at the height of the Harry Thaw trial scandal (when her husband was arraigned for shooting her lover, Stanford White) received $3,500.)

In some ways, this might not have seemed the kind of publicity Houdini should be seeking. In his book *Handcuff Secrets* he was emphatic as to the importance of stage manners. 'Nothing is more offensive to an audience than a performer to appear surly and bad tempered. He is there to please the public, and to do so he must be on the best of terms with himself and, I may add, in the best of humour.'

But that had been written some years earlier; and with every year that passed Houdini was gaining confidence in his ability to control an audience. By now he had this down to a fine art. Audiences were an instrument which he had learned to play just as he wished. If misdirection was to succeed, nothing was more essential than complete mastery in this department:

Suppose I want to use a short flight of steps from the stage down to the audience. I never have a carpet on them, because while I am transferring a watch or producing an egg from a hat I tramp heavily, and so draw your attention to my feet. If I think the audience is watching me too closely, I signal my assistant to drop something, or to make some sudden movement. If I want a chair, table, or basket brought on the stage, and don't want you to see it, I simply walk to the opposite side of the stage . . . All magicians know that the average person never raises or lowers his eyes very much. Most people just look on a straight level. Therefore, whenever we use tables fitted up with magic devices, we always raise them slightly above the level of the eye, so that when you think you are looking at the top of the table you are not. Really to see the top you would have to raise your eyes; and as this would be an effort you just don't do it.

Two years later, another free publicity opportunity presented itself. Sarah Bernhardt, then touring the States, was to be honoured by the American acting profession. They gave her a grand reception at the Metropolitan Opera House, New York, and presented her with a bronze statuette which they had had especially designed and made for the occasion. Unfortunately nobody had thought to pay for the statuette; and its maker, having failed elsewhere, sent the bill – for $350 – to Bernhardt. She, understandably, returned the object forthwith. Houdini, reading about this, immediately stepped in, paid the bill and saved the day. Within a fortnight he had received 3,756 newspaper clippings, all praising his action and linking his name with Bernhardt's. A newspaper columnist, estimating the advertising at the reading-matter rate of a dollar a line, worked out the sums. Houdini had received publicity worth $56,340 for an outlay of $350.

Bernhardt was nearing the end of her long and illustrious career. She had recently had a leg amputated. This tour was by way of a proof (to herself and others) that she was nevertheless undiminished. But the proud façade which she maintained so stoically, with her family no less than with her audiences, cracked before Houdini. She had heard that he had magic powers. Could he not (she begged him) restore her leg?

'Good heavens, Madame, certainly not; you cannot be serious. You know my powers are limited and you are actually asking me to do the impossible.'

'Yes,' she said as she leaned closer to me, 'but you do the impossible.' . . .

'Are you jesting?'

'*Mais non, Houdini, j'ai jamais été plus sérieuse dans ma vie,*' she answered.

Alas poor Sarah! She had fallen for the line Houdini was always promoting, that 'secret' of his that stood him, in the mind of the audience, on the very edge of real magic. 'It is when you do the "impossible" that people sit up and gasp,' he wrote. 'That is why I do a different sensational trick every year.'

Now, when he was thinking about moving from escapes into conjuring proper, he came up with his two most famous such tricks.

The first was walking through a wall, first performed in 1913. The stage was covered with a seamless carpet. On to this was wheeled a steel framework which stood about two inches clear of the ground and was several feet high. A team of bricklayers came onstage and built a solid brick wall inside this framework. When this was finished, Houdini stood on one side of the wall. Screens were placed at either end, and the stage committee was strategically stationed to ensure that there would be no slipping round the back. Houdini would wave his hands over the screen on one side of the wall and shout, 'Here I am!' A minute would elapse. Then his hands would be seen waving over the other side: 'And here I am now!' The screens would be drawn away. And there he was on the other side of the wall.

When rumours spread in some quarters that Houdini was able to dematerialise, this was one of the feats that was cited to prove it. But the secret, as with many tricks, was childishly simple. The wall was built over a trapdoor in the stage. This was covered by the carpet. Although this was seamless, it had enough give to produce a hollow deep enough for Houdini to crawl through. Then the trapdoor would be shut and all was as before. The trick made a great sensation. But he never repeated it after its single season (handing it over to Hardeen, who took it to Europe), because there were squabbles over the trick's provenance and ownership, and the secret had begun to leak out.

His other great illusion was the Vanishing Elephant.

'People are much more interested in seeing things disappear than seeing them appear,' Houdini wrote at about this time. 'When you make things appear they say, "Oh, he had it on him all the time!" But when you make things disappear, they are amazed.' Vanishing rabbits were literally child's play; vanishing ladies were a cliché. But a vanishing elephant was something else. A vanishing elephant was there for the headline value.

The elephant was vanished in the Hippodrome, where Houdini had first wowed New York. The effect of the trick was heightened by the fact that everyone knew that, whatever might be happening, the elephant could not simply drop through a trapdoor into the space below the stage. The reason was that the Hippodrome stage was built over a pool which was used for water spectaculars.

So what did happen? The procedure was simple. A large 'cabinet' was pushed onstage, and the elephant was led into it. The blinds were dropped. The cabinet was then turned sideways by a dozen stagehands, and two circular panels were dropped, giving the spectators a view through the cabinet. Where was the elephant? (And where was its trainer?) Various wise guys based their guesses on the facts that a) an elephant lying down is considerably flatter than an elephant standing up, and b) the floor of the cabinet was slightly raised. Others remember the cabinet as having had a square, curtained opening in front through which, when the curtain was raised, one could see through the circular opening at the back to the rear of the stage. In this version the elephant could not have been concealed by lying down, but was standing at what was (after the turn had been made) the side of the cabinet, which was wider than the uncurtained aperture. Houdini always said his cabinet for the Vanishing Elephant was eight feet square; in fact it was larger than this, and he gave the wrong size to put audiences off the scent. At any rate, the cabinet, which had been wheeled on by a mere three or four assistants, needed the round dozen to wheel it off. None of this mattered. What mattered were the headlines. These were only increased by the fact that the original elephant, Fannie, hired from Ringling's Circus, proved stage-shy. Nothing would induce her to enter the theatre. (The suspicion was that Ringling was not entirely surprised to hear this.) So another elephant, Lucy, had to be found to replace her.

Vanishing elephants and melting walls were certainly sensational. But they were crude, if clever – effect, not finesse. They achieved their end, which was to draw the headlines. But in a way they underlined the gulf between what Houdini did and what more conventional magicians did. 'He was a stunt man,' said Walter Gibson, who wrote books for and about him, 'and was so regarded in his lifetime.' Stage magic was not the compulsive stuff upon which Houdini's reputation was founded. He would have to look for something else, and he knew it.

So the movies seemed like an obvious answer. Their star was in the ascendant. Their mode was melodrama. It seemed as if Houdini was made for the movies, and they for him. He began to collect helpful clippings: 'Chaplin – And How He Does It'; 'At Work With Charlie Chaplin'; 'Mrs Fiske to the Actor-In-The-Making'. In June 1918, he wrote to a friend: 'I have signed to play the star part of a big serial movie and twill take up all my time in six weeks, when the plot is finished. Will play Master Detective part as I believe.'

The Master Detective was called Quentin Locke (presumably an allusion to the star's well-known skills). Locke was locked in combat with a criminal corporation called International Patents Inc., whose base was the castle of a wicked tycoon. The castle was built on a cliff overlooking a stretch of water whose continuity was somewhat shaky: it was sometimes the sea, sometimes a river. International Patents' main business was the suppression of new inventions which might interfere with the business of various vested interests. The models of these inventions were stored in a cellar beneath the castle, The Graveyard of Genius. The films also featured the tycoon's beautiful and terrified daughter, Eva, and a monstrous steel robot known as The Automaton. Upon this basis was constructed a thirteen-part cliffhanger. In it, Locke-Houdini is repeatedly trapped in lethal situations and as repeatedly escapes from them. He is bound with barbed wire in the path of a stream of acid; he is tied with ropes and rolled under a freight elevator which is slowly descending to crush him; he is nailed into a box and tossed into the sea, or maybe the river . . . Old obsessions also reappeared: one of Locke's escapes is from an electric chair.

The plots were ludicrous and the acting wooden. Houdini had no idea of acting. All he had ever done was be himself. This had not merely sufficed: it had earned him an international reputation. So why should it not do for the movies?

There were of course various reasons, all to do with the differences between the movies and vaudeville. Feature films, however sensational, could not be sustained by a string of escapes. They needed plot and character to hold the audience. But Houdini's plots (which he insisted upon writing himself) were nothing more than a framework for the escapes, which indeed provide the films' only moments of tension and life. The films were to be the public's big chance to see *how he did it*: using the slack in ropes that he was always able to gain because he was slightly bow-legged; untying knots with his toes; snapping the weakened links in chains . . . Unfortunately, however, they did not produce the same mesmerising effect on film as in real life.

Will Dexter, in his book *This Is Magic*, mentions a television film about Houdini in which the actor playing Houdini flaps his cloak at an elephant 'and the great beast vanished. Just like that. WHOOF! And the elephant had gone.' This was done by camera trickery. But Houdini himself would never have contemplated such a cheat. All his filmed magic was for real, and so were the risks he took – or at least as real as any risks he ever took.

But two things were missing in the films which were always there in a live performance. One was the possibility of a disaster. The compelling shadow of death was never present in the films. The other, however much the star might protest, was the certainty that what you were watching was the genuine article. The question was almost irrelevant, because everyone knew it *could have been* faked. So the tension of a live show was not there.

All this might have been offset by adequate plotting or characterisation. But Houdini was not a writer nor an actor. He was a magician. Not that that need have prevented him from making excellent films. Georges Méliès, one of the greatest of early film-makers, was originally a magician. Many of his delightful two- and three-minute shorts are about magical illusion; and although they clearly involve camera trickery rather than prestidigitation, this is of no account. The films are enchanting in their own right. But film as a working medium held no interest for Houdini. Its only appeal was that it allowed him to reach a wider public.

Moreover, the particular format upon which he had alighted for *The Master Mystery*, and to which he stuck throughout his film career, was in important ways peculiarly unsuited to him. Houdini saw himself as a romantic hero, a cross between Tarzan and the Scarlet Pimpernel, whose mission was to rescue fragile heroines from nameless fates by thrilling feats of derring-do. This is the fundamental storyline of all his films, and it is the basis of all the stories which he continued to produce even when there was no more need for film scenarios and which were ghosted for him by various hands (notably H. P. Lovecraft's in *Weird Tales* magazine). As far as Houdini was concerned, this was evidently *the* story from which all other stories were mere aberrations. The only variations he introduced were those of background. Sometimes his hero was a Neanderthal figure (as in *Yar the Primeval Man*), sometimes a secret policeman, sometimes the frozen relic of another century

(*The Man From Beyond*). But he was always fundamentally the same person.

This storyline, if it was to carry conviction, inevitably necessitated a certain amount of masterful cuddling of the heroine by Houdini. Unfortunately this was something he could not bring himself to indulge in. He had made his gesture in the direction of the opposite sex in his once-for-all pounce upon Bess twenty years earlier, and had hidden thankfully behind the role of model husband ever since. But this was no help when it came to being a film star. The customers did not care whether or not film stars were faithful to their wives. They wanted to be vicariously swept away by Rudolph Valentino or, in the present instance, Quentin Locke. But Mr Locke would be unable to oblige if Houdini could not forget his inhibitions. And he could not. He would never touch his leading lady if Bess was not right there to see that he did nothing immoral. He insisted on paying her five dollars for every kiss that passed between himself and his leading ladies. Not many did; and even those were hardly worth the money. One distraught director, after a wasted morning spent vainly trying to persuade Houdini to put a bit of enthusiasm into a kiss, requested Bess to leave the lot. He said: 'Whenever we get him to the point of kissing the girl he spoils the shot by glancing anxiously at you.'

The Master Mystery was made by a company called B. A. Rolfe Productions. Its appeal, even when it was made, was pretty much as kitsch. But Houdini's name was a draw. It did not do badly – in fact it made a considerable amount of money – and the new star moved a step up the ladder. Jesse Lasky, who had just joined with Zukor to form Famous Players-Lasky, signed Houdini for two films.

Interestingly, he now proposed to turn for his scenarios to Edgar Allan Poe, whose obsessions so closely mirrored his own. But although he sensed the affinity between them, that deep and genuine pairing of morbid imaginations, he was characteristically unable to recognise its nature. 'His tales,' Houdini commented, 'contain the desired amount of mysticism, danger and opportunity for physical exertion.' So much for the dark terrors of Poe's ghastly fantasies. He went on: 'I am told out here in California, where I am working away at my scenarios and productions, that my act is bound to go well in the movies; so, if you hear that the Famous Players have made a small fortune during the year 1919, you will know at whose door to lay the credit for it.'

In the event Poe was spared the Houdini treatment. Houdini's first film for Lasky was called *The Grim Game*, and, like *The Master Mystery*, it was written by Arthur B. Reeve and John W. Gray, with copious help from the star. In it, he broke out of a gaol cell, climbed the outside of the building to reach a dangling rope, and used it to slide to the street. He was captured after a fight and, as one might expect, taken up to the roof of the building, strapped into a straitjacket and suspended head down over the street below. (He freed himself, fell into an awning, rolled into the street under the wheels of a moving truck, grasped its underside and rode away.) Among various other heartstopping escapades, the script required him to jump from one plane to another in mid-air. Houdini, on a rope, was to do the jump: the cameraman would be filming from a third plane. The lower plane turned upwards: its propeller caught the upper plane. The cameraman, a true professional, kept on turning. Fortunately the two planes disengaged before they hit the ground. They crash-landed in a beanfield. No one was seriously hurt; the storyline was revised to include the crash, and the publicity featured it avidly. ('On June first 1919, the Associated Press carried from Los Angeles a story of the thrilling aeroplane accident that took place during the filming of "The Grim Game." . . . It's all in the picture – and lots more! The greatest thrill in the greatest thrill picture ever made!') What nobody was told was that Houdini had not been involved in the crash. His arm was in a sling at the time: he had broken his wrist falling three feet during a gaol escape. For the plane-to-plane descent they had had to use a double, Lieutenant Robert E. Kennedy. Other doubles, for even more dangerous feats, were dummies with Houdini's clothes and painted faces, seen in long-shot. Such is the deceptive world of film.

The Houdinis liked California. They rented a bungalow in Hollywood and enjoyed the unprecedented sensation of living in one place for months at a time. When Houdini was asked to name his favourite holiday spot, he nominated Hollywood. *Terror Island*, his next Lasky film, was shot on Catalina during the fall of 1919. It was the mixture as before. Harry Kellar, Houdini's old friend and mentor, enjoyed it. He wrote, 'What particularly left an impression on my mind was the fight in the submarine . . . where the water compartment was left open and the boat was being flooded . . . The scene where you rescue the girl from the safe . . . I just sat there and enjoyed it and shouted at the villain like a gallery kid. To me it was all real and I forgot I was looking at a movie.'

Houdini enjoyed making films. What was more, he found that they gave a new impetus to his act. They had made him more famous than ever. (He kept all his fan-letters, stuck neatly into scrapbooks together with their envelopes whose stamps record his various films' progress around the world.) And because of this new notoriety more people than ever wanted to see him perform live. His earning power in vaudeville rose to unprecedented heights. A record weekly salary of $3,750 offered by the London Palladium – the largest salary ever offered to a single entertainer – tempted him once more to Britain, where he had not performed for six years.

He sailed in December 1919, and the crowds flocked in. In financial terms the tour was his most successful ever. But despite general acclaim his act was not what it had been, and some people were beginning to point out that the emperor seemed to be losing his clothes. Houdini had scored some of his first great successes in the English provinces; now it looked as if he might be about to lose his reputation there. The Nottingham *Football News* ran a very disappointed review of his performances there in April 1920: 'Somebody in the head office of Moss Empires owes me an apology over the Houdini visit this week. After receiving a long and fulsome screed of preliminary matter (three large type-written pages of it) which, extravagantly worded, contained the definite statement: "He will present his water-torture sensation AMONG OTHER FEATS," I felt justified in saying that the show he would give would be well worth seeing, and should not be missed by anyone. In fact I boomed of the disadvantage of the rest of the bill.

'No one was more astounded than I was to see on Monday night Houdini's solitary feat, which of itself lasts only three minutes, and no one has more sympathy with the candid remarks of large numbers of the patrons after the act than I have . . . Why on earth Houdini should imagine that any audience would be entertained by hearing a long and uncalled-for account of what he has been doing during the past six years I am at a loss to understand.'

Terror Island was not a success, and Lasky did not renew his contract. Undeterred, Houdini determined to go into film production himself. He formed the Officers' Mystery Pictures Corp. Its president was Houdini and its vice-president, Hardeen. He also had a Film Development Corporation. In 1919, between *The Grim Game* and *Terror Island*, he had acquired Martinka's magic store in New York. Now he sold it again in order to have more cash to devote to movie-making. He had sunk $5,000 into his movie ventures before leaving for London, and had sent a further $10,000 from Britain. He had various movie ideas. There was a serial idea about 'a ring that stole five hundred motors' taken from a newspaper: 'can make use of the vanishing ideas I have also disappearing motors'. But he finally decided upon a story written by himself, called *The Man From Beyond*.

The Man from Beyond had, like the mammoth, been frozen in a block of ice for many years, and the film concerned his attempts, once defrosted, to come to terms with the modern world. This was the film that featured, among other thrilling stunts, the Niagara Falls rescue. Houdini boosted it to the skies. 'Greatest praise ever bestowed on any production,' trumpeted the full-page advertisements in the trade press. 'Territory available. Unlimited exploitation opportunities.'

But, like Houdini's other movies, it was a disappointment. It was not simply that they were not very good. There was also, always, the frustrating sense that they really should have been better. There was so much talent and energy in Houdini; but, in movies at any rate, it went unexpressed. 'It starts out promisingly,' wrote one critic of *The Man From Beyond*, 'with the assumption that a man incased in a cake of ice for a hundred years may be resuscitated and brought back from the Arctic to civilisation to find his sweetheart of a century ago reincarnated as a girl of identical appearance. Many things might be done with this fantastic conception. But none of them is done in "The Man from Beyond". Mr Houdini's imagination seems to have run out at the inception of his idea.'

What Houdini might have done with his plots, had he possessed an iota of creative imagination, is shown in the stories ghosted for him by H. P. Lovecraft, who did. *Weird Tales* for May 1924, ran a story from this team entitled 'Imprisoned with the Pharaohs' where Lovecraft's embroideries add the artistry missing from all Houdini's solo ventures into the non-vaudeville world: 'Far over the city toward the great Roman dome of the new museum; and beyond it over the cryptic yellow Nile that is the mother of eons and dynasties – lurked the menacing sands of the Libyan desert, undulant and iridescent and evil with older arcana . . .'

Nonetheless, and despite Houdini's ludicrous acting, *The Man From Beyond* did tolerably well, mostly on account of the Niagara Falls scene. It seemed for a while as though Houdini's movie career and his vaudeville career might keep each other going. He signed for nine weeks with the Keith Circuit at $3,000 a week for the first four theatres and $3,500 for the last five. The mixture was the one which had failed to excite the citizens of Nottingham. It opened with film of his bridge jumps, continued with talk of his adventures and the old needle-threading trick, and ended with the Water-Torture Cell. The tour ended in January 1922. The Keiths re-engaged him. 'I am working very hard, drawing bigger than ever,' he wrote, 'but must acknowledge that the publicity I have received in motion pictures is the prime cause of the big crowds . . . Every week is like an ovation . . . Despite my enormous salary they are engaging me for five more weeks.' Some of the components of his show had not seen the stage for so many years that they seemed new again. The Boston *Globe* remarked on a new sensation he was introducing: 'The exchange of human beings in a locked, sealed and corded trunk.'

The Man From Beyond opened in April 1920, at the Times Square Theater. To ensure attendances, Houdini made personal appearances in which he treated the patrons to a full-scale spectacular magic show, including the Vanishing Elephant, the needles trick, a straitjacket escape, and two illusions called Goodbye Winter and Welcome Summer. In Goodbye Winter a girl (Mrs Houdini) wearing furs stood on the top of three stacked tables. Houdini climbed a ladder to cover her with a cloth. When he pulled it away he shouted, 'Goodbye, Winter!' and the girl was gone. In Welcome Summer a cone-shaped wooden structure was shown empty. Houdini fired a pistol, shouted, 'Welcome Summer!' and up popped the girl garlanded with flowers.

The notes for the staging of these illusions are interesting, showing the kind of minutiae that have to be taken care of in a show of this kind. 'Things to look after on the new material,' noted Houdini. 'A run for Mrs. H. to go up into G.W.'

A sure fire cloth to pull away, and a sure string or tape for Mrs. H. to take hold of so it can be released when I pull at cloth.

Strap to pull extra gag back into place.

A string or strap to place against back to poles so Mrs H. cannot go back to far. Best to have a thin piece of bent tin or hoop iron.

Belt table together.

Get new square made for bottom table, and refix the second one.

Recover all tables with black velvet.

Get long white or gold stick to wave for other two trick.

Paint bottom of run white also ladder.

Make special bottom on Comet so I can open it myself from the back, after I turn it around towards audience.

Wire or cable to pull out Mrs H. Trapeze or swing for her to sit down on about 2 feet. try and make it pull square by having the upper ropes also have trapeze bar.

Measure cone inside, to show audience that it is just as long inside as outside, to do this turn cone sideways so that the top and bottom are away from audience.

Lay calico hopp or frame on floor to show nothing comes from under stage.

String to hold ring so it can be passed immediately to me into the box.

Fix doors with elastic so they will not swing open. doors at bottom must be practically the same.

None of this, however, could turn *The Man From Beyond* into a moneymaker – and this time it was Houdini's own money that was disappearing down the drain.

'My dear old friend,' Harry Kellar had written on the occasion of the founding of the Houdini Picture Corporation, 'don't be rash but weigh well what you do and if you find the enterprise a "dead one" don't let it swamp you. Remember Mark Twain lost nearly a million in a "dead sure proposition" which was a complete failure.'

This was sound advice, and now was the moment to take it. But Houdini could not believe his film career was over. He embarked upon yet another movie. After considering two or three ideas, he fixed upon another of his own creations. This had begun life as *The Mysterious Mr Yu* but hit the screens as *Haldane of the Secret Service*. It was the same preposterous mixture as before. Houdini boosted it with all his genius for publicity. He had thousands of small slips of paper printed with the message: 'This lock is not HOUDINI-proof. He could pick it as easily as you could pick a daisy. See the Master-Man of Mystery HOUDINI in "Haldane of the Secret Service." A picture that will thrill you to your marrows.' He had two men work an eyecatching street stunt. They were carrying identical black bags and they met on a busy street. One man shouted that the other had taken his bag. When the quarrel had drawn a good crowd, one of the bags was opened and the two men brought out a big cloth banner bearing the name of the film and the house where it was showing, and held it up for the delectation of the crowd. But in spite of all this the film flopped, definitively.

There were no more movies. It was clear, even to Houdini, that although this might be the wave of the future, he would not be riding it. Houdini the film star embodied nobody's fantasies but his own.

In 1952, a film was made about Houdini's life starring Tony Curtis. Its publicity included the following:

A set of amazing parallels surrounds the picture. Both Houdini and Curtis were born in New York. Their physical resemblance is staggering . . . Curtis' real name is Bernard Schwartz, while the man who owned the motion picture rights to 'Houdini' is Berman Swarttz. George Boston, Tony's magic teacher, is married to Janet Boston. Tony's wife is Janet Leigh. Houdini died 26 years ago at the age of 52. Twenty-six is half the count of a deck of cards. Fifty-two cards in a deck. Tony is 26 years old, again the count of a half-deck, and 'Houdini' went before the cameras on August 26th. There are three Georges connected with the production: George Pal, the producer, George Marshall, its director, and George Boston, Tony's trainer. Finally, Tony's middle name in Hebrew is Harry.

Such logic would hardly have been out of place in Houdini's own films.

14

Merlin's Cave

In his book *Miracle-Mongers and their Methods*, Houdini divulges various recipes supposed to induce heat-resistance, for the benefit of prospective fire-eaters.

The formula set down by Albertus Magnus was probably the first ever made public: the following translation of it is from the *London Mirror*:

> 'Take juice of marshmallow, and white of egg, flea-bane seeds, and lime; powder them and mix juice of radish with the white of egg; mix all thoroughly and with this composition annoint your body or hand and allow it to dry and afterwards annoint it again, and after this you may boldly take up hot iron without hurt.'

> . . . Another early formula is given in the 1763 edition of *Hocus Pocus*. Examination of the different editions of this book in my library discloses the fact that there are no fire formulas in the second edition, 1635, which is the earliest I have (first editions are very rare and there is only one record of a sale of that edition at auction). From the fact that this formula was published during the time that Powell was appearing in England I gather that that circumstance may account for its addition to the book. It does not appear in the German or Dutch editions . . .

> 'Take half an ounce of samphire, dissolve it in two ounces of aquaevitae, add to it one ounce of quicksilver, once ounce of liquid storax, which is the droppings of Myrrh and hinders the camphire from firing; take also two ounces of hematitus, a red stone to be had at the druggist's, and when you buy it let them beat it to powder in their great mortar, for it is so very hard that it cannot be done in a small one; put this to the afore-mentioned composition, and when you intend to walk on the bar you must annoint your feet

well therewith, and you may walk over without danger;
by this you may wash your hands in boiling lead.'

Houdini prefaces these disclosures by remarking, characteristically: 'The yellow thread of exposure seems to be inextricably
woven into all fabrics whose strength is secrecy.' But he hasn't
exposed very much here. These recipes never made anyone
fireproof. The secrets of fire-walking, fire-eating and flame
resistance in general lie more in the domain of 'natural magic' –
the imaginative use of the laws of physics. The skin does not
combust the instant it is brought into contact with flame: a
certain time is needed for it to reach the necessary temperature.
A fire-walking experiment conducted by the psychical researcher
Harry Price found that a man was burned crossing a trench of
coals in six steps, but another who crossed the same trench in
four steps was unharmed. (The trench temperature was
740°C.) Heat resistance is increased by the presence of a film of
water, or other liquid, which has to evaporate before the heat
can reach the skin. This is what makes fire-eating possible
(along with the fact that fire needs oxygen: if things get too
hot, all you need do is close your mouth, or breathe out: CO_2
will extinguish the flame). If you wet your feet before you
tread the burning coals, you will run even less risk. But don't
stop to take a photo in the middle of the trench, even so.

Prosaic details, however, were not what interested Houdini
in this instance. *Miracle-Mongers and their Methods* was not a
manual for aspiring magicians. It was, rather, an opportunity
for Houdini to display his scholarly prowess and its trappings:
his exhaustive acquaintance with magical arcana, his know-
ledgeability as a collector, the unparalleled extent of his library.

Of course it is not unusual for people to be interested in the
history of their profession. A great many magicians, amateur and
professional, collect magical memorabilia. Part of Houdini's
own collection was bought by a famous magician, John Mulholland, after he died, and is now owned by another, David
Copperfield. But Houdini's passion had deeper and more
obsessively complex roots than the average collector's.

In October 1925, just a year before he died, Houdini gave an interview to *Popular Science* that was inaccurate even by his relaxed standards. 'It may seem surprising,' his interviewer observed, 'that one whose chief fame has come from dexterity of hand and strength of body should possess so remarkable a passion for pursuits of the mind. Actually, though, there is nothing surprising about it; for Houdini was a scholar and teacher long before he became a magician. The son of a clergyman and educator, he was raised in a scholastic atmosphere, and almost before he was out of his knee pants, he taught modern and ancient languages in a school his father conducted in Wisconsin. "Books were my hobby, even as a child," he told me. "I read about every book in Milwaukee Public Library before I was fifteen . . . Some of the books I didn't understand – but I read them just the same. I believed, you see, that my life work would be teaching, so I wanted to learn everything I could about every possible subject." '

When people rearrange their childhood for public consumption, the result is often more interesting than any mere recital of the truth. The picture is not of reality, but of aspirations: not the childhood and family they actually had, but the one they would have wished for. Houdini here bends the facts of his past. They are distorted, but not unrecognisable. His father, Mayer Samuel Weiss, had attended rabbinical college in Hungary, served as a rabbi for a while in Appleton, Wisconsin, and thereafter taught Hebrew without much success: he could loosely be described as 'a clergyman and educator'. Naturally, then, the Weiss household possessed a rabbinical respect for learning. Houdini, né Ehrich Weiss, did speak one modern language other than English – German, which his parents spoke at home – and probably had a smattering of an ancient one – Hebrew. He may have sat in on his father's classes, although the notion that he would ever have taught them is laughable. And it is more than likely that he frequented Milwaukee Public Library.

As with the disquisitions on fireproofing, the important agenda here is about intellectual acceptability. He is really saying: I am a scholar, and I come from a long line of scholars. And this was, in a sense, true. One of the most extraordinary aspects of his career was that the first instinct of this in fact wholly uneducated vaudeville artist, as soon as he had a free moment in the struggle to keep body and soul together, was to write books. His first, *The Right Way to Do Wrong,* was published in 1906 when he was thirty-two; his second, *The Unmasking of Robert-Houdin,* in 1909.

Houdini made no secret of his wistful yearning for education. A clipping survives in his papers: 'IGNORANCE – Root of all Evil – This is the Master that Drives Human Beings Through Suffering to Misery.' After he died his one-time enemy and latter-day friend, Dr Archie Wilson, editor of *The Sphinx,* described a visit to the Houdini home: 'We talked for hours, not on magic but on his yearnings for a higher education, that he might qualify as a writer and lecturer on the deeper things of life than magic afforded. I outlined a course of study which he would have pursued had he lived.' Houdini described to Dr Wilson his plans for a University of Magic: 'Do you know that thoughts have come into my head, that when I get back to New York, I may start an organization for a sort of institution in which degrees will be given to the experienced and reputable magicians . . . Am being dubbed, "Doctor and Professor", and "Doctor of Tricks" in the colleges [he was then on a lecture-tour denouncing fake spirit mediums] and get scores of letters, Doctor Houdini, and would like to get your reaction to the thought.' The idea of being Professor Houdini appealed to him more than any other: 'The public knows me as a magician, a mystifier, and a Cinema star . . . It does not know that I possess one of the largest privately-owned libraries on occult subjects in the world . . . It does not realise that I am a student.'

But formal education never did come his way; and so he had to make do with what he had picked up. And in this respect, too, the *Popular Science* interview is revealing. For the mark of the autodidact is not so much what he doesn't know as what he can't bear to leave out. Education is not just about gathering facts but about learning how to organise them. Education enables you to select your books and avoid feeling that you must read every book in the library whether you understand it or not. That is simply a way of trying to engulf the magical essence of all knowledge which, for the wishful self-educator like Houdini, is embodied in the rows of books on the library shelves.

His need to possess a library of his own is therefore clear. Only so would all learning be, literally, within his grasp: his to contemplate and use whenever he wished: *his.* He collected in much the same way as he had used the Public Library: wholesale, indiscriminately. Bess called him a 'pack-rat'. She groaned whenever another crate of dusty papers was delivered to the house. Alfred Becks, Houdini's librarian for many years, devised a routine whereby the boxes would be elaborately smuggled into the house to avoid her disapproving eye. He would carry the boxes to the front stoop, leave them in the vestibule, and then run back to ring the basement bell. Meeting Bess's suspicious glance he would say, 'Madam, you see my hands are perfectly empty!'

Bess, faced with an ever-growing accumulation of dusty tomes and heaps of paper, saw only a never-ending, uncontrolled heaping-up of stuff. 'We have "arrived" home safe. Am having an awful time with the books I brought back. Never realized the amount, until I tried to get them into my home. Its a good thing I played my entire tour, and was too busy to look at all the bookshops', Houdini reported on a typical booty-laden return. He bought entire collections, warehouses full of dusty bales: after his death, the boxes kept on coming for months. 'Some of the important things I have collected lately,' he wrote in 1925. 'The Strobridge Lithograph Company went out of the theatrical business and they gave me a five ton truck full of lithographs which are reposing in my cellar. I am contemplating building a country home to house my entire collection. At the great Everett Wendell sale, I was the largest individual buyer, and it was only by the great collectors of the past two decades dying that I was able to accumulate some of my marvellous treasures. The great collectors of the past – Augustin Daly, Todeburg, Brown, Dick, Cox, Wright, Evans, Bement, Vail, Broadley, Morrow. It was only by the disposing of these collections that I was able to obtain their accumulation of years . . . In Edinborough, I walked into a book shop during the war and bought the entire stock on the fourth floor of the house built in 1700 . . . They tore down an Opera House in Iowa and I have the forty year accumulation of all letters . . . I bought a number of dramatic critics' letter files. Have important collection of Mansfield letters, I should judge about sixty and about one hundred Clyde Fitch letters, over a hundred of Edwin Booth, very scarce letters of Edmund Kean, the Siddons family, an enormous lot of writing of a great tragedian who lived to be over one hundred years of age [this was Charles Macklin].'

Collecting was a process that had begun on his first trip to Europe in 1900 – the first time he ever had spare cash in his pocket – and which had continued full spate ever since. Even when he was temporarily living with his brother's family in Flatbush he had continued to accumulate stuff. He advertised in the *New York Times*: 'As I possess the largest collection (private or public) in the world of material regarding magic, magicians, books, scripts, spiritualistic effects, documents, steel engravings, automata, am still looking for anything that would embellish my collection of interest on the subject of magic or mysteries.'

This compulsive need to accumulate *stuff* was part of Houdini's becoming a scholar like his father. (Asked 'Who is your favourite author?' he replied, unexpectedly, 'My dad.') But, as always when the question of ancestry was broached, things were less simple than they seemed.

Dr Weiss had had no problems about assimilating the lore of his fathers. One of the books which he would undoubtedly have studied at the Budapest rabbinical college is called just that: *Pirkei Avoth,* the Sayings of the Fathers. This archaic Aramaic tome would have been both inaccessible to Houdini, and, like Dr Weiss himself, irrelevant to his life. But his diligent search for new fathers, his fathers in magic, provided him with his own *Pirkei Avoth*. He spent his life collecting and chronicling an adopted heritage.

In it, he found that contentment which eluded him elsewhere. Vladimir Nabokov, as articulate about his sensations as Houdini was inarticulate about his, collected butterflies. He wrote movingly of the perfect happiness this passion afforded him: 'The highest enjoyment of timelessness . . . is when I stand among rare butterflies and their food plants. This is ecstasy, and behind the ecstasy is something else . . . It is like a momentary vacuum into which rushes all that I love.' I have little doubt that Nabokov here speaks for all collectors. Here, and perhaps here only, Houdini's tortured and obsessional soul found true and timeless happiness and peace.

Houdini's accumulation and study did bring with it the desired scholarly satisfaction and authority. In the summer of 1916, for instance, he developed an interest in the Booth family – Edwin Booth the actor and his brother John Wilkes Booth, the assassin of Abraham Lincoln (who interested him for both theatrical and ghoulish reasons). 'Yesterday I bot a book Edwin Booth and his art by W. Winter and shall "study" Booth so that I shall be able to talk intelligently about our great actor,' he reported. He soon felt the urge to know more but wrote: 'I know that I cannot go in for Drama collection, the field is stupendous, and I have thrown away many an opportunity of obtaining material in foreign countries as I only sought magic. And now I am in America, and could not tie up the money required, for I will admit (privately) that the Press Agents have made me a rich man (on paper).' That was on 4 July. But less than a fortnight later he had succumbed to temptation: 'I told Mr Becks [Alfred Becks, who was later to take the job of cataloguing Houdini's own collection, was then cataloguing the Robert Gould Shaw collection at Harvard] that I was going in for Booth material, and he started in to tell me about the Booth collection in the Shaw World of Drama, and I felt my feet grow cold.' And nine years later he was corresponding with a fellow-enthusiast about Booth esoterica:

'I have at least one hundred letters of Edwin Booth and one of every member of the family. I have the full account of the early marriage or the first marriage of Edwin Booth's father . . . If memory serves me right, the lady referred to as the first wife of Edwin Booth's father and her children are buried in Baltimore.' Characteristically, he suggested that his correspondent might be helped in his Booth research by visiting the grave of the first Mrs Booth. By the time he had finished, he was an expert on Booth.

Another collector's pleasure is that of context, 'a relationship to objects which does not emphasize their functional, utilitarian value . . . but studies and loves them as the scene, the stage, of their fate'. In this sense, his librarian Alfred Becks was, for Houdini, a collector's item in himself. Through him, it was possible to trace a direct connection back to David Garrick and Mrs Siddons, and (by stretching things slightly) almost as far as Shakespeare. The line (as Houdini described it) ran thus: 'Mrs Siddons knew Mrs Garrick; Mrs Garrick knew Edmund Kean; Edmund Kean had as an admirer Couldack and at that time Mrs Vestris was running a theatre. She was the great amorous actress of that time . . . At any rate, she married Charles Matthews, Jr., and Dion Boucicault who wrote a number of plays for them came to America right after Couldack and became one of the well-known authors . . . Mr Becks was his private secretary for years . . . and Couldack and Becks intimate friends . . . Edmund Kean knew Cook, who was the competitor of David Garrick, Barton Booth, even coming to Quinn and Betterton. They all received their stage business from one another and from Burbage and perhaps from Shakespeare himself.'

Once Houdini began discussing this kind of thing, he was oblivious to all else. He once took a cab to see a friend (Carl Brema) who made conjurers' apparatus, told it to wait for him, and only remembered he had done so when he emerged several hours later to find it still there. He and Brema had been immersed in magical discussions. Tiny slips of paper on which he noted items of interest are scattered through his letters: 'Linsky in a gun accident killed wife de Y'; 'Just run across the European Magazine and July first 1789 Thomas Denton was hanged in public with three other men . . . This occurred July and you will find full account of it in the European Magazine, it is a good life of Denton, states specifically that he wrote rather translated Pinetti's book.' He added: 'Save this Sargent [J. W. Sargent was his private secretary]. Sending it to you, as it records the only English magician ever hanged . . . The French Louis I was reprieved but Rollin had his head cut off during the reign of terror.'

But the thrill of the chase far exceeded such passing serendipitous chances. The chase is the essence of all collecting, in which the desired object is located, stalked, and finally, triumphantly, acquired. He had various trusted agents who would act for him at auctions. The English magical collector Harry Price bid for him on more than one occasion for items such as rare first editions which Price already possessed. On one occasion Alfred Becks brought a particular set of books to his attention. They were ones Becks himself particularly wanted, and he intended to bid for them. He returned from the auction crestfallen: he had been outbid by someone who could afford much more than he could. The mystery buyer had in fact been Houdini, who had also coveted the books. When he saw how disconsolate poor Becks was he felt very ashamed of himself, and the parcel of books lay hidden and unopened in his cellar. Some time later Becks died. Houdini was griefstricken. He visited three different florists and ordered three wreaths to be sent under assumed names to ensure that the funeral would be a fitting one. When he came home, he sat down and wept. Then he straightened up. 'Now I suppose I can get those books from the cellar!' he observed.

He wrote to Harry Price extolling his collection:

My Dear Mr Harry Price,
. . . My librian informs me that it will take more than a year to classify and arrange my library.

So I shall have to have a permanent man to fix my books. This will give you an index of the extent of my collection.

My dramatic portion is supposed to be the *greatest private* in this country. And that is saying a *great deal*, for there are quite a number of millionare collectors. I do not claim its the most expensive, for Folger of the Standard Oil has a few millions in Shakespeares but my rare tracts, makes my library one of The libraries of the world, and when I get it arranged you will hear about it. My Garrick (I have his private diary) Kean, Kemble etc. etc. would cause you to think you stept into the British Museum that is one corner of it.

That last phrase rings slightly false. 'One corner of it' is a mere afterthought. For Houdini it was necessary to believe, whatever lipservice he might pay to other people's mistaken prejudices, that his library was the best and the greatest with no exceptions at all. In this field as in all others, he 'vehemently wanted to be first.' But he admitted a few competitors for the sake of credibility. He classed his dramatic library as the fifth most important in the world (after Harvard, the British Museum, the Huntington, and the Folger). There was also his magic collection, the largest of its kind, and his materials concerning 'psychic phenomena, witchcraft and kindred subjects', also the largest of its kind.

If Houdini liked to see himself as a student, even a professor, the role which embodied the acme of his ambitions was that of author. He set out his thoughts on his literary career in a sketched obituary sent to his secretary Oscar Teale:

His research into the files of Magical History is entirely a labor of love, and though he may not be remunerated for his labor, perhaps when the years have passed, and when he has long received his Mandate for the other world, perhaps the first authentic history of magic his Robert Houdin unmasked will actually be his monument.

Like Sir Wren, to whom no monument has been erected, and who is resting in St Pauls London, when any one asks

where is his monument, they say 'Look around and see
them.'

So Houdini may have erected his own monument for at no
other period of printery has any one ever delved into the real
magicial history, and have same published.

. . . Like Alexander, (Teale was it Alexander who wept
because he had no more worlds to conquer) Houdini sought
for other worlds to enter.

Houdini's books, the proof of his scholarship, were little
more than distillations of his collection. Even the books he
wrote ostensibly based upon his own career, such as *Magical
Rope-Ties and Escapes* or *The Right Way to Do Wrong* or *Houdini's Paper Magic,* turned into historical compendia; *The
Unmasking of Robert-Houdin, Miracle-Mongers and their Methods*
and *A Magician among the Spirits,* were overtly such, while also
(in the case of *Robert-Houdin and A Magician among the Spirits*)
destroying the enemy of the moment. They are all profusely
illustrated from his own collection.

But his books present a problem of their own. Houdini's
writing style, as may be seen from his letters, was chaotic
and at times barely literate. His books are hardly models of
coherence. Nevertheless, it is hard to believe that they come
from the same untutored hand.

This is because, on the whole, they don't. 'When we speak
of the writings of Houdini, we must qualify the statement',
observes one commentator. 'To the best of my knowledge,
Houdini did very little writing himself. He always had at least
one secretary, and I have been told that at times he had as
many as three, all at work, on different projects. I know that
Messrs. Albert Guissart, Clinton Burgess and Oscar Teale all
worked on "Elliott's Last Legacy" . . . Another secretary was
Mr. John William Sargent and, in the later years, Mr. Bernard
M. L. Ernst, who was Houdini's attorney, also did some
writing for him. I believe he was at least partly responsible
for "A Magician Among the Spirits".' Others, too, were
involved in this factory. At the time of Houdini's death, Walter
B. Gibson was preparing three volumes on simple magic

which were to appear under Houdini's name. He employed ghosts, including H. P. Lovecraft, for several short stories based upon plots he provided.

His methods seem to have varied depending on his collaborator. With Lovecraft, Houdini provided the outline of the story and had the final say over the printer's proofs, while Lovecraft did all the actual writing. Oscar Teale, on the other hand, working on *A Magician among the Spirits* – in the preparation of which he played a large part – was faced with nothing so collected as an outline. The notebook from which Houdini collated this work contains pages and pages of instances of murder induced or committed by spirit mediums for various ends, and suicides induced by them. From these, something in the nature of a connected text had to be hewn by the factory. Teale groaned: 'This is a good example of the disjointed, irrational, irrelevant "composition" or dictation by Houdini – I have never known him to dictate more than *suggestive* thought, mere fragments – followed by instruction to "whip it into shape" and these fellows, being unfamiliar with the subject, often if not invariably confused the subject matter by erroneous statements.' Even where Houdini appeared to take pains checking the truth of his allegations and obtaining permissions, he refused to allow anything so inconvenient as a refusal to spoil his effects. When the editor of the London *Times,* in a handwritten note, 'present[ed] his compliments to Mr Houdini and desire[d] to inform him that he [was] unable to allow Mr Houdini to use the name of *The Times* in connexion with his book on Spiritualism', Houdini commented: 'This might have been written by the office boy! It bears no signature therefore cannot be proven by anyone.'

Thus he manipulated his books into existence. But, curiously (considering his methods), there is nothing impersonal about the end result. His voice – obsessional, overbearing, unmistakable – blares out from them. This is partly because, once the material had been 'whipped into shape', he made endless additions and corrections. Houdini was an editor's nightmare. The final corrections of *A Magician among the Spirits* consist of dozens of little bits of paper, some typed, some scrawled, corrections made on the back of letters, corrections made on tour . . .

But there is also another reason: and this is that although members of his factory might grumble about his methods, they absorbed his personality to the point where their own was completely subsumed within it. The corrections to the *A Magician among the Spirits* galleys were made by Teale; but he speaks with Houdini's voice to the extent that it is almost impossible to believe this is Teale, not Houdini, writing. The authentic aggressive, defensive tone is there: 'It would take the rest of Houdini's lifetime to read *all* the books in his library. He has never made such claims. Doyle [Sir Arthur Conan Doyle, with whom Houdini was then quarrelling about spiritualism] accuses him of saying that he *has attended 10,000 séances.* A statement Houdini never made.' It is easy to imagine Houdini carrying his battles to the very margins of his galley-proofs. That his secretary should feel impelled to do so on his behalf says something about the hypnotic quality of his persona.

The same quality was apparent when the question arose of credit and its apportionment. Houdini insisted upon claiming all credit for any book in which he was involved: his collaborators received little if any acknowledgement. *Elliott's Last Legacy,* mentioned above, was a case in point. Elliott was a magician and collector, and when he died his son asked Houdini to help in the collating of his memoirs and tricks. The son was outraged when Houdini's name appeared as virtual author on the title page. It read:

Elliott's Legacy
to the
Conjuring Fraternity

. . .

edited by
HOUDINI
compiled by Clinton Burgess   Illustrated by O. S. Teale

223

But, for Houdini, this was merely his usual practice: young Elliott's outrage would simply have surprised him.

When Henry Ridgely Evans, an old friend, was revising his *The Old and the New Magic*, Houdini contributed a good deal of information and went over the manuscript at Evans' request.

> My Dear Evans, [he wrote]
> It is three A.M. I have pored over the script since 7 o'clock, intending only to write a few lines, but I unpacked the script, and have reread it.
> . . . I think in the preface you might thank me for my anything you wish to call it [handwritten addition: 'kindness, co-ordination – or material?'], for honestly I am doing this so that the history of magic will be correct. Let OUR TIME start the acurate magic age.
> And if you will send me the proofs, and I can assist you, will do so with pleasure time permitting.
> I have so much material, that what you are writing does not even touch it in any way.
> There are a number of places where I could let you have some programmes, that would just fit.
> Think I have written enough for tonight, or morning, so will close.
> . . . Well so long good morning. H.Houdini.

Next day, Houdini wrote to Evans again. He said there was so much of his material in the book that the authorship should be credited: *As originally planned by Harry Houdini and Henry R. Evans Litt.D.* Houdini pointed out that he was asking no money – just credit. But by this time (1917) money meant little to him (though it meant plenty to Evans, who was hard up). Credit, on the other hand, was the whole point. Credit was everything. He begrudged every morsel of it shared with someone else.

Yet Evans put up with it. His references to Houdini in the edition of *The Old and the New Magic* published after the latter's death are consistently admiring and affectionate. His friends grumbled, but they remained his friends. They had joined his

cast, willingly: they accepted that the fulfilment of their allotted role, whatever that might be, was the price they had to
pay. He had them in his thrall.

As the years passed, the library began to work its magic.
People began to see Houdini as he dreamed of being seen. 'He
now appeared in his true role,' commented Edmund Wilson,
' . . . not precisely that of an entertainer, but of an expert on
magic, equipped for his peculiar field with more intelligence,
experience and learning than had perhaps ever before been
brought to it. At this period, he seemed to take more pleasure
in explaining how tricks were done than in astonishing people
with them.'

'I live in a treasure-house of mysticism and intensely interesting affairs,' he wrote. Visitors to his house were shown into
'a long room, rather too full of furniture, books and bric-a-
brac'. Here they waited before being shown up into the library;
and here, unknown to them, Houdini could, if he chose, listen
to everything they said. He had had the house specially wired,
and enjoyed impressing his visitors with his apparent 'second
sight.' This arrangement was satisfactory on two counts. It
gave Houdini an immediate advantage over the unsuspecting
visitors; and it could be used to practical effect. When psychical
research circles in London were bowled over by Professor
Gilbert Murray's demonstrations of kinaesthesia, in which he
told people what they had been discussing in distant rooms,
Houdini gleefully replicated his effects, to general consternation. (Whether Murray used a similar system is not known.
It seems improbable. But far more improbable things have
happened in the history of psychical research.)

The ante-room was full of souvenirs. 'On a massive table
stood a jewelled cup (presented to Houdini by Grand Duke
Sergius of Russia), a coin-studded vase (a token of admiration
from the management of the Essen Ruhr Coliseum where
Houdini broke all records) and a beautiful magician's wand (a
gift from the late King of Belgium) . . . In a tall case [were]

a large assortment of wands that had been wielded by famous magicians. John Henry Anderson's was there, Alexander Herrmann's (and his wife Adelaide Herrmann's) and, of course, Harry Kellar's . . . On a pedestal was a strikingly life-like head and bust of the Master Magician himself, done by Cassidy, an Irishman, to be set on Houdini's grave.'

These treasures meant a lot to Houdini. 'Did he feel that they linked him in some way with the original owners?' wondered one correspondent to whom he described them. He almost certainly did: owning the wands of his magical predecessors, he possessed himself of their magic. He especially treasured a writing-desk which had belonged to Edgar Allan Poe, that kindred spirit. The bust, meanwhile, towered over all these memorabilia, affirming his pre-eminence in this world. As for the next, he knew that matters regarding his own tomb, the monument that always loomed so large in his imagination, would be satisfactorily attended to. He had seen to it himself.

One visitor (who was frankly charmed) gives a graphic picture of Houdini at fifty: 'Dressed, according to the season, in light trousers, with shirt open at the throat and sleeves cut off at the elbows, he evidently had been hard at work earlier that evening. He is not a large man and, as he himself will frankly tell you, not a particularly young one, but he is well built, and so full of energy and enthusiasm that it is simply impossible to ticket and pigeonhole him in terms of years. At fifty he not only looks but seems forty; after thirty-one years of marriage, his wife is still his closest friend and active partner . . . I find it difficult to translate his charm and dynamic or rather magnetic vitality into words. There is a rare delightfulness in his personality . . . In his make-up there is a dash of Puck . . . Yet nothing could be more clear-cut than the workings of Houdini's versatile mind. His fine head is well set on splendid shoulders and I noticed, as he talked, how developed were the tendons as well as the muscles of his forearms. I think it rather significant that I did not, although I particularly intended to do so, notice his hands. I have a sort of confused recollection of them but my eyes seem, oddly enough, to have been both more occupied and less observant than usual. Frequently I was too absorbed in watching what he was doing to notice details – as when he broke off the first joint of his thumb and showed it to us entirely separated from the remaining part, then calmly setting it back again where it belonged, gave his thumb a little pull and held it up once more whole . . . I could almost have sworn I heard a brittle sounding snap as he broke it off . . . "Lady Conan Doyle nearly fainted," he commented, "when she first saw me do it." '

Thus Merlin in his cave. For what was Houdini now if not a mage? He had gathered up the wisdom of the centuries, and now it was he who controlled it, ensconced in its midst, the wizard in his lair.

Magic is the search for total control. 'As I do will, so mote it be', run the witchcraft spells. An adept describes the student's training in the rites of magic:

> During his process through the early grades he should be trained in emotional and mental control . . . After the individual has achieved the optimal mental, emotional and physical control over himself, which means control in function, not inhibition, it is his task to face the Dweller on the Threshold . . . [This involves] personal Agony in the Garden, Trial, Crucifixion, Descent into Hell and eventual Ascension . . . Once the process has been gone through, the individual is in a position to look everything in the face, without distortion or delusion, and to accept full realization for all that he does or has done . . . And how does he work out his destiny? By being himself – literally. By acting within the centre of his being, his essential self. Not by acting according to the dictates of his mind, his emotions or his instincts, but by using them according to his and their needs.

The allusion to the Christian Passion is evident. But what is described here is every shaman's journey. Houdini had trodden this path time after time. Now at last he had arrived, blowing his own trumpet as always, on the other side.

15

Magician Among the Spirits

The production of ghosts – visible yet intangible – is one of the most ancient and impressive branches of magic. These illusions are produced using mirrors. The mirrors used in the earliest such deceptions were almost certainly concave. If a strongly-lit object is placed where it will be reflected in the mirror, but in a position where it is invisible to the spectators of the illusion, an image of the object will be projected into the air of a darkened room. The image may be much strengthened if some sort of screen – for instance, a column of smoke – is provided for it. 'As in all experiments with concave mirrors, the size of the aerial image is to that of the real object as their distances from the mirror, we may, by varying the distance of the object, increase or diminish the size of the image. In doing this, however, the distance of the image from the mirror is at the same time changed, so that it would quit the place most suitable for its exhibition. This defect may be removed by simultaneously changing the place both of the mirror and the object, so that the image may remain stationary, expanding itself from a luminous spot to a gigantic size, and again passing through all intermediate magnitudes, till it vanishes in a cloud of light'. Such images are almost identical with those apparitions of the gods in their temples described by the ancients. They were intended to terrify, and doubtless that is just what they did. 'A national system of deception, intended as an instrument of government, must have brought into requisition, not merely the scientific skill of the age, but a variety of subsidiary contrivances, calculated to astonish the beholder, to confound his judgment, to fuddle his senses, and to give a predominant influence to the peculiar imposture which it was thought desirable to establish.' Thus Sir David

Brewster, author of a treatise on *Natural Magic*, whose intention was to demystify such tricks.

There is no record of any nineteenth-century medium using optical illusions of this kind to produce his or her effects. By then, such knowledge was no longer restricted to a few powerful people. Magic Lanterns were generally available, and ghosts were frequently produced in stage shows – though these, by now, generally used the flat mirror technique perfected by Professor John Henry Pepper of the Regent Street Polytechnic and commonly known as Pepper's Ghost.

Nevertheless, magical skill had not lost its power to inspire awe and terror when skilfully used, on or off the stage. The 'spirit-rapping' craze which swept Europe and America during the nineteenth century was proof of the effects which could be produced by even the crudest practitioners; while for the truly skilful and unscrupulous, it provided possibilities of real wealth and influence.

One of the fundamental skills any medium had to cultivate was some sort of technique for escaping from rope-ties or other constraints. For the most basic test of supernatural powers was his or her ability to produce phenomena while securely 'controlled'. The medium would be held or tied so that no hand or foot was free and no movement was possible; then spirit hands would brush the sitters in the darkened room, ghosts would walk, objects would move, and wonder reign.

Among the earliest and most successful exponents of these techniques were the Davenport brothers, William and Ira. Among many other refinements, they evolved the 'cabinet' in which manipulations might take place in decent privacy, and which was so central a part of Houdini's own equipment. Their cabinet was fitted with a bench on either side; into each bench two holes were drilled, a little distance apart. The brothers would seat themselves opposite each other, their feet squarely on the floor in front of them. 'The end of a rope was passed around the legs of one of the brothers, close up by the knees, and tied. The rope was then wound around the legs several times, fastened at the ankles, the remaining portion carried straight across the cabinet to the other brother's ankles, fastened, wound about his legs and tied at the knees. A shorter piece of rope was then tied to each of their wrists with the knots lying next to the pulse. These ropes were threaded through the holes and the wrists drawn down to the benches, and the ends of the ropes fastened to the ankles.' The room was then darkened; instruments played, bells rang, objects flew about; what could this be but a display of supernatural powers? The Davenports were a sensation. Myths flourished. Ira was supposed to have levitated across the Niagara River; to have risen during a seance until his head went through the ceiling; and to have escaped from prison by spiritual means.

The Davenports never claimed supernatural powers for themselves. But they allowed them to be claimed on their behalf by their manager, a Dr Ferguson. And they never disclosed the secret of how they managed to produce their phenomena – not to their children; not to their assistant, the young Harry Kellar. Kellar nevertheless worked it out, and the 'Davenport Rope-Tie' made his reputation as a magician. Some people are of the opinion that all magic as we know it today in America and Britain can be traced back to the Davenports, through Kellar and through J.N. Maskelyne, who as a young boy attended a Davenport show in the daytime when the curtain fell by accident and all was unintentionally revealed. Maskelyne later became a noted exposer of mediums. But those who wanted to believe remained unperturbed. 'If you think it is all juggling,' remarked Alfred Russel Wallace of Maskelyne, 'point out exactly where the difference lies between it and mediumistic phenomena.' Wallace had worked out the theory of evolution independently of Darwin, but believed avidly in spiritualism nonetheless. What he meant was that Maskelyne, contrary to his protestations, was a true medium. Maskelyne's assertion was of course just the opposite: that mediums are accomplished conjurers.

Years later, when Kellar had become the doyen of American magicians and the mentor of a new star, Harry Houdini, he revealed (to Houdini's surprise) that although William Davenport had died in 1877, Ira was still alive. He lived in Maysville, New York, where Houdini at once wrote to him. This was just before his tour of Australia, where he made a point of visiting and restoring William's grave.

On his return he hurried to visit Ira, who was the very type of those magical father-figures Houdini always loved to cultivate. They spent a long and happy day together, during which Ira revealed the Davenports' secret. 'Their method of releasing themselves was comparatively simple. While one extended his feet the other drew his in thus securing slack enough in the wrist ropes to permit working their hands out of the loops. (Note: They rubbed vaseline into their hands and wrists to facilitate their movements.) The second brother was released by reversing the action. After the demonstrations were completed the brothers slipped their hands back into the loops from which they had drawn them, placed their feet in the original positions and were ready to be examined. When the cabinet was opened the ropes appeared as taut as when put on by the committee.'

They never met again. Ira Davenport had survived many vicissitudes, but the curse of Houdini was too much for him. An appointment to meet the magician a second time had the same effect on the old showman as a similar appointment had had upon Wiljalba Frikell years before. 'Curiously enough, I had made an appointment with Ira E. for July 9th, 1911, and was making ready for my trip to his home in Maysville, N.Y., when the sad news reached me of his death on the 8th.' Houdini kept his secret until *A Magician among the Spirits* was published in 1924. Until then, all he would say was: 'Regarding the Davenport Brothers, I am afraid that I cannot say that all their work was accomplished by the spirits.'

The Davenports travelled the world, generally to great acclaim. They were twice almost exposed: once in Liverpool, when their cabinet was smashed and a near-riot ensued, and once in Paris. They were guyed, to great acclaim, by Sir Henry Irving in Manchester. (Irving was annoyed because the Davenports were proving to be a potent rival draw.) Yet this did not prevent a great many people from continuing to believe in them. The famous explorer Sir Richard Burton wrote, 'I have spent a great part of my life in oriental lands, and have seen there many magicians . . . I have read and listened to every explanation of the Davenport "tricks" hitherto placed before the English public, and, believe me, if anything would make me take that tremendous jump "from matter to spirit," it is the utter and complete unreason of the reasons by which the "manifestations" are explained.'

The Davenports rode the first tremendous wave of spiritualist enthusiasm in the 1860s and 70s. After that the general craze for it died down somewhat. But there was, as might be expected, a great revival during and after World War I, which cruelly robbed so many families of sons, brothers and husbands.

Among those who turned to spiritualism at this time was Sir Arthur Conan Doyle. He had for many years been interested in psychical research, but in a comparatively detached way. Now, however, like so many others, he clutched at this last straw to comfort himself in a time of terrible loss. The war saw the deaths of his son, Kingsley, and the brother of his second wife, Jean. Jean had at first tried to discourage his enthusiasm, but after her brother's death she became as committed as he, and discovered in herself a faculty for automatic writing: a gift she shared with her children's governess, who had also lost three brothers in the war.

Houdini and Doyle met in 1919, when Houdini was playing at Brighton, not far from Doyle's home in Crowborough, Sussex. The basis of their friendship was a shared interest in spiritualism. Houdini had always been fascinated by it. He knew of course that most 'spirit mediums' were fakes: he and Bess had themselves been fake mediums and in on the secrets of the trade. But part of him strongly resisted this knowledge. Despite all his inside information, he was never quite able to convince himself that there was no such thing as a true medium. As he himself wrote to Doyle early in their friendship: 'During my tour in Australia, I met the man who was supposed to lay low Mrs Piper [a famous medium, like all the others mentioned here]; I was in Berlin, Germany, at the trial of Miss Roth, the flower-medium; know the methods of the Bangs sisters, the famous Chicago mediums; was at the court when Ann Odelia Diss Debar was sentenced . . . And still I want to believe there is such a thing.' Houdini's first experience of spiritualism, he said, was at the age of fifteen when his father died. He had persuaded his mother to give him the last dollar in the house to pay a medium who would communicate with the deceased. Nothing however, had happened.

He had given up the trade himself on account of a number of coincidences (mentioned earlier) which had thoroughly unnerved him. 'Was doing mind-reading with my good wife,' he explained to a friend, 'and among the numerous questions, one inquired "Who killed -?" I have forgotten the name. At that time I was unable to answer, but the next day I made a detective of myself and haunted the place for three days, and eventually as I was getting shaved, the barber was telling how he had loaned a razor to the father of the girl, and from actual deduction, I believe to this day that the father dressed himself (disguised himself as a woman) went to the trysting place, beheld his daughter in the evolutions, and "finish" . . . If any one ever possessed second sight, twas my sainted Mother and I have inherited the "trait or ability" from Her.' This uncertainty, or hope, never quite left him. In 1906 he wrote, 'At one time I was almost a believer . . . I contemplate writing a book on spiritualistic methods, and how they do their tricks. I do not mean genuine spiritualists, who have no tricks, but those mediums who use their knowledge of magic to gain a living.' This book would eventually be published as *A Magician among the Spirits*.

At the time Houdini and Conan Doyle became friends, they were two of the most famous men in the world. No two people could have been more different. They were opposites in every way. But they were fascinated by each other. 'In a long life which has touched every side of humanity,' wrote Doyle, 'Houdini is far and away the most curious and intriguing character whom I have ever encountered. I have met better men, and I have certainly met very many worse ones, but I have never met a man who had such strange contrasts in his nature, and whose actions and motives it was more difficult to foresee or to reconcile.' Doyle dwelt on Houdini's immense physical courage, his cheery companion-ability, his devotion to his family, his impulsive charity – mixed with a curious frugality, so that 'while he was giving away his earnings at a rate which alarmed his wife, he would put an indignant comment in his diary because he had been charged two shillings for the pressing of his clothes'. He was at the same time repelled by Houdini's immense vanity and his mania for publicity.

Doyle was always conscious that he did not really under-stand Houdini. He put this down to the gulf between Houdini's 'Oriental' nature (which he shared with 'our own Disraeli') and Doyle's own 'colder Western blood'. (The Sherlock Holmes stories abound with sinister villains of foreign extraction.)

Houdini, for his part, viewed Doyle with a similar tempered enthusiasm. 'He is a brilliant man a deep thinker, well versed in every respect, and comes of a gifted family . . . His home life is beautiful and Lady Doyle has told me on numerous occasions that he never loses his temper and that his nature is at all times sunshiny and sweet. His children are a hundred per cent children in every way and it is beautiful to note the affection between the father, mother and the children. He is a great reader who absorbs what he reads but he believes what he sees in print *only* if it is favorable to Spiritualism.'

Houdini's interest in spiritualism had been reawakened by his mother's death. 'There is no sacrifice I would not make to be able to get in communication with my mother,' he wrote. 'After years of research I still hope that there is a way of communicating with her from this life . . . I have made defi-nite compacts with seven intimate friends and relatives to the effect that the one who died first would communicate with the others. All of my seven friends are dead. Up to the present time I have not received the slightest sign from any of them.'

Houdini was happy to put any effort into this desperate search. But he was terribly handicapped in it. Where Conan Doyle and his fellow enthusiasts would happily classify any effect which they could not otherwise explain as supernatural communication from the Other Side, Houdini was in the unfortunate position of always being able not only to explain the effects but to duplicate them. What he hoped for may be seen from his dedication in *A Magician among the Spirits:*

IN WORSHIPFUL HOMAGE
I
DEDICATE THIS BOOK
TO THE MEMORY OF MY SAINTED MOTHER
IF GOD
IN HIS INFINITE WISDOM
EVER SENT AN ANGEL UPON EARTH IN HUMAN FORM
IT WAS MY
MOTHER

Thus, while he dedicated to his father a book (*The Unmasking of Robert-Houdin*) about the destruction of a father-figure, the book he dedicated to his mother embodied his dashed hopes that even death need not come between them.

The repeated frustration of these hopes, and his fury at the cheating he was so easily able to detect, soon turned Houdini into the scourge of false mediums. He delighted in exposing them with the maximum possible theatrical publicity. He would take part in seances disguised in false beards and spectacles, and, at the crucial moment, flashing a light upon some tell-tale piece of apparatus, would tear off his costume and reveal himself as Houdini. Next day the newspapers would, naturally, be full of his exploits. Houdini had always delighted in the total destruction of anyone he saw as an enemy. And he saw all false mediums as his personal enemies in the fight to establish contact with his mother.

This fury naturally meant that the friendship between Houdini and Doyle could never be entirely easy, however much they liked each other personally and respected each other's sincerity. 'Our relations are certainly curious,' wrote Doyle, 'and likely to become more so, for as long as you attack what I *know* from experience to be true I have no alternative but to attack you in turn. How long a private friendship can survive such an ordeal I do not know.' And when, inevitably, the friendship ended, Conan Doyle could see nothing but a vindictive desire for personal publicity in Houdini's constant attacks on mediums. 'There was no consideration of any sort which would restrain him if he saw his way to an advertisement. Even when he laid flowers upon the graves of the dead it was in the prearranged presence of local photographers. It was this desire to play a constant public part which had a great deal to do with his constant campaign against Spiritualism.'

Of course this was partly true. Once again Houdini had found that the public appeasement of his personal furies was the surest route to the heroic notoriety he craved. Once again he was pitting himself against all comers. Edmund Wilson noted that 'Houdini says that he has never yet been duped, that he has been able to guess all the tricks that he has ever seen, but that he lives in constant terror of being outwitted by a telepathist or a medium – in which case his dogmatic denials would be made to look ridiculous. And this has given him a certain edge and excitement as of a man engaged in a critical fight: where he once challenged the world to tie him up, he now challenges it to convince him of the supernatural.'

Part of this 'edge and excitement' resulted from Houdini's ambivalence towards spiritualism. The magnetism of his escape acts lay, for both his audience and himself, in the alluring possibility of failure. He was never quite sure whether he really wanted to go on with life – whether he would not in the end prefer to die. This was what he had to prove to himself anew every day before the public. The excitement was as much a function of his own uncertainty as of theirs. Similarly with spiritualism: the driving fury arose not because he wanted to prove it was all false, but because he so much wanted to believe it might be true. He wrote to Doyle: 'I am willing to believe, if I can find a medium who, as you suggest, will not resort to "manipulation" when the Power does not "arrive" . . . Dean Harry Kellar, who lives in retirement in California, at one time had a standing challenge to all mediums (1876 to 1899), and even he will not come right out and say that all of it is humbug. And I think he knows *more* about the mysteries of magic than anyone living.' This truly expressed Houdini's state of mind. He terribly wanted to be convinced. That he could not be, was his tragedy.

There was, on the other hand, no difficulty about convincing Doyle of anything that smacked of the supernatural. His gullibility seemed limitless. Its most notorious manifestation was the episode described in his *The Coming of the Fairies*. This book is about two schoolgirls from Cottingley in Yorkshire who cut out drawings of fairies, set them in a woodland glade, and photographed the resulting scene. The fairy photographs came to the attention of a Miss Scatcherd, a well-known 'sensitive'; and she in turn told Doyle of them. He delegated a friend to look into the matter for him since he was just about to leave for Australia. The girls took more photographs. The friend was convinced. Doyle, on his return, was overcome. He knew, of course, that photographs could be faked. But he could not believe that two little girls could have hatched such a plot and seen it through as these two little girls had done. As far as Doyle was concerned, the Cottingley fairies lived.

You might say: If he could believe that, he could believe anything. Indeed, in this sense Conan Doyle himself was as much a mystery as any of his literary creations. How was it possible that the creator of Sherlock Holmes should turn out to be such a quintessential Dr Watson?

It was as if the person who produced those masterpieces of literary deduction was quite separate from Houdini's new acquaintance. No one knew more than the author of the Holmes stories about how mystifying things may seem before they are explained, and how simple after. 'I am afraid that I rather give myself away when I explain,' remarks Holmes on

one occasion. 'Results without causes are much more impressive.' And the formula of the stories is based upon exactly
this principle. They invariably begin with some mystifying
circumstance, or series of circumstances, which are by the end
of the story explained in a simple and logical manner. One
hardly dare ask what Holmes would have made of the Cottingley fairies, or of a man who could write (on the conditions of
life after death): 'The usual information is that any nutrition
is of a very light and delicate order, corresponding to the
delicate etheric body which requires it. Then there [is] the
question of marriage, and the old proposition of the much-
married man and which wife he should have. As there is no
sexual relation as we understand it, this problem is not very
complex and is naturally decided by soul affinity.'

But this combination of, on the one hand, outstanding ana-
lytic power and, on the other, apparently boundless credulity
regarding spiritualism, was by no means peculiar to Doyle.
The history of psychical research is crowded with comparable
figures – eminent savants who happily lent their names to
palpable hoaxes of the crudest nature. The celebrated physicists
Sir William Crookes, Sir Oliver Lodge, Sir William Barrett,
Lord Rayleigh; the naturalist Alfred Russel Wallace; the French
biologist and Nobel laureate Charles Richet; the vitalist philo-
sopher Hans Driesch; psychologists such as William McDougall and William James – these are just a few of the more
famous supporters of the spiritualist hypothesis. Parapsy-
chology today can cite similar names. At least one Nobel
laureate in physics believes that Uri Geller has supernatural
powers.

Why should these people have been – why should they still
be – so reluctant to believe that they were, and are, seeing
conjuring tricks?

Perhaps the answer may lie in the particular cast of mind
required of a physical scientist. The preponderance of physicists and engineers over psychologists among believers in psi
is marked. The physicist's world (in contrast to that of the
psychologist) is composed of more or less immutable laws

governing inanimate objects. The essence of physical science – as of Sherlock Holmes's technique – is close and accurate observation followed by deduction. The scientist has learned how to look; the best scientists are those who know what to look for and how to draw the right conclusions from what they see. In the very best scientists, these conclusions are often daring and original. The hypothesis of spiritualism is no stranger than many received scientific hypotheses. So the natural scientist who has become convinced of the paranormal hypothesis may well be more confident in his conclusions than the layman. He is accustomed to being right in what he takes to be comparable circumstances. Similarly, Conan Doyle, that veteran of the deductive art, felt that, whoever was likely to be deceived, he was not. 'In a fair light I saw my dead mother as clearly as ever I saw her in life. I am a cool observer and don't make mistakes.' While for Houdini, as for many others, the fact that people like Doyle could be convinced was a large factor in their own willingness to believe. 'It is only by knowing that Analytical Minds are going in for it, that I am treating this matter seriously,' he wrote Doyle early in their acquaintance.

But there is one big difference between the phenomena generally observed by scientists in the course of their work, and the phenomena of spiritualism. Scientific phenomena may be deceptive, but this is not on account of a will to deceive. Alfred Einstein, who propounded the most daring theory of all, said: 'God is subtle, but He is not malicious.' But false mediums, unlike God, certainly are, in this sense, malicious. The process, as in any display of illusions, is one of dissimulation and misdirection. The vital thing is to control the audience without its being aware of that control. The scientist, confident of his trained powers of observation and experimentation, draws his conclusions. Because he has not seen what he thought he saw, those conclusions are incorrect. He is applying the laws of physical observation to a different world in which everything is designed to make the laws of physics seemingly stand on their head. So the physicist, metaphorically, stands on his head, confidence unimpaired. This was Conan Doyle's position.

Like Alfred Russel Wallace with J. N. Maskelyne, Conan Doyle was faced, in Houdini, with a conjurer who was able to replicate the feats of the mediums. His response, like Wallace's, was not to disbelieve in the mediums, but to attribute supernatural powers to the conjurer. 'My dear chap,' he wrote, 'why go round the world seeking a demonstration of the occult when you are giving one all the time? Mrs Guppy [a well-known and hugely fat medium who allegedly travelled by telekinesis from Highbury to Bloomsbury] could dematerialize, and so could many folk in Holy Writ, and I do honestly believe that you can also.'

Houdini, of course, vehemently denied this. He repeated, and went on repeating, that everything he did was done by natural means. But he had a problem. He could not prove this without revealing his secrets. Thus, when Hewat Mackenzie, the president of the London College of Psychic Science, asserted in his book *Spirit Intercourse* that Houdini escaped from the Water-Torture Cell by dematerialisation, the magician was stymied. Mackenzie wrote: 'The body was completely dematerialized within this tank within one and a half minutes, while the author stood immediately over it. Without disturbing any of the locks, Houdini was transferred from the tank direct to the back of the stage in a dematerialized state. He was there materialized, and returned to the stage front dripping with water and attired in the blue jersey suit in which he entered the tank . . . Dematerialization is performed by methods similar in operation to those in which the psycho-plastic essence is drawn from the medium. The body of the medium may be reduced to half its ordinary weight in the materializing seance room, but in the case of dematerialization the essence continues to be drawn until the whole physical body vanishes, and the substance composing it is held in suspension within the atmosphere, much in the same way as moisture is held by evaporation. While in this state Houdini was transferred from the stage to the retiring-room behind, and there almost instantaneously materialized.'

What could be said or done to counter this short of demonstrating exactly how the Water-Torture Cell worked? Doyle himself recognised this dilemma and drew the conclusion which was, to him, inevitable: 'It is said, "How absurd for Doyle to attribute possible psychic powers to a man who himself denies them!" Is it not perfectly evident that if he did not deny them his occupation would have been gone forever? What would his brother magicians have to say to a man who admitted that half his tricks were done by what they would regard as illicit powers? It would be *exit* Houdini.'

Part of Houdini's difficulty when he protested that he was in no way a magical personage was that, in symbolic terms, that was exactly what he *was*. All his power lay in his embodiment of the idea that lay at the very root of spiritualism: immortality.

Carl Jung, who defended the idea of a life after death, wrote: '. . . beyond [the intellect] there is a thinking in primordial images – in symbols that are older than historical man; which have been ingrained in him from earliest times, and, eternally living, outlasting all generations, still make up the groundwork of the human psyche. It is possible to live the fullest life only when we are in harmony with these symbols; wisdom is a return to them. It is a question neither of belief nor knowledge, but of the agreement of our thinking with the primordial images of the unconscious. They are the source of all our conscious thoughts, and one of these primordial images is the idea of life after death.' Houdini, in his (literally) death-defying stunts, brought this 'primordial image' to the level of conscious experience, both for himself and on behalf of his audience.

That was real magic. Descending to the trivia that constituted the everyday currency of most mediums – disembodied voices speaking through trumpets, unexplained noises, small tables rising from the ground, ouija-boards – he was forced to confront the fundamental dilemma of spiritualism: the contrast between the enormous emotional and intellectual issues at stake and the poverty of their expression in mediumistic drawing-rooms. If he, who had repeatedly dared the entry to the underworld, had not been able to contact his mother, how was it possible that some 'trumpet-medium' should dare pretend to do so? And yet – what other means offered? *That* was the source of his fury.

This terrible, disproportionate triviality has always been one of the problems with spiritualism. The psychologist William James was particularly bothered by what he called 'this particularly crass and low type of supernatural phenomena'. James and Houdini may perhaps be said to have approached the question from opposite poles. Both spent their lives arriving at the same conclusion: that the question of life after death was the most important question of all. Houdini arrived at it instinctively; James, intellectually and emotionally. 'All argument is against it,' said Dr Johnson, 'but all belief is for it.' Houdini, approaching the question as, so to speak, the embodiment of belief – but without argument – found spiritualism emotionally impossible and exploded in indignation. James, feeling the same way, tried to reconcile himself by intellectual means. When T. H. Huxley said, 'Better live a crossing-sweeper, than die and be made to talk twaddle by a "medium" hired at a guinea a Seance,' James riposted: 'The odd point is that so few of those who talk in this way realize that they and the spiritists are using the same major premise and differing only in the minor. The major premise is: "Any spirit-revelation must be romantic." The minor of the spiritist is: "This is romantic"; that of the Huxleyan is "This is dingy twaddle" – whence their opposite conclusions!'

The friendship of the Doyles and the Houdinis developed apace. The families lunched together at Crowborough; Houdini sent tickets for his Palladium show. Receiving a batch of stamps from all round the world – probably from fan-mail following *The Man From Beyond* – he sent them on to Lady

Doyle, who collected stamps. Doyle wrote that he had been 'planting seeds in the West – Bristol, Bath, Swindon, and now back in London. I go to the famous spirit photographer Hope to-day.' Spirit photographers specialised in producing photographs of ghosts. The ghost Doyle was hoping for was that of his son Kingsley, who had appeared previously on a photograph.

Meanwhile, Houdini was investigating a very famous medium. She was known as Eva C., and had begun her career fifteen years earlier in Algiers, where she had been the means by which Charles Richet, the eminent biologist, proved that spirits were warm, had hair, and exhaled carbon dioxide. At that time she had been called Marthe Béraud; but there had been a scandal and Marthe had disappeared, to re-emerge as Eva. Since 1911 she had been under the protection of Mme Juliette Bisson, the wife of a well-known Parisian playwright. With Mme Bisson, Eva had gone through a series of tests with a German sexologist named Schrenck-Notzing, who was a friend of Richet's. In the course of these tests she had developed a technique for producing a substance known as ectoplasm, which took many curious and revolting forms. She was still producing it in 1920 when Houdini took part in some of her seances.

Well, we had success at the seance last night, as far as productions were concerned [he told Conan Doyle], but I am not prepared to say that they were supernormal.

I assure you I did not control the medium, so the suggestions were not mine. They made Mlle. Eva drink a cup of coffee and eat some cake (I presume to fill her up with some food stuff) and after she had been sewn into the tights, and a net over her face, she 'manifested'.

1st. Some frothlike substance, inside of net. It was about 5 inches long; she said it was 'elevating', but none of us four watchers saw it 'elevate'.

Committee, Messrs. Feilding, Baggally, Dingwall and myself. 2nd. A white plaster-looking affair over her right eye.

3rd. Something that looked like a small face, say 4 inches

in circumference. Was terra-cotta coloured, and Dingwall, who held her hands, had the best look at the 'object'.

4th. Some substance, frothlike, 'exuding from her nose'. Baggally and Feilding say it protruded from her nose, but Dingwall and I are positive that it was inside of net and was not extending from her nose; I had the best view from two different places. I deliberately took advantage to see just what it was.

It was a surprise effect indeed!

5th. Medium asked permission to remove something in her mouth; showed her hands empty, and took out what appeared to be a rubberish substance, which she disengaged and showed us plainly; we held the electric torch; all saw it plainly, when presto! it vanished.

The seance started at 7.30 and lasted until midnight.

Such was the bizarre world of spiritualism in its more 'scientific' form (as Mme Bisson expressed it). Houdini was convinced that Eva had 'vanished' the rubbery substance by sleight-of-handing it into her mouth while pretending to have it between her fingers – the same move he used in his old Hindoo needle trick. He attended various other seances with Eva during his time in England, but, much to Doyle's disappointment, remained unconvinced.

Soon after this, in the summer of 1920, Houdini returned to the United States. He wrote from there that his house had been 'all fixed up' and cordially invited the Doyles to 'make [it] your home when you visit New York City'. Doyle tactfully deflected this invitation: 'You will understand that I have to be semi-public for my job's sake.' Despite his conviction that Houdini had magic powers, he worried about his new friend's safety. 'All good wishes to you, my dear Houdini. Do drop these dangerous stunts', he urged him; and, again, 'Our best remembrances to your wife and self. For God's sake be careful in these fearsome feats of yours. Surely you could retire now.'

Conan Doyle was preparing a lecture-tour of America in which he would spread the spiritualist word. Jean and their three children were to accompany him. They arrived in New York in the spring of 1922. Sir Arthur's first lecture took place

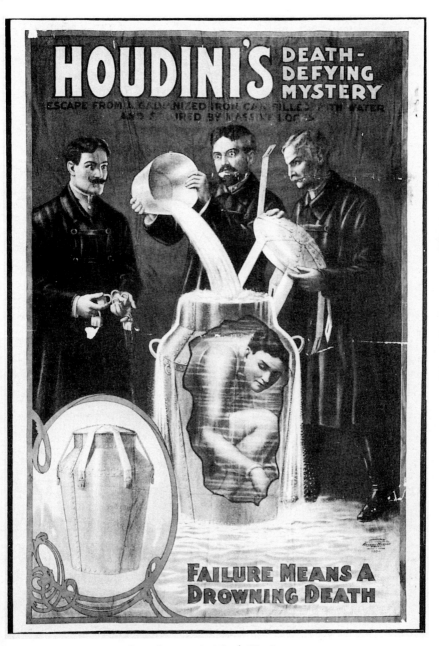

Back to the womb: The Milk Can act

What the crowd saw:
Houdini, hanging from the top
of a skyscraper, escapes from
yet another straitjacket.

What Houdini saw:
a sea of hats and marooned
tramcars as he stops traffic.

After Houdini's mother's death, his brother Leopold was cut out of the family photograph.

The same photo as later reproduced. Leopold has now been airbrushed out.

Taken on Board the
Hamburg American Liner "IMPERATOR"
In Mid Ocean June 23. 1914.

Two versions of Houdini with Teddy Roosevelt. In photographs, but not in life, unwelcome intruders could simply be airbrushed out.

Houdini performs a particularly
gymnastic screen rescue.

Houdini with
Sir Arthur Conan Doyle.

The face that captivated a
thousand professors: Mrs Mina
Crandon, aka 'Margery',
the medium.

'Ectoplasm' emerges from
Margery's nose and/or mouth. This
variety bears a strong resemblance
to crumpled fabric.

Houdini meets the ghost of Abraham Lincoln
in a demonstration of spirit photography.

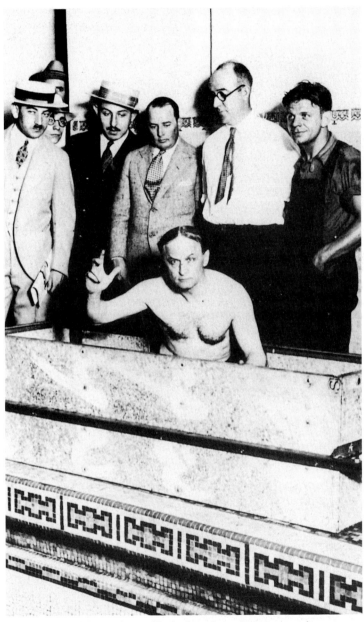

Houdini in his coffin before the swimming-pool
underwater test, 1924. The years are beginning to tell.

At the grave of old magicians: Lafayette and Bosco

Houdini poses with the bust destined for his tomb.

Hardeen and Bess at Houdini's grave,
finally complete with bust and plaque to mark his
presidency of the Society of American Magicians.

in Carnegie Hall before a packed house. There followed a crowded couple of weeks in New York, then in April a short rest on the Jersey shore before the family set off on its tour across America. May saw them back in New York, where they visited the Houdinis. On 10 May Houdini noted in his day-book: 'To-day at 11 o'clock Sir Arthur and Lady Doyle came up to 278, for a visit. Sir Arthur was very anxious to see my collection of books and became very much interested. I went all over the house and got together all my rare tracts, and he seemed very much surprised at my collection of literature on Spiritualism.' Doyle, however, was disappointed to see that Houdini's collection was 'very short of positive books'. A fortnight later Doyle attended, at Houdini's invitation, the annual banquet of the Society of American Magicians. He had at first been reluctant to do so, feeling that magicians and spiritualists were ranged in opposite camps and that his views would be attacked. But Houdini persuaded him that nothing was further from his mind, and in the event it was Sir Arthur who amazed the magicians by showing them the dinosaur footage from the film which had recently been made of his novel *The Lost World*.

The friendship between the two families was by now so warm that, when the Doyles went to Atlantic City for a short holiday in June, they invited the Houdinis to join them there. 'The children would teach you to swim! and the change would do you good.' Houdini replied, 'Mrs Houdini joins me in thanking you for the invitation to come to Atlantic City, and if you will be there next Saturday or Sunday, Mrs Houdini and I would like to spend the weekend with you . . . Most important of all, if the kiddies want to teach me to swim I will be there, and in return will show them how to do one or two things that will make it very interesting.'

The afternoon of June 17th was to be a momentous one. It began innocently enough: 'As Sir Arthur, Mrs Houdini and I were sitting on the sand skylarking with the children Sir Arthur excused himself saying that he was going to have his usual afternoon nap. He left us but returned in a short time and said "Houdini, if agreeable, Lady Doyle will give you a special seance, as she has a feeling that she might have a message coming through. At any rate, she is willing to try." '

That, at any rate, was Houdini's account of how the affair began. In *Our American Adventure* Doyle says, 'It was sudden inspiration of mine to ask him up to our room and see if we could get any evidence or consolation for him,' while in his *On the Edge of the Unknown,* which was written after Houdini's death, he ascribes the whole thing to Houdini: 'The method in which Houdini tried to explain away, minimize and contort our attempt at consolation, which was given *entirely at his own urgent request* and against my wife's desire, has left a deplorable shadow in my mind.'

It seems, all in all, most probable that the suggestion did originate with the Doyles. Doyle's view at this time was expressed in a note to an American medium, Ada Besinnet (later exposed by Houdini): 'Mr Houdini is deeply interested and quite sympathetic but has never had a chance of getting good evidence . . . He deserves more than has come to him, for he is a patient and sympathetic observer.' What the Doyles now felt was that they might be able to provide this evidence themselves.

Houdini goes on to explain how Bess cued him as to what all this was probably about, using the system of signs they had evolved for their 'second sight' act twenty years before. 'In that manner Mrs. Houdini told me that on the night previous she had gone into detail with Lady Doyle about the great love I bear for my Mother. She related to her a number of instances, such as, my returning home from long trips, sometimes as far away as Australia, and spending months with my Mother and wearing only the clothes that she had given me because I thought it would please her and give her some happiness . . . I walked with Sir Arthur to the Doyles' suite. Sir Arthur drew down the shades so as to exclude the bright light. We three, Lady Doyle, Sir Arthur and I, sat around the table on which were a number of pencils and a writing pad, placing our hands on the surface of the table.

'Sir Arthur started the seance with a devout prayer. I had made up my mind that I would be as religious as it was within my power to be and not at any time did I scoff at the ceremony. I excluded all earthly thoughts and gave my whole soul to the seance.'

Conan Doyle takes up the tale: 'It was a singular scene, my wife with her hand flying wildly, beating the table while she scribbled at a furious rate, I sitting opposite and tearing sheet after sheet from the block as it was filled up, and tossing each across to Houdini, while he sat silent, looking grimmer and paler every moment.'

The first question Jean Doyle asked of the spirit which had taken hold of her so energetically was, 'Do you believe in God?' Her hand beat the table three times: affirmative. She said, 'Then I will make the sign of the Cross.' She marked a cross on the edge of the pad on which she was writing. Then she asked who was there, and whether it was Houdini's mother. Her hand struck the table three times once more. Then she began to write:

Oh, my darling, thank God, thank God, at last I'm through
– I've tried, oh so often – now I am happy. Why, of course,
I want to talk to my boy – my own beloved boy – Friends,
thank you, with all my heart for this.

You have answered the cry of my heart – and of his – God
bless him – a thousand fold, for all his life for me – never
had a mother such a son – tell him not to grieve, soon he'll
get all the evidence he is anxious for – Yes, we know – tell
him, I want him to try to write in his own home. It will be
far better so.

I will work with him – he is so, so dear to me – I am
preparing so sweet a home for him which one day in God's
good time he will come to – it is one of my great joys
preparing it for our future –

I am so happy in this life – it is so full and joyous – my
only shadow has been that my beloved one hasn't known
how often I have been with him all the while – here away
from my heart's darling – combining my work thus in this
life of mine.

It is so different over here, so much larger and bigger and more beautiful – so lofty – all sweetness around one – nothing that hurts and we see our beloved ones on earth – that is such a joy and comfort to us – Tell him I love him more than ever – the years only increase it – and his goodness fills my soul with gladness and thankfulness. Oh, just this, it *is* me. I want him only to know that – that – I have bridged the gulf – that is what I wanted, oh, so much – Now I can rest in peace – How soon –

At this point, Doyle requested Houdini to ask some question that would prove to him that his mother really was with them. 'Lady Doyle did not seem to think that the spirit would answer direct questions, and I purposely evaded asking anything which might embarrass the medium, as I wanted to help all I could, so I thought of the question proposed by Sir Arthur, "Can my mother read my mind?" in this way answering any question of which I might think.'
The spirit resumed:

I *always* read my beloved son's mind – his dear mind – there is so much I want to say to him – but – I am almost overwhelmed by this joy of talking to him once more – it is almost too much to get through – the joy of it – thank you, thank you, friend, with all my heart for what you have done for me this day – God bless you too, Sir Arthur, for what you are doing for us – for us over here – who so need to get in touch with our beloved ones on the earth plane -
If only the world knew this great truth – how different – life would be for men and women – Go on, let nothing stop you – great will be your reward hereafter – Good-bye – I brought you, Sir Arthur, and my darling son together – I felt you as the one man who might help us to pierce the veil – and I was right – Bless him, bless him, bless him, I say from the depths of my soul – he fills my heart and later we shall be together – oh, so happy – a happiness awaits him that he has never dreamed of – tell him I am with him – just tell him that I'll soon make him know how close I am all the while – his eyes will soon be opened – Good-bye again – God's blessing on you all –

When Jean had finally stopped writing, Houdini asked about trying the automatic writing in his own home. He took up a pencil to see what would happen, and wrote, apparently without volition, the name 'Powell'.

Now it so happened that both Doyle and Houdini had close friends of this name, who were on their minds at this particular time. Houdini's old friend, F.E. Powell, was in some trouble. His wife had been paralysed by a stroke and could no longer work with him; he was wondering whether he should engage a young woman as his assistant. The Houdinis had recently had an argument about this. Mrs Houdini maintained that it would be unfair of Powell to engage a girl; Houdini, on the other hand, could see no reason why he should not do so. This was what Houdini asserted he had in mind when he wrote 'Powell'. But Sir Arthur could not accept this explanation; for an old spiritualist ally of his, also named Powell, had died only the previous week. He jumped up and said, 'The Spirits have directed you in writing the name of my dear fighting partner in Spiritualism, Dr Ellis Powell, who has just died in England. I am the person he is most likely to signal to, and here is his name coming through your hands. Truly Saul is among the Prophets.'

When Houdini got home he found a letter from his Powell awaiting him, which he sent on to Conan Doyle with the comment 'I judge it was just one of those coincidences.' But Doyle could not accept this. Three days later he wrote: 'My dear Houdini – No, the Powell explanation won't do. Not only is he the one man who would wish to get me, but in the evening, Mrs M., the lady medium, got "there is a man here. He wants to say that he is sorry he had to speak so abruptly this afternoon." '

This incident, as one might expect, simply confirmed each of the men more strongly in his original attitude. Doyle was happily convinced that the spirit of Houdini's mother had indeed spoken through Jean Doyle and that he had made his friend a wonderful gift for which Houdini was duly grateful. 'I see you sometime,' he wrote, 'as your true experiences accumulate, giving a wonderful lecture, "Phenomenal Spiritualism – True and False". In which, giving an account of your adventures with Fakes you will also give an account of those which bear inspection. It would be a very great draw . . . I may say your mother again came back with words of passionate love through Mrs Metcalfe of Brooklyn last night.' His view of the incident remained that 'It was a long and very moving message and bore every internal sign of being genuine. There is no question at all in my mind that Houdini was greatly shaken at the time and for some days afterwards. His objections were all afterthoughts in order to save the situation.'

'I was *willing* to believe, even wanted to believe,' Houdini noted. 'It was weird to me and with a beating heart I waited, hoping that I might feel once more the presence of my beloved Mother . . . I especially wanted to speak to my Mother, because that day, *June 17*, . . . was her birthday.' This was just one of the many personal facts she had failed to mention. Indeed, the message had been couched in terms of the widest generality: there was nothing particular to Houdini in it at all. But Doyle was not persuaded. 'What are birthdays on the other side?' he wanted to know. 'It is the death day which is the real birthday.' Houdini could still not convince himself that this was the real thing. In the margin of the letter he noted: 'Message written by Lady Doyle claiming the spirit of my dear mother had control of her hand – my sainted mother could not write English and spoke broken English.' And how was it possible that his mother, an orthodox Jewess, should have begun her outpourings with the sign of the cross? No wonder he looked shaken. This appeal to the very deepest of his emotions, the hopes it raised, the dashing of those hopes, the consciousness that he could say nothing without mortally offending a good friend – how could all this fail to unsettle him?

Relations between the two families remained cordial for the few days remaining to the Doyles in America. On their last night, June 22, which was the Houdinis' wedding anniversary, they all went to see Raymond Hitchcock's *Pinwheel Revue* at the Carroll Theater. The evening was a great success in a somewhat unexpected way, for Hitchcock, recognising who was in the audience, insisted upon inviting Houdini on to the stage to perform one of his tricks. He agreed, and performed the needle trick to wild applause; after which the rest of the show was scrapped and the orchestra struck up the closing number. The Doyles were duly impressed by this unique example of an artist 'not only stopping but curtailing a show in which he was not programmed to have a part'. They sailed next day; a telegram from Houdini wishing them bon voyage and hoping they would soon return was placed in Sir Arthur's hands as he stepped on to the gangway.

No more passed between them concerning the seance until November, when Houdini published an article in the New York *Sun* violently attacking spiritualism and mentioning his experience with the Doyles. This naturally infuriated Doyle. 'I feel rather sore about it,' he wrote. ' . . . When you say that you have had no evidence of survival, you say what I cannot reconcile with what I saw with my own eyes. I know by many examples the purity of my wife's mediumship, and I saw what you got and what the effect was upon you at the time . . . However, I don't propose to discuss the subject any more with you, for I consider that you have had your proofs and that the responsibility of accepting or rejecting is with you.'

Regretfully, Houdini replied: 'You write that you are very "sore". I trust it is not with me, because you, having been truthful and manly all your life, naturally must admire the same traits in other human beings.' He rehearsed all the reasons why he could not accept the letter as a true communication from his mother, and the Powell explanation, and ended, 'I trust my clearing up the seance from my point of view is satisfactory, and that you do not harbour any ill feeling, because I hold both Lady Doyle and yourself in the highest esteem. I know you treat this as a religion, but personally I cannot do so, for, up to the present time, and with all my experiences, I have never seen or heard anything that could really convert me.'

They continued to correspond for a while. But the friendship was irremediably undermined. What had happened was too personal, on both sides, ever to be forgotten or laid aside. Houdini continued to attack false mediums (which effectively meant all mediums) with renewed fury; the Doyles watched from afar in increasing anger and perplexity.

'You are to me a perpetual mystery,' Doyle had written early in their acquaintance. 'But no doubt you are to many. You do (and say) things that are beyond me. As an example of the latter, you said that Ira Davenport did his phenomena by normal means. But if he did (which I really don't believe) then he is manifestly not only a liar but a blasphemer, as he went round with Mr Ferguson, a clergyman, and mixed it all up with religion. And yet you are photographed as a friend with one whom, under those circumstances, one would not touch with a muck-rake. Now how can one reconcile that? It interests me as a problem.'

During the years of gradual estrangement which inevitably followed the fatal seance, Houdini mercilessly attacked Doyle's credulity in his lectures while the good-hearted Doyle followed his erstwhile friend's career more in sorrow than in anger. Like Houdini, his views remained unaltered. Considering the mystery after Houdini had died, he reconciled his difficulties by reverting once more to the Davenports. 'If it be true that the Davenports were real mediums (and let the inquirer really read their record before he denies it), and if Houdini produced exactly similar results, which have in each case been inexplicable to their contemporaries, then is it conceivable that they were produced in entirely different ways? If Ira Davenport was a medium, then there is a strong prima facie case that Houdini was a medium too.'

16

Margery

The fiasco of the Jean Doyle seance and the collapse of his friendship with Sir Arthur resulted in a stepping-up of Houdini's campaign against fraudulent mediums. The most continual and unbroken disappointment was never going to kill his desperate desire to be 'united in happiness' with his mother. But it could and did embitter him, and he expressed this bitterness in the increasing intensity of his campaign against fraud.

He employed two investigators full-time – Julia Sawyer, a niece of Bess's, and a Miss Rose Mackenberg. He even went so far as to buy a spiritualist church in Worcester, Mass., and the title of Reverend that went with it, where he installed Miss Mackenberg under the name of the Revd. F(rances) Raud. This somewhat crude exploit gained the headlines he craved. Others demanded more skill. It took all his powers, for example, to find out how one particularly baffling slatewriter worked his tricks. (Slatewriters produced spirit messages written on slates which had been shown to be blank and to which they could have had no apparent access.) 'When he did the slatewriting at this sitting I felt someone's presence and, sure enough, when he took the slates away there was an almost imperceptible hesitation. In this fraction of a second the slates were switched through a *trap in the panel* behind me. I had a mirror on a rubber elastic fastened to my vest and as I took my seat I pulled the elastic so I could sit on it. I managed to secure the mirror and keep it palmed in my hand, and with it saw the panel slide open, the arm extended with the duplicate slates, and the exchange made.'

In 1924 the House of Representatives of the District of Columbia set up a judiciary committee to discuss whether fortune-telling should be banned in Washington. During the

1920s as during the 1980s, prophets of the paranormal held sway at the White House. It was well-known that Mrs Coolidge, the President's wife, frequently attended seances, and many of the senators were in regular contact with mediums.

Of course Houdini insisted on appearing before the Judiciary Committee. And of course the mediums tried to discredit him. Naturally Houdini's appearance made the headlines; and naturally the mediums all suggested that his crusade was conducted, and he was now appearing, solely to gain publicity.

Perish the thought! However, he could point out that he certainly wasn't making any money out of it. In the interests of his crusade, he explained, 'I positively spend between $40,000 and $50,000 every year. I brought my staff up here. They are under salary; they are under expenses.' He then performed a couple of tricks popular with spiritualists and explained how they were done.

One of these was the most fundamental spiritualist trick of all. It is known as 'fishing'. Its most famous recent exponent was the late Mrs Doris Stokes. Out of the blue Houdini asked, 'Is there anybody here by the name of Mrs Florence Kahn?' Of course, there was.

HOUDINI: My spirit guide tells me – George Washington is my spirit guide – he tells me in a picture. I see a lady in a ferryboat in a big, wide stream. Where is there a lady, please? Have you ever been in a ferryboat in a great broad beautiful stream? Is that right? Have I ever spoken to you, Mrs Kahn?

MRS KAHN: Never.

HOUDINI: Did you get a most important letter four days ago that you decided not to answer? Yes or no?

MRS KAHN: Sixty-eight of them.

HOUDINI: This is a very particular one from a very dear old friend, Yes or no?

MRS KAHN: Yes . . .

HOUDINI: Then, the message. I am just doing the inspirational stuff for you, and I now will give you evidence of my wonderful power. This is addressed to Florence P. Kahn: 'Good work. You are going to find that Julius P.'s efforts

were appreciated. (Signed) Benjamin Franklin.' . . .
[Laughter and applause]

Houdini went on to explain how he did it:

> HOUDINI: First of all when I came in, I can guess and pick out
> and say, 'Clara is present' and make a guess. If I hit it, all
> right. If I did not hit it I say Thelma or Mary, and it fits
> some one. Then I inquire, 'Who is that lady?' I heard Mrs
> Kahn say, 'I would like to get a message.' Didn't you say
> that, Mrs Kahn?
> MRS KAHN: Yes.
> HOUDINI: I heard you. And you were back of me and I did
> not turn around. I was purposely impolite and I hereby
> apologize for my apparent impoliteness. I found out about
> you and was able to give you a life history, and I simply
> exchanged, deducted, and made guesses; and that is all there
> is to it.

Manoeuvres such as this seem so childishly simple when
they are explained that it is hard to believe anyone can be
taken in by them. But they *are* taken in: partly because they
want to be and partly because, well-performed by an experienced practitioner, the effect can be unnerving in the extreme.
As tricks, however, they are commonplace.

But Houdini was soon to meet a medium who was his
worthy adversary.

Conan Doyle's American tours had been accompanied by
enormous publicity. In December 1922, the publisher of the
Scientific American, Orson Munn, decided to cash in on this.
He announced that the magazine would award $2,500 to the
first person producing a genuine spirit photograph and $2,500
to the first person producing genuine phenomena in the seance
room. The genuineness or otherwise of entries would be
judged by a committee consisting of the Harvard psychologist
Dr William McDougall, Hereward Carrington, a well-known
psychical researcher, Dr Daniel Frost Comstock, the developer
of Technicolor, Dr Walter Franklin Prince, a minister and
psychologist, and Houdini. Conan Doyle was much annoyed

by Houdini's inclusion. 'My dear Houdini,' he wrote (from the heights of his own impartiality),

> I see that you are on the *Scientific American* Committee, but how can it be called an Impartial Committee when you have committed yourself to such statements as that some Spiritualists pass away before they realize how they have been deluded, etc.? You have every right to hold such an opinion, but you can't sit on an Impartial Committee afterwards. It becomes biased at once. What I wanted was five good clear-headed men.

The kind of person Conan Doyle had in mind was the journalist and mathematician Malcolm Bird, an associate editor of the magazine. Early in 1923 Bird had visited Britain and spent some time with Conan Doyle investigating various mediums. They returned to the United States together in April 1923. Although they had found no one who seemed to qualify for the award, Bird reported on his return that he was 'convinced that these phenomena do occur without fraud. I distinctly saw phosphorescent lights, heard trumpet voices and witnessed the movement of material objects under circumstances which satisfied me personally that there was no fraud.' He added: 'Don't assume for a moment that this means I am endorsing spiritualism.' Bird then took up the secretaryship of the committee. Conan Doyle, just before he left New York for a nationwide tour, recommended a friend of his to the committee's attention. Her name was Mina Crandon, a young Canadian woman (she was then twenty-six) married to a wealthy and fashionable Boston surgeon, Dr LeRoi Goddard Crandon.

It was Dr Crandon who had become interested in spiritualism first. He had read a book called *The Psychic Structures of the Goligher Circle,* published in 1919 by a Dr W. J. Crawford. Dr Crawford was a Belfast engineer who had become convinced that various members of a local family, the Golighers, were moving objects by means of supernaturally produced structures he called *teleplasm*. Photographs taken of this teleplasm reveal it to be something very like a rod draped in a net curtain. However, Dr Crandon was much excited by Dr Crawford's book, and showed it to his wife. They visited a medium who assured them that Mina possessed strong mediumistic powers. They tried some seances at home, using a table built exactly to Crawford's specifications, and to Dr Crandon's delight it not only moved but seemed almost to dance across the room on two legs. Soon afterwards they took off on a tour of Europe during which they visited all the most august names in psychical research, including Professor Richet (who had discovered Eva C.) and Conan Doyle. All these people were much impressed by Mina's powers.

The *Scientific American* committee had been meeting with little success. Nobody of any real interest had turned up. Mr Munn was therefore prevailed upon to increase the award to $5,000 to see if this would bring forward someone more serious. It was now, in November 1923, that Dr Crandon contacted the magazine. He was not interested in the money, nor was Mrs Crandon prepared to go to New York to be investigated. But if the committee would conduct its investigations in Boston, Mina (who for mediumistic purposes called herself Margery) was prepared to co-operate with them. As several of them anyway lived nearby, this was no problem.

Malcolm Bird paid the first visit. Margery's psychic abilities had progressed. She was now able to make bugle-calls without a bugle and rattle a non-existent chain. There were flashes of light in the dark. She could stop the clock just by concentrating upon it; she produced a two-dollar bill and a live pigeon. She had also developed a spirit alter ego: when she went into trance it was her brother Walter who spoke through her. Walter had been killed when still a young man some years previously: he had been crushed by a train. Speaking through Margery's lips he had a gruff voice, a penchant for repartee and an outstandingly profane vocabulary. He also had a notably cool head. Once, when Dr Comstock brought an intricate mechanical device to a seance with a request that Walter operate it, he asked, 'How long did it take you to make that thing, Comstock?'

'About three days, Walter.'

'Well, if you expect me to work it in three minutes you're mistaken,' Walter replied. 'I have to experiment and work out things in my sphere just as you do in yours, and I may have to try it forty times before I can do it. If you think I'm here just to wander around the room making demonstrations, you're damn mistaken. I have to work hard and gather force for you people here, and light dissipates it just as water interferes with your activities.' Thus Walter ensured that the seance conditions suited him. As to the provenance of his voice, Dr Comstock said: 'One time I placed one hand over Mrs Crandon's mouth and nose, and the other over Dr Crandon's mouth and nose, and pressed hard, so hard that I must have hurt them. And Walter's voice – a hoarse whisper – came as clearly as it did before.'

Bird was much impressed. He recommended Margery to the committee, which paid her a number of visits. In the July 1924 issue of the *Scientific American* he published an article describing the investigations and hinting that the prize was as good as won.

Houdini, although he was nominally on the committee, had known nothing about Margery. The first he heard of the affair was when he received a letter from Bird: 'As you will observe when you get your July *Scientific American*, we are engaged in the investigation of another case of mediumship. Our original idea was not to bother you with it unless, and until, it got to a stage where there seemed serious prospects that it was either genuine or a type of fraud which our other committeemen could deal with . . . Mr Munn feels that the case has taken a turn that makes it desirable for us to discuss it with you.'

Houdini was beside himself. It was clear from Bird's article that the committee was on the point of giving Margery the award. How could they have gone so far without him? He rushed to New York and confronted Munn and Bird. It was essential that he and Munn go to Boston at once. The Cran-

dons were happy to offer hospitality to any visiting members
of the committee, but Houdini was adamant that neither he
nor Munn should accept this offer. It would put them at a
disadvantage *vis-à-vis* Margery. They booked into the Copley-
Plaza Hotel, but accepted the Crandons' invitation to dine.

It was clear from the start that Houdini's relations with the
Crandons were going to be tense. Houdini thought that they
had been trying to keep him away from the investigation.
This only made him feel the more combative. Despite his
protestations, it clearly never entered his mind that Margery
could be anything more than a clever trickster. She had duped
the scientists, as clever mediums always had duped scientists –
but she would not dupe him. 'The truth is,' observed Edmund
Wilson, ' . . . that in a committee of scientists of which
Houdini is a member it is Houdini who is the scientist. Doctors, psychologists and physicists are no better qualified to
check up on spiritualistic phenomena than lawyers, artists or
clergymen.'

Houdini's suspicions that the Crandons had been trying to
keep him away were not without substance. In May Dr Crandon had got hold of an advance copy of A *Magician among the
Spirits*. He reported to Conan Doyle, to whom he wrote
weekly, that Houdini was 'not in any way held back by ability
or intent to tell the truth'. He was disgusted at the way
Houdini had used Doyle's private letters as evidence of his
credulity. Walter, who was able to express Margery's real
feelings when Mina might have felt constrained, had burst out
against Houdini several times – more than once in verse. And
if Houdini was determined to 'get' Margery, his sentiments
were cordially reciprocated. Crandon told Doyle that they
planned to 'crucify' Houdini and so prove Margery 'the most
extraordinary mediumship in modern history'. On the morning of 23 July, the day of Margery's first seance with Houdini,
the tension was palpable. Crandon told Doyle that Margery
was 'vomiting merrily' at the prospect of the evening's activities and 'general nastiness'.

The evening produced its fair share of phenomena. Houdini

was sitting on Margery's left, 'controlling' her left hand and left foot (i.e. he kept hold of them, or kept in contact with them, ensuring that she could not use them to produce any effects). Bird was on her right. The other members of the committee were all present. The seance was conducted for the most part in darkness. Margery, apparently fully controlled, rang a bell situated in a box on the floor; Walter threw a megaphone which landed at Houdini's feet, as requested; a heavy cabinet was tilted over. Next day (24 July) there was another seance, this time at Dr Comstock's hotel. Houdini, once again, had charge of Margery's left side. The bell-box that evening was on the table; it mysteriously fell to the floor, and, later, the table itself tilted over.

That evening, back at their hotel, Houdini wrote Munn a letter. His emotion is evident in his syntax, which is more than usually contorted:

Dear Mr. Munn,
   Please, if I may, allow me to see the exposed article before it is published, as all of the other articles were not written so as to properly place the real thing before the public.
   Mr. Bird in your presence, said he believed the medium was fifty per cent genuine, when this evening there was no chance of anything she pretended to have been accomplished by 'Walter,' but was so done by herself. In fact she is *one hundred per cent trickster or fraud* judging by the first seance I attended, after forty or more were given . . .
   I have been unfairly treated in this case being only called in when according to Mr. Bird's personal statement and in print made, to the effect that the medium, Mrs Crandon, was fifty per cent genuine . . . facts such that could not have been written by a competent investigator, and I would like a personally written statement from all those who were present on the Committee, to check their findings.

To Harry Price Houdini wrote: 'There is no doubt in my mind, whatsoever, that this lady who has been "fooling" the scientists for months resorted to some of the slickest methods

I have ever known and honestly it has taken my thirty years of experience to detect her in her various moves.'

Later, Houdini revealed just how he had detected what Margery was up to. Before the first seance he had begun his precautions early:

> All that day I had worn a silk rubber bandage around [his right] leg just below the knee. By night the part of the leg below the bandage had become swollen and painfully tender, thus giving me a much keener sense of feeling and making it easier to notice the slightest sliding of Mrs Crandon's ankle or flexing of her muscles. She wore silk stockings and during the seance had her skirts pulled up well above her knees . . .
>
> On the evening in question the bell-box was placed between my feet with my right foot between it and Mrs Crandon's left foot. As the seance progressed I could distinctly feel her ankle slowly and spasmodically sliding as it pressed against mine while she gained space to raise her foot off the floor and touch the top of the box. To the ordinary sense of touch the contact would seem the same while this was being done. At times she would say:
>
> 'Just press hard against my ankle so you can see that my ankle is there,' and as she pressed I could feel her gain another half inch.
>
> When she had finally maneuvered her foot around to a point where she could get at the top of the box the bell ringing began and *I positively felt* the tendons of her leg flex and tighten as she repeatedly touched the ringing apparatus. There is no question in my mind about it. *She did this.* Then, when the ringing was over, I plainly *felt her leg slide back* into its original position with her foot on the floor beside mine.

The trick with the megaphone was Margery's masterpiece.

> During the second intermission 'Walter' asked for an illuminated plaque to be placed on the lid of the box which held the bell and Bird went to get it. This left the right hand and foot of the medium free. ['When Bird left the circle it was *pitch dark*,' Houdini wrote Bess that same evening.] Bird had difficulty in finding the plaque and while he was searching 'Walter' suddenly called for 'control'.

Mrs Crandon placed her right hand in mine and gave me to understand that I had both her hands. Bird was requested to stand in the doorway, but without any warning, before he could obey, the cabinet was thrown over backwards violently. *The medium then gave me her right foot also*, saying: 'You have now both hands and both feet.'

Then 'Walter' called out:

'The megaphone is in the air. Have Houdini tell me where to throw it.'

'Towards me,' I replied, and in an instant it fell at my feet.

The way she did these two tricks is as follows: when Bird left the room it freed her right foot and hand. With her right hand she tilted the corner of the cabinet enough to get her free foot under it, then picking up the megaphone she placed it on her head, dunce-cap fashion. Then she threw the cabinet over with her right foot. Then she simply jerked her head, causing the megaphone to fall at my feet. Of course with the megaphone on her head it was easy and simple for her to ask me or anyone else to hold both of her feet and also her hands, and still she could snap the megaphone off her head in any direction requested. This is the *slickest* ruse I have ever detected, and it has converted all skeptics.

Houdini had not yet finished with Margery. He now had his assistant Jim Collins construct a box which would contain her. It was shaped like a fall-front bureau and its effect was something like a pillory. Margery sat on a chair inside; the lid was closed, leaving only her head and arms sticking out, and the box was locked. Margery was now challenged to produce her usual phenomena. Malcolm Bird was no longer present at the seances: Houdini had objected that he was betraying the committee's secret deliberations to the Crandons.

The first box seance was to take place on 25 August 1924. The Crandons and their supporters did not welcome the innovation, since it was their contention that Margery produced her phenomena by means of a pseudopod, or supernormal limb, which emanated from between her legs. Dr Crandon announced: 'The psychic does not refuse to sit in the cage made by Houdini for the committee; but she makes the reservation that she knows no precedent in psychic research where a medium has been so enclosed: and she believes that a closed cage gives little or no regard for the theory and experience of the psychic structure or mediumism.'

On the first evening, however, the box proved useless. It was broken open, possibly by the psychic structure. Somehow the bell was rung: it was contended that Margery was using her head. Next day the locks were strengthened and the contest resumed.

The activities of 26 August began with Malcolm Bird bursting in and demanding to know why he was being excluded. Houdini confronted him with accusations of betrayal. Bird at first blustered, then resigned from the committee and flounced out. The seance began.

According to Houdini, he suspected from the start that Margery had something concealed inside the box and repeatedly warned Dr Prince *'not to let go of her right hand until after the seance was over and the cabinet-box unlocked'*. She offered to be physically searched, but this was too much for Houdini. He declined, saying, 'No, never mind, let it go, I am not a physician.' 'Walter' then said: 'Houdini, you are very clever indeed, but it won't work. I suppose it was an accident those things were left in the cabinet?' Houdini asked what was left in the cabinet? 'Pure accident, was it? You were not here, but your assistant was,' said Walter, and stated that a ruler would be found in the cabinet-box under a pillow at the medium's feet, 'and virtually accused me of putting it there to throw suspicion on his sister winding up with a violent outburst in which he exclaimed: "Houdini, you goddamned sonofabitch, get the hell out of here and never come back. If you don't, I will!" '

'This just expressed Mrs Crandon's feelings towards me,' says Houdini.

The seance proceeded: nothing happened. Houdini wrote Bess that night: 'As I asked permission to have the red light turned on as soon as the bell rang as I knew she cried out take the gimmick back with the cabinet, if she used a foot rule – so she gave a complete blank seance.' He added: ' "Walter" begged my pardon for calling me names and wanted it crost out of the record but it remains as is.' At the end, the box was opened and, as Walter had predicted, a ruler – in fact, a folding two-foot rule – was found, with which Margery could have rung her bell.

Who planted the ruler? Houdini said it was the Crandons. The Crandons said it was Houdini, who wanted to make sure Margery would be discredited. After Houdini's death, Jim Collins is supposed to have confessed to the deed. In that case Houdini would have known about the ruler (which would be why he drew Dr Prince's attention so repeatedly to the possibility of some such thing) but could truthfully deny having planted it himself. This seems distinctly possible. He had never been bothered by scruples when it came to showing up the unscrupulous behaviour of hated opponents.

Houdini was appearing at Keith's Theater in Boston to coincide with his investigations there. He reports an exchange between himself and Margery, who evidently thought that he was going to denounce her from the stage there during the part of his show devoted to fraudulent mediums. (His regular show at this time began with a lecture on this topic, going on to some 'small magic' and finishing with the perennial Water-Torture Cell.) She said, 'If you misrepresent me from the stage at Keith's some of my friends will come up and give you a good beating.'

'I am not going to misrepresent you,' [Houdini] replied, 'they are not coming on the stage and I am not going to get a beating.'

'Then it is your wits against mine,' she said . . .

'Yes, certainly, that is just what it is,' [Houdini] told her.

'She repeatedly told [Houdini] of her boy twelve years old and said that she would not want him to grow up and read that his mother was a fraud, to which [Houdini] replied: "Then don't be a fraud." '

If ever two people were destined to hate each other, it was

Margery and Houdini. It was inevitable given what they were each trying to do – Margery to play her role, Houdini to destroy it and her. Margery's feelings were expressed through Walter, who took to predicting that Houdini would be dead in 'a year or less'. Houdini scornfully dismissed this: 'In the last 10 years my death has been predicted dozens of times, and if the spiritualists(?) guess often enough some time they will guess correctly.' Nevertheless, he was deeply unsettled by Margery. For she embodied everything that made him feel most miserable and uncomfortable.

Everyone agrees that she was a beautiful and very sexy woman who had no compunction about displaying her highly desirable body. For seances during the hot summer weather she liked to wear a kimono with nothing underneath. This served two purposes. It facilitated the production of 'pseudo-pods', which tended to emanate from her vagina. But it also distracted members of the committee – which by now was considerably enlarged.

Mediums had rarely hesitated to use their sexual charms wherever this seemed appropriate. Eusapia Palladino, who had convinced (among others) William James, had (Houdini reported 'on good authority') '[thrown] her legs into the laps of her male sitters! . . . She placed her head upon the shoulders of men sitters, and . . . she did various other things calculated to confuse and muddle men.' Margery, too, relied on being able to dazzle her sitters; and she usually succeeded. Malcolm Bird was undoubtedly in love with her (he later wrote a whole book about her). So was Hereward Carrington. And so was Eric Dingwall, a psychical researcher from England who now came over to Boston to see what was going on.

Dingwall seems principally to have interested himself in the more pornographic aspects of Margery's mediumship. Indeed, pornography was a prime interest of his. He was for some years Keeper of the closed shelves in the British Museum Library; and Houdini had previously met him when they were both investigating Eva C., whose manifestations were also decidedly *louche*.

His relations with the prudish and puritanical Houdini on this occasion were strained from the outset. Houdini made strenuous attempts to contact Dingwall while he was in Boston and find out whose side he was on – for in this affair there could be no more pretence of impartiality: you were either on Margery's side or Houdini's. But Dingwall was not to be pinned down. 'A statement which I heard, and which he did not deny, was that the London Psychic Research sent him over especially to investigate Mrs Crandon,' Houdini told Harry Price. 'But not having spoken to him, I cannot say he makes the statement but he allows people to believe they are bearing the expenses . . . Since he has been over here he states she has ectoplastic arms which exude from her body and ring the bells. What do you think of this? . . . *I would appreciate anything you could tell me about what Dingwall knows about ectoplasm, if there is anything to be told.*'

It may be remembered that the original creator of ectoplasm was Eva C. Eva's ectoplasmic productions took many curious and horrid forms, but they did not resemble Margery's, which were large, floppy, hand-like exudations of some meaty substance (possibly lungs) appearing from beneath her kimono. If they were not paranormal (Dingwall speculated in a report on the sittings) then they were presumably secreted in her vagina.

These 'pseudopods' fascinated Dingwall, who took copious photographs of them for the *Proceedings of the Society for Psychical Research* and described at great length the seances at which they were produced. In the end, reluctantly, he conceded that he was not convinced, but it took time for him to arrive at this conclusion. While the seances were going on he wrote to Eva's promoter and investigator, Schrenck-Notzing: 'It is the most beautiful case of teleplasm and telekinesis with which I am acquainted. One is able to handle the teleplasm freely. The materialized hands are connected by an umbilical cord to the medium; they seize upon objects and displace them . . . The control is irreproachable.' He described 'A cold, clammy, dark brown or grayish ectoplasmic substance that exuded from the medium's mouth and head and slowly extended to ring bells and flip papers on the floor from a nearby table.' But a few months later he had concluded that 'normal' production was far the most likely explanation. 'By the way,' Houdini queried of Harry Price, 'is there any truth in the report that Dingwall was observed making ectoplasmic hands out of liver and lights. I presume for experimental purposes.'

Things came to a head between Houdini and Dingwall – and indeed between Houdini and Margery – in January 1925. The previous month, Dr William McDougall, the Harvard psychologist who was also on the Margery committee, had publicly accused Houdini of adopting an unfair and prejudiced attitude towards Mrs Crandon. Houdini riposted by wagering $5,000 that he could reproduce every one of Margery's supposedly supernatural effects by pure trickery. At the beginning of January he presented an evening exposé where he did just that. Among other things, 'with the aid of the Spirit slates I produced a photograph of Mrs Crandon's brother "Walter" who was killed and of all the miracles in the world – I ran across the photograph of the boy as he was crushed between the engine and the tender of the train, and which was taken one minute before he died. Can you imagine the sensation she would have created had she come across this photograph first – planted them and then have "Walter" tell her where his last photograph could be found?' Dingwall was present at this lecture and took Margery's part. He demanded to see a trick bell-box Houdini had had constructed which rang 'at command'. Houdini, very much in control, turned the audience against him much as he had done with Jess Willard some years before.

' "Will you let me see that box," the voice shouted out in a challenging tone. Just as I was reaching over to hand the person the box I was thunder-struck to see that the *person* was Eric Dingwall.

'I said "Well, Dingwall, you here and challenging me when you know that any secret I have in Spiritualism is yours simply for the asking? you ought to be ashamed of yourself . . ."

'I turned to the audience, told them that he had been sent here specially by the Psychic Research Association of England, and here he was sneaking in to see me work, when he was a member of two of the Organizations to which I belong and said, "Dingwall, this is not cricket." . . . He was crestfallen, he flushed and when they yelled for him to stand up so that they could see him he said, "Kindly address your remarks to the lecturer," and sank into his seat.'

The exposé finally did the trick. The committee, with the exception of Hereward Carrington, announced that it agreed with Houdini. Margery did not qualify for the *Scientific American* award.

All this stuff – flying megaphones, spirit hands carved out of liver and lights, bells being rung by mysterious agencies – now seems so ludicrous that it is hard to see how it can have been taken seriously at the time. Just how seriously it was taken, however, may be judged from the thousands of words and acres of newspaper space devoted to the Margery affair by such grave journals as the Boston *Transcript,* the New York *Times* and the Boston *Herald.* There were not merely headlines but enormous articles, accusations, rebuttals, justifications, discussions, Houdini's denunciations of fraud, Dr Crandon's outrage at the slur on his wife's good name, Professor McDougall's arrival at a verdict adverse to Margery, the *Scientific American's* withdrawal of its award, the announcement of another award by another Harvard professor, Dr Morton Prince, Houdini's offer of $5,000 if Margery could prove herself genuine . . .

Houdini claimed the moral high ground. He had exposed a fraud and saved the *Scientific American* from making a fool of itself. Dr Crandon, not to be outdone, took refuge in respectability. He presented his wife and himself as a decent couple of exalted intellectual and social standing who had exposed themselves to a publicity-seeking trickster purely in the interests of the higher truth. Conan Doyle supported him in weary outrage and invited Margery to England.

Margery declined Conan Doyle's invitation. 'MARGERY

FEARS FOG MAY BLOCK LONDON SEANCES', reported the *New York Times*. 'MEDIUM WHO FAILED TO WIN $2,500 PRIZE NOT SURE DAMP AIR WILL AGREE WITH "WALTER" HER CONTROL'.

One of the most interesting aspects of the Margery mediumship is the role played in the affair by Dr Crandon.

That he was his wife's accomplice as well as her impresario seems beyond doubt. Dingwall observed that hand control of Margery by her husband 'must be regarded as non-existent'. Even the Spiritualist *Banner of Light* pointed out that 'In the absence of Dr Crandon there has been a dearth of phenomena.'

Dr Crandon's sincerity, the genuineness of his beliefs, impressed everyone who met him. But if he was helping to produce the phenomena, how was it possible that he could *also* believe in their supernormal nature? And if he knew what was going on, how could he have imagined that he would not be found out?

The last question, at least, seems clearly answered by his undisguised fury at Houdini's presence. The part of him that did acknowledge what was going on also knew exactly what would happen once Houdini arrived (as, of course, did Margery and 'Walter'). One of Houdini's main crimes, in Dr Crandon's eyes, was perhaps that he forced this suppressed knowledge – as it might be, a sleight-of-mind – into Dr Crandon's consciousness.

In a sense, 'Margery' was entirely her husband's creation. It was he who was interested in the occult, he who induced her to try her hand at mediumship – for which she proved to have a hitherto unsuspected talent. Looked at in this way, they appear as almost a cliché spiritualist couple. The besotted older man and the beautiful young medium appear frequently in spiritualist annals. One thinks, for example, of Sir William Crookes, who fell comprehensively for young Florrie Cook and her 'spirit' alter ego, Katie King (while professing to be a detached observer, he wrote hymns of love to Katie and conducted an altogether more material relationship with Florrie).

In such circumstances, the girl's motivation is usually clear. Put crudely, this is a poor girl's chance of respectability and a decent life. Once the man has succumbed, he lays himself open in every possible way. If he will not co-operate willingly, then he can be forced to do so. Annie Eva Fay, another of William Crookes's young protégées, took him to court alleging 'more than gallantry on his part towards her' when it seemed that she might be losing her influence over him.

Mina Crandon had not needed to resort to blackmail of this sort. She had previously been married to a grocer, Earl P. Rand. They had met in church, and had married in 1909. He was just starting up the grocery business, so that they 'did not live luxuriously'. But they enjoyed making themselves financially independent, and were contented with their life and their little boy, Allan. Then, in the summer of 1917, Mina needed an operation. It was performed by Dr Crandon. He was then still married to his second wife, although he had filed for divorce.

In November 1917 the grocer and his wife had their first quarrel. Their relations after that were strained, and they separated on Christmas Day, Mina going to her mother's home, Earl staying with the business. On 18 January 1918, Mina filed for divorce on grounds of cruel and abusive treatment. During this period, Earl said, he felt 'dazed'. He decided not to contest the divorce for the sake of Allan, who was then five years old. It was granted in March: Mina received custody of Allan and $7 a week alimony. Shortly after the decree nisi became final Mina married Dr Crandon, who had meantime finalised his own divorce. Allan lived with them: in the doctor's Lime Street house he was known as 'John'. The Crandons, at the time of the 'Margery' seances, still bought their groceries from Earl Rand – for what mixture of motives may be conjectured. He had not seen Mina since the divorce, but assured journalists that while she had been his wife 'she never had any spiritualistic powers. She took lessons on the cornet . . . she tried the cello and she could play a few pieces on the piano, but I never knew her to be able to talk to ghosts.'

From Mina's point of view, the attractions of the wealthy Brahmin Dr Crandon were obvious. He might be thirty years older than she was, but he could offer her a life such as Mrs Earl P. Rand could never dream of. If he wanted her to be a medium, she would be a medium. She approached the job with her customary charm, intelligence and thoroughness. He, meanwhile, saw and did not see what was going on. He had friends at Harvard. The Department of Psychology, founded by William James, had long-standing connections with psychical research. William McDougall held the chair there largely on account of his interest in it. Margery gave her seances before eminent men experienced in the field. She convinced them. Why not go for the *Scientific American* prize? Houdini, the potential fly in the ointment, was busy elsewhere. Why not present him with a *fait accompli*? Unfortunately for them, Houdini was not to be fobbed off; and not only could he see through Margery, but he was uniquely impervious to her charms. Rather, he was revolted by their display. That was Margery's bad luck.

Mina, of course, was irretrievably stuck with Margery once she had made her appearance. Her marriage probably depended increasingly upon Dr Crandon's collusion, acknowledged or unacknowledged, in the seances. And she must have got a good deal of fun out of it all. She could express herself through Walter as she never could through the mouth of the respectable Mrs Crandon. She could bamboozle respectable professors. She could flirt with all the men.

'It is the belief of all the committee,' reported Hudson Hoagland, writing in the *Atlantic Monthly* after the event, 'that Dr Crandon is sincere in his belief in Walter as a supernormal reality – as the returned spirit, in fact, of his dead brother-in-law . . . Walter seems to most of us to be a delightful and wholly dramatic impersonation – witty, tactful, obliging, entertaining, full of wonders and tricks, swaggering with confidence, joking with the most boisterous joker, and then in a moment all sympathy and wisdom, ready with advice and counsel. Of course, with the reality of a supernormal Walter established, it becomes a rather easy matter for the medium and sympathetic attendants to help him consciously at times as one would help any friend to demonstrate important truths, although this is not in the spirit of the scientific method.'

After his destruction of Margery, Houdini continued his crusade against false mediums with redoubled vigour. When he was in London he had wanted to replicate the exploit of the famous D. D. Home, who had (according to detailed reports) flown out of one third-storey window and in at another. These windows were reputedly eighty-five feet above the ground. 'Tall stories,' Houdini remarked then of Home's witnesses, 'appear to have been a specialty of these remarkably observant gentlemen.'

Tall stories in all their guises were his concern now. He exposed 'trumpet mediums' in Denver and New York, revealing himself at the crucial moment with a triumphant cry to the consternation of all concerned. He employed his intrepid lady secretaries to uncover fraud where he might be recognised. He was especially interested in spirit photographers, always having been a dab hand with a camera himself.

In a sense, this had become another field for his collector's instinct. He was a connoisseur of fake mediums. 'Have run across 2 very fine "trick" mediums. Best ever,' he crowed to Harry Price. And after another exposure: 'Last night pandemonium rained supreme.'

He had intended to leave all his books on spiritualism to the American Society for Psychical Research. But when they elected Malcolm Bird to be a research officer for them, he cancelled the bequest. The Margery grudge, of all grudges, was not one to be abandoned merely at death.

17

Inside the Coffin

The only member of the *Scientific American* committee who continued to endorse Margery's claim to mediumship was Hereward Carrington. Carrington was an enterprising figure. He made his living as an author and showman, specialising in subjects related to conjuring and mediumship. He had for a time been the manager of Eusapia Palladino, the leg-waving Neapolitan medium who convinced many of the world's most distinguished scientists, from the Italian criminologist Cesare Lombroso and the French biologist Charles Richet in 1893 to the American psychologist William James just before his death in 1909, that she possessed supernatural powers. In November 1909, Carrington brought Eusapia to Harvard at the invitation of James's successor, Hugo Muensterberg: on that occasion she was comprehensively exposed.

Eusapia faded away, but Carrington carried on regardless. Now, in 1926, he was promoting a supposedly Egyptian dervish and fakir called Rahman Bey. The choice of nationality was a shrewd one. The East had always been the home of magic and mystery. Houdini's needle trick – 'presented to me in the White Silences of the Ganges by an old Hindu priest' – was Indian for no other reason. But the East is a big place: Far, Near or Middle might all be equally apposite for presentation purposes. It happened that at this time the Middle East carried the greatest magical charge. A passion for all things Egyptian was sweeping the world. In 1922 Sir Howard Carter and his team had unearthed the lost tomb of Tutankhamun with the immortal question and answer: 'What do you see?' 'Wonderful things!' – and had ever since been falling like flies, victims of the fatal and inexplicable Mummy's Curse. The ancient magic of the Pharaohs had evidently lost none of its potency.

Rahman Bey purveyed mystical and possibly supernatural

powers of mind over matter. In May 1926, he opened at the Selwyn Theater on Broadway. He began with a selection of familiar yogic tricks – thrusting a steel pin through his cheek, sticking a thin knife into his neck, pushing skewers through the skin of his chest. He lay on a bed of nails (placed very close together so that they didn't stick into him), increased the pulse rate in one wrist while decreasing it in the other, lay on two swords while a stone slab was hammered to bits on his midriff. Carrington provided a running commentary from the side of the stage. For the climax of his act the fakir threw himself into a trance and was buried in a coffin under a mound of sand. For ten minutes Carrington lectured the audience on living burials and suspended animation. Then Rahman Bey was disinterred, brought himself out of trance, and was applauded wildly.

All this belonged to the realm of 'Natural Magic' – the use of material properties to produce apparently wonderful effects. Most of it was regular dime-show stuff. But it might have been designed specifically to infuriate Houdini. Firstly it was produced by his *bête noire* Carrington. Houdini and Carrington were old enemies. Carrington, a supporter of Mrs Crandon, had denounced Houdini over the Margery affair and accused him of having 'No Standing as a Psychist' and of being a 'pure publicist'. In retaliation, Houdini leaked the *Scientific American* article which would have awarded Margery the prize, had he not turned up in the nick of time, put his spoke in the wheel and had Orson Munn stop the presses. When Dr E. E. Free, the magazine's editor, protested at this unauthorised behaviour, Houdini's reply revealed his target: 'I have never at any time asked that the "Margery" case be reopened,' he wrote. 'What I have suggested, however, is that "Dr" Carrington's actions in the "Margery" incident, should be investigated . . . I regret to note, nevertheless, that both you and Mr O. D. Munn think my opinion concerning the fitness of "Dr" Carrington "is entirely beside the point." Since this is your estimate of the matter, I think I may, in all modesty, contravert it.'

As though Carrington's presence were not in itself enough to turn Rahman Bey into a focus for Houdini's outrage, his act did what, for Houdini, was the most unforgivable thing of all. It infused a succession of simple tricks with a whiff of the supposed supernatural. More: Rahman Bey, with his coffin trick, was trespassing directly on Houdini's territory. He was both usurping the panoply of death and performing supposedly impossible feats of physical endurance. He even (in July) had himself thrown into the Hudson River in his coffin. This was a failure – the alarm bell with which the coffin was fitted went off, apparently inadvertently, almost as soon as he had hit the water. But in a swimming-pool a little later he stayed underwater, in his coffin, for a full hour. After that Carrington challenged Houdini, who had been loud in his criticisms of the 'Egyptian Miracle Man', to duplicate this feat – if he could.

Houdini lost no time about it. He ordered a galvanized-iron box six-foot-six long, twenty-two inches wide and twenty-two inches high. It was fitted with both an alarm bell and a telephone. Then, in his basement workshop, he prepared to test out his theories and Rahman Bey's claims.

The Egyptian (who turned out to be more of an Italian) claimed, or Carrington claimed on his behalf, that his survival in the coffin was due to his assumption of a trance state in which both respiration and circulation stopped. But there was no proof of this, and Houdini did not believe it. Much of his own act was based upon controlled breathing. And although he had never tried what Rahman Bey was now doing – his act, on the contrary, having hitherto been based upon the principle that he would stay in the box for as *short* a time as possible – he suspected that the secret here, too, lay in breath control rather than suspended animation.

Houdini made three tests in his new coffin, two in private, one in public. He wrote them all up in a report which he then submitted to the U.S. Department of Mines: he hoped his experiences might prove useful to miners or sailors caught in an accident. For the first two tests, he recorded, he had 24,428 cubic inches of air in the box; for the third, 34,398 cubic inches.

For the first test, Houdini's coffin was not submerged, and he remained in the box for one hour, ten minutes. He reported: 'Was comfortable which leaves me to believe that some air must have seeped through, though very little, it helped. I started to perspire after being in about forty-five minutes, and was completely saturated with perspiration, but at no time was I in agony. I scarcely moved. With my years of training, I can remain apparently motionless without an effort. I kept my eyes open for fear I would go to sleep.'

The second test took place underwater at noon on 4 August. The coffin had been strengthened and tested until it was airtight. When Houdini was inside, it was placed in a large box and lowered underwater. 'This time I was comfortable – somewhat cold,' he reported. 'There was plenty of moisture on the inside – I should judge that about an inch and a half water on the top of the coffin . . . Was much more comfortable than at the first test as far as my body was concerned. Started to draw long breaths after about fifty minutes. There was always an irritability there and thought it was simply temperament on my part . . . I gave the signal to let me out at seventy minutes and believe it took three minutes to unscrew the thirty-two bolts and screws on the coffin. There was no suffering.'

The third test took place in public next day, 5 August 1926, in the swimming-pool of the Hotel Shelton. Before he was submerged, Houdini made a little tension-raising speech. 'If I die,' he said, 'it will be the will of God and my own foolishness.' He added, 'I am going to prove the copybook maxims are wrong when they say a man can live but three minutes without air, and I am not going to pretend to be in a cataleptic state either.' (Of course he did not mention that the coffin was full of air, 34,398 cubic inches of it, to be precise.) The area round the swimming-pool was filled with spectators from the press, including Hereward Carrington. They watched as it was submerged, and held underwater by several men standing on top of it. Then the counting began.

'As a matter of fact I was not comfortable at all,' reported Houdini, 'and attribute it to the warmth of the place and the mechanical means of drawing air into the pool . . . It was warm in the coffin before the two round plates were screwed on . . . At no time can I say I was as comfortable as during the other tests. The first day, the anxiety of an accident retarded me somewhat, but as you know I trained for many years as an escape artist . . . In this test I had to breathe heavily after about fifty minutes and was not sure of staying under. I hung along over an hour and thought I would do at least ten minutes more. By this time I commenced to pant, that is draw rather long slow breaths. As I remembered in the first two tests, the temperature was less at my feet than at my head, I slid towards the foot of the box . . . When the coffin was out of the water, there was a relief all over my body . . . I counted my respirations and averaged seventeen. When I dictated this I still had that metallic taste in my stomach and mouth. Felt rather weak in the knees . . .

'When my assistant phoned me to say that I had been in there for one hour and twelve minutes, I was going to stay in three more minutes, but watching my lungs rise and fall thought I could stand the strain for another fifteen minutes . . . In ordinary circumstances I can remain under water two minutes without any trouble. When I was a boy 16–18 I could do four minutes in a bath tub where there was not much pressure.

'Am having a coffin made with a glass top and as soon as it is ready will let you know.'

In fact the new coffin was not glass-topped but bronze. It was a magnificent thing. Having worsted Rahman Bey, Houdini had decided to co-opt his crowd-puller and take it on tour with him that autumn. It would be a welcome novelty. He also co-opted Rahman Bey's adoptive nationality. The poster he had printed to advertise his new act was as Egyptian as could be, with the Sphinx lowering over a painted sarcophagus containing Houdini. 'Buried Alive!' it proclaimed. 'Egyptian Fakirs Outdone – the Greatest Necromancer of the Age – Perhaps of all times.'

In 1926, Houdini was fifty-two. He was in perfect health. Conan Doyle, who was a doctor as well as a writer, said: 'I suppose at that time Houdini was, from an insurance point of view, so far as bodily health goes, the best life of his age in America. He was in constant training and he used neither alcohol nor tobacco.' This opinion was echoed by his insurer, who ended one letter, 'Would there were many more like you.'

But the fact remained that he was getting older. He was about to embark on another gruelling tour. How much longer could he go on with this life? He showed no more sign of stopping than he ever had done. From the moment of his first great success he had been assuring correspondents that, on the completion of his next contract, he was going to retire. But he had never done so. Now that the moment might seem to be approaching, he made no such pretences. 'We all have our hobbies,' he wrote at this time, 'and it is natural that each year I have an inclination to return to my first love – vaudeville – because it was Mr Albee, of the B. F. Keith Circuit, who gave me an opportunity to make my name known throughout the civilized world as an entertainer. While others go to Palm Beach in the winter for a vacation, I go into vaudeville. I get paid for it, a very good salary, but I don't have to do it.'

He might be impervious to age: Bess was not. She was by now drinking heavily. Her make-up was applied ever more thickly and luxuriantly: a gaudy face which did not disguise the sad middle-aged lady beneath. There is a certain charm in Houdini's dismissal of her worries. 'Stop thinking that at 48½ years you are old – tush-tush – and a couple of *fiddle-de-dees*. We have our best mature years before us,' he told her, adding: 'I have a list of men and women at home who only started to think and act after *three* score years had flitted by.'

Things started to go wrong in October. While they were playing the Opera House in Providence, Rhode Island, Bess was taken ill. Ptomaine poisoning was diagnosed: she needed rest and constant care. A nurse, Sophie Rosenblatt, was engaged for her, and one of the girls in the show took her place onstage as Houdini's partner in Goodbye Winter, Welcome Summer and the rest of the show. On the Friday evening, 8 October, Bess had a high fever and Harry sat up with her all night. The fever went down Saturday morning; he snatched a few hours' sleep between the matinée and the evening performance. They were due to open in Albany on Monday. After the Saturday night show, Harry saw Bess and the troupe off to Albany, and himself took the last train to New York, where he had an appointment with his lawyer, Bernard Ernst. They were to discuss how the many libel suits instigated against him by outraged spiritualists ought to be handled, and some other matters. When he arrived, the Ernsts were not at home: Houdini snatched a little sleep on the living-room sofa. Then they arrived, and Houdini retired with Ernst to the study. He phoned Albany: Bess was still ill. He went down to Martinka's to pick up some pieces of apparatus he needed for the show, then phoned Albany again. Miss Rosenblatt assured him she would stay with Bess through the night.

Houdini took the early morning train to Albany, and when he arrived, found Bess a little better. He slept briefly, and then it was time for the opening performance.

The first act went well. The second act began as usual with the needles trick; then it was time for the Water-Torture Cell. He changed into a bathing-suit and sat down to have himself closed into the mahogany stocks. Then the metal frame which held the stocks in place was passed over him. After that he was ready to be hoisted into place; but this did not go smoothly. The hoist jerked suddenly, he heard a snap and felt a sharp pain in his ankle. He signalled to be lowered again, and found he was unable to stand. Jim Collins asked if there was a doctor in the house. There was, and he diagnosed a broken ankle. The diagnosis was confirmed that night in hospital, where the ankle was bandaged and splinted. Back at the hotel he constructed a leg brace which would get him through the next days in Albany and then Schenectady. After that it was on to Montreal where, on 18 October, he opened at the Princess Theater.

A doctor examined his ankle and told him to keep off his feet, in which case the bone would knit. Houdini did not take this advice. On Tuesday morning he lectured to the police, and in the afternoon he was due to fulfil a long-standing engagement at McGill University, where he would lecture about spirit fraud and the various mediums he had exposed. After the lecture he sat while faculty members and students came to talk to him. One young man had made a sketch of him: Houdini admired it and invited him backstage to make a proper portrait later in the week.

The young man, whose name was Samuel J. Smilovitch, or Smiley, kept the appointment that Friday, 22 October. He and a friend, Jack Price, met Houdini in the Princess Theater lobby at eleven in the morning. Houdini arrived with Bess, Sophie Rosenblatt the nurse, and a young woman called Julia Sawyer, Bess's niece, who had been acting as his secretary. They all went through to the dressing-room. A few minutes later there was a knock on the door, and Julia showed in another young man, a first-year McGill student called Whitehead.

Jack Price told what happened next:

> Houdini was facing us and lying down on a couch at the time reading some mail, his right side nearest us. This first-year student engaged Houdini more or less continually in a conversation whilst my friend Mr Smilovitch continued to sketch Houdini. This student was the first to raise the question of Houdini's strength. My friend and I were not so much interested in his strength as we were in his mental acuteness, his skill, his beliefs and his personal experiences. Houdini stated that he had extraordinary muscles in his forearms, in his shoulders and in his back, and he asked all of us present to feel them, which we did.
>
> The first-year McGill student asked Houdini whether it was true that punches in the stomach did not hurt him. Houdini remarked rather unenthusiastically that his stomach could resist much, though he did not speak of it in superlative

terms. Thereupon he gave Houdini some very hammer-like blows below the belt, first securing Houdini's permission to strike him. Houdini was reclining at the time with his right side nearest Whitehead, and the said student was more or less bending over him. These blows fell on that part of the stomach to the right of the navel, and were struck on the side nearest to us, which was in fact Houdini's right side; I do not remember exactly how many blows were struck. I am certain, however, of at least four very hard and severe body blows, because at the end of the second or third blow I verbally protested against this sudden onslaught on the part of this first-year student, using the words, 'Hey there. You must be crazy, what are you doing?' or words to that effect, but Whitehead continued striking Houdini with all his strength.

Houdini stopped him suddenly in the midst of a punch, with a gesture that he had had enough. At the time Whitehead was striking Houdini, the latter looked as though he was in extreme pain and winced as each blow was struck.

Houdini immediately after stated that he had had no opportunity to prepare himself against the blows, as he did not think that Whitehead would strike him as suddenly as he did and with such force, but that he would have been in a better position to prepare for the blows if he had risen from his couch for this purpose, but the injury to his foot prevented him from getting about rapidly.

At first the blows seemed to have had no ill effect. But by mid-afternoon Houdini was aware of a nagging ache and tenderness in his stomach, and by the evening both his ankle and his stomach were giving him great pain. However, as usual the show went on. Houdini was Superman, the death and resurrection hero. Such a figure is not deterred by trifling discomforts such as a broken ankle or a stomach-ache. So, in his dressing-room between the acts, he sat on the couch and doggedly dictated letters to old collaborators about a projected new collection of mathematical problems and tricks. On one, to Will Goldston, he scrawled, 'Broke a bone in my left leg.' He did not mention the stomach-ache.

All that night he suffered terrible pain in his stomach. At

about two a.m. he told Bess he thought he had a cramp or a strained muscle. She massaged him and he said he felt better. When she awoke next morning she found a note:

> *Champagne* coquette
> I'll be at theatre about 12.00 –
> H H
> Fall Guy

Bess wrote on this note: 'This is the last letter my darling wrote to me. We had a Champagne party in his room, Julia the nurse and I, and made him pay the bill.'

Houdini closed in Montreal that Saturday, 23 October, and was due to open in Detroit the following Monday for a two-week run. On the train he was no longer able to conceal his suffering. Bess, distraught, and barely recovered from her own illness, telegraphed ahead to the show's Detroit advance man instructing him to get the best doctor in Detroit ready to examine Houdini before the opening.

The train was late – too late for them to check in at the hotel before leaving for the theatre. The doctor was waiting, meanwhile, in the hotel lobby. Finally the advance man thought to telephone the theatre. The doctor rushed round and examined Houdini on the dressing-room floor, there being nowhere else he could lie down. He diagnosed acute appendicitis and said an ambulance should be called at once to take Houdini to hospital. Bess did not hear this, and Houdini did not tell her. Nor did the theatre manager, who was present during the examination. He had his own worries. The house was sold out and queues were still waiting outside the theatre. He said, 'We have a $15,000 advance sale. What are we going to do?' to which Houdini replied, 'I'll do this show if it's my last.'

He was by now running a temperature of 104°. Several times during the show he nearly collapsed. Spectators reported that he was nervous, was missing his cues, and was hurrying the show along. Between the first and second acts he was taken to his dressing-room and ice-packs placed upon him, and the same thing was done between the second and third acts. He did the 'little magic' with silks and coins, the card sleights, the lecture exposing fraudulent mediums, the questions and challenges from the audience. Just before the third act he turned around to his chief assistant and said, 'Drop the curtain, Collins, I can't go any further.' He returned to his dressing-room, changed his clothes, and still would not go to hospital.

The impulse to suicide, which was such a fundamental part of his make-up, had hitherto always been thwarted by the reflex which compelled him to save himself each time. But now it had found an ally stronger than any reflex: Houdini's cult of bodily imperviousness, which denied his own mortality. This became the instrument by which his death, so often sought, was finally to be achieved.

Back at the hotel, Bess threw a tantrum – her weapon of last resort. The hotel physician was called. He summoned a surgeon who arrived at three a.m. and said Houdini must be rushed to hospital at once: his condition was critical. Houdini still demurred. He insisted on calling his personal physician, Dr William Stone, in New York. Stone talked to the doctors in the hotel room. Then he spoke to Houdini again. Houdini gave in. He was taken to Grace Hospital, where his gangrenous appendix was removed that afternoon. Dr. Kennedy, the surgeon who performed the operation, said: 'We found that his appendix was a great long affair which started in the right lower pelvis where it normally should, extended across the mid-line and lay in his left pelvis, exactly where the blow had been struck. Reconsidering the history afterwards, we concluded that his appendix had ruptured some place near St Thomas, Ontario, and that he had carried on the entire performance the same evening at the Garrick Theatre with a ruptured appendix spreading peritonitis.'

Now, at last, no effort or expense was spared. A specialist in post-operative technique was called from a nearby hospital. The family was summoned, all except Leopold, the errant brother, whom Houdini had still not forgiven for the fact that he, Ehrich, had not been present at his mother's death.

'As I entered the lobby, Dr Kennedy, the doctor who had performed the operation, was just coming out of the operating room,' Theo recalled. 'I asked him, "How is he?" Dr Kennedy . . . said, "He will never get well." . . . He said he might live twenty-four hours at the most. Houdini was powerfully built and fooled the doctor. Monday, Tuesday, Wednesday and Thursday went by and the doctor came to me and said "We must perform another operation on Houdini as the bowels have become paralyzed." . . . All Houdini said was, "You are the doctor. Go ahead." . . . During all the hours of agony Houdini never thought he was dying – never gave that a thought. All he talked about was having to lay off work for six or seven weeks and keep his assistants out of work that long. After the second operation [he] seemed to get stronger. In fact on Friday he was stronger still, but on Saturday afternoon Dr Kennedy came and told me that it was a matter of a few hours . . . Sunday at eleven o'clock Dr Kennedy came out of the sick-room and I could see tears streaming from his eyes. He did not say a word to me but I went in and sat alongside of Houdini's bed. Houdini reached over and took my hand in his and said, "Dash, I'm getting tired and I can't fight any more." '

He died in Bess's arms at one-twenty-six that afternoon. The Detroit *Free Press* reported: 'He . . . closed his eyes for all time with the name of Robert Ingersoll on his lips.' Ingersoll was a writer and lecturer on agnosticism who had been one of Houdini's heroes all his life. 'It was a beautiful sunny day,' Theo remembered, 'and when the doctor said "He is gone" the heavens clouded over and it poured rain like I have never seen it pour before.'

It was 31 October, Halloween. He was fifty-two years old.

All the properties for the show had been crated up and shipped to New York when Houdini was taken to hospital. But Jim Collins was notified by the Detroit Transfer Co. on the Friday that one crate had been left behind accidentally.

This, when investigated, turned out to be the box containing the bronze casket which had been the chief prop for the Rahman Bey exposure. Houdini's attorney, telephoning from New York, disclosed that one of the first provisions of the will was a desire to be buried in this casket in the event of death. So fate and Houdini remained in cahoots until the end.

The body in its casket was taken by train to New York. Houdini had left meticulous instructions regarding the conduct of his funeral. It was held at the huge Elks Lodge Ballroom on West 43rd Street. Two rabbis officiated: the crowd was two thousand strong.

All his life Houdini had been a joiner. He liked belonging to clubs, societies and lodges. Perhaps they enhanced that sense of rootedness he was always looking for. All of them took part in his funeral. A cedarwood wand was broken in half over the coffin to a funeral chant by members of the Society of American Magicians, of which he had for so long been President. There were tributes from the National Vaudeville Artists, the Jewish Theatrical Guild, and rites by the St Cecile Masonic Lodge, the Mount Zion Congregation and the Elks. The cortège taking the body to Machpelah Cemetery was twenty-five cars long. The honorary pallbearers included E.F. Albee, Martin Beck, Marcus Loew, Lee Shubert, Charles Dillingham, Adolph S. Ochs, Adolph Zukor and many others. As the coffin was lowered one pallbearer whispered to another (the impresario Florenz Ziegfeld), 'Suppose he isn't in it!'

Theo, Nat and Gladys were there, but not Leopold. Houdini's assistants, James Collins, James Vickery, Frank Williamson, John Arden, Beppo Vitorelli and Elliott Sandford, lowered the coffin into its place by the side of his mother. As he had requested, his head rested on a black bag containing her letters to him.

A year later, as Jewish custom requires, the bust which had been waiting for so long in his living-room was set in its appointed place atop the enormous tomb. Beneath it, under a plaque recording his presidency of the Society of American

Magicians from 1912 until 1926, enormous letters read simply **HOUDINI**.

Mystery continued to surround him. Even the circumstances of his death were (and remain) slightly mysterious. Indeed, Robert Lund, a magic collector who worked for many years in Detroit and took a particular interest in the details of the death, found no fewer than seven different versions of how it occurred:

> And there you have the true story of Houdini's death. How he died in the arms of Larry Lewis and Beatrice Houdini in Boston and Chicago while suspended upside down in a glass tank on the stage of the Oriental Theatre while performing on the bottom of the river locked in a casket and suffering from a ruptured appendix and hardening of the arteries, the same afternoon, within twenty-four hours, or five days later. Truth will out.

What really happened is in a sense clear: he died of peritonitis brought on by a ruptured appendix. But how did that appendix rupture in the first place?

The assumption (not unnaturally) was that the blows to the stomach were the precipitating factor. But the consensus is that this is medically impossible. Bernard Meyer conducted a computerised search of the medical literature and talked to a number of experienced surgeons, and could find not a single instance of acute appendicitis being caused by physical injury. Such a trauma can rupture the large intestine, and in fact this was the initial diagnosis of Dr Charles Kennedy, the surgeon who examined Houdini in his hotel room and later operated on him. But what he found was a ruptured appendix. He said, 'It is the only case of traumatic appendicitis I have ever seen in my lifetime, but the logic of the thing seemed to indicate that Mr Houdini died of appendicitis, the direct result of the injury.'

What seems most likely is that Houdini was already suffering from appendicitis before the famous incident, and that this either aggravated it or prevented him from realising that his condition was something more than a mere bruise until it was too late. It will be remembered that Jack Price had noticed that 'at the time Whitehead was hitting Houdini the latter looked as though he was in extreme pain and winced as each blow was struck'. And after his death, Professor William Tait, who introduced him at the McGill lecture, remarked how precipitately he had sat down at its conclusion, as though he were in some pain. Tait concluded at the time that this was due to the pain from his ankle, but it might have been abdominal; the fracture was by then eight days old. This possibility is borne out by a letter written by one Gertrude Hills to the New York *Sun* some time later. Ms Hills described how, during the summer, Houdini had agreed to take part in a charity fund-raising show. 'He was delighted to be of assistance and promised to perform his "straitjacket" act and to try to beat his own record in escaping. In attempting to do so he hurt himself so badly that for a number of days he suffered pain in his side. Closely following upon this injury he had an attack of what was diagnosed as "ptomaine poisoning". From this he really never seemed to recover. When he left on his tour he told me that the effects of the injury and "poisoning" were still evident.'

Meanwhile, reports from clairvoyants who claimed to have predicted Houdini's death and to have witnessed signs and portents began to flood in. A Mr Gysel reported that at ten-fifty-eight on the evening of 24 October 1926, a photograph of Houdini which he had framed and hung on the wall 'fell to the ground, breaking the glass. I now know that Houdini will die.'

Mr Gysel's experience would have come as no surprise to Houdini's spiritualist adversaries, for (as he himself had noted) they had been predicting his death for years, and one day they would inevitably get it right. In 1924 'Walter' had given him 'a year or less'. Then the Crandons had foretold the event for 25 December 1925. Conan Doyle recorded that 'In my own home circle I had the message some months before his death, "Houdini is doomed, doomed, doomed!" ' On 13 October a medium called Mrs Wood wrote a letter to the novelist Fulton Oursler: 'Three years ago the spirit of Dr Hyslop said, "The waters are black for Houdini," and he foretold that disaster would befall him while performing before an audience in a theatre. Dr Hyslop now says that the injury is more serious than has been reported, and that Houdini's days as a magician are over.'

Houdini himself had apparently had his own premonitions of the coming event. Among his clippings is one from 1919 recording the collapse, onstage at Detroit, of a comedian named Sidney Drew. Drew had been taken ill in St Louis, but had continued to play, against all advice, until in Detroit he could go no further . . .

A friend and fellow-magician, Joe Dunninger, reported that one morning in October Houdini called him in New York with a request to come at once with his car to West 113th Street as he was in a hurry and had to move some stuff. When the car was loaded he said, 'Drive through the park, Joe.'

> When we got to the exit on Central Park West around 72nd Street he grabbed my arm; in a hollow, tragic voice he said, 'Go back, Joe!'
> 'Go back where?'
> 'Go back to the house, Joe.'
> 'Why – did you forget something?'
> 'Don't ask questions, Joe. Just turn around and go back.'
> I drove back to the house. By this time it was raining even harder, if that was possible, but Houdini ignored it; he got out of the car, took off the straw hat, and stood looking up at the dark house with rain streaming down his face. Then he got back in the car saying nothing. When we again approached the western exit of the park his shoulders began to shake. He was crying. Finally he said, 'I've seen my house for the last time, Joe. I'll never see my house again.' As far as I know he never did.

Nevertheless, it seems clear from Theo's account that, even

in the agonies of appendicitis, Houdini had no morbid present-
iments. Fulton Oursler, who shared Houdini's interest in
spiritualism (but was more inclined to believe), noted: 'I had
written to Houdini in care of the Garrick Theater in Detroit,
and when he arrived there on Sunday [after Montreal and the
fatal blow] he found my letter waiting for him. In his dressing
room he typed me a note in which he stated that he hoped to
go to Toledo and have a seance with Ada Bessinet. Here . . .
is evidence that he had no real suspicion his days were numbered. A few hours afterwards he was stricken and taken to
the hospital from which he never emerged alive.' And as late
as 30 October – the day before his death – he wrote to a
friend: 'Box offices here are S.R.O. which certainly makes me
sunny and quite happy. Except that I feel none too well at the
moment, but suppose I will get over this waviness in no time.'

Houdini thus proved that, as he always insisted (but never
really believed), he was not clairvoyant.

18

HOUDINI LIVES!

Last Halloween I attended a seance. It was held at the Holiday Inn, Rochester, N.Y., an improbable venue for the supernatural. There were nine participants besides myself and the medium. We were trying, on the anniversary of his death, to raise Houdini. 'If it is possible for anyone to get through after death,' he always asserted, 'that person will be me.'

The eleven of us sat around a table on a kind of dais. Apart from a surviving niece, the medium and myself, the participants were male, mostly middle-aged or elderly, dressed in tuxedos: a family gathering, a group of uncles. Everyone knew each other well. They had met on countless Houdini-related occasions in the past. Several were noted collectors of Houdiniana, for which there is an avid and ever-growing market. Around us clustered a bevy of press photographers and television crews. The body of the room was filled with wives, friends and spectators. In the middle of the table were a bust of Houdini, a pair of his handcuffs and an envelope containing the message he promised to send Conan Doyle, should he ever return. The message has never yet been transmitted. Would it be received today? Would the spirit of Houdini accept us as satisfactory Doyle substitutes?

Most of the participants seemed to assume that this or any other manifestation was unlikely. Still, at the appointed hour – one in the afternoon, twenty-six minutes before the moment of death – we all joined hands and shut our eyes. The medium told us to relax. As my chair was very close to the edge of the dais the fear of falling over backwards made this hard for me. But I did my best, although it must be said that this was not a relaxing occasion. The medium, a healthy-looking lady with very red cheeks and a black dress, intoned from time to time, 'Houdini, are you there?' We kept our eyes shut.

Nothing happened. After a while Mrs Blood, Houdini's niece, announced that she had felt someone touch her. But it was a press photographer, not a spirit. This was the nearest we got to a sign.

Past seances have tried more tangible temptations. In 1978, at the American Museum of Magic in Marshall, Michigan – an altogether more conducive location – an attempt was made to lure the elusive spirit with a basket of his favourite snack, bagels and lox. But Houdini did not descend. He might have reacted more favourably to bread-and-butter custard, the recipe he contributed to 'A collection of the Favorite Foods of Famous Players': 'I happen to have a weakness for sweets, and this one you will not find in any other cookbook.'

The Houdini seances did not start out in such light-hearted fashion.

After her husband died, Bess found herself even more at a loss than most widows. Since the age of eighteen she had lived inside Houdini's closed world. Every member of this tiny circle had his or her particular role, from which no deviation was tolerated. All these roles were strictly relative to Houdini, planets to his sun. So his death presented all his close associates with problems of identity and occupation. What were they to do next? They had never really lived their own lives – they had simply been bit players in Houdini's.

For Theo Hardeen, the answer was straightforward. He had always been his brother's copy – 'Houdini der zweite'. Now the original was gone, he was free at last to 'come into his own'. This turned out to mean that he remained his brother's copy. That was all he knew: it was too late for him to redesign himself as himself. He inherited all Houdini's illusions and apparatus (though he could never use the Water-Torture Cell, as he was much too big for it). He also took over Jim Collins. Together they finished Houdini's uncompleted tour, and started on further tours of their own. Eventually he became, as his brother had been for so many years, President of the Society of American Magicians.

From time to time, Theo tried to contact his brother. He

did not really believe he would succeed. After the death of their brother Bill in 1925, 'We . . . agreed that . . . the first Sunday we were to go to Houdini's office at midnight and wait to see whether we would get any sign from Bill. . . . We did as arranged . . . and, as expected, nothing happened. It was also agreed that if nothing should happen on Sunday night, then we were to go out to the cemetery and sit at Bill's grave, midnight on Wednesday, this we did, and again nothing happened except that we got wringing wet as it was pouring with rain.

'It was then that Houdini turned to me and said, "We will keep the same code between you and me. Whichever one of us passes away first, if the other one should ever receive a message from any medium and it does not contain any of the ten words of our compact, he will know that the message must be a fake." This is ten years ago,' Hardeen added, 'and up to the present time, I have not had as much as a peep from Houdini.'

For Hardeen, this was just one part of a crowded life. He had his family, he had his work. But for Bess, the emptiness was complete. She had not only lived through her husband: more than most wives, she had lived *with* him. They had been partners in a very real sense. When his safe was opened after his death, a bundle of photographic negatives was found. He bequeathed them to 'My beloved wife Beatrice Houdini and the only one who has actually helped me in my work.' Their life together had not been perfect. But it had never been dull. And, however intolerable his huge ego may have been, he had never made any secret of the fact that he depended upon her utterly. He had once been asked his idea of perfect pleasure. He replied, 'Sitting in a comfortable chair in my library and hearing Mrs Houdini call up the stairs "Young man, your lunch is ready." ' As an image of married life after thirty years, this has much to commend it.

Of course, this life had been distinctly lopsided: his, not hers. That was a fact that all the declarations of undying devotion could not negate. 'Dear Mrs Houdini,' ran a typical missive in that voluminous, one-sided domestic correspondence. 'Professor Brainien, Astronomer of Columbia College, has been invited for luncheon, for 12.30 on Tuesday next, provided you OK same. If quite all right, get in touch with Houdini himself, in person, notifying him of what's what. If you refuse I will have a hell of a time squaring him, because the invitation has already been given and accepted.' The letter was signed 'Your fond Husband, Houdini,' and there was a postscript: 'It has been so long since I have written you a letter, so hope this is the proper way to address a loving wife.' And a terrible poem about nightingales was cut out and stuck on the end. But the meat of the communication was clear. The professor was coming and that was that. This might sound like a request, but it was purely informative.

Bess's increasing reliance on the bottle indicates that she did not find this life easy. She put up a certain resistance. There were the tantrums, the disapproval he dreaded, the grumbles in the dressing-room. But in the end life went on – *his* life: and hers followed in its wake.

Now not only was he not there, but there was nothing to do. She could hardly go on tour with Hardeen. And there was never any prospect of her carrying on the act as Adelaide Herrmann had done with such success on the death of her husband Alexander 'The Great' Herrmann. It was not that kind of act; she could never be anything but a secondary participant.

Nor was she rich. Houdini had earned enormous amounts of money, but he had spent it as fast as he earned it. The motion-picture ventures had swallowed up oceans of dollars, and were in chaos. Prints of Houdini's films had been widely distributed with no records to show who had them: anyone might exhibit them, and nobody would be any the wiser. Boxes of books he had bought kept arriving for months after his death, and had to be paid for. The terms of Houdini's will provided for a trust fund to be set up; but when B. M. L. Ernst, his lawyer and old friend, showed the prospective trustees the accounts relating to the estate, they declined to take on the position as there was no fund with which to set up any trust. Bess advanced money out of her own funds (all the real estate was in her name) to pay administration expenses, debts and inheritance taxes. She might have sold the library to pay for all this, but preferred to donate it, as Houdini had wished, to the Library of Congress in Washington – such as was left after friends and collectors had possessed themselves of many of the choicer items. Ernst never charged her for all the work his own firm did on behalf of the estate: 'Because of my long and close personal friendship with Houdini, such services were rendered even though there were no funds to pay for them.'

Bess was not left penniless, however. For years Houdini had spent substantial sums on life-insurance policies. These (as his publicity liked to announce) provided for double indemnity in the event of accidental death. One of the insurance companies, New York Life Insurance, conducted a special investigation to ascertain what had really happened in Montréal and Detroit. After getting signed statements from all concerned, they accepted that the blow to the stomach had been the precipitating factor. When they agreed to pay the double indemnity, all the other companies followed suit. Mr Ernst estimated that Bess would receive half a million dollars in insurance payments. She would have to pay heavy inheritance taxes, but even so, there would be enough to live on comfortably for the rest of her life.

But what was she to do with it?

She sold the house on West 113th Street to Rose Bonanno, whose father had for years looked after it when the Houdinis were away. As time went on and the locality got rougher, Rose's connections with the famous (or infamous) Bonanno Family stood her in good stead. She lived in the basement, along with trunkfuls of neatly piled photographs, and did nothing to dispel the legend of Houdini's secrets. She would never open the padlocked attic because 'Mrs Houdini wouldn't like it'. And there were all Houdini's mahogany bookcases, with their extra-deep ceilings and bases. What was hidden in those? Rose didn't know, or wasn't telling; and after her death, it was too late to find out. The collectors moved in *en masse* and everything movable disappeared.

Bess moved to Payson Avenue in another part of the city. There, for a while, she lapsed into drink and misery. A glimpse into her sad life at this time is given by a diary she began to keep in 1927. On its cover she wrote: 'One of the few happy days.' She had spent it visiting cemeteries – 'How peacefull. Home early, only one drink.'

Clearly life could not go on like this. For a while she tried a few desultory occupations. She opened a tearoom in Manhattan, in a building later torn down to make room for the Rockefeller Center. She thought of taking a vaudeville act on the road, in which a man was to be frozen into a block of ice from which he would make his escape (a stunt from *The Man From Beyond*). But the freezing and subsequent melting processes took too long, and the act never got past the try-out stage.

Most of her life, however, was still spent in the company of her husband. She commissioned and helped with the preparation of his biography, which appeared in 1928. And she spent a good deal of time trying to contact him. Every Sunday at the hour of his death she shut herself in her room opposite his photograph and waited for a sign. There was a standing offer of $10,000 for any medium who could produce the secret message Houdini had arranged to send her, and of which he had reminded her on his deathbed. No one did; and towards the end of 1928 the offer was withdrawn.

But it was clear that any medium who could come up with the message would put him or herself in the way of a good deal more than $10,000. The publicity alone would be worth ten times that.

It was, therefore, hardly surprising that a possible medium did eventually present himself. This was the Revd. Arthur Ford, who was at this time pastor of the First Spiritualist Church of Manhattan. He had recently distinguished himself by challenging the famous magician Howard Thurston to a debate at Carnegie Hall – a debate which Ford won. Thurston had been continuing the magical tradition of exposing fake mediums, but Ford was able to produce some effects which he could not explain. Rumour now had it that he was planning a lecture tour with Bess. He meanwhile did his very best to get in touch with Houdini. On 8 February 1928, he claimed to have done so, or at any rate to have contacted old Mrs Weiss, which was the next best thing. While in trance, she had apparently transmitted, via Ford's control, the word *'Forgive'* – the last word she had ever spoken. 'Capitalize that,' the old lady was quoted as having instructed through Ford's 'control', 'and put it in quotation marks. His wife knew the word, and no one else in all the world knew it. Ask her if the word which I tried to get back all these years was not "Forgive".' It will in fact be recalled that Mrs Weiss's last word, whatever it may have been, was spoken to Hardeen, not Houdini or Bess, so that she can hardly have been the only person who knew it. But maybe Mrs Weiss's spirit was carried away by the emotion of contact.

All this came to the attention of one of the reporters for a notorious scandal-sheet, the New York *Graphic*. She was called Rea Jaure. Jaure was interested in Bess Houdini for her own reasons.

These, predictably, were to do with Houdini's supposed love-life. In the 1928 Kellock biography, which was very much Bess's view of things, the picture given of her relations with her husband was an idyllic one (though not without its wholly unintended bizarreries). But there were those who were ready to hint that this was not the way things had been at all. One of these was a pretty redhead named Daisy White.

Daisy White had been a magician's assistant, and had later become a popular member of Martinka's staff. She, like all the close-knit magic community, knew about Houdini's terror when faced with flirtatious ladies. So, as a joke, she had sent him some steamy love-letters. He never replied. But he kept them, together with various other such letters that he received from time to time. Inevitably, Bess found them after his death.

The story was that she gave a tea-party for the various ladies concerned, at which nothing was said, but which ended with each, as a farewell present, being given a packet which proved to contain her letters. It would be nice to believe this. Bess's feelings when she discovered the letters must have been mixed, although, knowing her husband as she did, she cannot have believed he ever did more than read them.

In the end, Bess and Daisy White became good friends. But this was not before Rea Jaure had done her worst.

Rea Jaure met Daisy White one lucky day, and forthwith decided to approach Mrs Houdini for the *real* story – the story that had not been told in the biography. In December 1928, she managed to get Bess to agree to a series for the *Graphic*, to be written by Jaure and signed by Bess. It was to be called *The Life and Loves of Houdini*. There was also a question of some letters supposed to have been written to Bess by Charles Chapin, a former New York newspaper editor serving a life sentence for murder in Sing Sing, whom the Houdinis had befriended: the linking of his name with Mrs Houdini's might provide a sensational story. But before any of this could be put into effect Bess became ill and went to hospital.

This should have presented no problem. After all, it was not Bess who was writing the pieces. But Jaure wanted a picture of Mrs Houdini to go with them, and when the hospital staff would not allow anyone in to visit her, got one of the *Graphic*'s photographers to smuggle himself in disguised as a doctor. However, when he got to the ward, his magnesium flash set a Christmas tree on fire. In the ensuing uproar, Bess let it be known that the series was off and that she never wanted anything to do with the *Graphic* again.

Rea Jaure was furious, and determined to have her revenge. On 8 January 1929, the *Graphic* ran a report of a seance which Arthur Ford had held at Bess's sick-bed. This was the culmination of a number of seances – eight separate sittings, beginning on 8 November 1928 – at each of which one word of the message from Houdini to his wife was received by Arthur Ford's 'control'. The first word was ROSABELLE – the word, said Ford, which was going to unlock the rest. Two weeks later a second word – NOW – was added; and on 18 December LOOK – the sixth word in the code, said Ford – was transmitted by a lady believed to be Houdini's mother. The next word to be added was NOW. Then came ROSABELLE once more, together with ANSWER, PRAY and TELL. Finally, on the evening of 5 January 1925, came the final seance at which the entire message was to be transmitted. The sitters were an associate editor of the *Scientific American*, John Stafford, and his wife Dorothy, Francis R. Fast, Mrs Helen E. Morris, and of course Arthur Ford. All except Ford were strangers to Mrs Houdini. Ford was in deep trance. His 'control' said, 'A man who says he is Harry Houdini, but whose real name was Ehrich Weiss is here, and wishes to send to his wife, Beatrice Houdini, the ten-word code, which he agreed to do if it were possible for him to communicate. He says you are to take this message to her, and, upon acceptance of it, he wishes her to follow out the plan they agreed upon before his passing. This is the code: ROSABELLE ANSWER TELL PRAY ANSWER LOOK TELL ANSWER ANSWER TELL!'

The message was duly carried to Bess by John Stafford and Francis Fast. She had by now returned home, though she was still not very well. She read the letter, then dropped it and said, 'It is right.' Then, 'Did he say ROSABELLE?' Then, 'My God!' Another seance was then arranged at Bess's house for the second day following, 8 January, when all would be elucidated.

At this decisive seance, Rea Jaure was present, along with three of Ford's group and, of course, Bess. Ford went into trance: the voice of his 'control' came through. 'This man is coming now, the same one who came the other night. He tells me to say, "Hello, Bess, sweetheart," and he wants to repeat the message and finish it for you. The code . . . is one that you used to use in one of your secret mind-reading acts.' The ten words were repeated; Mrs Houdini confirmed that they were correct. 'He smiles and says "Thank you", now I can go on,' said the 'control'. 'He tells you to take off your wedding-ring and tell them what ROSABELLE means.'

Bess drew her left hand from under the cover and took off the ring. Holding it in front of her she sang softly:

> Rosabelle, sweet Rosabelle,
> I love you more than I can tell;
> O'er me you cast a spell,
> I love you! My Rosabelle!

It was the song the Floral Sisters had been singing on Coney Island on the night when they had first met the Houdini Brothers.

The seance continued. Houdini, through Ford's 'control', explained the code governing the next nine words of the message: 'The second word in our code was ANSWER. B is the second letter of the alphabet, so ANSWER spells B. The next word in the code is TELL, and the fifth letter of the alphabet is E. The twelfth letter of the alphabet is L and to make up twelve we have to use the first and second words of the code.'

The code he was referring to was the one (described in Chapter 6) used by Harry and Bess in their mind-reading act many years before. The nine words which had been 'transmitted' spelt: BELIEVE.

'The message I want to send back to my wife is, ROSA-BELLE, BELIEVE!' 'Is that right?' the 'control' asked, and Bess replied, with great feeling, 'Yes.' She was reported as adding: 'Later when I get well I shall open the vault in your presence and prove it.'

The next day she signed a message which was witnessed by three independent persons: 'Regardless of any statement made to the contrary, I wish to declare that the message, in its entirety, and in the agreed upon sequence, given to me by Arthur Ford, is the correct message pre-arranged between Mr. Houdini and myself. Beatrice Houdini.' The St Louis *Post-Dispatch* commented:

'It is too bad we are deprived of the comment of the earthly Houdini on this extraordinary occurrence.'

The *Graphic* reported the 8 January seance in appropriately sensational style. But on 10 January, Rea Jaure produced an even greater sensation. It was headlined 'HOUDINI HOAX EXPOSED!' – ' "Seance" Prearranged by "Medium" and Widow' – and it alleged that it was Beatrice herself who had given the code to Ford. Rea Jaure recounted how she had lured Ford to her apartment where, overheard by two witnesses hidden in a convenient steamer trunk, he admitted the hoax, declaring that he and Bess were indeed planning a tour. He would finance it; 'Mrs Houdini supplied the code as her part of the bargain.'

This of course caused an uproar, as it was intended to do. Bess indignantly denied having passed him the code. She wrote to Walter Winchell, who was also at that time on the *Graphic:* 'I am writing you this personally because I wish to tell you emphatically that I was no party to any fraud . . . When the real message, THE message that Houdini and I had agreed upon, came to me, and I accepted it as the truth, I was greeted by jeers? Why? Those who denounced the entire thing as a fraud claim that I had given Mr. Arthur Ford the message. If Mr. Ford said this I brand him as a liar. Mr. Ford has stoutly denied saying this ugly thing, and knowing the reporter as well as I do I prefer to believe Mr. Ford . . . However, when anyone accuses me of GIVING the words that my husband and I labored so long to convince ourselves of the truth of communication, then I will fight and fight until the breath leaves my body.'

But how else would he know it? Joseph Dunninger, entering the fray, pointed out some possibilities. The code, he reminded everyone, had been printed in the Kellock biography only the previous year (it is on page 105). As for *'Rosabelle, Believe'* – Mrs Houdini had not been alone with her husband when he had murmured it to her. The nurse, Sophie Rosenblatt, had also been in the room; she might have mentioned it to someone, and it might have reached Arthur Ford's ears. Another possibility raised, once again, the spectre of Daisy White. A fish-peddler who had a girlfriend who was a friend of Miss White's declared that Daisy White had learned the secret message from Houdini before he died. The New York *Telegram* ran this story: it ended, 'Little Daisy White at Ford's apartment admitted knowing the fish-peddler slightly but denied everything else!'

Poor Bess relapsed into illness, muddle and despair. Ford was using a copy of her signed statement in some advertisements. 'I wish to say that I did sign that letter', she wrote Ernst. ' . . . I did not say that I believed that the message came through spiritual aid or that I believed in spiritualism. I did say the words I heard were the words I expected to hear, etc . . . I had a copy of the original letter I wrote to him somewhere but I am too ill to look for it and I really don't care. I never said I believed the letter came from Houdini. I never said I believed in spiritualism and I still say the same. I don't care what Sir Arthur Conan Doyle or Will Goldston say or do. I don't and never did believe the message genuine nor did I believe in spiritualism. I will write you clearly later if you will just give me a chance to get well. I don't care what you do to or about Mr Ford.'

Shortly afterwards, Arthur Ford was expelled from the United Spiritualist League of New York. He denied Jaure's story, and shortly afterwards was reinstated 'on the ground of insufficient proof'. He continued to maintain that the message was authentic. 'Until the message was proved false, he would consider the Houdini matter closed.'

Bess thrashed about for some years in this unsatisfactory world of spirit mediums and disappointed hopes. 'There was a period when I was ill – really mentally ill as well as physically,' she told an interviewer some years later. 'I wanted so intensely to hear from Harry that spiritualists were able to prey on my mind and make me believe they really had heard from him.' She was only finally disillusioned when he gave her, via a medium, some bad business advice: 'I asked him about signing certain papers – I did what he was supposed to have advised and it was all wrong. Harry wouldn't have done that.'

She was finally rescued by another denizen of that world of carny-shows and freak-stages where she and Houdini had always felt at home. His name was Edward Saint; he had once been a living statue, and had done a little magic.

His was not altogether a chance appearance. Bess's friends were worried by her vulnerability. So they introduced her to Eddy Saint, and suggested that he might act as her manager. In fact (although Bess never realised this), his duties were more those of a watchdog. A genuine affection soon arose between them, and eventually they shared a small Spanish-style bungalow in Hollywood. She had enjoyed living there with Houdini during his film-making period, and it is clear that she enjoyed living there with Eddy Saint. Everyone found him a charming, amiable and dignified figure. 'Mrs Houdini,' recalled the magician John Booth who visited them at this period, 'was a white-haired, gracious and lively little lady of complete naturalness. Edward Saint was an immaculately dressed elderly man of refined manners whose most noticeable characteristic was a goatee with waxed mustache pointed and turned up at the ends.' They enjoyed playing practical jokes on some of their visitors. When Booth first telephoned for an appointment, 'a male voice answered the phone. There was an unusually long delay while Mrs Houdini gaily answered. We talked for several minutes.' That was the day before his visit. During it, 'We were sitting in the small living-room talking when the spooky voices began. I was absent-mindedly gazing up at an heroic sized portrait photograph of Houdini, on the wall opposite, when I became aware of other voices in the room. They were coming from an indeterminate source. My friends had stopped talking. We listened. It was as though radio voices had suddenly begun to penetrate the air around us . . . I noticed the trace of smiles in the expression of Mrs Houdini and Mr Saint. Then I recognized my own voice. I was chatting with a woman. When had this happened?' It was a recording of his conversation with Bess the previous day.

She had delayed answering until the machine was set up. She was making a collection of recordings of her conversations with famous magicians. None of them knew they were being recorded, so all spoke quite spontaneously. She must have got the idea from Houdini, who had regularly eavesdropped on his visitors. But the effect was quite different, the flavour Bess's, not Houdini's. With him, it had been a question of power; with Bess and Eddy Saint, the whole thing was a gentle joke.

It was not until Bess left for California that she began to free herself from Houdini's spell. Not that life with Eddy Saint was life without Houdini. Much of their time was taken up with Bess's unique position as Houdini's widow. 'We spent the morning engrossed in talk about the late showman, going over mementoes of a lifetime. I suspected that Mrs Houdini had been through this routine a thousand times since his death. I also felt that both she and Saint had assumed a duty to keep alive his memory wherever possible in the world outside,' remarked John Booth.

It was Eddy Saint who was with Bess for what was billed as the Final Houdini Seance. This took place on top of a skyscraper in Hollywood on 31 October 1936, the tenth anniversary of the magician's death. Coverage of this event, which was broadcast live to a waiting world, was enormous. Saint's scrapbook of clippings concerning it is three feet by two, six inches thick, and can barely be lifted. Every page is thick with clippings. One picture of Bess and Saint appeared in seventy different publications. 'Over 300 invited guests formed the outer circle, while 13 scientists, occultologists, newspapermen, world famous magicians, spiritual leaders, boyhood friends of Houdini, joined Madame Houdini in the Inner circle,' intoned the commentator. 'Bathed in the weird glow of ruby light, trained observers and spirit mediums joined under controlled conditions to evoke the shade of the late mystifier.'

Saint – referred to in this account as 'Dr Saint', perhaps because of his distinguished and doctorly appearance, immaculately bearded and moustached – took charge of the proceedings. They were heralded by the playing of Elgar's 'Pomp and Circumstance' march, which Houdini had used as his entry music during the latter years of his life (it would boom out and he would come bounding on to the stage, tearing off his false sleeves above the elbow and crying, 'Hi, everyone, I'm Harry Houdini!' in that lightly accented Central European voice of his). He noted that 'Every facility has been provided tonight, that might aid in opening a pathway to the spirit world. Here in the Inner Circle, reposes a "Medium's Trumpet", a pair of slates with chalk, a writing tablet and pencil, a small bell, and in the center reposes a huge pair of silver handcuffs on a silk cushion. Facing the Inner Circle stands the famous "Houdini Shrine", with its doors ajar.'

Eddy Saint talked on. Everyone waited. 'Houdini! Are you here?' he cried. 'Are you here, Houdini? Please manifest yourself in any way possible . . . We have waited, Houdini, oh, so long! Never have you been able to present the evidence you promised. And now – this, the night of nights. The world is listening, Harry . . . Levitate the table! Move it! Lift the table! Move it or rap it! SPELL OUT A CODE, HARRY! Please! Ring the bell! Let its tinkle be heard around the world!'

But all was in vain. Nothing happened. Finally Dr Saint said to Mrs Houdini, 'Mrs Houdini, the zero hour has passed. The ten years are up. Have you reached a decision?' She replied, 'Yes. Houdini did not come through. My last hope is gone. I do not believe that Houdini can come back to me – or to anyone. . . . The Houdini Shrine has burned for ten years. I now, reverently – turn out the light. It is finished. Good Night, Harry!'

But of course she was wrong. It wasn't finished at all.

Discussing this book at a dinner party, my neighbour expressed surprise that it was to be a biography. 'You mean he really existed?' she said.

This, it seems to me, is an extraordinary confirmation of Houdini's ascent to the level of myth. He embodied it: now he has become it. It was not that my neighbour had never heard of Houdini. Far from it. How could she have failed to do so? His name is constantly in the newspapers. While he was alive, his publicity frequently mentioned the fact that he had become a verb. 'To houdinize' was listed in Funk and Wagnall's Dictionary, meaning, to escape from an apparently impossible situation. I have never heard it used. Even so, this was a legitimate source of pride: it is not given to many of us to become a part of speech. And Houdini's name is constantly invoked to symbolise the slippery skills needed or displayed by sportsmen or politicians. It was used in this way twice in one paper last Sunday – both times with reference to politics. The week before that, it described the feat of a football team – 'Luton Town Houdinis Snatch Victory'. He may not be a verb, but he has undoubtedly become a metaphor.

Moreover, he appears in countless works of reference. Robert Lund of the American Museum of Magic in Marshall, Michigan, has made a collection of reference books – dictionaries, encyclopedias, etc. – in which Houdini's name appears. His rule is that none of them must cost more than one dollar. He reckons to possess several hundred of these books. How many would there be had he not imposed the one-dollar rule? This notoriety does not please Lund, who is no fan of Houdini's. 'Houdini's name gets bigger and bigger – but several others who were as big a draw in his lifetime are unheard of now,' he grumbles.

But the myth refuses to fade. The Library of Congress lists thirteen children's books about Houdini, four of them published within the past three years. The rare books room of the Library holds one of his early scrapbooks. The librarian reckons it is their most-requested item. Parents and children come in together to look at it. He has at least one notorious soi-disant descendant: Frank Gilmore, father of the mass murderer Gary Gilmore, was the son of a circus medium and always averred he was Houdini's bastard son. So the Handcuff King maintains his grip upon the world's imagination.

Part of the reason is of course that Houdini epitomised an

aspect of the human condition. This is in itself a mythic attribute. But it was not his only mythic attribute. Perhaps as
important was the timing and manner of his death.

Jack Flosso, talking about this, said, 'The timing was a very
important thing. Had he lived on – Imagine it! Here's a man
selling virility, with flabby flesh and varicose veins.'

He was right. In life, as onstage, timing is important. Would
Marilyn still be Marilyn if she had sunk, like Elizabeth Taylor,
into fat, alcoholism, and husbands of ever-decreasing stature?
Big stars die young. The statistics prove it. *Variety* magazine
reports that 'the average American lifespan is 71.9 years, the
average star dies at age 58.7. The normal American woman
dies at age 75.8, while female stars die at the age of 54.3.'

'Death defines life,' says the Mexican poet Octavio Paz.
'Our deaths illuminate our lives . . . Each of us dies the death
he is looking for, the death he has made for himself . . . If we
do not die as we lived, it is because the life we lived was not
really ours; it did not belong to us, just as the bad death that
kills us does not belong to us.'

This is especially true of those symbolic figures who,
through their early deaths, achieve an immortality quite disproportionate to their lives. From the days of the ritual king
killed every year in the Attic grove, the human imagination
has fed upon these untimely deaths. In some cases, as with
Jesus, the death becomes an icon in itself. In others – JFK,
John Lennon – the death defines the life by framing it at its
peak. So they achieve the immortality that speaks to us, Kennedy forever unsullied by Vietnam, Lennon shrouded in mysterious glamour. Superstars are bathed in media-inspired love.
Martyrdom, added to that love, resulting from it, ensures a
continuing cult.

This is the kind of death Houdini achieved. It was poetic,
appropriate to the life he had led. It was not the prosaic details
of either his life or his death (the arrays of keys and miniature
jacks, peritonitis) that mattered. What mattered was the effect
they achieved. The important things were the appropriate
framing (the impregnable box, the fatal blow), the suspense

(the spellbound audience, the refusal to succumb), the right equipment (the Water-Torture Cell, the bronze coffin). And the aura of magic: Houdini's secrets; the plethora of stories surrounding his death. He mystifies us to the end and beyond.

This is a biography. Biography ends in death. But this is Houdini's biography; and Houdini, who defied death so many times while he lived, finally defeated it – after he had died.

Notes

List of abbreviations used:

HH:	Harry Houdini
ACD:	Sir Arthur Conan Doyle
BRTC:	Billy Rose Theater Collection, New York Public Library
HC:	Houdini Collection, Library of Congress
HPL:	Harry Price Library, University of London
HTC:	Harvard Theater Collection, Harvard University
McMYC:	McManus-Young Collection, Library of Congress
MKC:	Messmore Kendall Collection, Harry Ransom Humanities Research Center (HRHRC), University of Texas at Austin
RLC:	Robert Lund Collection, Marshall, Michigan (private)
SRC:	Sidney Radner Collection, Appleton

1: The Manacled Diver

p.1 'Houdini . . . arrived at the dock gates . . .': Aberdeen *Daily Free Press*, 1 July 1909.
p.2 'I expect . . .': Liverpool *Daily Post*, 8 – 13 December 1908.
p.3 List of fifteen different preferred types of cuff: McMYC.

2: Rabbits from a Hat

p.6 'all magicians are shy . . .': *Strand Magazine*, January 1919.
p.8 'Father insulted by Prince Erik . . .': facsimile in *Houdini Birth Research Committee's Report:* from the Stanley Palm Collection, Brooklyn, New York.
p.9 'You must remember . . .': facsimile in *Houdini Birth Research Committee's Report*.
p.10 The rumour about Samuel Weiss being Houdini's stepfather was brought to my attention by Charles Reynolds, and it is mentioned in the book he wrote with Doug Henning, *Houdini: His Legend and His Magic*, p.24. He attributed it to J.G. Frazee.

p. 11 'Re the Birthdays . . .': facsimile in *Houdini Birth Research Committee's Report*.

3: Metamorphosis

p. 12: As with most illusions, the secrets of the Substitution Trunk are simple. They rely on the fact that people will look for what they expect to see. Because the lid of the trunk opens upwards, the assumption will be that ties must be loosened if it is to be opened again; but the exit from the trunk is effected via an inward-opening panel in the side, worked by a secret lock. Likewise with the bag: because it was entered from the top, all the audience's attention is concentrated on the original ties and seals. But the exit is made through the bottom: the original occupant carries a small razor and makes a neat slit, or cuts a seam. And when the substitute occupant is discovered, he of course makes his final exit from the top of the bag (after the knots have been untied, seals broken, etc.) and remains standing on the slit at the bottom. Finally, as to the speed which is essential for the effective execution of this trick – the expectation is that the occupant of the trunk will not start preparations for the escape until the screen conceals the apparatus. On the contrary: by that time, he will already be out of the bag. The rest is practice, and presentation.

p. 13 'Polish . . . is becoming . . .': Eva Hoffman, *Lost in Translation*, London, 1989, pp. 120–2.

p. 13 'My mother . . .': note in Houdini's annotated copy of *A Magician among the Spirits*, p. 157, Hoblitzelle Theater Arts Library, HRHRC.

p. 13 The one extant recording is in the possession of Mr Jay Marshall, of Chicago.

p. 14 'Who that has seen Appleton . . .': *Appleton Crescent*, 14 February 1874.

p. 14 'My parents spent . . .': HH to Edna Ferber, 1 November 1914, SRC, Appleton.

p. 14 'I actually dreampt . . .': facsimile in Walter B. Gibson, *The Original Houdini Scrapbook*.

p. 15 'It may interest you to know . . .': HH to Dr Waitt, 8 September 1907, HTC.

p. 17 'twenty-eight years . . .': Milbourne Christopher, *Houdini: The Untold Story*, p. 18.

p. 18 'Such hardships . . .': ibid., p. 10.

p. 18 'I did not like it . . .': HH to Augustus Rapp, 24 December 1912, SRC.

p. 18 'darling mother . . .': note, MKC.

p. 19 'I am going . . .': from a scrapbook, McMYC.

p. 19 'We lived there . . .': Christopher(1969), p. 13.

p. 20 'Shake me! I'm magic!': this story is told in Christopher (1969), pp. 13–14.

p.20 'Compars is the real name . . .': letter, MKC.

p.20 The fact that Compars performed for President Lincoln appears in a letter from Houdini to Dr A.M. Wilson, HC.

p.21 'My dear old Dad and Compars . . .': letter to F.E. Powell, 30 December 1916.

p.21 'You know how a fresh kid is . . .': *Haldeman-Julius Monthly*, October 1925.

p.21 'a circus coming to the town . . .': Houdini souvenir programme.

p.22 'I really believed . . .': quoted in Bernard Meyer, *Houdini: A Mind in Chains*, p.11.

p.23 'Thus, to any young man . . .': Houdini, 'Confessions of a Jail-Breaker', 1919.

p.23 'One day the son . . .': *Photoplay*, June 1920.

p.24 'I want to be first' . . .: Sydney *Daily Telegraph*, 16 April 1910.

p.25 Mrs Williams 'held forth in a house . . .': Joseph Rinn, *Searchlight on Psychical Research*, p.69.

p.26 'My interest in conjuring . . .': Houdini, *The Unmasking of Robert-Houdin*, p.7.

4: Aaron's Rod

p.29 'And Moses and Aaron . . .': Exodus 7:10–12.

p.29 For an extended discussion of Moses' secret magical texts, see Paul Kurtz, *The Transcendental Temptation*, pp.179ff.

p.29 'all the people . . .': Exodus 20:20.

p.30 And it came to pass . . .': Exodus 33:9–11.

p.31 'All the folk in our circle . . .': Isaac Babel, 'Awakening', *Collected Stories*, London, 1961 (Penguin edn.), p.267.

p.31 'I register tomorrow . . .': William L. Gresham, *Houdini: The Man Who Walked Through Walls* p.201.

p.33 'It may exist . . .': HH to Dr Waitt, 8 September 1902, HTC.

p.33 'I don't want anything to do with your cause . . .': Philip French, *The Movie Moguls*, pp.111–2.

p.34 'To be a Jew in New York . . .': John Lahr, 'No Way Back to Kansas', *New Statesman and Society*, 29 May 1992.

5: Two Ladies

p.36 The secret of Houdini's version of sawing a woman in half, as with many such tricks, lies in the platform, which is hollow. The hinged bottom of the box tips the original woman down into it; the 'twins' have crept out from inside it under cover of the open doors and lid and concealed themselves behind it before these are shut. The girls are of course dressed exactly like the original woman. From Gibson, *Houdini's Escapes and Magic*, pp.214 ff.

p.36 'One day I was hired . . .': *Photoplay*, June 1920.

p.37 Mrs Houdini's own recollections appear in Harold Kellock, *Houdini: The Life Story*, p.44.

p.37 'properly married . . .': ibid., p.46.

p.38 'The brothers Houdini . . .': ibid., p.55.

p.38 'Risey . . .': quoted in Gresham pp.25-6. The clipping is in an early scrapbook, SRC.

p.38 The holy water story is according to Meyer, p.55.

p.39 'I was perhaps fortunate . . .': Kellock, p.47.

p.40 'My dear girl . . .': MKC.

p.41 '[Mrs Weiss's] instant acceptance . . .': Kellock, pp.47-8.

p.41 'We were romantically in love . . .': ibid., p.46.

p.41 'still a Honeymoon . . .': letter, MKC.

p.41 'Adorable . . .': MKC.

p.43 'Within a few days . . .': Kellock, p.51.

p.43 'Houdini asked his brother . . .': ibid., pp.52-3.

p.44 'He said the show . . .': ibid., pp.80-1.

p.45 'To be delivered . . .': ibid., pp.81-2.

p.45 'My own entire family . . .': ibid., p.51.

p.45 'I was paralyzed . . .': ibid., p.54.

p.46 The theory that Bess was simply a more suitable stage partner than Dash is given by Goldston in *Sensational Tales of Mystery Men*, p.115.

p.47 'What the hell . . .': Kellock, p.60.

p.47 'It was pleasant . . .': ibid., p.52.

p.47 'Bess had a brain storm', etc.: quoted in Meyer, p.56.

p.47 'Listen to him! . . .': personal communication from James Randi.

p.48 'Houdini created a dream child . . .': interview with Bess, Philadelphia *Evening Bulletin*, 9 January 1933.

p.48 Bess's X-ray theory appears in *Houdini's Strange Tales*, ed. Patrick Culliton and T.L. Williams, Los Angeles 1992, p.5.

p.49 'your husband until . . .': HH to Bess, September 1926, MKC.

p.49 'a girlish woman . . .': *The Marvelous Adventures of Houdini*, quoted in Meyer, p.57.

p.49 'I'm afraid I'm not much of a ladies' man . . .': Kellock, p.293.

p.49 'I have uncanny feelings . . .': letter to Quincy Kilby, 5 September 1915, MKC.

p.50 'stopped sharply in the doorway . . .',: Kellock, pp.295-6.

p.51 'Houdini: Step this way . . .': 'Fortune Telling' Hearings 1924.

p.51 'Mrs Houdini . . .': Kellock, p.194.

6: Freaks

p.53 'I have often sat . . .': New York *Tribune*, 1 November 1921.

p.55 'Houdini always missed it . . .': Kellock, p.64.

p.55 'The pain . . .': 'Handcuff Secrets Exposed', *Conjurer's Magazine*, 1908.

p.56 'NOTICE TO MANAGERS . . .': Rinn, p.86.

p.57 'Your attention . . .': New York *Tribune*, 1 November 1921.

p.57 'when I was playing . . .': HH to Quincy Kilby, 22 June 1916, MKC.

p.58 'stumbled about . . .': Kellock, p.72.

p.59 'The ringmaster . . .': Kellock, p.71.

p.60 'In the lock-up . . .': Kellock, pp.76–7.

p.63 'Even a small stake . . .': Houdini, *The Right Way to Do Wrong*, p.80.

p.64 'You're a monkey . . .': Freedland, *Al Jolson*, p.40.

p.65 An effective technique was that known as 'one ahead'. Sealed messages are collected in a basket. The medium lifts one to her forehead, holds it there and 'reads' it. But the message she is reading (and replying to) is one that she has made up. Then she hands the 'used' message to her partner, who has opened it and conveyed its contents to her before she takes up the next. And so on.

p.66 'Where is my brother John? . . .': Kellock, pp.107–9.

p.66 The story about the boy with the broken arm comes from Kellock, pp.123–4.

p.68 'Get me to the theatre . . .': Christopher (1969), p.35.

p.69 Jack Flosso told me about the book on freaks – his father, Al Flosso, was helping with the illustrations.

7: Handcuff King

p.70 'I started in the show business . . .': Washington *Times*, 7 January 1906.

p.71 'It was opened . . .': Morris N. Young M.D., 'Houdini's Trunk No.8', *Houdini Historical Center Newsletter*, vol. 2 no.2, originally published in *M.U.M.*, December 1951.

p.73 'The key in this set . . .': Letter, MKC.

p.73 'In Berlin . . .': Gibson and Young, *Houdini on Magic*, p.14.

p.74 'for it is obvious . . .': Hereward Carrington, *The Physical Phenomena of Spiritualism*, quoted in H.R. Evans, *The Old and the New Magic*, p.489.

p.74 'The primary lesson . . .': Houdini 'Handcuff Secrets Exposed', quoted in Gibson, *Houdini's Escapes and Magic*, p.17.

p.76 'While in St Johns . . .': Houdini, 'Handcuff Secrets Exposed', *Conjurer's Magazine*, 1908; reprinted *Genii*, October 1972.

p.77 'He lived his own drama . . .': Edmund Wilson, 'A Great Magician', *New Republic*, 17 October 1928.

p.78 'MANACLES DO NOT HOLD HIM': Omaha *World Herald*, 1 April 1899.

p.78 'The ad man put a pair . . .': Kansas City *Star*, 21 August 1899.

p.80 'so I trust you will . . .': HH to Dr Waitt, 18 February 1900, HTC.

p.80 'I have no room . . .': quoted in Edwin Dawes, *The Great Illusionists*.

p.80 'Who created . . .': Christopher (1969), p.39.

p.81 'Possibly we may sail . . .': HH to Dr Waitt, 21 May 1900, HTC.

8: With One Bound He Was Free

p.83 'headliner' . . . 'at the salary of . . .': Christopher (1969), p.42.

p.84 'That is not true . . .': Kellock, p.141.

p.84 'Properly presented . . .': MKC.

p.85 'Cirnoc is dead . . .': 13 November 1903, MKC.

p.85 'It appears he must have . . .': 'Houdini Issues Challenge to "Spirit" of Northcliffe', newspaper cutting c. 1925, McMYC.

p.86 'You can well imagine my feelings . . .': quoted in Christopher (1969), p.46.

p.87 'THEATRICAL NEWS . . .': HTC.

p.88 'because he is a *native* . . .': Christopher (1969), p.47.

p.88 'COME OVER . . .': ibid.

p.88 Al Flosso, for instance, spoke of the rumour about Dash having killed someone to his son Jack, who told me of it.

p.88 'Why, you have acted . . .': quoted in Meyer, p.42.

p.88 'Theo Hardeen . . .': ibid.

p.89 'I don't think . . .': HH to Dr Waitt, HTC.

p.89 'My Dear Bro. Dash . . .': Bess to Hardeen, 1911, SRC.

p.90 'He did it by saying . . .': Conan Doyle, *On the Edge of the Unknown*, p.5.

p.90 'When Harry passed on . . .': 'My Pal Dash', by Joe Hayman, *Conjuror's Magazine*, Hardeen Memorial Issue, July 1945.

p.90 '*which is something* . . .': Houdini, *The Adventurous Life of a Versatile Artist*, p.7.

p.90 'It would be boastful . . .': HH to Dr Waitt, 7 January 1901, HTC.

p.90 'We closed . . .': HH to Dr Waitt, 21 February 1901, HTC.

p.91 'To avert suspicion . . .': Houdini, 'The Thrills in the Life of a Magician', *Strand Magazine*, 5 January 1919.

p.92 'I am not well . . .': HH to Dr Waitt, 31 March 1901, HTC.

p.92 'The "digs" . . .': *Vaudeville News*, 20 August 1920.

p.92 'To tell the truth . . .': HH to Dr Waitt, May 1901, HTC.

p.93 'Letters starting with . . .': typed note, McMYC.

p.95 'stood up and cheered . . .': Blackburn *Star*, 25 October 1902. I should like to thank Frank Koval for giving me the background to this incident.

p.97 The third commentator is quoted in Arthur Setterington, 'Houdini and the Hippodrome Handcuffs', *The Linking Ring*, October 1966.

p.97 The correspondent was Pat Culliton, to the author, 27 May 1992.

p.98 For a detailed discussion of relations between performer and audience, see Richard Sennett's *The Fall of Public Man*.

p.101 'It does seem strange . . .': HH to Dr Waitt, 30 November 1901, HTC.

p.102 'My God, we should be ruined! . . .': Kellock, p.164.

p.103 'carrying their black . . .': quoted in Christopher (1969), p.70.

p.104 'On the inside . . .': Kellock, pp.166–7.

p.104 'The lithograph . . .': Christopher (1969), p.71.

p.104 'The superstitious court . . .: Minneapolis *Star*, 1928, McMYC.

p.105 'Have managed to send . . .': to Dr Waitt, 11 August 1903, HTC.

p.105 'After you leave Russia . . .': Christopher (1969), p.75.

p.106 'After listening . . .': quoted in Kellock, pp.147–8.

9: The Disappearing Fathers Trick

p.108 'I borrowed . . .': Robert-Houdin, *Memoirs*, quoted in Jean Hugard, *Houdini's 'Unmasking'*, pp.49–53.

p.110 'Any unprejudiced . . .': ibid., p.54.

p.110 'My interest . . .': Houdini, *The Unmasking of Robert-Houdin*, pp.7–8.

p.111 'My investigations . . .': ibid., p.8.

p.111 'I am the Great . . .': Hugard, pp.13–14.

p.112 'At that time . . .': *Conjurer's Magazine*, first issue, 15 September 1906.

p.112 'I, as a representative . . .': Christopher (1969), pp.55–6.

p.113 'What a great difference . . .': *Conjurer's Magazine*, 15 September 1906.

p.113 'Visited the grave . . .': postcard, MKC.

p.115 'Horace Goldin has arrived . . .': *Conjurer's Magazine*, 15 September 1906.

p.115 'W.T. STEAD FOOLED AGAIN . . .': ibid., 15 January 1907.

p.115 'The master-magician . . .': Houdini, *The Unmasking of Robert-Houdin*, pp.318–9.

p.116 'Wrote until 2.30 . . .': Kellock, p.182.

p.117 'Darling Kadaria . . .': 28 March 1903, MKC.

p.117 'your husband . . .': MKC.

p.117 'The rare signature . . .': MKC.

p.117 'My legal name . . .': to H.R. Evans, 14 December 1917, MKC.

p.118 'Q: What kind of magicians . . .': I am indebted to Jack Flosso for this one.

p.118 'The money mentioned here . . .': Gibson (1976), p.178.

p.118 'We have decided . . .': *M.U.M.* November 1917.

p.118 'Old Mortality of Magic' . . .: Evans, p.495.

p.120 'The cemetery of a little Jewish town. . . .': Isaac Babel, 'The

Cemetery at Kozin', *Collected Stories*, London, 1961 (Penguin Edition), p.93.

p.120 'It's a bit like collecting . . .': James Hamilton, in conversation with the author.

p.120 'Cemeteries . . . induce the triumphant . . .': Elias Canetti, *On Crowds and Power*, p.275.

p.121 'I have had an argument . . .': HH to Hardeen, 11 October 1903.

p.124 'It appears . . .': HH to F.E. Powell, 24 February 1919, MKC.

p.125 'Poor Evanion . . .': quoted in Kellock, pp.180–1.

p.125 'For every conjurer . . .': *Conjurer's Magazine*, 15 April 1907.

p.125 'In my many conversations . . .': Gibson and Young, p.xi.

p.126 'When a magician advertizes . . .': HH to F.E. Powell, 1919, MKC.

10: All In the Mind

p.128 This version of the story appeared in 'Thrills in the Life of a Magician', *Strand Magazine*, January 1919.

p.129 ' "HANDCUFF KING" JUMPS . . .': quoted in Gresham, p.141.

p.129 'If I don't come to America . . .': quoted in Christopher (1969), p.64.

p.129 'There is no possible chance . . .': HH to Dr Waitt, 25 March 1904, HTC.

p.130 'Saw all that was left . . .': quoted in Meyer, p.81.

p.130 'He is a quick nervous chap . . .': *Appleton Crescent*, 23 July 1904.

p.131 'Better give this . . .': Edna Ferber, *A Peculiar Treasure*, New York, 1939, pp.114–5.

p.131 'Then I will return . . .': HH to Dr Waitt, 2 June 1905, HTC.

p.132 'A rich man . . .': Canetti p.397.

p.132 The stories about Adolph Zukor and Louis B. Mayer appear in Neal Gabler, *An Empire of Their Own*.

p.132 'You should rather . . .': scrapbook, BRTC.

p.133 'The Northern District . . .': *Glasgow Herald*, 23 September 1904.

p.135 'In my own particular work . . .': Houdini, *The Right Way to Do Wrong*, p.89.

p.136 'Disgraced, they are . . .': ibid., pp.9,11.

p.136 'Guess he didn't know . . .': quoted Edmund Wilson, 'A Great Magician', *New Republic*, 17 October 1928.

p.136 'A despot . . .': Canetti p.377.

p.136 'I am induced . . .': Houdini, 'Light on the subject of Jail-breaking as done by my Imitators', Gibson and Young, p.3.

p.137 Houdini's methods for escaping from coffins are outlined in Gresham, pp.122–3.

p.138 'I am strong . . .': Sydney *Daily Telegraph*, 16 April 1910.

p.140 . . . 'unquestionably better . . .': Christopher (1969), p.98.

p.140 'Manager Tate informs me . . . ': Kellock, p.199.

p.141 'Downs has retired . . .': MKC.

p.142 'I never do handcuffs . . .': HH to Augustus Rapp, 24 December 1912, RLC.

p.142 '. . . 1910 New York Can . . .', etc.: Kenneth Silverman, 'More Houdini Trunks', Houdini Historical Center *Newsletter*, vol.: 2 no.2.

p.142 'This stunt . . .': Kellock, p.200.

p.142 The explanation of how the Milk Can worked is from Gresham, pp.151–2.

p.143 'His act . . .': Augustus Roterberg to HH, 20 July 1910, SRC.

p.143 'To ease your mind . . .': Horace Goldin to HH, 5 April 1909, MKC.

11: The Death and Resurrection Show

p.145 'The Death and Resurrection Show': Apologies to Rogan Taylor, the title of whose excellent book I have stolen for this chapter.

p.145 'February 24 . . .': quoted in Meyer, p.81.

p.146 Notes written in 1911 on 'buried alive' appear in Walter Gibson (1932), p.139.

p.146 'I tried out "Buried Alive" . . .': ibid., p.138.

p.147 'Despair . . .': E.A. Poe, 'The Premature Burial', *Tales of Mystery and Imagination*, Everyman edition, London 1966 p.278.

p.150 'I smashed . . .': Christopher (1969), p.112.

p.150 'They charge you . . .': ibid., p.114.

p.151 'We, the undersigned . . .': Henning and Reynolds.

p.151 'Never in any fear . . .': Kellock, p.217.

p.152 'But when only . . .': Sydney *Herald*, 2 April 1910.

p.152 'As soon as I was aloft . . .': ibid.

p.152 'I have been very bisy . . .': HH to Mr Fay, 6 May 1910, MKC.

p.152 'It is time . . .': Kellock, p.218.

p.152 'in which I offered you . . .': MKC.

p.153 'I knew . . .': Houdini, 'Nearly Dying for a Living'.

p.153 'He had . . .': Doyle (1930), p.2.

p.154 'I carry 40 pieces . . .': HH to Augustus Rapp, 24 December 1912, RLC.

p.154 'Laying off . . .': Kellock, pp.281–2.

p.155 'In the first place . . .': Houdini, *Magical Rope-Ties and Escapes*, pp.56–7.

p.156 'No matter what . . .': Dawes, p.183.

p.157 'The moment of *survival* . . .': Canetti, p.227.

p.158 'On the one hand . . .': Robert Jay Lifton, *The Broken Connection*, p.272.

p.158 'Sometimes I think . . .': Houdini, 'The Thrills in the Life of a Magician', *Strand Magazine*, 5 January 1919.

p.159 'The list . . .': Lifton, p.25.

p.159 'It all comes . . .': Doyle, pp.2–3.

p.159 'The practice . . .': McMYC.

p.162 For a discussion of magic as a religion see T.M. Luhrman, *Persuasions of the Witch's Craft*, esp. p.258.

p.163 'When I was twenty . . .': Rogan Taylor, *The Death and Resurrection Show*, p.24.

p.163 'No, no, . . .': Kellock, pp.277–8.

p.164 The remains of shamanism have been traced by Rogan Taylor in *The Death and Resurrection Show*.

p.165 'organization of mythological symbols': Joseph Campbell, *Myths to Live By*, p.97.

12: The Lady Vanishes

p.169 Description of how 'Gone' is performed from Will Dexter, *This Is Magic*, pp.59–60.

p.170 'It is his act . . .': quoted in Christopher (1969), p.131.

p.170 'I am doing . . .': HH to T. Nelson Downs, 7 October 1901, MKC.

p.171 'Think I started . . .': Houdini's diary, quoted in Kellock, p.229.

p.172 'This day Cecilia . . .': diary, Kellock, p.235.

p.172 'Mother-fixated men . . .': Erich Fromm, *The Anatomy of Human Destructiveness*, p.360.

p.173 For discussion of birth as causation of Houdini's neuroses see Otto Rank's remarks in Louis Bragman, 'Houdini Escapes from Reality', *Psychoanalytic Review*, 14 October 1929.

p.173 'in order to hear her heart . . .': Houdini, *A Magician among the Spirits*, p.151.

p.175 'Some time ago . . .': HH to Ottakar Fischer, 4 May 1909, MKC.

p.175 'Have no desire . . .': HH to Harry Price, October 1926, HPL.

p.175 'It hurts me to think . . .': HH to Hardeen, 22 November 1913, Gibson (1976).

p.176 'This is my new letterhead . . .': ibid.

p.176 'I never knew . . .': 5 July 1915, SRC.

p.176 'Dash, I knew . . .': HH to Hardeen, 23 September 1913, SRC.

p.176 'Time heals . . .': HH to Hardeen, 22 November 1913, SRC.

p.177 'I hope [Nat] . . .': HH to Hardeen, 19 January 1914, Gibson (1976).

p.177 'This is the picture . . .': Meyer, pp.35–6.

p.177 'It is my express . . .': ibid., pp.36–7.

p.179 'I was about to sail . . .': Houdini, 'Confessions of a Jail-breaker', 1918.

p.180 'last resting places for Houdini's . . .': scrapbook, BRTC.

p.182 'January First . . .': HH to Bess, 1 January 1916, MKC.

p.183 'Monday Feb 15 . . .': MKC.

p.184 'Good Morning . . .': MKC.

p.184 'Am doing needle trick . . .': MKC.

p.185 'Dismal day . . .': Kellock, pp.237–8.

p.185 'When you say . . .': HH to Dan Turley, 1915, MKC.

p.186 'almost every stunt . . .': Bragman, 'Houdini Escapes from Reality'.

p.186 'A number of times . . .': Boston *Post*, n.d., McMYC.

p.187 ' . . . Urbane, smiling . . .': *The Sun*, Pittsburg, 6 November 1916.

p.189 'I don't know how long . . .': scrapbook, BRTC.

13: Film Star

p.190 'The idea . . .': Gibson (1932), pp.126–7.

p.191 'It was said later . . .': Christopher (1969), p.164.

p.192 'filled . . . with . . .': Gabler p.18.

p.192 'Fifty-five percent . . .': ibid., p.67.

p.193 'Our fur offices . . .': ibid., p.18.

p.193 'that these short . . .': ibid., pp.24–5.

p.194 'movies . . . now almost monopolize . . .': *M.U.M.*, December 1913.

p.194 'I don't like his style . . .': Bob Lund, magic collector *par excellence* and owner of the Museum of Magic in Marshall, Michigan, to the author.

p.195 'My Dear Sister . . .': Kellock, pp.258–62.

p.196 'Nothing is more offensive . . .': Houdini, 'Handcuff Secrets Exposed', quoted in Meyer p.45.

p.196 'Suppose I want . . .': Houdini, 'The Thrills in the Life of a Magician', *Strand Magazine*, 5 January 1919.

p.197 The Bernhardt story appears in Kellock, p.264.

p.197 'Good heavens . . .': Houdini, *A Magician among the Spirits*, p.xv.

p.198 'It is when . . .': Houdini, 'The Thrills in the Life of a Magician', *Strand* magazine, 5 January 1919.

p.199 'People are much more interested . . .': ibid.

p.200 The helpful clippings on acting are now in McMYC.

p.200 'I have signed . . .': HH to O.S. Teale, 17 June 1918.

p.201 'and the great beast . . .': Dexter, p.128.

p.203 'Whenever we get him . . .': Kellock, pp.267–8.

p.203 'His tales . . .': Houdini, 'Confessions of a Jail-breaker'.

p.204 The aeroplane stunt is described in Christopher (1969), pp.156–7.

p.205 'What particularly . . .': ibid., pp.157–8.

p.205 'Somebody in the head office . . .': Nottingham *Football News*, 3 April 1920.

p.206 'a ring that stole . . .': note in MKC.

p.207 'It starts out promisingly . . .': clipping, MKC.

p.208 'I am working very hard . . .': Christopher (1969), p.165.

p.208 'The exchange of . . .': Boston *Globe*, 9 September 1924.

p.208 'Things to look after . . .': MKC.

p.209 'My dear old friend . . .': Harry Kellar to HH, 24 April 1918, RLC.

p.210 'This lock is not . . .': Milbourne Christopher (1969), p.174.

p.210 'A set of amazing parallels . . .': quoted in Robert Lund, 'Afterword on Houdini,' No. 3, *Abracadabra*, 1956.

14: Merlin's Cave

p.211 'The formula . . .': Houdini, *Miracle-Mongers and their Methods*, ch.6.

p.212 The firewalking experiments by Harry Price: *Two Experimental Firewalks* and *Three Experimental Firewalks*, University of London Council for Psychical Investigation, Bulletins II and IV (1936 and 1938).

p.213 'It may seem surprising . . .': *Popular Science*, October 1925.

p.214 'IGNORANCE . . .': *The Star* n.d., HC.

p.214 'We talked . . .': *The Sphinx*, November 1926.

p.214 'Do you know . . .': HH to A.M. Wilson, 17 March 1926, McMYC.

p.214 'The public knows me . . .': interview by George Dilnot for Associated Press, n.d.

p.215 'Madam, you see . . .': Kellock, p.282.

p.215 'We have "arrived" . . .': HH to Harry Price, 1 August 1920, HPL.

p.215 'Some of the important things . . .': HH to Fred Black, quoted in Robert Lund, 'Afterword on Houdini', no.4.

p.216 'As I possess . . .': *New York Times*, 18 June 1916.

p.216 'Who is your . . .': *Picture Plays Confessions Album*, in Gibson (1976), p.170.

p.217 'The highest enjoyment . . .': Nabokov, *Speak, Memory* quoted in Danet and Katriel, 'Books, Butterflies, Botticellis – A Life-span on Collecting', p.1.

p.217 'Yesterday I bot . . .': HH to Quincy Kilby, 27 June 1916, MKC.

p.217 'I know that I cannot . . .': HH to Quincy Kilby, 4 July 1916.

p.217 'I told Mr Becks . . .': HH to Quincy Kilby, 16 July 1916.

p.218 'I have at least . . .': HH to Fred Black, quoted in Lund, 'Afterword on Houdini', no.2.

p.218 'a relationship . . .': Walter Benjamin, quoted in Danet and Katriel, p.5.

p.218 'Mrs Siddons . . .': HH to Fred Black, 5 May 1925, RLC.

p.219 'Just run across . . .': 14 May 1920, MKC.

p.219 'My Dear Mr Harry Price . . .': HH to Harry Price, 5 September 1920, HPL.

p.220 'His research . . .': HH to O.S. Teale, McMYC.

p.221 'When we speak . . .': *Genii*, October 1967. Preface to Manuel Weltman's *Houdini: A Definitive Bibliography*.

p.222 Regarding Lovecraft, see introduction to reprint of 'Imprisoned with the Pharaohs', scrapbook, McMYC.

p.222 This notebook is in McMYC.

p.222 'This is a good example . . .': Teale correspondence, McMYC.

p.222 'present[ed] his compliments . . .': MKC.

p.222 The final corrections to *A Magician* . . . are in the Hoblitzelle Theater Arts Library, HRHRC.

p.223 'It would take . . .': galleys, McMYC.

p.224 'My Dear Evans . . .': HH to H.R. Evans, 14 December 1917, MKC.

p.225 'He now appeared . . .': Edmund Wilson, 'A Great Magician', *New Republic*, 17 October 1928.

p.225 'I live in a treasure-house . . .': HH to Fred Black, 5 May 1925, RLC.

p.225 'On a massive table . . .': Marcet Haldeman-Julius; 'An Interview with Harry Houdini', *Haldeman-Julius Monthly*, Girard, Kansas, October 1925.

p.226 'Did he feel . . .': Fred Black, quoted in Lund 'Afterword on Houdini', no.2.

p.226 'Dressed, according . . .': Haldeman-Julius.

p.227 'Magic is the search . . .': Luhrmans, p.258.

p.227 'During his process . . .': 'Knight in Fortune', quoted in Luhrmans, p.258.

15: Magician Among the Spirits

p.228 'As in all experiments . . .': Sir David Brewster, *Letters on Natural Magic*, p.65.

p.228 'A national system . . .': ibid.

p.229 'The end of a rope . . .': Houdini, *A Magician among the Spirits*, p.21.

p.230 'If you think . . .': quoted in Brandon, *The Spiritualists*, p.168.

p.231 'Their method . . .': Houdini, *A Magician among the Spirits*, pp.21–2.

p.231 'Curiously enough . . .':HH to ACD, 28 March 1920.

p.231 'Regarding . . .': HH to ACD, quoted in Carrington and Ernst, *Houdini and Conan Doyle*, p.87.

p.232 'I have spent . . .': ibid., p.35.

p.232 'During my tour . . .': HH to ACD, 30 March 1920, McMYC.

p.233 Houdini told the story of his first experience with a medium in a lecture on spiritualism to Springfield Union YMCA, 1925, McMYC.

p.233 'Was doing mind-reading . . .': HH to Quincy Kilby, 5 September 1915, MKC.

p.233 'At one time . . .': Houdini, *The Right Way to Do Wrong*, p.6.

p.233 'In a long life . . .': Doyle (1930), p.2.

p.234 'while he was . . .': ibid., p.5.

p.234 'He is a brilliant . . .': Houdini, *A Magician among the Spirits*, pp.138–9.

p.234 'There is no sacrifice . . .': Houdini, 'Ghosts that Talk – By Radio', *Popular Radio*.

p.236 'Our relations . . .': Houdini, *A Magician among the Spirits*, p.164.

p.236 'There was no consideration . . .': Doyle (1930) p.5.

p.236 'Houdini says . . .': Edmund Wilson, 'Houdini', *New Republic*, 24 June 1925.

p.237 'I am willing . . .': Carrington and Ernst, p.88.

p.237 'I am afraid . . .': Doyle, 'The Stockbroker's Clerk', from *The Memoirs of Sherlock Holmes*, London, 1893.

p.238 'The usual information . . .': Doyle, *Our American Adventure*, p.16.

p.239 'In a fair light . . .': ACD to HH, 26 January 1922, McMYC.

p.239 'It is only by knowing . . .': HH to ACD, 3 April 1920, McMYC.

p.240 'My dear chap . . .': quoted in 'The Case of Doyle versus Houdini', *The Month*, August 1930.

p.240 'The body . . .': J. Hewat Mackenzie, *Spirit Intercourse*, pp.86–7.

p.241 'It is said . . .': Carrington and Ernst, p.47.

p.241 '. . . beyond [the intellect] . . .': quoted in Lifton, p.15.

p.242 'this particularly crass . . .': William James, *The Last Report*, quoted in Brandon, The Spiritualists, p.230.

p.242 'Better live . . .': T.H. Huxley, *Life and Letters*, vol.1, quoted in Brandon, ibid.

p.242 'The odd point . . .': James, *The Last Report*, quoted in Brandon, ibid.

p.243 'planting seeds . . .': Carrington and Ernst, p.129.

p.243 'Well, we had . . .': ibid., pp.59–60.

p.244 'all fixed up' . . .: HH to ACD, 27 July 1920.

p.244 'You will understand . . .': Carrington and Ernst, pp.132–3.

p.245 'To-day at 11 o'clock . . .': ibid., p.143.

p.245 'very short . . .': ibid., p.144.

p.245 'The children . . .': ibid., p.159.

p.245 'As Sir Arthur . . .': Houdini, *A Magician among the Spirits*, p.150.

p.246 'The method . . .': Carrington and Ernst, p.162.

p.246 'Mr Houdini . . .': ACD to Ada Besinnet, 3 June 1922, McMYC.

p.246 'In that manner . . .': Houdini, *A Magician among the Spirits*, p.151.

p.247 'It was a singular . . .': Doyle, *Our American Adventure*, quoted in Carrington and Ernst, p.162.

p.247 'Oh, my darling . . .': Carrington and Ernst, pp.165–6.

p.248 'I *always* . . .': Houdini's memorandum of 18 June 1922, quoted in Carrington and Ernst, p.162.

p.249 'My dear Houdini . . .': Houdini, *A Magician among the Spirits*, p.155.

p.249 'I see you . . .': ACD to HH, 19 June 1922, McMYC.

p.250 'It was a long . . .': Doyle (1930), p.43.

p.250 'I was *willing* . . .': Houdini, *A Magician among the Spirits*, p.152.

p.251 'I feel rather sore . . .': Carrington and Ernst, pp.172–3.

p.252 'You are to me . . .': ACD to HH, 26 January 1922, quoted in Carrington and Ernst, p.46.

p.252 'If it be true . . .': Doyle (1930), pp.47–8.

16: Margery

p.253 'When he did the slatewriting . . .': notes, HC.

p.254 'I positively spend . . .': 'Fortune Telling' Hearings, p.70.

p.254 'Is there anybody here . . .': ibid., pp.171–2.

p.256 'My dear Houdini . . .': quoted in Houdini, *A Magician Among the Spirits*, pp.159–160.

p.256 'convinced that these . . .': New York *Tribune*, 6 April 1923.

p.258 'How long did . . .': Boston *Herald*, 19 December 1924.

p.258 'As you will observe . . .': quoted in Christopher (1969), p.189.

p.259 'The truth is . . .': Wilson, 'Houdini', *New Republic* 24 June 1924.

p.259 'not in any way . . .' 'crucify', 'the most extraordinary . . .', etc.: Meikle, Jeffrey; ' "Over There": Arthur Conan Doyle and Spiritualism', University of Texas at Austin Library *Journal*, 1974, p.33.

p.260 'Dear Mr. Munn . . .': Houdini, 'Houdini Exposes the Tricks Used by the Boston Medium Margery', New York, 1924, p.11.

p.260 'There is no doubt . . .': HH to Harry Price, 28 September, 1924, HPL.

p.261 'All that day . . .': Houdini, 'Houdini Exposes . . .', p.7.

p.261 'During the second intermission . . .': Houdini, 'Houdini Exposes . . .', pp.7–8.

p.261 'When Bird left the circle . . .': HH to Bess, 24 July 1924, MKC.

p.263 'not to let go . . .': Houdini, 'Houdini Exposes . . .', pp.17–18.

p.263 'As I asked . . .': HH to Bess, 26 August 1924, MKC.

p.264 'If you misrepresent . . .': Houdini, 'Houdini Exposes . . .', p.21.

p.265 'In the last 10 years . . .': Boston *Herald*, 22 December 1924.

p.265 '[thrown] her legs . . .': handwritten correction to *A Magician among the Spirits*, HRHRC.

p.266 'A statement . . .': HH to Harry Price, 8 February 1925, HPL.

p.266 'It is the most beautiful . . .': E.J. Dingwall to Schrenck-Notzing, *Progressive Thinker*, 18 April 1925.

p.266 'A cold, clammy . . .': Boston *Herald*, 1 February 1925.

p.267 'By the way . . .': HH to Harry Price, 4 July 1925, HPL.

p.267 'with the aid of the Spirit slates . . .': HH to Harry Price, 5 January 1925, HPL.

p.267 'Will you let me see . . .': ibid.

p.269 'must be regarded . . .': 'A Report on a Series of Sittings with the Medium Margery', *Journal of the Society for Psychical Research*, 1926.

p.269 'In the absence . . .': *Banner of Light*, 30 May 1925.

p.270 'more than gallantry . . .': reported in *The Manufacturer and Builder*, December 1876.

p.270 'she never had any . . .': *Boston American*, 20 December 1924.

p.271 'It is the belief . . .': Hudson Hoagland, 'Science and the Medium', *Atlantic Monthly*, November 1925.

p.272 '*Tall stories*' . . .: Houdini, *A Magician among the Spirits*, p.48.

p.272 'Have run across . . .': HH to Harry Price, 20 March 1925, HPL.

p.272 'Last night . . .': HH to Fred Black, quoted in Lund, no. 7.

17: Inside the Coffin

p.274 'No standing . . .': Boston *Herald*, 22 December 1924.

p.274 'I have never . . .': HH to Dr E.E. Free, 5 March 1925.

p.276 'Was comfortable . . .': this and the following quotes are taken from Houdini's report on the tests written to Dr W.J. McConnell of the U.S. Department of Mines. He liked to think that his experiences would be of some use to miners or sailors involved in an accident. The letter is in the Library of Congress.

p.276 'If I die . . .': Christopher (1969), p.231.

p.277 'As a matter of fact . . .': letter to Dr McConnell, U.S. Dept of Mines.

p.278 'I suppose . . .': Doyle (1930), p.15.

p.278 'Would there were . . .': H.W. Bateson to HH, 1917, SRC.

p.278 'We all have our hobbies . . .': letter to editors of Cleveland newspapers denouncing Malcolm Bird, McMYC.

p.278 'Stop thinking . . .': HH to Bess, MKC.

p.280 'Houdini was facing us . . .': Doyle (1930), pp.18–19.

p.281 'Broke a bone . . .': Christopher (1969), p.243.

p.282 '*Champagne* coquette . . .': MKC.

p.282 'We have a $15,000 advance . . .': Hardeen, Lecture on Houdini to Chicago Kiwanis, 1936, McMYC.

p.282 The spectators' reports appear in Robert Lund, 'The Final Chapter', *The Sphinx*, December 1952.

p.283 'Drop the curtain . . .': Hardeen lecture, 1936.

p.283 'We found that his appendix . . .': Lund, 'The Final Chapter'.

p.284 'As I entered the lobby . . .': Hardeen lecture, 1936.

p.284 'He . . . closed his eyes . . .': Detroit *Free Press*, 1 November 1926.

p.284 'It was a beautiful sunny day . . .': Hardeen lecture, 1936.

p.284 The story of the coffin having been left behind comes from Lund, 'The Final Chapter'.

p.286 'And there you have . . .': quoted in Dawes, p.202.

p.286 Bernard Meyer's findings from Meyer, p.176.

p.286 'It is the only case . . .': Lund, 'The Final Chapter'.

p.287 'He was delighted . . .': cutting, SRC.

p.287 'fell to the ground . . .': Doyle (1930), p.22.

p.287 The Crandons' prophecy appears in Samri Frikell (Fulton Oursler), *Ghost Stories*, cutting in scrapbook, McMYC.

p.287 'In my own home . . .': Doyle (1930), p.15.

p.288 'Three years ago . . .': ibid., p.17.

p.288 'Drive through . . .': quoted in Gresham, p.278.

p.289 'I had written . . .': Oursler, *Ghost stories*.

p.289 'Box offices . . .': letter, RLC.

18: HOUDINI LIVES!

p.291 'I happen to have . . .': Dan Waldron, 'Houdini's Favourite Food', *Magicol*, November 1984, pp.6–7.

p.292 'We . . . agreed . . .': Hardeen, Lecture to Chicago Kiwanis, 1936, McMYC.

p.292 'My beloved wife . . .': MKC.

p.292 'Sitting in a comfortable chair . . .': *Picture Plays Confessions Album*, in Gibson, (1976), p.170.

p.293 'Professor Brainien . . .': 28 July 1926, MKC.

p.293 The chaos of the motion-picture ventures is described in a letter from B.M.L. Ernst to Hardeen, McMYC.

p.294 'Because of my long . . .': B.M.L. Ernst to Theodore Hardeen Jr., 16 January 1937, in the possession of Robert Lund.

p.294 'Mrs Houdini wouldn't like it': I am indebted to James Randi for this information on Rose Bonanno.

p.295 'One of the few . . .': diary, MKC.

p.296 'Capitalize that . . .': Francis Fast, *The Houdini Messages*, p.3.

p.298 'A man who says . . .' a seance which Arthur Ford had held: ibid., pp.5–9.

p.298 'This man is coming now . . .': ibid., pp.9–10.

p.299 'The message I want to send . . .': report for U.P., New York, January 1929, scrapbook, McMYC.

p.299 'Regardless of any statement . . .': scrapbook, McMYC.

p.300 'HOUDINI HOAX EXPOSED!': Gresham, p.294.

p.300 'I am writing you this personally . . .': Christopher (1969), p.237.

p.301 'Little Daisy White . . .': ibid., p.258.

p.301 'I wish to say . . .': Gresham, p.296.

p.301 'on the ground of . . .': New York *Telegram*, 25 February 1929, quoted in Christopher (1969), p.259.

p.301 'There was a period . . .': Philadelphia *Evening Bulletin*, 9 January 1933.

p.302 'Mrs Houdini . . . was a white-haired . . .': John Booth, 'Memoirs of a Magician's Ghost', *The Linking Ring*, August 1966, p.25.

p.302 'a male voice . . .': ibid.

p.303 'We spent the morning . . .': ibid.

p.303 'Over 300 invited guests . . .': *Genii*, 20, 1955, pp.81–83.

p.305 Frank Gilmore's claim appears in Mikal Gilmore, 'Family Album', *Granta*, 'They Fuck You Up', Vol. 41, 1992, p.13.

p.306 'the average American lifespan . . .': *Variety*, 25 May 1992.

p.306 'Death defines life . . .': quoted in Lifton, p.100.

Bibliography

In addition to published works, I have made use of the following specialist and manuscript collections:

McManus-Young and Houdini Collections, Library of Congress, Washington D.C.
Messmore Kendall Collection and Hoblitzelle Theater Arts Library, Harry Ransom Humanities Research Center, University of Texas at Austin.
Sidney Radner Collection, Houdini Historical Center, Appleton, Wis.
Harry Price Library, University of London.
Waitt Letters, Harvard Theater Collection, Harvard University.
Billy Rose Theater Collection, New York Public Library.
Robert Lund Collection, Marshall, Michigan (private).

Arcuri, Lawrence, ed., *The Houdini Birth Research Committee's Report*, reprint with additional material (originally compiled by Milbourne Christopher, 1972).
Barnouw, Erik, *The Magician and the Cinema*, Oxford, 1981.
Bergreen, Laurence, *As Thousands Cheer: The Life of Irving Berlin*, London, 1990.
Berlin, Isaiah, *Against the Current, Essays in the History of Ideas*, London, 1979.
Brewster, Sir David, *Letters on Natural Magic*, London, 1833.
Campbell, Joseph, *The Hero with a Thousand Faces*, New York, 1949.
Campbell, Joseph, *Myths to Live By*, New York, 1972.
Cane, Melville, *The First Firefly*, New York, 1974.
Canetti, Elias, *On Crowds and Power*, tr. Carol Stewart, London, 1972.
Carrington Hereward, and Ernst, B.M.L., *Houdini and Conan Doyle: The Story of a Strange Friendship*, London, 1933.
Christopher, Milbourne, *Houdini: The Untold Story*, New York, London, 1969.
Christopher, Milbourne, *Mediums, Mystics and the Occult*, New York, 1975.
Crandon, L.R.G., *The Margery Mediumship: Unofficial Sittings at the Laboratory of the Society for Psychical Research, London, December 6, 7 and 8, 1929*, Boston, 1930.

Dawes, Edwin, *The Great Illusionists*, Newton Abbott, 1979.

De Camp, L. Sprague, *Lovecraft, a Biography*, New York, 1975.

Dexter, Will, *This Is Magic*, London, 1958.

Doerr, H.R., *The Secrets of Houdini's Feats Explained*, Philadelphia n.d.

Doyle, A. Conan, *On the Edge of the Unknown*, London, 1930.

Doyle, A. Conan, *Our American Adventure*, London, 1923.

Dunninger, Joseph, *Houdini's Spirit Exposés*, New York, 1928.

Evans, Henry Ridgely, *The Old and the New Magic*, Chicago, 1906.

Fast, Francis, *The Houdini Messages*, New York, 1929.

Fitzsimons, Raimund, *Death and the Magician: The Mystery of Houdini*, London, 1980.

French, Philip, *The Movie Moguls: An Informal History of the Hollywood Tycoons*, London, 1969.

Fromm, Erich, *The Anatomy of Human Destructiveness*, London, 1974.

Gabler, Neal, *An Empire of their Own: How the Jews invented Hollywood*, New York, 1988.

Gibson, Walter B., *Dunninger's Secrets*, Secaucus, N.J., 1974.

Gibson, Walter B., *Houdini's Escapes and Magic*, New York, 1932.

Gibson, Walter B., *Houdini's Fabulous Magic*, New York, 1961.

Gibson, Walter B., *The Original Houdini Scrapbook*, New York, 1976.

Gibson, Walter B., and Young, Morris N., eds. *Houdini on Magic*, New York, 1953.

Goldston, Will, *Sensational Tales of Mystery Men*, London, 1929.

Gresham, William L., *Houdini: The Man who Walked through Walls*, New York, 1959.

Grey, Margot, *Return from Death*, London, 1985.

Hammond, Paul, *Marvellous Méliès*, London, 1974.

Hardeen, Theodore, *Life and History of Hardeen*, California, 1926.

Henning, Doug, with Charles Reynolds, *Houdini: His Legend and His Magic*, New York, 1977.

'Hoffman, Professor' (Angelo Lewis), *Modern Magic*, London, 1874.

Houdini, Harry, *The Adventurous Life of a Versatile Artist*, 1906.

Houdini, Harry, *Magical Rope-Ties and Escapes*, London, 1920.

Houdini, Harry, *A Magician among the Spirits*, New York, 1924.

Houdini, Harry, *Miracle-Mongers and their Methods*, New York, 1920.

Houdini, Harry, *Houdini's Paper Magic*, New York, 1922.

Houdini, Harry, *The Right Way to Do Wrong: An Exposé*, Boston, 1906.

Houdini, Harry, *The Unmasking of Robert-Houdin*, London, 1909.

Huntington, Richard, and Peter Metcalf, *Celebrations of Death: The Anthropology of Mortuary Ritual*, Cambridge, Mass., 1979.

Hugard, Jean, *Houdini's 'Unmasking'; Fact vs Fiction* (With an Introduction and Supplementary Chapter by Milbourne Christopher, 1957–9), reprinted in book form, New York, 1989.

Jastrow, Joseph, *Wish and Wisdom*, New York, 1935.

Jung, C.G., 'On the Psychology and Pathology of So-called Occult Phenomena', *Collected Works*, pp.3–92, London, 1953.

Kellock, Harold, *Houdini: The Life Story (From the Recollections and Documents of Beatrice Houdini)*, New York, 1928.

Kurtz, Paul, *The Transcendental Temptation*, Buffalo, N.Y., 1991.

Leach, Edmund, *On Culture and Communication*, Cambridge, 1976.

Lifton, Robert Jay, *The Broken Connection: On Death and the Continuity of Life*, New York, 1983.

Luhrman, T.M., *Persuasions of the Witch's Craft*, Cambridge, Mass., 1989.

MacKenzie, J. Hewat, *Spirit Intercourse*, London, 1916.

Menninger, Karl, *Man Against Himself*, London, 1938.

Meyer, Bernard C., M.D., *Houdini: A Mind in Chains: A Psychoanalytic Portrait*, New York, 1976.

Mitchell, Adrian, *Houdini: A Circus Opera*, Amsterdam, 1974–6.

Mulholland, John, *Quicker than the Eye*, Indianapolis, 1932.

Napier, A. David, *Masks, Transformations and Paradox*, California, 1989.

Oursler, Fulton (Anthony Abbott), *Behold This Dream*, New York, 1964.

Oursler, Fulton, *These Are Strange Tales*, Philadelphia, 1948.

Randi, James, and Singer, H., *Houdini: His Life and Art*, New York, 1976.

Reik, Theodor, *The Temptation*, New York, 1961.

Rinn, Joseph F., *Searchlight on Psychical Research*, New York, 1950.

Robert-Houdin, Jean Eugène, *Memoirs of Robert-Houdin, King of Conjurers*, London, 1859.

Sardina, Maurice, *Where Houdini was Wrong*, Tr. and ed. Victor Farelli, London, 1950.

Sennett, Richard, *The Fall of Public Man*, New York, 1976.

Sharpe, S.H., *Introducing Houdini versus Robert-Houdin: The Whole Truth*, Reighton, 1955.

Taylor, Rogan, *The Death and Resurrection Show*, London, 1985.

Tietze, Thomas R., *Margery*, New York, 1973.

Urbain, Jean-Didier, *L'archipel des morts*, Paris, 1980.

Wilson, Edmund, *Classics and Commercials*, New York, 1950.

Magazine Articles and Papers

Bragman, Louis J., 'Houdini Escapes from Reality', *Psychoanalytic Review*, 14:404, October 1929.

Danet, Brenda and Tamar Katriel, 'Books, Butterflies, Botticellis – A Life-span on Collecting', paper for 6th international conference on Culture and Communication, Philadelphia, 1986.

Dingwall, E.J., 'A Report on a Series of Sittings with the Medium Margery', *Journal of the Society for Psychical Research*, vol. XXXVI, June 1926.

'Fortune Telling', Hearings before the Subcommittee on Judiciary of the

Committee on the District of Columbia House of Representatives Sixty-Ninth Congress, First Session, on H.R. 8969, February 26, May 18, 20 and 21, 1924, Washington, 1924.
Frazee, William, 'When Houdini was President', *M.U.M.*, November 1953.
Houdini, Harry, 'Confessions of a Jail-breaker', 1918.
Houdini, Harry, 'Handcuff Secrets Exposed', *Conjurer's Magazine*, 1908.
Houdini, Harry, 'Houdini Exposes the Tricks used by the Boston Medium Margery', New York, 1924.
Houdini, Harry, 'The Thrills in the Life of a Magician', *Strand Magazine*, 5 January 1919.
Lund, Robert, 'Afterword on Houdini', seven articles in *Abracadabra*, 561–7, October–December 1956.
Lund, Robert, 'The Final Chapter', *The Sphinx*, December 1952.
Silverman, Julian, 'Shamans and Acute Schizophrenia', *American Anthropologist*, vol. 69, no. 1, February 1967.
Wilson, Edmund, 'A Great Magician', *New Republic*, 17 October 1928.
Wilson, Edmund, 'Houdini', *New Republic*, 24 June 1925.
Young, Maurice N., 'Houdini's Trunk No. 8', *M.U.M.*, December 1951.
Zolotow, Maurice, *New York Times Book Review*, 23 March 1969.

Index

BEETROOT AND MUSHROOM SALAD WITH EGG

Calories 125; Fibre 4g

3oz (85g) cooked beetroot, peeled and cubed
2oz (55g) mushrooms, thinly sliced
1 egg (size 3), hard-boiled, quartered lengthwise
sprigs of watercress for garnish

Mix beetroot and mushrooms together and serve with hard-boiled egg.
Garnish with sprigs of watercress.
    Suggested dressing: tangy tomato dressing (p. 145).

BEETROOT, CARROT AND SHRIMP SALAD

Calories 125; Fibre 8g

2oz (55g) cooked beetroot, peeled and finely diced
3oz (85g) carrot, peeled and finely diced
1 tablespoon low-fat natural yogurt
1 teaspoon horseradish relish
2oz (55g) watercress sprigs
2oz (55g) beansprouts
2oz (55g) canned shrimps, drained

Put the beetroot and carrot in a basin. Mix the yogurt with the horseradish relish and stir into the beetroot and carrot. Spoon it into the
centre of a shallow dish. Surround with watercress sprigs and
beansprouts. Add the shrimps or serve separately.

HAM WITH TOMATO AND FRENCH BEAN SALAD

Calories 150; Fibre 3g

2 tomatoes, sliced
2oz (55g) whole French beans, fresh or frozen, slightly undercooked

1 tablespoon chopped chives or spring onions
2oz (55g) lean ham

Arrange the tomatoes and beans on a plate, sprinkle with chives or spring onions. Trim off and discard any fat from the ham and serve with the salad.

Suggested dressing: Dietade Low-Calorie Salad Dressing without Oil *or* Waistline Oil-Free French Dressing *or* tangy tomato dressing (p. 145).

CAULIFLOWER, PEAS, PEPPER AND CHEESE SALAD

Calories 150; Fibre 4g

2oz (55g) cauliflower sprigs
2oz (55g) cooked peas, fresh or frozen
1oz (25g) chopped green pepper
1oz (25g) Edam cheese, cubed or grated
1 tablespoon Heinz Slimway Low Calorie Salad Dressing
salt and pepper

Mix all the ingredients together and season to taste with salt and pepper.

CHICKEN WITH CELERY, APPLE AND WATERCRESS SALAD

Calories 150; Fibre 4g

5oz (140g) apple, cored and thinly sliced
1 teaspoon lemon juice
2oz (55g) celery, thinly sliced
2oz (55g) watercress sprigs
2oz (55g) lean roast chicken, sliced

Toss the apple slices in the lemon juice and combine with the celery and watercress. Remove and discard any skin from the sliced chicken and serve with the salad.

Suggested dressing: 1 tablespoon Waistline Vinegar and Oil Dressing *or* Heinz Slimway Low-Calorie Salad Dressing.

COLESLAW WITH FISH

Calories 150; Fibre 5g

3oz (85g) firm white cabbage, shredded
2oz (55g) carrot, grated
1 stick celery, finely chopped
1 tablespoon chopped chives or spring onion
1 tablespoon low-calorie salad dressing
1 tablespoon low-fat natural yogurt
a pinch of curry powder
4oz (115g) poached white fish, cooled and flaked

Mix the cabbage, carrot, celery and chives together in a basin. Blend the low-calorie salad dressing with the yogurt and curry powder. Add to the vegetables and mix well. Lightly stir in the flaked fish and serve.

PEACH AND COTTAGE CHEESE SALAD

Calories 175; Fibre 4g

2oz (55g) Chinese cabbage leaves, thinly sliced crossways
2oz (55g) mushrooms, thinly sliced
4oz (115g) fresh peach, sliced
1 tablespoon Waistline Oil-Free French Dressing
1 tablespoon low-fat natural yogurt
4oz (115g) cottage cheese
1oz (25g) parsley, finely chopped

Combine the cabbage, mushrooms and peach. Add the oil-free dressing and yogurt and toss well together. Mix the cottage cheese with the parsley and serve with the salad vegetables.

HAM WITH COLESLAW

Calories 175; Fibre 6g

3oz (85g) firm white cabbage, shredded
1 tablespoon finely chopped onion
2oz (55g) carrot, grated
1 tablespoon Oil-Free French Dressing
2oz (55g) lean boiled ham, sliced
2 medium tomatoes, halved and sliced

Mix the cabbage with the onion, carrot and dressing. Serve with the ham and tomatoes.

FRUIT AND CABBAGE SALAD

Calories 175; Fibre 13g

1oz (25g) dried apricots, chopped
½oz (15g) raisins
2 tablespoons orange juice
4oz (115g) eating apple
1 tablespoon lemon juice
3oz (85g) white or red cabbage, chopped
1 stick celery, chopped

Soak the dried apricots and raisins in the orange juice for half an hour. Core and chop the apple and toss in the lemon juice until coated to prevent discoloration. Add the fruits to the chopped cabbage and celery and toss well to mix.

BEAN-STUFFED TOMATOES

Calories 175; Fibre 16g

2 large tomatoes, 4oz (115g) each
1 stick celery, finely chopped
6oz (170g) baked beans with tomato sauce

salt and pepper
2oz (55g) white cabbage, chopped

Cut a lid off both tomatoes and remove the centre pulp; chop finely.
Mix with the celery, beans and seasoning to taste. Pile back into the
tomato cases. Serve on a bed of chopped white cabbage.

POTATO, BEETROOT AND PRAWN SALAD

Calories 200; Fibre 5g

3oz (85g) cooked beetroot, peeled and diced
4oz (115g) new potatoes, boiled and diced
1 small onion, peeled and finely chopped
1oz (25g) parsley, finely chopped
1 tablespoon Waistline Oil-Free French Dressing
2oz (55g) prawns

Mix the beetroot and potatoes together. Add the onion, parsley and
dressing and toss together until well mixed. Top with the prawns.

ORANGE, BROAD BEAN, CELERY AND COTTAGE CHEESE SALAD

Calories 200; Fibre 7g

1 medium orange, peeled and sliced
2oz (55g) broad beans, boiled and drained
2oz (55g) celery, thinly sliced
½oz (15g) almonds, chopped
2oz (55g) cottage cheese

Combine the orange, broad beans and celery. Sprinkle with almonds
and serve with the cottage cheese.

Suggested dressing: yogurt mint dressing (p. 146) *or* 1 tablespoon
Waistline Oil-Free French Dressing.

POTATO AND TUNA SALAD

Calories 200; Fibre 7g

4oz (115g) new potatoes, boiled and diced
1 tablespoon Waistline Oil-Free French Dressing
1 tablespoon low-fat natural yogurt
salt and pepper
2oz (55g) fresh or thawed frozen garden peas
1oz (25g) red pepper, chopped
1 tablespoon chopped chives
2oz (55g) tuna in brine, drained and flaked

Put the potatoes while still warm in a basin. Mix the oil-free dressing, yogurt and seasoning together and stir into the warm potatoes. Leave to get cold, then add the peas, red pepper, chives and tuna. Toss well and serve.

SUMMER SALAD

Calories 200; Fibre 8g

2oz (55g) new turnips, grated
2oz (55g) new carrots, grated
2oz (55g) cooked peas
1oz (25g) raisins
1 hard-boiled egg, thickly sliced

Mix the grated vegetables with peas and raisins and top with slices of egg.

Suggested dressing: 1 tablespoon Waistline Low-Calorie Vinegar and Oil Dressing *or* Heinz Slimway Low-Calorie Salad Dressing.

SPINACH, CARROT, NUT AND TURKEY SALAD

Calories 200; Fibre 11g

4oz (115g) spinach leaves, shredded
2oz (55g) carrots, coarsely grated

½oz (15g) almonds, chopped
2oz (55g) roast turkey

Mix the spinach leaves with carrots and almonds. Add dressing if wished and serve with turkey.

Suggested dressing: tangy tomato dressing (p. 145).

BROCCOLI, RED PEPPER AND GRAPE SALAD WITH CORNED BEEF

Calories 225; Fibre 5g

4oz (115g) broccoli, fresh or frozen, cooked and well drained
1 canned red pepper, drained and chopped
4oz (115g) white grapes
1 tablespoon Waistline Oil-Free French Dressing
2oz (55g) corned beef, sliced

Mix the broccoli and red pepper. Halve the grapes, remove seeds and add to the vegetables, with the dressing. Toss well and chill for 30 minutes. Serve with the corned beef.

SAVOY SALAD

Calories 225; Fibre 7g

4oz (115g) Savoy cabbage, thinly sliced
1oz (25g) currants
4oz (115g) fresh or canned pineapple in natural juice, cut into small chunks
1 tablespoon natural pineapple juice
2oz (55g) lean roast chicken

Combine Savoy cabbage, currants, pineapple and juice. Remove and discard any skin from the chicken. Cut the meat into bite-size pieces and mix with the remaining ingredients.

LEEK, KIDNEY BEAN AND CAULIFLOWER SALAD WITH SMOKED MACKEREL

Calories 225; Fibre 8g

4oz (115g) leeks (white part only), sliced
2oz (55g) canned red kidney beans, rinsed and well drained
2oz (55g) raw cauliflower sprigs
1 tablespoon lemon juice or wine vinegar
2oz (55g) smoked mackerel

Mix the leeks with the kidney beans and cauliflower sprigs. Sprinkle with lemon juice or vinegar, and toss well. Serve smoked mackerel separately.

AMERICAN BEAN SALAD AND COTTAGE CHEESE

Calories 225; Fibre 7g

half 1lb 1oz (482g) can Green Giant American Bean Salad
4oz (113g) carton Eden Vale Cottage Cheese with Onion and Peppers

Drain the bean salad and serve with the cottage cheese.

TWO-BEAN SALAD WITH COTTAGE CHEESE

Calories 250; Fibre 12g

2oz (55g) canned red kidney beans, rinsed and drained
2oz (55g) runner beans, cooked
2oz (55g) sweetcorn kernels
½oz (15g) peanuts
2 tablespoons Waistline Oil-Free French Dressing
2oz (55g) cottage cheese
1 tablespoon finely chopped parsley
1 teaspoon chopped chives *or* spring onion

Mix together the kidney beans, runner beans, sweetcorn and peanuts, and toss in the French dressing. Serve with cottage cheese mixed with the parsley and chives or spring onion.

NUTTY COLESLAW

Calories 275; Fibre 13g

4oz (115g) firm white cabbage, shredded
2oz (55g) carrot, grated
2oz (55g) fresh peas *or* frozen peas, cooked
2oz (55g) sweetcorn kernels, cooked
1oz (25g) walnut pieces, roughly chopped
yogurt mint dressing (p. 146)

Mix all the prepared vegetables and nuts together in a bowl. Stir in the yogurt mint dressing and serve.

BOLOGNA AND BEAN SALAD

Calories 300; Fibre 12g

one-third 10oz (283g) can Granose Bologna
1 tomato, sliced
one-third 1lb 1oz (482g) can Green Giant American Bean Salad
4 black or green olives
2 Ideal Bran Crispbreads

Slice the Bologna thinly and arrange in a circle around a serving plate. Pile the bean salad in the centre. Garnish with the sliced tomato and olives. Chill before serving. Accompany with the crispbreads.

KIDNEY BEAN, ONION, APPLE AND CHEESE SALAD

Calories 300; Fibre 10g

3oz (85g) canned red kidney beans, drained and rinsed
2 spring onions, chopped
4oz (115g) eating apple
1 tablespoon (15ml) lemon juice
1½oz (40g) mature Cheddar cheese, diced
2 tablespoons (30ml) oil-free French dressing

Mix the kidney beans and chopped spring onions together in a bowl.
Core and chop the apple then toss in the lemon juice. Add the apple,
diced cheese and oil-free French dressing to the kidney beans and onion
and toss well. Chill before serving.

CORNED BEEF SALAD

Calories 350; Fibre 15g

half 1lb 1oz (482g) can Green Giant American Bean Salad
half 7oz (198g) can sweetcorn kernels
2oz (55g) corned beef, diced
2 tablespoons (30ml) oil-free French dressing
few lettuce leaves
1 Ideal Bran Crispbread

Drain the bean salad and the sweetcorn kernels and place in a bowl.
Add the diced corned beef and the dressing and toss well together.
Serve on a bed of lettuce. Serve the crispbread with the salad.

HI-FI SOUP SNACK MEALS

Some soups can provide super fibre-rich meals. Here we give basic recipes for pea, lentil and sweetcorn soups and show you how you can use them to make a whole variety of easy F-Plan meals.

No one wants to go to the bother of making their own soup for one meal, so we have given quantities for four portions with each basic recipe. The idea is that you should divide the quantity into four, use one and deep freeze the other three in individual rigid plastic containers – empty cartons, for instance.

In the meal section, beneath each soup, we show how adding a bit of this and that can ring the changes on your basic soup.

In giving the calorie and fibre count for each soup we have included one slice of wholemeal bread (1¼oz, 35g) to eat with it. This is not buttered. If you spread your bread, add the following calories:

¼oz (7g) butter or margarine	50 calories
¼oz (7g) low-fat spread (Outline, St Ivel Gold)	25 calories
¼oz (7g) peanut butter	45 calories
½oz (15g) cheese spread (a good alternative for dieters)	35 calories

LENTIL SOUP – BASIC RECIPE, FOUR PORTIONS

Four portions: 600 calories; 25g fibre
Individual portion: 150 calories; 6g fibre
Individual portion plus slice of wholemeal
   bread: 225 calories; 9g fibre

Basic four-portion recipe to make and freeze for lentil soup meals.

6oz (170g) dried lentils
2 pints (1l) water or stock
1 lemon, rind and juice
1 clove garlic, crushed
4oz (115g) onions, chopped
2oz (55g) carrot, chopped
1 clove
salt and freshly ground black pepper

Soak the lentils in water or stock overnight. Put the lemon rind and juice in a heavy-based saucepan and gently sweat the garlic, onions and carrot with the lid on for about 10 minutes, until softened. Add the lentils with the soaking liquid, clove and seasoning. Cover, bring to the boil. Boil for 10 minutes, then simmer for 1–2 hours until the lentils are soft and mushy. For a smooth soup, blend the soup in a liquidizer, first removing the clove.

LENTIL AND VEGETABLE SOUP

Calories 250; Fibre 12g

4oz (115g) tomatoes, chopped
2oz (55g) mushrooms, chopped
1 portion basic lentil soup (see previous page)

Simmer the vegetables in the soup for about 5 minutes. Eat with wholemeal bread.

CURRY-FLAVOURED LENTIL SOUP

Calories 250; Fibre 10g

1 portion basic lentil soup (see previous page)
2oz (55g) apple, chopped
$\frac{1}{2}$ teaspoon curry powder
2 teaspoons chutney

Simmer all the ingredients in the soup for about 5 minutes. Eat with wholemeal bread.

LENTIL, CHICKEN AND LEEK SOUP

Calories 275; Fibre 11g

1oz (25g) white chicken or turkey meat, cooked and chopped
2oz (55g) leeks, sliced
1 portion basic lentil soup (see previous page)

Simmer the poultry meat and leeks in the soup for about 5 minutes. Eat with wholemeal bread.

PEA SOUP – BASIC RECIPE, FOUR PORTIONS

Four portions: 520 calories; 32g fibre
Individual portion: 130 calories; 8g fibre
Individual portion plus slice of wholemeal
bread: 205 calories; 11g fibre

Basic four-portion recipe to make and freeze for pea soup meals.

6oz (170g) dried peas
2 pints (1l) water or stock
4oz (115g) onion, chopped
2oz (55g) celery, chopped
$\frac{1}{4}$ teaspoon dried sage or savory
2 tablespoons fresh chopped parsley
salt and freshly ground black pepper

Soak the peas overnight in the water or stock. Put about two tablespoons of the soaking water in the base of a heavy saucepan and add the onion and celery; cover and gently sweat the vegetables for about 10 minutes. Do not allow to burn. Then pour in the rest of the liquid and peas. Add the herbs and seasoning. Bring to the boil and simmer, covered, for about 2 hours until the peas are soft. For a smooth creamy soup, blend in a liquidizer.

One slice of wholemeal bread (see introduction to the soup section) is included in both the calorie and fibre count of each of these snack meals.

CHUNKY PEA SOUP

Calories 250; Fibre 13g

1 portion basic pea soup (see above)
2oz (55g) carrots, chopped
2oz (55g) apple, chopped
1oz (25g) low-fat natural yogurt

Simmer the carrot and apple in the soup for about 5 minutes. Stir in the yogurt before serving. Eat with wholemeal bread.

PEA SOUP WITH HAM

Calories 275; Fibre 11g

1 portion basic pea soup (see previous page)
1oz (25g) lean boiled ham, chopped

Simmer the ham in the soup for about 5 minutes. Eat with wholemeal bread.

PEA SOUP WITH LEEK AND EGG

Calories 300; Fibre 14g

1 portion basic pea soup (see previous page)
3oz (85g) leeks, sliced thinly
1 egg (size 5 or 6)

Simmer the leeks in the soup for about 5 minutes. Hard-boil the egg, and chop. Crumble the chopped egg into the soup before serving. Eat with wholemeal bread.

SWEETCORN SOUP – BASIC RECIPE, FOUR PORTIONS

Four portions: 260 calories; 12g fibre
Individual portion: 65 calories; 3g fibre
Individual portion plus slice of wholemeal
bread: 140 calories; 6g fibre

Basic four-portion recipe to make and freeze for sweetcorn soup meals.

6oz (170g) sweetcorn kernels, frozen or canned
1½ pints (9dl) water or stock
4oz (115g) onion, chopped

$\frac{1}{2}$ teaspoon sugar
$\frac{1}{2}$ teaspoon dry mustard powder
1 tablespoon lemon juice
3 drops tabasco sauce
1 tablespoon Worcestershire sauce
salt and freshly ground black pepper
$\frac{1}{2}$ pint (3dl) skimmed milk, additional to daily allowance

Put all the ingredients, except the milk, into a saucepan. Bring to the boil, cover and simmer for about 30 minutes. Add the milk. If preferred, blend until smooth in a liquidizer – otherwise leave chunky.

One slice of wholemeal bread (see introduction to the soup section) is included in both the calorie and fibre count of each of these snack meals.

SWEETCORN SOUP WITH CHICKEN AND BEANSPROUTS

Calories 175; Fibre 7g

10z (25g) cooked chicken or turkey meat, chopped
1 portion basic sweetcorn soup (see left)
10z (25g) fresh beansprouts

Simmer the chicken or turkey in the soup for about 5 minutes, then stir in the beansprouts. Leave them crisp. Eat with wholemeal bread.

SWEETCORN SOUP WITH VEGETABLES

Calories 175; Fibre 7g

1 portion basic sweetcorn soup (see left)
20z (55g) tomato, chopped
40z (115g) courgettes, sliced

Add the vegetables to the soup and simmer for about 5 minutes. Eat with wholemeal bread.

SWEETCORN SOUP WITH CRAB

Calories 200; Fibre 6g

1oz (25g) canned crab meat
1oz (25g) apple, chopped
1 portion basic sweetcorn soup (p. 160)

Add the crab meat and apple to the soup and simmer for about 5 minutes. Eat with wholemeal bread.

SWEETCORN CHOWDER

Calories 200; Fibre 6g

2oz (55g) any white fish, cooked and flaked, *or* peeled prawns
1 portion basic sweetcorn soup (p. 160)

Add the flaked fish or prawns to the soup and simmer for about 5 minutes. Eat with wholemeal bread.

HI-FI CRISPBREADS

All these crispbread snacks are served on Energen Brancrisp crisp-breads. We have included two – supplying 50 calories and 2·6g fibre in total – in the calorie and fibre count for each meal. Don't use other crispbreads because the alternative well-known brands are lower in fibre content.

These snacks, perhaps eaten with fruit from the daily allowance, could be useful for those who like to follow a little-and-often pattern of eating. Alternatively they could provide a suppertime snack for those with calories to spare, or even a very light lunch for those who like to save most of their calories for the evening.

CURRIED CHEESE

Calories 125; Fibre 3g

4 tablespoons cottage cheese
2 teaspoons curry paste
2 teaspoons sweet pickle

Mix the cottage cheese and curry paste and spread over the crispbreads. Spoon the pickle in the centre of each.

CHEESE AND SWEETCORN PICKLE

Calories 125; Fibre 4g

½oz (15g) or 1 triangle cheese spread
1oz (25g) cucumber, sliced
1oz (25g) corn relish

Spread the crispbreads with the cheese spread. Top with the cucumber slices and the corn relish.

PEANUT BUTTER AND CRESS

Calories 150; Fibre 4g

4 teaspoons peanut butter
1 stick celery, chopped
½ carton mustard and cress

Mix the peanut butter and celery. Spread on the crispbreads and garnish with the mustard and cress.

CHEESE AND ONION

Calories 150; Fibre 4g

1 small onion, chopped
1oz (25g) cheese spread
8 potato crisps

Mix the onion and cheese spread and four of the crisps. Spread on the crispbreads and crush the other crisps. Sprinkle over the top.

PIQUANT FISH

Calories 150; Fibre 5g

3oz (85g) cod or haddock
1 tablespoon low-calorie tartare sauce (Waistline)
1 tablespoon peas, cooked
ground pepper
2 lemon wedges

Poach the fish, flake and cool. Mix it with the dressing, peas and pepper. Spread on the crispbreads and top with lemon wedges.

CHOCOLATE AND BANANA

Calories 150; Fibre 5g

2 teaspoons chocolate spread
1 small banana (4½oz, 130g)
1 teaspoon lemon juice

Spread a teaspoonful of chocolate spread on each crispbread. Slice the banana and arrange on top of the crispbreads. Sprinkle with the lemon juice.

PRAWN AND CELERY

Calories 150; Fibre 5g

2 sticks celery
1 tablespoon low-calorie salad dressing
2oz (55g) prawns

Finely chop the celery and mix with the salad dressing. Spread over the crispbreads and top with the prawns.

HAM AND PEA

Calories 150; Fibre 5g

1 large slice lean ham (1oz, 25g)
½ small onion, finely chopped
1oz (25g) peas, cooked
1 tablespoon low-calorie salad dressing

Chop the ham and mix it with the other ingredients. Spread on the crispbreads.

FRUIT, VEGETABLES AND CHEESE

Calories 150; Fibre 7g

1oz (25g) peas, cooked
1oz (25g) canned sweetcorn
1oz (25g) low-fat curd cheese
¼oz (7g) raisins

Mix all the ingredients together and spread on the crispbreads.

EGG AND SWEETCORN

Calories 175; Fibre 4g

1 hard-boiled egg (size 3)
1oz (25g) canned sweetcorn
1 tablespoon low-calorie salad dressing
salt and pepper

Chop the egg. Mix with the other ingredients and spread over the crispbreads.

CHICKEN AND MUSHROOM

Calories 175; Fibre 4g

2oz (55g) cooked chicken meat, chopped
4 button mushrooms, chopped
salt and pepper
1 tablespoon low-calorie salad dressing
1 tablespoon chopped walnuts

Mix the chicken, mushrooms, seasoning and salad dressing together. Spread on the crispbreads and garnish with the chopped nuts.

COTTAGE CHEESE, RAISIN AND APPLE

Calories 175; Fibre 5g

2oz (55g) cottage cheese
½oz (15g) raisins
4oz (115g) eating apple, cored and sliced

Mix the cottage cheese and raisins and spread over the crispbreads.
Cover with the apple slices.

PORK AND APPLE

Calories 175; Fibre 7g

2oz (55g) cooked lean pork
4 prunes (soaked if dried)
½oz (15g) low-fat spread
1 tablespoon apple sauce

Chop the pork finely. Remove the stones from the prunes and chop
the flesh. Add to the pork. Spread the low-fat spread on the crispbreads, and then the pork mixture. Top with a little apple sauce.

COTTAGE CHEESE WITH APRICOTS

Calories 225; Fibre 14g

4oz (113g) carton Eden Vale Cottage Cheese with Pineapple
2oz (56g) Whitworths No-need-to-soak Dried Apricots

Mix together the cottage cheese with the chopped dried apricots. Serve
with the crispbreads.

MEALS ON TOAST

The meals in this section are all served on two slices of wholemeal or whole-wheat bread, toasted. Maximum total weight for the two slices must be 2½oz (70g). The calories for this quantity of bread, and the 6g fibre they supply, are included in the totals for each meal. If you use high bran bread, add another 2g fibre to the total for each meal.

With some meals we have relied on the bread alone to provide dietary fibre. With others we have added more dietary fibre in the ingredients used for the topping.

Some of these meals on toast are as simple as a can of baked beans or a couple of poached eggs. Others are more imaginative for the adventurous!

Do not butter toast or spread it with any other fat unless the recipe indicates that you should. Calories given are for butter, but subtract 50 calories for each ½oz (15g) fat if you use low-fat spread.

RED BEEF

Calories 250; Fibre 8g

¼ bunch watercress
1oz (25g) cooked lean beef, thinly sliced
2 teaspoons tomato chutney
2oz (55g) cooked beetroot, sliced

Cover the toast with the watercress; cut the beef into thin shreds and mix with the chutney. Pile on to the watercress and garnish with beetroot.

CREAMY MUSHROOMS

Calories 250; Fibre 9g

4oz (115g) button mushrooms
4fl oz (115ml) skimmed milk
2 teaspoons cornflour
1 tablespoon low-fat natural yogurt

salt and pepper
a dash of Worcestershire sauce

Poach the mushrooms in the milk for 5 minutes. Blend the cornflour with a little cold water and stir into the mushrooms. Bring to the boil, stirring, and cook for 2 minutes until thickened. Add the yogurt, seasoning to taste and Worcestershire sauce. Serve on toast.

BANANA SPECIAL

Calories 275; Fibre 12g

1 banana (6oz, 170g)
2 teaspoons lemon juice
a little grated lemon rind
a small fresh peach (4oz, 115g)
ground cinnamon

Mash the banana with the lemon juice and rind, and spread over toast. Peel and slice the peach, arrange on the banana and sprinkle lightly with cinnamon.

Other fruit in season can replace the peach; melon, for instance.

DEVILLED KIDNEY

Calories 300; Fibre 6g

$\frac{1}{4}$oz (7g) butter
5oz (140g) sliced lamb's kidneys
1oz (25g) onion, chopped
salt and-pepper
4 teaspoons made mustard
2 teaspoons tomato ketchup
2 large lettuce leaves
parsley for garnish

Melt the butter in a non-stick pan and fry the kidneys and onion. Off the heat add the seasonings, mustard and ketchup, and stir well. Cover the toast with the lettuce leaves. Pile the kidneys on top and sprinkle with parsley.

TOMATO BONANZA

Calories 300; Fibre 9g

½oz (15g) butter
2 teaspoons fresh basil, chopped, *or* 1 teaspoon dried basil
8oz (225g) tomatoes, thinly sliced
salt and pepper

Mix the butter and herbs together and spread over the toast. Arrange tomatoes on top, making sure the toast is completely covered. Season. Grill until the tomatoes are cooked.

CHINESE VEGETABLE TOP

Calories 300; Fibre 10g

1 large Chinese leaf
½ tablespoon oil
1 clove garlic, crushed
2oz (55g) mushrooms, thinly sliced
2oz (55g) leek, thinly sliced
2oz (55g) courgettes, thinly sliced
½ teaspoon soy sauce
1 tablespoon stock, wine, cider or water
pepper

Put half a Chinese leaf on each slice of toast. Heat the oil, add the vegetables and fry quickly for 3 minutes. Add the soy sauce, liquid and pepper. Cook for a further minute and then pile on to the leaves and serve.

HOT INDIAN CHICKEN

Calories 325; Fibre 6g

2oz (55g) curd cheese
$\frac{1}{4}-\frac{1}{2}$ teaspoon curry or vindaloo paste
2oz (55g) cooked chicken, sliced
1 teaspoon mango chutney
coriander leaves or parsley

Mix curd cheese and curry paste, and spread over the toast. Arrange the chicken slices on top. Put chutney in centre of each and garnish with the leaves.

TUNA MIX

Calories 325; Fibre 7g

3½oz (100g) can tuna in brine, drained
1 medium onion, peeled
1 tablespoon Hellman's Reduced Calorie Lemon Mayonnaise
1 tablespoon chopped parsley
cayenne pepper
parsley

Flake the tuna. Cut the onion into halves and then into very thin slices. Mix with mayonnaise, parsley and pepper. Spread on toast. Garnish with parsley sprigs.

SMOKED MACKEREL SPREAD

Calories 325; Fibre 7g

2oz (55g) curd cheese
1oz (25g) smoked or kippered mackerel, flaked
pepper
2oz (55g) tomato
2 black olives

Mix the curd cheese and mackerel until smooth. Season with pepper and spread on toast. Thinly slice the tomato and olives and arrange on top.

COTTAGE CHEESE AND PINEAPPLE

Calories 325; Fibre 7g

4oz (115g) cottage cheese (natural or with onion and peppers)
salt and pepper
2 slices canned pineapple in natural juice, drained
sprigs of watercress

Season the cottage cheese to taste and spread over the toast. Top each with a ring of pineapple and heat through under the grill. Garnish with watercress.

MUSHROOM SCRAMBLE

Calories 325; Fibre 7g

2fl oz (55ml) skimmed milk
2oz (55g) mushrooms, sliced
2 eggs (size 4)
salt and pepper

Put the milk and mushrooms in a saucepan. Heat gently for 3 minutes. Beat the eggs with the seasoning and stir into the mushrooms. Cook, stirring continuously until the eggs are creamy. Serve on toast.

CRANBERRY TONGUE TREAT

Calories 350; Fibre 6g

½oz (15g) cranberry sauce
2oz (55g) tongue
1in (2·5cm) unpeeled cucumber

Spread the sauce on toast. Cut the tongue into strips and pile on top. Cut the cucumber into small dice and scatter over the tongue.

DUTCH CHEESE SAVOURY

Calories 350; Fibre 7g

2oz (55g) Edam cheese, grated
1 tablespoon horseradish sauce
2 pickled onions, thinly sliced
paprika

Mix the cheese and sauce, spread on toast and, if wished, grill until the cheese melts. Garnish with onions and paprika. Serve hot or cold.

MOCK PIZZA

Calories 350; Fibre 8g

2 small or 1 large tomato, sliced
salt and pepper
$\frac{1}{4}$ teaspoon dried mixed herbs
2oz (55g) Edam cheese, grated
2 stuffed olives, sliced

Cover the toast with the sliced tomatoes. Season to taste and sprinkle over the herbs. Top with the grated cheese and add the slices of olive for garnish. Grill until the cheese is melted.

LEMON AND PEAR SWEETENER

Calories 350; Fibre 9g

$2\frac{1}{2}$oz (70g)
1 tablespoon lemon curd
1 small ripe pear
$\frac{1}{2}$oz (15g) raisins

Mix the cottage cheese and lemon curd and spread over toast. Halve the pear, remove the core and slice thinly. Arrange on toast, sprinkle with raisins and serve at once.

BAKED BEAN MEDLEY

Calories 350; Fibre 22g

8oz (225g) baked beans with tomato sauce
2 tablespoons low-fat natural yogurt
salt and pepper
2 teaspoons chopped mint
2 lettuce leaves, shredded
a few beansprouts (optional)

Mash the baked beans and stir in the remaining ingredients. Spread on toast. If wished, arrange a few beansprouts in the centre of each.

BAKED BEANS

Calories 350; Fibre 22g

8oz (225g) baked beans with tomato sauce

Heat and serve on toast.

APPLE AND CHEESE

Calories 375; Fibre 9g

2 tablespoons sweet pickle
4oz (115g) eating apple, cored and thinly sliced
2 processed cheese slices

Spread each piece of toast with pickle and cover with sliced apple. Arrange a cheese slice on top of each and grill until the cheese has melted.

CORN, CELERY AND CHEESE GRILL

Calories 375; Fibre 14g

half a 12oz (340g) can sweetcorn
salt and pepper
2 sticks celery
1oz (25g) Lancashire cheese
paprika
2 cocktail gherkins

Liquidize the corn and its liquid and season. Slice the celery thinly and cut the cheese into small dice. Arrange the celery on toast, coat with the sweetcorn, scatter the cheese on top and grill until the cheese melts and browns. Sprinkle with paprika and garnish each with a gherkin fan.

SWEETCORN SCRAMBLE

Calories 375; Fibre 11g

2 tablespoons (30ml) skimmed milk
2 eggs (size 4)
salt and pepper
3oz (85g) canned sweetcorn, drained
1 teaspoon chopped fresh parsley

Beat the milk, eggs and seasoning together. Pour into a non-stick pan and stir in the sweetcorn. Heat gently, stirring continuously, until the egg is just set. Spoon on to toast and sprinkle with the chopped parsley.

CHICKEN LIVER SAVOURY

Calories 400; Fibre 6g

4oz (115g) chicken livers
salt and pepper
$\frac{1}{4}$ teaspoon butter
2 tablespoons low-calorie tartare sauce
$\frac{1}{2}$oz (15g) grated carrot
2 pieces celery leaf

Put livers on foil, season and flake butter on top. Grill until lightly cooked, turning once. Meanwhile spread toast with tartare sauce and cover with carrot. Slice livers and arrange on top. Garnish with the celery leaf or a sprig of any suitable herb.

EGG, PEA AND HAM

Calories 400; Fibre 9g

2 small eggs, size 5
$1\frac{1}{2}$oz (40g) frozen peas
1 tablespoon low-fat natural yogurt
salt and pepper
1oz (25g) lean cooked ham, shredded

Hard-boil eggs, cook peas and chop together while hot. Stir in yogurt and seasonings. Spread on toast, make a border with the ham and serve at once.

GLAZED PEANUT AND APPLE

Calories 400; Fibre 10g

2 teaspoons crunchy peanut butter
2 teaspoons redcurrant jelly
1 teaspoon lemon, orange or other unsweetened fruit juice
1 unpeeled, small crisp apple, quartered and cored

Spread peanut butter over toast. Soften the jelly in the fruit juice over a low heat. Slice the apple thinly and stir into the jelly until the slices are coated. Arrange the apple on butter, pour any remaining jelly on top and leave for a few minutes to set.

MEXICAN SPREAD

Calories 400; Fibre 13g

2oz (55g) Mattesson's Liver & Bacon Spreading Pâté
half a 10oz (283g) can red kidney beans, drained
$\frac{1}{2}$ stick celery, thinly sliced
1 small tomato, chopped
4 drops tabasco or pepper sauce

Chop pâté and put into a pan with the other ingredients. Heat very gently, stirring until blended and hot. Spread over toast.

DATE AND ORANGE TOPPING

Calories 400; Fibre 14g

2oz (55g) dried dates
2 small oranges
$\frac{1}{4}$oz (7g) flaked almonds

Stew the dates with the juice of 1 orange and beat smooth. Cool; spread on toast. Top with the second orange, divided into segments, and scatter the almonds on top.

POACHED EGGS

Calories 425; Fibre 6g

2 medium eggs, size 3, poached without fat
$\frac{1}{2}$oz (15g) butter

Serve poached eggs on buttered toast.

CRUNCH CAMEMBERT

Calories 425; Fibre 7g

2oz (55g) Camembert cheese
½oz (15g) dry roasted peanuts, chopped
cayenne pepper
sprigs of watercress

Slice the Camembert very thinly and cover the toast with cheese. Sprinkle the peanuts on top and press into cheese. Grill until the cheese melts and then sprinkle with a pinch of cayenne and garnish with watercress sprigs.

SEAFOOD TOPS

Calories 425; Fibre 7g

1½oz (40g) taramasalata
6 small green pepper rings
2oz (55g) peeled prawns

Spread the toast with taramasalata. Arrange 3 pepper rings overlapping, diagonally, on each. Divide the prawns between the rings.

SCRAMBLED EGG AND KIPPER

Calories 450; Fibre 6g

2oz (55g) skinned kipper fillet
2 small eggs, size 5
salt and pepper
1 tablespoon skimmed milk
¼oz (7g) butter
2 large lettuce leaves
4 thin slices cucumber

Cut the kipper fillets into strips. Beat the eggs with the seasonings and milk. Melt the butter in a non-stick pan and pour in all but 1 tablespoon of the egg mixture; stir over moderate heat until just set. Stir in the remaining egg. Put a lettuce leaf on each toast; divide the egg between them. Arrange the kipper strips on top and decorate each with two cucumber twists. Serve at once, hot or cold.

SANDWICH SECTION

Wholemeal bread, as everyone knows, is a good source of dietary fibre. So a sandwich made from wholemeal bread makes a quick and satisfying little meal.

Those who eat a desk lunch might carry one of these sandwiches with them to work, with the two pieces of fruit allowed on the daily eating plan. At home, a sandwich might suit the housewife who wants to save most of her calories and culinary effort for the evening.

We have divided the sandwiches into three sections: simple sandwiches, for those who like to keep to old favourites; sandwiches for those who like to experiment a little; and toasted sandwiches.

Important: all the sandwiches, in both sections, must be made with two slices of wholemeal bread weighing no more than 2½oz (70g) in total. This provides you with 6g dietary fibre and 150 calories. These figures, along with the sandwich filling, are included when we list the calorie and fibre total for each sandwich. Make sure the bread is wholemeal – not just brown!

Very important: do not butter the bread, or spread even with low-fat spreads, unless this is indicated in the instructions.

SIMPLE SANDWICHES

COTTAGE CHEESE AND CUCUMBER

Calories 200; Fibre 6g

2oz (55g) cottage cheese (natural, with chives, with onions and peppers, or with pineapple)
1oz (25g) cucumber, sliced

Fill the bread with the cottage cheese and cucumber slices.

SARDINE AND TOMATO

Calories 225; Fibre 7g

1 teaspoon low-fat spread
1 sardine in tomato sauce
a dash of vinegar
1 tomato, sliced
salt and pepper

Spread one slice of the bread with the low-fat spread. Mash the sardine with the vinegar and spread on the bread. Cover with the tomato slices. Season to taste and top with the second slice of bread.

CHICKEN AND CORN RELISH

Calories 225; Fibre 7g

1¼oz (35g) pot minced chicken in jelly
1 tablespoon corn relish

Spread the bread with the minced chicken and the corn relish.

BEEF, ONION AND TOMATO

Calories 225; Fibre 7g

1¼oz (35g) pot beef paste
1 tablespoon chopped onion
1 small tomato, sliced
salt and pepper

Spread both slices of bread with the beef paste and fill with the chopped onion and sliced tomato. Season to taste.

PRAWN AND SALAD SANDWICH

Calories 225; Fibre 7g

1 tablespoon low-calorie salad dressing
1oz (25g) prawns
1 lettuce leaf
1 tomato, sliced
a few slices of cucumber
a few sprigs of watercress

Spread both slices of bread with the salad dressing and fill with the remaining ingredients.

EGG AND CRESS

Calories 250; Fibre 6g

1 tablespoon Waistline Low-Calorie Vegetable Spread
1 egg (size 3), hard-boiled and chopped
½ carton mustard and cress
salt and pepper

Spread the bread with the low-calorie vegetable spread. Fill with the egg and cress, and season to taste.

CORNED BEEF AND PICKLE

Calories 250; Fibre 6g

1 level teaspoon low-fat spread
1oz (25g) corned beef
1 tablespoon sweet pickle

Spread the bread with the low-fat spread. Fill with the corned beef and pickle.

CHEESE AND PICCALILLI

Calories 250; Fibre 7g

1oz (25g) Edam cheese, grated
1oz (25g) piccalilli, chopped finely

Mix the cheese with the piccalilli and use to fill the sandwich.

PEANUT BUTTER

Calories 325; Fibre 8g

1oz (25g) peanut butter
½ carton mustard and cress

Spread the bread with the peanut butter and fill with the mustard and cress.

SOMETHING-DIFFERENT SANDWICHES

Note: use wholemeal bread (2½oz, 70g, for two slices) as in the previous section.

COTTAGE CHEESE AND MUSHROOMS

Calories 175; Fibre 7g

1oz (25g) cottage cheese
a pinch of mixed dried herbs
2oz (55g) mushrooms, thinly sliced

Mix the cottage cheese with the herbs and spread over one slice of bread, then add the mushrooms and top with the second slice of bread.

SOFT CHEESE AND PRUNES

Calories 225; Fibre 10g

1oz (25g) Sainsbury's Low Fat Soft Cheese
1oz (25g) prunes, stoned and chopped

Combine the cheese and prunes and fill the bread.

COTTAGE CHEESE, CAPER, SWEETCORN AND OLIVES

Calories 225; Fibre 9g

1oz (25g) cottage cheese
6 capers, drained and chopped
1oz (25g) sweetcorn
½oz (15g) olives, stoned and chopped

Mix all the ingredients together and season with pepper and mild paprika. Spread on one slice of bread and top with second slice.

PEANUT BUTTER AND BEANSPROUTS

Calories 250; Fibre 8g

½oz (15g) peanut butter
1oz (25g) beansprouts

Rinse, drain and chop the beansprouts. Spread one slice of bread with peanut butter; add the beansprouts and the second slice of bread.

PEANUT BUTTER, WATERCRESS AND MUSHROOMS

Calories 250; Fibre 9g

½oz (15g) peanut butter
1 tablespoon watercress, chopped
2oz (55g) mushrooms, finely chopped
1 teaspoon lemon juice

Spread the bread with the peanut butter. Mix the watercress, mushrooms and lemon juice together and use to fill the sandwich.

COTTAGE CHEESE, HAM AND SWEETCORN

Calories 250; Fibre 8g

1 oz (25g) cottage cheese
1 teaspoon French mustard
1oz (25g) sweetcorn
1oz (25g) lean ham

Mix the cottage cheese with the mustard and corn, and spread it over one slice of bread. Top with the ham and the second slice of bread.

EGG, COTTAGE CHEESE AND RED PEPPER

Calories 250; Fibre 7g

1oz (25g) cottage cheese
1 canned red pepper, well drained and chopped
1 egg (size 4), hard-boiled and chopped
salt and pepper
2 drops tabasco sauce

Mash together the cottage cheese, red pepper and egg. Season with salt, pepper and tabasco sauce and fill the sandwich.

CRAB AND BEANSPROUTS

Calories 275; Fibre 7g

½oz (15g) Primula or Dairylea cheese spread
1½oz (40g) canned crab meat
1oz (25g) beansprouts, chopped

Spread the cheese on the bread. Flake the crab meat, mix it with the beansprouts and fill the sandwich with it.

CRAB AND MUSHROOM

Calories 275; Fibre 6g

1 teaspoon low-fat spread
2oz (55g) canned crab meat, drained
1 tablespoon low-calorie salad dressing
1oz (25g) mushrooms, chopped

Spread the bread with the low-fat spread. Flake the crab meat and mix with the dressing and mushrooms. Fill the sandwich.

PEANUT BUTTER AND CHICKEN

Calories 300; Fibre 7g

½oz (15g) peanut butter
1oz (25g) lean roast chicken

Spread one slice of bread with the peanut butter. Top with the chicken and the second slice of bread.

BANANA, HONEY AND RAISINS

Calories 300; Fibre 11g

1 medium banana (6oz, 170g)
2 teaspoons honey
1oz (25g) raisins

Peel and mash the banana with the honey and raisins. Spread the bread with the mixture.

PEANUT BUTTER AND PRAWNS

Calories 300; Fibre 7g

½oz (15g) peanut butter
2oz (55g) prawns
thin slices of cucumber

Spread the bread with the peanut butter, and fill with the prawns and cucumber.

PEANUT BUTTER AND RAISINS

Calories 300; Fibre 9g

½oz (15g) peanut butter
1oz (25g) raisins

Mix together the peanut butter and raisins and spread on one slice of bread. Top with the second slice.

DATE AND NUT

Calories 325; Fibre 9g

1oz (25g) Sainsbury's Low Fat Soft Cheese
1oz (25g) dates, washed, dried and chopped
½oz (15g) peanuts, chopped

Spread the cheese on one slice of bread; sprinkle the nuts and dates over the surface. Top with the second slice of bread.

TURKEY AND APPLE

Calories 325; Fibre 8g

½oz (15g) cheese spread
2oz (55g) roast turkey
5oz (140g) apple, cored and thinly sliced
1 teaspoon lemon juice

Spread the cheese on the bread. Fill with the turkey and the apple slices, sprinkled with lemon juice.

TOASTED SANDWICHES

MUSHROOM AND HAM

Calories 300; Fibre 11g

half 7½oz (213g) can Chesswood Sliced Large Mushrooms in Brine
1oz (28g) boiled ham, lean only
1 tablespoon (15ml) tomato ketchup or brown sauce
½ carton mustard and cress

Drain the mushrooms. Chop the ham and mix with the mushrooms and tomato ketchup or brown sauce to make the filling. Toast the two slices of bread on one side only. Spread the filling between the toasted sides of bread. Toast the sandwich on the outside. Cut into four and garnish with mustard and cress.

DATE AND CHEESE

Calories 375; Fibre 14g

1oz (28g) stoned dates
1oz (28g) curd cheese
4oz (115g) eating apple, cored and cut into wedges

Chop the dates finely and mix with the curd cheese. Toast the two slices of bread on one side only. Spread the date and cheese filling between the two toasted sides of bread. Toast the sandwich on the outside. Cut into four and serve with the wedges of apple.

SWEETCORN AND CHICKEN

Calories 375; Fibre 12g

2oz (56g) canned sweetcorn kernels, drained
2oz (56g) cooked chicken, finely chopped
1 tablespoon (15ml) low-calorie salad cream

salt and pepper
$\frac{1}{2}$ carton mustard and cress

Mix the sweetcorn kernels, chopped chicken and low-calorie salad cream together to make the filling. Season to taste. Toast the two slices of bread on one side only. Spread the filling between the toasted sides of bread. Toast the sandwich on the outside. Cut into four and serve with mustard and cress.

ADDING FRUIT TO YOUR DAILY MENU

Two items of fruit, an apple or pear plus an orange (to ensure Vitamin C), are included as a basic part of your F-Plan menu. However, there is no reason why you should not add extra fruit as long as it is included in your total daily calorie allowance. In the case of fresh fruit this can be an easy way to add extra fibre at a modest cost in calories. Raspberries and blackberries when in season (or bought frozen) are unbeatable sources of low-calorie dietary fibre.

The chart gives close approximate calorie values of the most popular fruits in easy-to-add figures and the fibre supplied in each case.

With dried fruit, eaten neat, you have to be more restrained as the calorie count is higher. We have listed calories and grams of fibre per ounce of these dried fruits.

Fruit	Quantity	Calories	Fibre (g)
Raspberries	4oz (115g)	30	8
Blackberries	4oz (115g)	30	8
Fresh figs	2½oz (70g), one whole fruit	30	2
Strawberries	4oz (115g)	30	3
Peach	4 oz (115g), one medium-sized fruit	35	1
Plums	4oz (115g)	40	2
Orange	6oz (170g), one medium-sized fruit	40	3
Pears	5oz (140g), one medium-sized fruit	40	2
Apple	5oz (140g), one medium-sized fruit	50	2
Cherries	4oz (115g)	50	2
White grapes	4oz (115g)	70	1
Banana	6oz (170g), one medium-sized fruit	80	3
Dried fruit			
Prunes	1oz (25g) raw weight	45	4

Fruit	Quantity	Calories	Fibre (g)
Apricots	1oz (25g) raw weight	55	6
Dried figs	1oz (25g) raw weight	60	5
Dried dates (weighed with stones)	1oz (25g)	60	2
Sultanas	1oz (25g) raw weight	70	2
Raisins	1oz (25g) raw weight	70	2
Dried dates (weighed without stones)	1oz (25g)	70	3

HI-FI YOGURT DESSERTS

BLACKBERRY YOGURT

Calories 100; Fibre 4g

5oz (140g) low-fat natural yogurt
2oz (55g) blackberries
Liquid or powdered artificial sweetener (optional)

Stew the blackberries with a tablespoon water until just tender. Sweeten to taste with liquid or powdered artificial sweetener, if liked, then cool. Stir the yogurt into the cooled stewed blackberries and serve.

RASPBERRY YOGURT

Calories 125; Fibre 4g

2oz (55g) raspberries, fresh, or frozen and thawed
2 teaspoons icing sugar
5oz (140g) low-fat natural yogurt

Crush the raspberries with the icing sugar, then stir into the yogurt and chill before serving.

PEAR AND HAZELNUT YOGURT

Calories 150; Fibre 3g

5oz (140g) low-fat natural yogurt
5oz (140g) eating pear, cored and chopped
6 shelled hazelnuts, chopped

Mix the yogurt with the chopped pear and hazelnuts and serve.

HONEY BRAN AND SULTANA YOGURT

Calories 150; Fibre 4g

½oz (15g) Allinson's Honey Bran
½oz (15g) sultanas
5oz (140g) low-fat natural yogurt

Stir the Honey Bran and sultanas into the yogurt and serve.

APPLE AND RAISIN YOGURT

Calories 175; Fibre 3g

5oz (140g) low-fat natural yogurt
5oz (140g) eating apple, cored and chopped
½oz (15g) raisins
1 walnut half, chopped

Mix the yogurt with the chopped apple, raisins and walnut.

RAISIN AND BRAN YOGURT

Calories 175; Fibre 3g

1oz (25g) raisins, chopped
3 tablespoons unsweetened or fresh orange juice
5oz (140g) low-fat natural yogurt
1 tablespoon bran

Soak the raisins in the orange juice for ½ hour, then stir in the yogurt and bran.

BANANA AND WALNUT YOGURT

Calories 175; Fibre 4g

6oz (170g) banana, peeled and sliced
1 walnut half, chopped
5oz (140g) low-fat natural yogurt

Stir the sliced banana and chopped walnut into the yogurt and serve.

PRUNE YOGURT

Calories 175; Fibre 8g

2oz (55g) dried prunes *or*
    4oz (115g) cooked prunes (unsweetened)
1 tablespoon unsweetened orange juice
5oz (140g) low-fat natural yogurt

If using dried prunes, either cover with cold water and soak overnight
or cover with boiling water and soak for 1 hour, then bring to the boil,
cover and simmer for 15–20 minutes. Drain and cool. Halve the cooked
prunes and remove stones. Stir the prunes and orange juice into the
yogurt. Chill and serve.

ORANGE AND COCONUT YOGURT

Calories 200; Fibre 5g

5oz (140g) low-fat natural yogurt
5oz (140g) orange, segmented
½oz (15g) desiccated coconut

Mix the yogurt with the orange segments and coconut. Leave to stand
for ½ hour before serving to allow the flavours to blend.

APRICOT YOGURT

Calories 200; Fibre 9g

5oz (140g) low-fat natural yogurt
2oz (55g) dried apricots, chopped
1 teaspoon liquid honey

Mix the yogurt and chopped apricots together and leave to stand for a minimum of 12 hours for the apricots to soften. Stir in the honey just before serving.

BLACKCURRANTS WITH YOGURT AND BISCUITS

Calories 275; Fibre 8g

half 10·6oz (300g) can Ribena Blackcurrants in Syrup
2 tablespoons (30ml) low-fat natural yogurt
2 Country Basket Six Grains or Yogurt Biscuits

Mix the canned blackcurrants with the yogurt and serve with the biscuits.

APPLE AND DATE DESSERT BAR AND YOGURT

Calories 250; Fibre 6g

5·3oz (150g) carton low-fat natural yogurt
1 level teaspoon (5ml) liquid honey
2 level tablespoons ($\frac{1}{4}$oz/7g) Meadow Farm Toasted Bran
1 Prewett's Apple and Date Dessert Bar

Spoon the yogurt into a dish. Stir in the honey and sprinkle the top with the toasted bran. Serve with the apple and date dessert bar.

HI-FI BAKED APPLES

Baked apples make ideal low-calorie, high-fibre desserts or snack meals. The different fillings help to ring the changes and enable you to serve baked apples frequently without boredom creeping in.

BAKED APPLE – BASIC RECIPE

Calories 60; Fibre 5g

8oz (225g) cooking apple
filling as given in recipes

Wash the apple and remove the core, leaving a hole for filling. Cut through the skin round the centre of the apple with a sharp knife to prevent it bursting during cooking. Place the apple in a small ovenproof dish and pour 2–4 tablespoons water round the apple. Cover with a lid or foil and bake at 350°F (180°C, gas 4) for 30–40 minutes or until the apple is tender right through but not overcooked. Serve hot or cold.

Note: Some fillings are added after the apple is baked and some are added before baking. Each recipe will indicate at which stage the filling is added.

BAKED APPLE WITH BLACKBERRIES

Calories 100; Fibre 13g

8oz (225g) cooking apple
4oz (115g) blackberries
1 teaspoon sugar
liquid sweetener to taste (optional)

Prepare the apple for baking (see above). Pack 1oz (25g) blackberries into core hole of apple. Pour 2–4 tablespoons water around the apple. Cover with a lid or foil and bake at 350°F (180°C, gas 4) for 30 minutes or until apple is cooked through. Cook the remaining black-berries in a little water until tender, then stir in the sugar. Mash the blackberries with a fork or purée in an electric blender, and sweeten to taste with liquid sweetener, if wished. Serve baked apple with the hot blackberry sauce poured over.

BAKED APPLE WITH ORANGE AND CHERRY

Calories 125; Fibre 6g

8oz (225g) cooking apple
4oz (115g) orange
1 teaspoon honey
1 glacé cherry, quartered

Bake the apple without stuffing (see opposite). Meanwhile grate a little rind from the orange. Halve the orange – squeeze the juice from one half and remove the segments from the other half. Heat the orange juice with the honey in a small pan. Off the heat add the orange segments, grated rind and glacé cherry. Spoon into the centre of the baked apple.

MINCEMEAT STUFFED BAKED APPLE

Calories 125; Fibre 6g

8oz (225g) cooking apple
1oz (25g) mincemeat

Fill the centre of the apple with the mincemeat. Bake (see opposite). Serve hot.

BAKED APPLE WITH APRICOT AND CINNAMON

Calories 125; Fibre 9g

1oz (25g) dried apricots
2 tablespoons unsweetened orange juice
8oz (225g) cooking apple
a pinch of ground cinnamon

Chop the apricots and place in a small basin or cup with the orange juice. Leave to stand overnight. Sprinkle the cut surface on the inside of the apple with ground cinnamon. Spoon in the apricots and any remaining juice. Bake (see p. 196). Serve hot.

DATE AND HONEY STUFFED BAKED APPLE

Calories 150; Fibre 7g

1oz (25g) stoned dates, chopped
1 teaspoon clear honey
8oz (225g) cooking apple

Mix the chopped dates with the honey and spoon into the centre of the apple. Bake (see p. 196). Serve hot.

FRUIT AND NUT STUFFED BAKED APPLE

Calories 175; Fibre 6g

8oz (225g) cooking apple
½oz (15g) mixed raisins and sultanas
1 tablespoon unsweetened orange juice
½oz (15g) chopped mixed nuts

Bake the apple without stuffing (see p. 196). Meanwhile soak the raisins and sultanas in the orange juice for 30 minutes. Mix with the nuts and spoon into the centre of the baked apple. Serve hot.

BAKED APPLE WITH BANANA AND WALNUT

Calories 175; Fibre 8g

8oz (225g) cooking apple
1 small banana (about 5oz, 140g)
1 tablespoon low-fat natural yogurt
¼oz (7g) walnut pieces

Bake the apple without stuffing (see p. 196). Mash the banana until soft and stir in the yogurt and walnut pieces. Spoon into the centre of the hot baked apple and serve.

STEWED FRUIT DESSERTS

In this section you will find mostly simple stewed fruit desserts. For some stewed fruits variations have been given where appropriate.

We have used a little sugar to sweeten those fruits which we feel require sweetening; however, if you prefer to save calories by using a non-sugar sweetener, you can subtract 16 calories for each level teaspoon of sugar replaced. (Remember that where a spoonful of sugar is indicated this always means a *level* spoonful.)

STEWED BLACKBERRIES

Calories 50; Fibre 8g

4oz (115g) blackberries
1 level teaspoon granulated sugar

Stew the blackberries with 2 tablespoons water in a covered pan until softened. Stir in the sugar.

STEWED PEAR

Calories 75; Fibre 2g

a 5oz (140g) dessert pear
1 teaspoon lemon juice
a strip of lemon rind
a pinch of ground cinnamon
2 teaspoons granulated sugar

Peel, halve and core the pear. Place the pear halves in a pan with the lemon juice, lemon rind, cinnamon, sugar and 2½fl oz (70ml) water. Cover and simmer until the pear is tender but not mushy. Lift out the pear halves and boil the liquid rapidly until reduced by half. Discard the lemon rind. Pour the liquid over the stewed pears. Serve hot or cold.

STEWED RHUBARB

Calories 75; Fibre 3g

4oz (115g) rhubarb
2 tablespoons unsweetened orange juice
a pinch of ground ginger
½oz (15g) granulated sugar

Cut the rhubarb into 1in (2·5cm) lengths and place in a small pan with the orange juice, ginger and sugar. Cover and simmer until the rhubarb is just tender. Serve hot or cold.

STEWED GOOSEBERRIES

Calories 75; Fibre 4g

4oz (115g) gooseberries
1 elderflower head, if available
½oz (15g) granulated sugar

Stew the gooseberries with 2 tablespoons water and the elderflower head, if used, in a covered saucepan, until just tender. Remove the elderflower head and stir in the sugar.

STEWED BLACKBERRIES AND APPLE

Calories 75; Fibre 6g

2oz (55g) blackberries
4oz (115g) cooking apple, peeled, cored and sliced
1½ teaspoons granulated sugar

Stew the blackberries and apple with 2 tablespoons water in a covered pan until the fruits are tender. Stir in the sugar.

STEWED BLACKCURRANTS

Calories 75; Fibre 10g

4oz (115g) blackcurrants
1 sprig mint
2½ teaspoons granulated sugar

Stew the blackcurrants with 2 tablespoons water and the mint in a covered pan until softened. Stir in the sugar.

STEWED PLUMS WITH ALMONDS

Calories 100; Fibre 3g

4oz (115g) Victoria plums
2½fl oz (70ml) unsweetened orange juice
¼oz (7g) flaked almonds

Stew the plums in the orange juice until just tender. Serve hot or chilled, topped with the flaked almonds.

STEWED APPLE

Calories 100; Fibre 4g

8oz (225g) cooking apple, peeled, cored and sliced
a strip of lemon rind
2 cloves
2½ teaspoons granulated sugar

Put the apple, lemon rind and cloves with 2 tablespoons water in a pan and simmer, covered, until the apple is softened. Remove the lemon rind and cloves and stir in the sugar. Serve hot or cold.

RHUBARB AND BANANA

Calories 150; Fibre 6g

5oz (140g) banana, sliced
1 portion stewed rhubarb
1 walnut half, chopped

Mix the sliced banana with the rhubarb and top with the chopped walnut.

STEWED PRUNES

Calories 100; Fibre 8g

2oz (55g) dried prunes
water or cold tea to cover
4 drops angostura bitters
a strip of lemon peel
$\frac{1}{2}$ teaspoon sugar

Cover the prunes with cold water or strained tea and leave to stand overnight. Place the prunes and soaking liquid in a pan and add the angostura bitters and lemon peel. Cover and simmer for 20 minutes. Remove the lemon peel, stir in the sugar and serve hot or cold.

STEWED DRIED FIGS

Calories 125; Fibre 10g

2oz (55g) dried figs
a strip of lemon rind

Cover the figs with water and soak overnight. Turn the figs and liquid into a pan, add the lemon rind and cover and simmer for about 40 minutes, until the figs are tender. Serve hot or cold.

STEWED DRIED APRICOTS

Calories 125; Fibre 14g

2oz (55g) dried apricots
4 tablespoons unsweetened orange juice

Put the dried apricots in a bowl with the orange juice and water to cover and leave to soak overnight. Turn the apricots and soaking liquid into a pan and simmer, covered, for 30 minutes or until the apricots are tender. Serve hot or cold.

APPLE WITH SULTANAS AND NUTS

Calories 150; Fibre 6g

a pinch of ground cinnamon
½oz (15g) sultanas
8oz (225g) cooking apple, stewed as above
1 walnut half, chopped

Stir the cinnamon and sultanas into the apple and heat gently for 2 minutes. Serve topped with the chopped walnut.

APPLE WITH ORANGE

Calories 150; Fibre 6g

8oz (225g) cooking apple, stewed as above
4oz (115g) orange, peeled and segmented
1 glacé cherry

Allow the stewed apple to become cold. Stir in the orange segments and decorate with the glacé cherry.

STEWED PRUNES WITH BANANA

Calories 150; Fibre 11g

1 small banana (4½oz, 115g), sliced
1 portion stewed prunes, without sugar

Add the sliced banana to the hot or cold stewed prunes and serve.

STEWED PEAR IN RED WINE WITH FLAKED ALMONDS

Calories 150; Fibre 3g

a 5oz (140g) dessert pear
a strip of lemon rind
2½fl oz (70ml) red wine
2 teaspoons soft brown sugar
¼oz (7g) flaked almonds

Peel the pear and leave whole. Place in a small pan with the lemon rind, red wine and brown sugar. Cover and simmer on one side until tender. Turn the pear over and cover and simmer until the other side is tender. Stand the pear upright in a serving dish and stick the flaked almonds in it. Pour the cooking liquid round it and serve.

DRIED FRUIT SALAD

Calories 150; Fibre 13g

3oz (85g) mixed dried fruit (prunes, apricots, peaches and pears)
2 tablespoons concentrated low-calorie orange squash
¼ teaspoon ground cinnamon

Put the fruit, orange squash and water to cover the fruit in a bowl and leave to soak overnight. Place fruit and liquid in a pan, add cinnamon, cover and simmer for 30–40 minutes, until tender. Serve hot or cold.

SOME SAMPLE MENUS

Here, and on the following pages, you will see some examples of the many ways in which F-Plan meals can be put together to suit your own way of life and preferred eating pattern.

As you follow the diet you will probably – in the typical way of many slimmers – keep returning to some favourite meals which you learn off by heart. But do try to keep sampling some new dishes as well, from the very wide selection in this book, to keep your diet interesting and nutritious.

1,000 CALORIE MENU

The kind of meal selection which would suit a busy working girl, taking her lunch to work and cooking something quick and easy for her evening meal.

	Calories	Fibre (g)
Daily allowances: Fibre-Filler, $\frac{1}{2}$ pint (3dl) skimmed milk, two items of fruit	400	20
Breakfast Half portion of Fibre-Filler with milk from allowance		
Office lunch Cottage cheese, ham and sweetcorn sandwich (p. 185); apple and orange from allowance	250	8
Evening meal Frankfurter bean bake (p. 135)	350	16
Suppertime snack Remaining portion of Fibre-Filler		
TOTAL	1,000	44

1,000 CALORIE MENU

A 'little and often' meal selection for the housewife at home with a tendency to eat frequent snacks.

	Calories	Fibre (g)
Daily allowances: Fibre-Filler, ½ pint (3dl) skimmed milk, two items of fruit	400	20
Mid-morning Late breakfast on half portion of Fibre-Filler with milk from allowance		
Lunch Sweetcorn chowder with wholemeal bread (p. 162); orange from allowance	200	6
Teatime Remaining portion of Fibre-Filler; an apple from allowance		
Evening meal Creamy mushrooms on toast (p. 168)	250	9
Suppertime snack Fruit, veg and cheese on crispbread (p. 166)	150	7
TOTAL	1,000	42

1,250 CALORIE MENU

The meals on this menu are particularly quick and easy to make.

	Calories	Fibre (g)
Daily allowances: Fibre-Filler, ½ pint (3dl) skimmed milk, two items of fruit	400	20
Breakfast Half portion of Fibre-Filler with milk from allowance; an orange from allowance		
Lunch Bacon and baked beans (p. 132); an apple or pear from allowance	275	16
Evening meal Apple and cheese on toast (p. 174);	375	9
orange and coconut yogurt (p. 194)	200	5
Suppertime snack Remaining portion of Fibre-Filler		
TOTAL	1,250	50

1,250 CALORIE MENU

The pattern of this menu is based on the common slimmer's preference for being 'strict' during the day – when it is often easier – and saving most calories for the hungry hours of the evening.

	Calories	Fibre (g)
Daily allowances: Fibre-Filler, $\frac{1}{2}$ pint (3dl) skimmed milk, two items of fruit	400	20
Breakfast Half portion of Fibre-Filler with milk from allowance; an orange from allowance		
Lunch Prawn and pepper salad (p. 146); a pear from allowance	100	5
Late afternoon Remaining portion of Fibre-Filler to bridge the gap		
Evening meal Grilled bacon steak with baked jacket potato and baked beans (p. 101);	375	8
for dessert, mincemeat stuffed baked apple (p. 197)	125	6
Late supper Egg and cress sandwich (p. 182)	250	6
TOTAL	1,250	45

1,500 CALORIE BACHELOR MENU

No-bother meals for the man who has to make them for himself.

	Calories	Fibre (g)
Daily allowances: Fibre-Filler, $\frac{1}{2}$ pint (3dl) skimmed milk, two items of fruit	400	20
Breakfast Full daily allowance of Fibre-Filler with milk from allowance; an orange from allowance		
Lunch Two peanut butter and prawn sandwiches (p. 186); an apple from allowance	600	14
Evening meal Baked chicken, jacket potato and sweetcorn (p. 103);	400	8
large (8oz, 225g) banana (figures calculated from chart on p. 288)	100	4
TOTAL	1,500	46

1,500 CALORIE DRINKING MAN'S MENU

This menu illustrates how you can allow yourself some alcohol by using the chart on p. 281.

	Calories	Fibre (g)
Daily allowances: Fibre-Filler, ½ pint (3dl) skimmed milk, two items of fruit	400	20
Breakfast Full daily allowance of Fibre-Filler with milk from allowance		
Lunch Two corned beef and pickle sandwiches (p. 182); an apple and an orange from allowance	500	12
Evening meal Pease pudding with lamb's liver (p. 129)	450	10
Alcohol Three pub singles of whisky, gin or vodka	150	
TOTAL	1,500	42

The F-Plan Calorie and Fibre Chart

On the following pages you will find calorie and fibre charts which will make it easy for you to plan your own high-fibre meals if you prefer to do so rather than follow the ready-planned meal suggestions.

Instant calorie and fibre guide

Is it very fattening? Is it rich in fibre? Because this chart gives the calorie and dietary fibre contents of average or easily recognizable portions of all the basic foods, it provides an instant answer to these questions.

Few of us can picture an ounce of lamb chop or an ounce of apple, pear or peach, but we do get a clear picture of an average-sized whole loin chop, or an apple, pear or peach. Are these foods costing us much in calories and what, if anything, is each one contributing to our intake of dietary fibre? The answers emerge clearly here, as do the foods which will be of greatest value in boosting our fibre intake as we follow the F-Plan method of dieting.

Only foods which are most easily recognizable on a 'per ounce' basis are listed in that form in this chart. However, as you measure your food to keep within your calorie total, your portion or piece of a particular food may be larger or smaller than the average one itemized here. For this reason we also provide a Basic Calorie and Fibre Chart, starting on page 287, which reveals the calories and dietary fibre in a single ounce of each of the foods listed here.

In this guide we list only very basic packaged foods like cornflakes. But these days, with a growing awareness of the value of dietary fibre for health and weight control, many manufacturers are packaging useful fibre-rich foods. Some other canned, frozen and packaged foods just happen to be useful sources of dietary fibre because of the nature of their contents. You will find our valuable Calorie and Fibre Guide to Packaged Foods on page 244.

In this next chart, calorie figures are rounded off to the nearest 5, and fibre figures to the nearest half gram, for easy calculation. Dietary fibre figures should always be considered as an approximate rather than a precise guide. The figures we give are sufficiently dependable to take your daily intake up to the right level to help reduce your weight and protect your health.

Use the Instant Calorie and Fibre Chart to check which foods are low enough in calories to help you keep within your total and high enough in fibre to help you to reach that daily target.

Instant Calorie and Fibre Chart

Food	Portion	Calories	Fibre g
All Bran	1½oz (42g), average breakfast bowl	105	11·5
Almonds	1 shelled almond	10	0·5
ground	1 level tablespoon (15ml)	30	1·0
Apples			
eating	5oz (142g), average-sized fruit	50	2·0
cooking			
baked	8oz (227g), average-sized baking apple	70	4·5
stewed without sugar	6oz (170g)	55	3·5
Apricots			
fresh			
weighed with stone	1oz (28g), average-sized fruit	5	0·5
stoned and stewed without sugar	6oz (170g)	40	3·0
dried, stewed without sugar	4oz (113g) cooked weight	75	10·0
dried, raw	1oz (28g)	50	6·5
canned	4oz (113g), fruit and syrup	120	1·5

Food	Portion	Calories	Fibre g
Arrowroot	1 level teaspoon (5ml)	**10**	**0**
Asparagus, boiled	1 spear	**5**	**0·5**
Aubergines, raw, flesh only	1 aubergine, 7oz (200g)	**30**	**5·0**
Avocado, flesh only	½ avocado, 3½oz (99g)	**215**	**2·0**
Bacon	1 bacon steak, grilled, 3½oz (99g) raw weight	**105**	**0**
	1 back rasher		
	raw	**150**	**0**
	grilled	**85**	**0**
	fried	**95**	**0**
	1 streaky rasher		
	raw	**85**	**0**
	grilled	**60**	**0**
	fried	**70**	**0**
Banana	6oz (110g), average-sized fruit	**80**	**3·5**
Barcelona nuts, shelled	1oz (28g)	**180**	**3·0**

Barley, pearl	½oz (14g) raw weight, amount in average portion of thick broth	50	1·0
Bean sprouts			
raw	2oz (56g), average salad portion	15	0·5
cooked	2oz (56g)	20	0·5
Beans			
adzuki, uncooked	1oz (28g) dry weight	90	7·0
baked, canned in tomato sauce	8oz (227g), one small can	145	16·5
black-eyed, uncooked	1oz (28g) dry weight	95	7·0
broad, boiled	4oz (113g)	50	5·0
butter, canned	4oz (113g) drained weight	110	5·5
French, boiled	4oz (113g)	10	3·5
haricot, uncooked	1oz (28g) dry weight	75	7·0
red kidney			
uncooked	1oz (28g) dry weight, usual portion in a dish like chilli con carne	75	7·0
boiled	3oz (85g), average portion in salad	75	7·0
canned	3oz (85g) drained weight, average portion in a dish like chilli con carne	75	7·0
runner, boiled	4oz (113g)	20	4·0
soya, uncooked	1oz (28g) dry weight	110	4·0

Food	Portion	Calories	Fibre g
Beef			
beefburgers, frozen	average 2oz (56g) beefburger		
	grilled	130	0
	well grilled	85	0
brisket, boiled	3oz (85g)	275	0
corned, canned	2oz (56g)	120	0
forerib, roast	3oz (85g), lean only	190	0
mince, stewed	3oz (85g)	180	0
rump steak, grilled	4oz (113g), lean only	190	0
silverside, salted, boiled	3oz (85g), lean only	145	0
sirloin, roast	3oz (85g), lean only	160	0
stewing steak, stewed	3oz (85g)	185	0
topside, roast	3oz (85g), lean only	130	0
Beef sausages	1 large sausage, grilled	130	0
	1 small sausage (chipolata), grilled	60	0
Beef and pork sausages	1 large sausage, grilled	135	0
	1 small sausage (chipolata), grilled	65	0
Beetroot, boiled	2oz (56g)	25	1·5
Bemax (wheatgerm)	¼oz (7g), 1 level tablespoon (15ml)	25	0·5

Biscuits, *see* Packaged Food Chart			
Black pudding, fried	2oz (56g)	170	0·5
Blackberries, stewed without sugar	4oz (113g)	30	7·0
Blackcurrants, stewed without sugar	4oz (113g)	30	8·5
Bran	¼oz (7g), 2½ level tablespoons (37ml)	15	3·0
Brawn	2oz (56g)	85	0
Brazil nuts	1 shelled brazil nut	20	0·5
Bread (*see also* p. 251 for individual manufacturers' breads)			
brown	2½oz (70g), two average slices	155	3·5
wheatgerm (e.g. Hovis)	2oz (56g), two average slices	130	2·5
white	2½oz (70g), two average slices	160	2·0
wholemeal	2½oz (70g), two average slices	150	6·0

Food	Portion	Calories	Fibre g
Bread rolls			
brown			
crusty	2oz (56g), average size	160	3·5
soft	2oz (56g), average size	170	3·0
white			
crusty	2oz (56g), average size	160	2·0
soft	2oz (56g), average size	170	1·5
wholemeal (e.g. Allinson)	1½oz (42g), average size	90	3·5
Broccoli tops, boiled	4oz (113g)	20	4·5
Brussels sprouts, boiled	4oz (113g)	20	3·0
Butter	½oz (14g), average daily allowance on a calorie-controlled diet	105	0
Cabbage			
red, raw	1oz (28g), average serving of pickled cabbage	5	1·0
savoy, boiled	4oz (113g)	10	3·0
spring, boiled	4oz (113g)	10	2·5
white, raw	3oz (85g), average portion in coleslaw	20	2·5
winter, boiled	4oz (113g)	15	3·0

Cake			
fruit			
plain	2oz (56g), average slice	200	1·5
rich, iced	1oz (28g), 1 small slice	100	1·0
sponge, with fat, jam-filled	2oz (56g), 1 average slice	170	0·5
Carrots			
raw	2oz (56g), 1 medium-sized whole carrot	10	1·5
boiled	4oz (113g)	20	3·5
canned	4oz (113g) drained weight	20	4·0
Cashew nuts	1oz (28g)	150	0·5
Cauliflower			
raw	2oz (56g), average amount in a salad	10	1·0
boiled	4oz (113g)	10	2·0
Celeriac, boiled	4oz (113g)	15	5·5
Celery			
raw	2oz (56g), 1 large stick	5	1·0
boiled	4oz (113g)	5	2·5
Cherries			
eating	4oz (113g)	45	1·5
glacé	1 cherry	10	0

Food	Portion	Calories	Fibre g
Chestnuts, shelled	1oz (28g)	50	2·0
Chicken			
roast	3oz (85g), meat only, no skin	125	0
drumstick, grilled	3½oz (99g) weight before cooking	90	0
Chicken joint, baked or grilled	8oz (227g) weight before cooking	180	0
Chicory, raw	1oz (28g), salad serving	3	0·5
Chinese leaves, raw	2oz (56g), salad serving	5	1·0
Chips, fried in deep fat	4oz (113g), small portion	280	2·0
Chocolate, drinking	2 rounded teaspoons (20ml)	40	0
Christmas pudding	2oz (56g), small portion	170	1·0
Cocoa powder	1 rounded teaspoon (10ml)	20	0
Coconut, fresh	1oz (28g)	100	4·0
Cod			
fillet, fresh, steamed or poached	6oz (170g) weight before cooking	125	0
steak, frozen, raw	4oz (113g)	80	0

		Calories	Fibre
Coffee, instant, powder or granules	1 rounded teaspoon (10ml)	0	0
Coffee and chicory essence	1 teaspoon (5ml)	10	0
Coley, raw	6oz (170g)	120	0
Condensed milk, whole, sweetened	1 tablespoon (15ml)	50	0
Corn oil	1 tablespoon (15ml)	125	0
Corned beef	2oz (56g)	120	0
Cornflakes	1oz (28g), average breakfast bowl	105	0·8
Cornflour	1 level tablespoon (15ml)	35	0·5
Cottage cheese	4oz (113g) carton	110	0
Crab, canned	1½oz (42g) can	60	0
Cream	1 tablespoon (15ml) double	60	0
	1 tablespoon (15ml) single	30	0
Crispbreads, *see* p. 250 for individual manufacturers' crispbreads			
Crisps, potato	0.88oz (25g), 1 small packet	130	3·0

Food	Portion	Calories	Fibre g
Cucumber	2oz (56g), salad serving	5	0
Currants, dried	½oz (14g)	35	1·0
Custard powder	1 level tablespoon (15ml)	35	0·5
Damsons, stewed without sugar	4oz (113g)	30	3·5
Dates, dried, stoneless	2oz (56g)	140	5·0
Egg, whole, raw, boiled or poached in water	size 1	95	0
	size 2	90	0
	size 3	80	0
	size 4	75	0
	size 5	70	0
	size 6	60	0
Egg white	1 white of size 3 egg	15	0
Egg yolk	1 yolk of size 3 egg	65	0
Eggplant, *see* **Aubergines**			

Endive, raw	2 oz (56g), salad serving	5	1·0
Evaporated milk, whole	1 tablespoon (15ml)	25	0
Figs			
fresh, raw	1oz (28g), average-sized fruit	10	0·5
dried	2oz (56g) dry weight, about three dried figs	120	10·5
dried, stewed without sugar	4oz (113g)	130	11·5
Fish fingers, frozen	1 fish finger, grilled without fat	50	0
Flour, *see* Your Basic Calorie and Fibre Chart			
Fruit salad, canned	4oz (113g) fruit and juice	110	1·0
Glacé cherries, *see under* **Cherries**			
Golden syrup	1 tablespoon (15ml)	60	0
Goose, roast	3oz (85g), meat only	265	0
Gooseberries			
ripe, raw	2oz (56g)	20	2·0
stewed without sugar	4oz (113g)	15	3·0

Food	Portion	Calories	Fibre g
Grapefruit			
whole	5oz (142g), half average-sized fruit	15	0.5
canned in natural juice	4oz (113g)	45	0.5
Grapenuts	1½oz (42g), average breakfast bowl	150	3.0
Grapes			
black	4oz (113g)	55	0.5
white (green)	4oz (113g)	70	1.0
Greengages, stewed without			
sugar	4oz (113g)	45	2.5
Guavas, canned	4oz (113g)	70	4.0
Haddock			
fillets, fresh	6oz (170g) raw weight	120	0
smoked, steamed	6oz (170g) cooked weight	170	0
Ham			
boiled	2oz (56g), lean only	95	0
cooked and vacuum-packed	2oz (56g), 2–3 slices	80	0
canned	3oz (85g), salad serving	100	0

Food	Description	Calories	Fibre
Hazelnuts	1oz (28g) shelled weight	105	1·5
Heart, lamb's, roast	4oz (113g), average-sized heart	270	0
Herring, grilled	5oz (142g), whole herring weighed raw after head and bones removed	280	0
Honey	1 level teaspoon (5ml)	15	0
Ice cream	2oz (56g)	95	0
Jam	1 level teaspoon (5ml)	15	0
Jelly, made up with water	4oz (113g)	70	0
Kidney lamb	2oz (56g), average raw weight	50	0
ox	2oz (56g), average portion in a steak-and-kidney casserole	50	0
Kipper, grilled	6oz (170g), whole kipper weighed before cooking	280	0

Food	Portion	Calories	Fibre g
Lamb			
breast, roast	4oz (113g), lean and fat, no bone	460	0
leg, roast	3oz (85g), lean only	162	0
loin chops, grilled	5oz (142g), average-sized chop, raw weight	310	0
shoulder, roast	3oz (85g), lean only	165	0
Lard	½oz (14g)	125	0
Leeks, boiled	4oz (113g)	30	4·0
Lemon sole, fried coated in crumbs	4oz (113g), average-sized fish	190	0·5
Lentils, uncooked	1½oz (42g), in portion of soup	125	5·0
Lettuce, raw	1oz (28g), salad serving	5	0·5
Liver			
calf	4oz (113g) raw weight, average serving for grilling	170	0
chicken	2oz (56g) raw weight, average amount in chicken liver pâté or for fried livers on toast	75	0

Food	Portion	Calories	Fibre
lamb	4oz (113g) raw weight, average casserole serving	200	0
Liver sausage	1oz (28g), sufficient for one round of sandwiches	85	0
Loganberries stewed without sugar	4oz (113g)	15	6·5
canned in syrup	4oz (113g), fruit and syrup	110	3·5
Low-fat spread (e.g. Outline, St Ivel Gold)	1oz (28g), average daily allowance in a calorie-controlled diet	105	0
Luncheon meat, canned	2oz (56g)	175	0
Lychees, canned	4oz (113g), fruit and syrup	75	0·5
Macaroni, wholewheat	2oz (56g) dry weight	195	5·5
Mackerel whole, raw	8oz (227g)	320	0
smoked	6oz (170g)	420	0
Mandarin oranges, canned in syrup	4oz (113g), fruit and syrup	65	0·5

Food	Portion	Calories	Fibre g
Mangoes, canned	4oz (113g), fruit and syrup	90	1·0
Margarine, all brands	½oz (14g), usual daily allowance in a calorie-controlled diet	105	0
Marmalade	1 level teaspoon (5ml)	15	0
Marrow, boiled	4oz (113g)	10	1·0
Marzipan	½oz (14g)	60	1·0
Mayonnaise	1 tablespoon (15ml)	95	0
Melon cantaloup, honeydew or yellow ogen water	8oz (227g), average slice with skin 12oz (340g), average whole melon 8oz (227g), average slice with skin	30 60 25	1·0 2·5 1·0
Milk, dried, skimmed	1 rounded teaspoon (10ml), average serving in tea or coffee	10	0
Mincemeat	½oz (14g), average weight in a mince pie	35	0·5
Muesli, base mixture	2oz (56g), average breakfast bowl	205	4·0

Mulberries	4oz (113g) raw weight	40	2·0
Mushrooms	4oz (113g) raw weight	15	3·0
Mustard and cress	¼oz (7g), salad or sandwich serving	1	0
Nectarines	5oz (142g), average-sized whole fruit	65	3·0
Oatcakes	1oz (28g)	125	1·0
Oatmeal	1oz (28g) raw weight, to make average bowl of porridge	110	2·0
Olive oil	1 tablespoon (15ml)	125	0
Onion boiled raw	4oz (113g) ½oz (14g), salad serving	15 5	1·5 0
Orange, whole	6oz (170g), average-sized fruit	40	2·5
Parsley	½oz (14g)	5	1·5
Parsnips, boiled	4oz (113g)	65	3·0

Food	Portion	Calories	Fibre g
Passion fruit, raw	3oz (85g), average-sized fruit	10	5·5
Pawpaw, canned	4oz (113g)	70	0·5
Peach, whole	4oz (113g), average-sized fruit	35	1·5
Peaches, canned	4oz (113g), fruit and syrup	95	1·0
Peanuts, shelled	1oz (28g)	160	2·5
Peanut butter	½oz (14g), sufficient for one sandwich	88	1·0
Pearl barley, *see* **Barley, pearl**			
Pear, whole	5oz (142g), average-sized fruit	40	2·5
Pears, canned	4oz (113g), fruit and syrup	90	2·0
Peas			
fresh, raw	1oz (28g), salad serving	20	1·5
fresh or frozen, boiled	4oz (113g) raw weight	60	9·0
garden, canned	3½oz (99g), half the drained contents of a 10oz (283g) can	45	6·0
processed, canned	3½oz (99g)	75	7·5

dried, uncooked	1½oz (42g), in average portion of pea soup	120	7·0
split	2oz (56g) dry weight, amount in average portion pease pudding	175	6·5
chick			
raw	1oz (28g) dry weight	90	4·0
boiled	3oz (85g) cooked weight	90	5·0
Pepper, green			
raw	1oz (28g), salad serving	5	0·5
cooked	5oz (142g), average-sized pepper	20	1·5
Piccalilli	1oz (28g), 1 rounded tablespoon (30ml)	10	0·5
Pickle, sweet	1oz (28g), 1 rounded tablespoon (30ml)	40	0·5
Pilchards, canned in tomato sauce	2½oz (70g), average-sized pilchard	85	0
Pineapple			
fresh	2oz (56g), average slice without skin and core	25	0·5
canned in syrup	4oz (113g), fruit and syrup	90	1·0

Food	Portion	Calories	Fibre g
Plaice, fillets, fried in crumbs	6oz (170g) raw weight	435	1·0
Plums Victoria, dessert	2½oz (70g), average-sized fruit	15	1·5
cooking, stewed without sugar, weighed with stones	6oz (170g)	40	3·5
Pork chop, grilled	7oz (200g) raw weight, fat cut off after grilling	315	0
leg, roast	3oz (85g), lean only	155	0
Pork sausages, grilled	2oz (56g), large sausage, raw weight	135	0
	1oz (28g), 1 chipolata, raw weight	65	0
Porridge	1oz (28g), oatmeal or porridge oats made up with water	110	2·0
Potato baked	7oz (200g), eaten with skin	170	5·0
roast	2oz (56g)	90	1·0
instant, mashed	1oz (28g) dry weight	90	4·5

		Calories	Fibre
old, boiled and mashed new	4oz (113g)	90	1·0
boiled	4oz (113g)	85	2·5
canned	4oz (113g) drained weight	60	3·0
Prawns, shelled	2oz (56g)	60	0
Prunes, dried with stones	1oz (28g), four to five prunes	38	3·8
stewed without sugar	4oz (113g) cooked weight	85	8·5
Puffed wheat	¾oz (21g), average breakfast bowl	70	3·5
Rabbit, stewed	6oz (170g), weighed on the bone	150	0
Radishes, raw	1oz (28g), salad serving	5	0·5
Raisins	½oz (14g), serving with cereal etc.	35	1·0
Raspberries raw	4oz (113g)	30	8·5
canned in syrup	4oz (113g), fruit and syrup	95	5·5
Redcurrants, stewed without sugar	4oz (113g)	20	8·0

Food	Portion	Calories	Fibre g
Rhubarb	4oz (113g) raw weight	10	3·0
Rice Krispies	1oz (28g), average breakfast bowl	105	1·0
Rice brown white	2oz (56g) dry weight, usual amount for a rice-based meal 2oz (56g) dry weight	200 205	2·5 1·5
Rock salmon, fried in batter	6oz (170g)	445	0·5
Sago	½oz (14g) raw weight, usual amount in a serving of milk pudding	50	0·5
Salad cream	1 level tablespoon (15ml)	50	0
Salad dressing, low-calorie (e.g. Waistline, Heinz)	1 level tablespoon (15ml)	25	0
Salami	1oz (28g)	135	0
Salmon, canned	3oz (85g) drained weight	170	0
Salsify, boiled	4oz (113g)	20	1·0

Sardines			
canned in oil	2oz (56g), weighed after draining off oil	120	0
canned in tomato sauce	2oz (56g)	100	0
Scampi, in breadcrumbs, fried	3oz (85g)	265	1·0
Sea-kale, boiled	4oz (113g)	10	1·0
Semolina	½oz (14g) dry weight, amount in a serving of milk pudding	50	0·5
Shortcrust pastry			
white flour, cooked	1½oz (42g), usual amount in a serving of flan	220	1·0
wholemeal flour, cooked	1½oz (42g)	210	3·0
Shredded Wheat	¾oz (21g), one Shredded Wheat	70	2·5
Spaghetti			
white	2oz (56g), dry weight, usual amount in a pasta dish	210	1·5
brown wholewheat	2oz (56g) dry weight	195	5·5
canned in tomato sauce	7oz (200g), half large can	120	2·0
Spinach, boiled	4oz (113g)	30	7·0

Food	Portion	Calories	Fibre g
Spring greens, boiled	4oz (113g)	10	4·5
Spring onions	½oz (14g), salad serving	5	0·5
Strawberries, raw	4oz (113g)	30	2·5
Sugar	1 rounded teaspoon (10ml)	35	0
Sugar Puffs	1oz (28g), average breakfast bowl	95	1·5
Sultanas	½oz (14g), serving with cereal etc.	35	1·0
Sunflower seeds	¼oz (7g), just a nibble	35	0·5
Swedes, boiled	4oz (113g)	20	3·0
Sweetcorn kernels, canned	3½oz (99g)	75	5·5
Syrup, golden	1 level tablespoon (15ml)	60	0
Tangerine	3oz (85g), average-sized fruit	60	1·0
Tapioca	½oz (14g) dry weight, usual amount in a serving of milk pudding	50	0·5

		Calories	Fibre
Tomatoes			
fresh	4oz (113g), two, average-sized	15	1.5
canned	4oz (113g)	10	1.0
Tongue, ox, pickled, boiled	2oz (56g)	165	0
Treacle, black	1 level tablespoon (15ml)	50	0
Tripe, stewed	6oz (170g)	170	0
Trout	6oz (170g) raw weight	150	0
Tuna			
canned in brine	7oz (198g) can	230	0
canned in oil	7oz (198g) can	365	0
Turnips, boiled	4oz (113g)	15	2.5
Turkey, roast	3oz (85g), meat only, no skin	115	0
Veal			
cutlet, coated in egg and breadcrumbs, fried	3oz (85g)	180	0
fillet, roast	3oz (85g)	190	0
Vegetable oil	1 level tablespoon (15ml)	125	0

Food	Portion	Calories	Fibre g
Walnuts	1oz (28g) shelled weight	**145**	**1·5**
Watercress	1oz (28g), generous salad serving	**5**	**1·0**
Weetabix	two biscuits	**115**	**4·5**
Wheatgerm	½oz (15g), 1 rounded tablespoon (30ml)	**45**	**0·5**
Whitecurrants, stewed without sugar	4oz (113g)	**25**	**6·5**
Yogurt, low-fat			
natural	5·3oz (150g) carton	**80**	**0**
flavoured	5·3oz (150g) carton	**120**	**0**
hazelnut	5·3oz (150g) carton	**160**	**2·5**

Calorie and fibre guide
to packaged foods

Here, available to the public for the first time, is a comprehensive guide to the useful fibre-supplying packaged foods.

Dietary fibre is not an easy substance to measure, and in order to reveal this valuable information we have had to draw on the assistance of the manufacturers themselves in some cases, and in others on the help of the technicians at London University and the analytical experts working for Dr David Southgate at the Food Research Institute.

It is important to emphasize that the values given for fibre are approximate. Fibre-measuring methods are still in their infancy. Different brands and packages of the same type of food will differ a little in their precise composition. But the figures here will provide you with a good enough guide to ensure that you reach that 30-grams-plus daily fibre total to ease and speed your slimming and help protect your health.

The quantities given in this guide are those which we feel will be most convenient to you in planning your menus. Usually we list the number of calories and the amount of dietary fibre in a whole can or package. From the weight of the can or package you will easily be able to assess whether this is an individual portion or multi-portion pack.

In the case of some foods we felt that other measures would help you more. The fibre content of different breads, for instance, is given on a per-ounce basis. Slices and sizes vary so much that it makes most sense to weigh your own average slice of your own chosen loaf to reveal the calories and fibre in that. With biscuits, the calories and dietary fibre in one or two whole biscuits is obviously of more instant value than that in a whole package. Throughout this guide we have used this kind of commonsense flexibility to make calorie- and fibre-counting easy for you.

The same principle has been applied in 'rounding off' calorie and fibre figures for easy calculation. Where the contents of a whole pack are given we round off to the nearest 5 calories and half-gram of fibre, which gives a close enough guide.

In selecting and rejecting the foods to be included in this guide we have been equally realistic. All canned fruits, for instance, will provide at least a little dietary fibre. However, with some the fibre quantity is small in relation to the calorie cost. For this reason we have listed only the canned fruits which are free of added sugar, apart from those, like raspberries and prunes, which are particularly rich sources of dietary fibre.

Canned and packaged foods can play a valuable role in modern weight-conscious and health-conscious eating – when you use the information in this guide.

Ready packaged foods can help to provide an alternative. One of the remarkable effects of the F-Plan diet is the major influence it has already had on the sales pattern of foods in Britain, signalling a major upswing in the consumption of foods like wholewheat and granary bread, bran, and bran cereals.

Britain is at last beginning to eat in the way that our medical and nutritional advisers have been urging us to eat – and, quick to spot the trend, manufacturers already have new fibre-rich foods in the pipeline which are likely to start appearing in the shops soon. So, with the aid of these and the fibre figures revealed for the first time in this book, it becomes easier and easier to shed weight and improve health with the F-Plan.

Calorie and Fibre Chart of Packaged Foods

	Calories	*Fibre g*
Biscuits		

	Calories	*Fibre g*
Bran biscuits, per biscuit		
Allinson		
Bran Biscuit	78	1·0
Bran Oatcake	39	1·0
Boots Second Nature Bran	44	1·3
Country Basket Wholewheat		
Bran	32	1·7
Crawfords Bran Oatcake	50	1·3
Fox's		
Wholemeal Bran	67	1·0
Bran Crunch	32	0·4
Holly Mill Natural Bran	33	0·8
R. M. Scott Husky Wholemeal		
Bran	37	0·2
St Michael Wholemeal Bran	65	1·0
Coconut biscuits, per biscuit		
Allinson Coconut	70	0·9
Fox's Coconut Cookies	74	0·8
Digestive biscuits, per biscuit		
Burton's Digestive Sweetmeal,		
from 200g pack	47	0·5
Hovis Digestive	56	0·7
Huntley & Palmer Digestive	63	0·5
McVitie Digestive Wheatmeal,		
from 400g pack	70	0·8
Mitchelhill's Digestive	63	0·1
Sainsbury's Sweetmeal Digestive,		
from 400g pack	60	0·5
Tesco Digestive, from 250g pack	65	0·8

	Calories	*Fibre g*
Fig biscuits, per biscuit		
Jacob's Fig Roll	53	0·7
Prewett's Fig	60	0·7
Fruit and/or nut biscuits, per biscuit		
Allinson		
Carob-coated Fruit & Nut	62	0·2
Fruit & Nut	77	0·6
Hazelnut	63	0·5
Peanut	61	0·4
Walnut	65	0·5
Boots		
Second Nature Wholemeal Fruit		
Bran	33	1·1
Second Nature Wholemeal		
Hazelnut	37	0·5
Country Basket Hazelnut	34	1·2
Fox's Oat & Fruit	77	0·6
Garibaldi biscuits, per biscuit		
Peak Frean Garibaldi	30	0·3
Muesli-type biscuits, per biscuit		
Allinson Muesli	61	0·7
Boots Second Nature Wholemeal		
Muesli Fruit	38	0·4
Country Basket Muesli Fruit	37	1·0
Fox's Muesli Finger	63	0·7
Oatmeal and oatflake biscuits,		
per biscuit		
Allinson		
Oatmeal	74	0·4
Bran Oatcake	39	1·0
Carob-coated Oatmeal	62	0·2
Country Basket Oatmeal	34	1·6
Crawford's Bran Oatcake	50	1·3

	Calories	Fibre g
Fox's		
Oaten Crunch	36	0·3
Oatflake Cookie	69	0·4
Oat & Fruit Biscuit	77	0·6
Paterson's		
Girdle Oatcake	50	0·5
Farmhouse Oatcake	90	0·8

Shortbread, per piece		
Allinson Wholemeal Shortbread	82	1·2

Wheaten biscuits, per biscuit		
Fox's Wheaten Cookies	69	0·5
Prewett's Wholemeal	65	0·4

Miscellaneous biscuits, per biscuit		
Allinson		
Carob-coated Ginger/Bran	61	0·4
Demerara	66	0·4
Ginger	49	0·6
Honey	57	0·7
Boots Second Nature Wholemeal		
Six Grains	37	0·4
Country Basket		
Six Grains	34	1·5
Yogurt	34	1·2
Fox's		
Fivers	85	0·8
Nice	39	0·3
Itona Granny Ann High Fibre	100	5·0
Jacob's Farmhouse	34	0·4
Mitchelhill's Healthy Life	61	0·1
Prewett's		
Carob Chip Cookies	65	0·4
Sesame & Sunflower Cookies	67	0·5
Stem Ginger Cookies	59	0·4

	Calories	Fibre g
Crispbreads and crackers, per biscuit		
Country Basket Wholewheat		
Crispbread	32	0·7
Crisp-i-Bran	19	2·9
Energen		
Brancrisp	23	1·3
Starch Reduced Bran	18	0·7
Starch Reduced Brown Wheat	17	0·4
Starch Reduced Cheese	19	0·3
Starch Reduced Rye	17	0·4
Starch Reduced Wheat	18	0·2
Jacob's		
Vitawheat	28	0·7
Vitawheat, Rye	28	0·7
Parkstone Bakeries Crackerbread	23	0·3
Primula Extra Thin	20	0·1
Ryvita		
Brown	25	0·9
Original	25	0·9
Salt-free	25	0·9

Brans

	Calories	Fibre g
Soya brans, per oz (28g)		
Direct Foods Soya Bran	24	9·9
Granose Soya Bran	60	9·9

	Calories	Fibre g
Wheat brans, per oz (28g)		
Allinson		
Bran Plus	63	7·1
Broad Bran	43	12·5
Boots Second Nature Natural		
Unprocessed Bran	56	12·4
Itona Wheat Bran	43	12·5
Prewett's Natural Wheat Bran	43	12·5

	Calories	*Fibre g*

Breads

Bran loaves, per oz (28g)

Nimble Family Bran	70	1·3
Sunblest Hi Bran	57	3·1
Sunblest Sunbran	62	1·3
Windmill Bran	64	1·8

Granary, per oz (28g)

Windmill Granary	67	1·6

Wheatgerm loaves, per oz (28g)

Hovis

Family Loaf	63	1·4
Handy Loaf	66	1·4
Original	66	1·4
Vitbe Wheatgerm	65	1·4

Wheatmeal (brown) loaves, per oz (28g)

Mothers Pride Brown Long Loaf	64	1·6
Windmill Country Brown	64	1·6

White loaves, per oz (28g)

Mothers Pride

Danish Toaster	71	0·9
Danish White	71	0·9
White Long Loaf	66	0·8
Nimble		
Family White	71	0·9
Long White	74	0·8
Sunblest White	65	0·8
Windmill White Fibre	64	1·7

Wholemeal loaves, per oz (28g)

Allinson Wholemeal	61	2·4
Windmill		
Wholemeal, small loaf, 400g	64	2·6
Wholemeal, large loaf, 800g	61	2·4

	Calories	Fibre g
Bread rolls, per oz (28g)		
Granose Wheatmeal Rolls	100	1·0
Granose White Rolls	101	0·5
Bread mixes, per packet dry mix		
Allinson		
Bran Bread Mix, 1¼lb pack	2,050	75·0
Wholewheat Bread Mix, 1¼lb pack	1,845	57·0
Prewett's Ever-ready Bread Mix,		
1¼lb pack	1,895	48·0

Breakfast Cereals

	Calories	Fibre g
Maize (corn) breakfast cereals, per oz (28g)		
Cornflakes, *see* Your Basic Calorie and Fibre Chart		
Kellogg's		
Crunchy Nut Corn Flakes	107	0·5
Frosties	100	0·3
Muesli-type and crunchy breakfast cereals,		
per oz (28g) except where stated		
Boots		
Second Nature Honey Muesli	118	2·2
Second Nature Muesli	103	2·1
Cheshire		
Wholefoods Muesli	104	0·8
Wholefoods Economy Muesli	93	0·5
Familia		
Birchermuesli	115	2·0
Muesli (Swiss Mixed Cereal),		
1 portion pack, 2½oz (71g)	285	5·5
Holly Mill		
Muesli	103	1·8
Muesli Base	101	2·1
Sugar Free Muesli	98	2·0
Jordans		
Country Muesli	103	0·7
Muesli Tub, Banana and Brazil,		
2½oz (71g) tub	305	3·6

	Calories	Fibre g
Muesli Tub, Coconut and Sultana, 2½oz (71g) tub	260	3·6
Muesli Tub, Date and Cashew, 2½oz (71g) tub	263	3·6
Original Crunchy Natural	123	0·4
Original Crunchy with Honey, Almonds and Raisins	121	0·4
Original Crunchy with Bran and Apple	116	0·7
Kellogg's Country Store	100	1·4
Prewett's		
Bran Muesli	87	6·2
Honey Muesli	104	1·8
Muesli Base	105	2·1
Muesli Deluxe	111	2·1
Muesli	102	1·9
Quaker		
Harvest Crunch	126	2·6
Harvest Crunch, Bran & Apple	129	3·9
Safeway Swiss Style Breakfast Cereal	110	2·0
Sainsbury's Swiss Style Breakfast Cereal	100	2·0
Sunwheel Natural Foods Fruit and Nut Muesli	103	3·0
Tesco Swiss Style Breakfast Cereal	105	2·0
Weetabix Alpen	105	1·9
Oat breakfast cereals, per oz (28g)		
Boots Second Nature Bran & Oat Crunch	103	5·4
Lyons Tetley		
Ready Brek, Butter Flavour	110	2·2
Ready Brek, Standard Flavour	110	2·2
Prewett's		
Breakfast Oats	115	2·0
Oatmeal, fine/medium/coarse	115	2·0
Porridge, wheatmeal	95	2·7

	Calories	*Fibre g*
Oat breakfast cereals, *cont*.		
Quaker		
Golden Oaties	107	2·3
Oats	105	4·3
Oat Krunchies	108	3·4
Warm Start	107	4·3
Safeway		
Hot Oat Cereal	115	2·2
Quick Cooking Oats	105	4·0
Sainsbury's Scotch Porridge		
Oats	105	4·0
Scotts Porage Oats	115	4·0
Tesco		
Instant Oats	115	2·2
Scotch Porridge Oats	115	4·0
Waitrose Instant Porridge	115	2·2
Whitworth's Porridge Oats	114	2·0
Rice breakfast cereals, per oz (28g)		
Kellogg's		
Rice Krispies	99	0·3
Ricicles	100	0·3
Coco Pops	101	0·3
Puffa Puffa Rice	117	0·1
Wheat (including bran) breakfast cereals, per oz (28g) except where stated		
Allinson Crunchy Bran	64	7·7
Boots Second Nature Bran & Oat		
Crunch	103	5·4
Energen		
Brancrunch	115	4·3
Wheatflakes	100	4·2
Granose		
Fruit Bran	86	3·5
Sunnybisk, each	50	1·1
Holly Mill Wheat-Heart	117	1·0

	Calories	Fibre g
Kellogg's		
All-Bran	70	8·0
Bran Buds	74	7·4
Bran Flakes	85	4·2
Sultana Bran	82	3·6
Smacks	106	0·2
Meadow Farm Toasted Bran	100	8·2
Nabisco		
Bran Flakes	105	3·4
Shredded Wheat, each	80	2·4
Shreddies	105	2·3
Spoonsize	100	3·1
Prewett's Whole Wheat Flakes	102	2·6
Quaker		
Puffed Wheat	106	4·3
Sugar Puffs	104	2·1
Safeway Biskwheat, each	68	2·5
Sainsbury's		
Puffed Wheat	100	4·3
Whole Wheat Bisk, each	70	2·5
Weetabix		
Bran Fare	75	8·2
Farmhouse Bran	85	5·7
Weetabix, per biscuit	58	2·2
Weetaflakes	96	3·6
Miscellaneous breakfast cereals, per oz (28g)		
Bird's Grape-Nuts	99	2·0
Holly Mill		
Day Brek	118	5·2
Bran Brek	123	2·3
Kellogg's Special K	101	0·5
Prewett's Golden Grains	105	1·6
Pronutro	105	3·4
Chutneys and Pickles		
Bicks Corn Relish, per oz (28g)	30	1·3

	Calories	*Fibre g*
Chutneys and Pickles, *cont.*		
Happy Farm		
Piccalilli, per oz (28g)	9	0·5
Sweet Pickle, per oz (28g)	38	0·5
Tomato & Apple Chutney, per oz (28g)	48	0·5
Dehydrated Meals		
Vesta Chilli con Carne with Rice, pack, serves two	800	19·0
Flour		
Rye flour, per oz (28g)		
Prewett's Rye Flour	96	0·3
Soya flour, per oz (28g)		
Prewett's Soya Flour	123	3·4
White flour (plain, self-raising and strong flours), per oz (28g)		
Allinson		
81% Farmhouse (plain)	100	2·3
81% Farmhouse (self-raising)	100	2·3
Strong White	97	1·1
Prewett's		
Millstone Flour 81% (plain)	97	2·3
Millstone Flour 81% (self-raising)	100	2·3
Strong White Bread Flour (unbleached)	97	1·1
Super White Unbleached Flour (plain)	97	1·4
Super White Unbleached Flour (self-raising)	97	1·1
Whitworths		
Plain White Flour	99	1·0
Self-Raising White Flour	96	1·0
Wholemeal flour		
Allinson		
100% Wholemeal Flour (plain)	96	3·1

	Calories	Fibre g
Cerea 100% Flour	96	3·1
Boots Second Nature Stoneground Wholemeal Flour	89	2·7
Jordans 100% Wholewheat Flour	91	0·7
Prewett's		
100% Organic Wholemeal Flour	96	3·1
100% Wholemeal Flour (plain)	96	3·1
100% Wholemeal Flour (self-raising)	96	3·1

Fruit, Canned

Apples

Waitrose Apple Slices in Natural Juice, 7¾oz (219g) can	75	4·5

Apricots

Boots Shapers Apricots in Low-calorie Syrup, 7¾oz (220g) can	35	3·0
Dietade Apricots in Water, 7oz (198g) can	35	2·5
Frank Cooper's Apricots in Water, 7oz (198g) can	25	2·5
Sainsbury's Apricot Halves in Apple Juice, 14½oz (411g) can	185	5·5

Blackberries

Sainsbury's Blackberries in Syrup, 7½oz (213g) can	210	10·5
Smedley Blackberries in Syrup, 7½oz (213g) can	145	10·0
Weight Watchers Blackberries in Low-calorie Syrup, 7oz (198g) can	50	10·0

Blackcurrants

Ribena Blackcurrants in Syrup, 300g can	345	13·0
Sainsbury's Blackcurrants in Syrup, 7½oz (213g) can	210	9·0
Smedley Blackcurrants in Syrup, 7½oz (213g) can	145	9·0

	Calories	Fibre g
Fruit salad		
Dietade		
Fruit Salad in Water, 7oz (198g) can	35	2·0
Fruit Salad in Fruit-sugar Syrup,		
8oz (227g) can	90	2·5
Frank Cooper's Fruit Salad in Water,		
7oz (198g) can	35	2·0
Weight Watchers Fruit Salad in		
Low-calorie Syrup, 7oz (198g) can	35	2·0
Gooseberries		
Hartley's Gooseberries,		
10oz (283g) can	240	5·5
Safeway Gooseberries, 10oz (283g) can	180	5·5
Sainsbury's Gooseberries,		
10½oz (298g) can	210	6·0
Smedley Gooseberries, 10oz (283g) can	180	5·0
Grapefruit		
John West Grapefruit Segments in		
Natural Juice, 10oz (283g) can	120	1·0
Libby's Grapefruit Segments,		
sweetened, 19oz (538g) can	380	2·0
Princes Grapefruit Segments,		
10oz (283g) can	170	1·0
Sainsbury's Grapefruit Segments in		
Natural Juice, 19oz (539g) can	210	2·0
Tesco Grapefruit Segments,		
sweetened, 19oz (539g) can	340	2·0
Waitrose Grapefruit in Natural Juice,		
7¾oz (219g) can	75	1·0
Weight Watchers Grapefruit		
Segments in Low-calorie Syrup		
7oz (198g) can	50	1·0
Loganberries		
Tesco Loganberries in Syrup,		
14½oz (411g)	320	13·5

	Calories	*Fibre g*
Mandarin oranges		
John West Mandarin Orange		
Segments in Natural Juice,		
10½oz (298g) can	80	1·0
Peaches		
Boots Shapers Peaches in Low-calorie		
Syrup, 7¾oz (220g) can	45	2·0
Dietade Peaches in Water, 7oz (198g) can	35	2·0
Frank Cooper's Peaches in Water,		
7oz (198g) can	35	2·0
John West Peach Slices in Fruit Juice,		
10oz (283g) can	130	3·0
Koo Peach Slices in Apple Juice,		
8oz (227g) can	95	2·5
Sainsbury's Peaches in Apple Juice,		
14½oz (411g) can	185	4·0
Waitrose Peaches in Apple Juice,		
7¾oz (219g) can	75	2·0
Weight Watchers Peaches in Low-		
calorie Syrup, 7oz (198g) can	40	2·0
Pears		
Boots Shapers Pears in Low-calorie		
Syrup, 7¾oz (220g) can	50	3·5
Dietade		
Pears in Water, 7oz (198g) can	35	3·5
Pears in Fruit-sugar Syrup,		
8oz (227g) can	95	4·0
Frank Cooper's Pears in Water,		
7oz (198g) can	35	3·5
John West Pear Quarters in Fruit		
Juice, 10oz (283g) can	110	5·0
Koo Pear Halves in Apple Juice,		
8oz (227g) can	105	4·0
Sainsbury's Pear Halves in Apple Juice,		
14½oz (411g) can	185	7·0

	Calories	Fibre g
Pears, *cont.*		
Waitrose Pears in Apple Juice, 7¾oz (219g) can	75	3·5
Weight Watchers Pears in Low-calorie Syrup, 7oz (198g) can	40	3·5
Pineapple		
Boots Shapers Pineapple in Low-calorie Syrup, 7¾oz (220g) can	55	2·0
Del Monte Pineapple Slices in Natural Juice, 8oz (227g) can	150	2·0
Dietade		
Pineapple in Water, 7oz (198g) can	35	2·0
Pineapple in Fruit-sugar Syrup, 8oz (227g) can	100	2·0
Frank Cooper's Pineapple in Water, 7oz (198g) can	40	2·0
John West Pineapple Rings in Natural Juice, 8oz (227g) can	130	2·0
Sainsbury's Pineapple Slices in Natural Juice, 8oz (227g) can	105	2·0
Waitrose Pineapple in Natural Juice, 8oz (227g) can	120	2·0
Weight Watchers Pineapple Rings in Low-calorie Syrup, 7oz (198g) can	70	2·0
Prunes		
Pickering Prunes in Syrup, 7½oz (213g) can	220	7·5
Tesco Prunes in Syrup, 7½oz (213g) can	235	9·0
Raspberries		
Baxters		
Raspberries in Syrup, 10¼oz (290g) can	250	14·5
Raspberries in Syrup, 15oz (425g) can	365	21·0

	Calories	Fibre g
Hartleys Raspberries in Syrup, 15oz (425g) can	400	21·0
Sainsbury's Raspberries in Syrup, 7½oz (213g) can	155	10·5
Smedley Raspberries in Syrup, 7½oz (213g) can	155	9·0
Weight Watchers Raspberries in Low-calorie Syrup, 7oz (198g) can	50	10·0

Strawberries
Baxters
  Strawberries in Syrup,
    10¼oz (290g) can — 250 · 3·0
  Strawberries in Syrup,
    15oz (425g) can — 365 4·0
Weight Watchers Strawberries in
    Low-calorie Syrup, 7oz (198g) can — 50 2·0

Fruit, Dried

Whitworths		
Apricots, no-need-to-soak, 8·8oz (250g)	385	52·5
Chopped Dates, sugar rolled, 8·8oz (250g)	680	17·5
Dessert Dates, with stones, 8·8oz (250g)	530	18·5
Stoned Dates, 8·8oz (250g)	620	21·5
Figs, 8·8oz (250g)	450	37·5
Prunes, no-need-to-soak, 8·8oz (250g)	290	30·0

Pasta

Wholewheat Pasta, per oz (28g)
Newform Foods Limited Country
    Basket Spaghetti — 99 2·3
Record
  Whole Wheat Lasagne, uncooked — 105 2·8

	Calories	Fibre g
Wholewheat Pasta (Record), *cont.*		
Whole Wheat Long Spaghetti, uncooked	105	2·8
Whole Wheat Short Cut Macaroni, uncooked	105	2·8
Whole Wheat Spaghetti Rings, uncooked	105	2·8

Rice

	Calories	Fibre g
Brown Rice, per oz (28g)		
Prewett's Unpolished Rice, long/short grain	97	1·4
Whitworths Brown Rice	102	0·3

	Calories	Fibre g
White Rice, per oz (28g)		
Kellogg's Boil-in-bag rice, uncooked	93	0·1
Whitworths		
Basmati Rice, uncooked	103	0·1
Ground Rice, uncooked	103	0·1
Rice, long/short grain, uncooked	103	0·1
Rice Easy Cook, uncooked	105	0·1

Savoury Pot Snacks

	Calories	Fibre g
Noodle snacks, per pot made up		
Golden Wonder		
Beef & Tomato Pot Noodle	370	1·5
Cheese & Tomato Pot Noodle	345	2·0
Chicken & Mushroom Pot Noodle	380	8·5
Spicy Curry Pot Noodle	380	4·5
Sweet & Sour Pot Noodle	345	1·0

	Calories	Fibre g
Rice snacks, per pot made up		
Golden Wonder		
Chicken Curry	265	2·5
Chicken Risotto	270	1·0

	Calories	Fibre g
Savoury Beef	255	1·5
Spicy Tomato	250	1·5

Slimmers Products

Meal replacements
Balance, per serving

(26g) with 175ml milk	198	2·0
Crunch'n'Slim		
Coconut & Currant Bars, per meal	230	2·8
Orange & Raisin Bars, per meal	230	2·8
Sultana & Hazelnut Bars, per meal	230	2·8
Limits		
Cheese Flavour Cracker Biscuits		
with Bran	250	2·5
Chocolate Biscuits with Bran	250	2·5
Chocolate Flavour Wafer with Bran	250	2·5
Chocolate Mint Biscuits with Bran	250	2·5
Coffee Flavour Biscuits with Bran	250	2·5
Lemon & Lime Flavour Biscuits		
with Bran	250	2·5
Milk Chocolate Sweetmeal Biscuits		
with Bran	250	2·5
Orange Flavour Biscuits with Bran	250	2·5
Plain Sweetmeal Digestive with		
Bran	250	2·5
Vanilla Flavour Biscuits with Bran	250	2·5
SlimGard, per daily quota of 1 Bar,		
1 Drink and 2 Inbetweeners	333	1·7

Starch-reduced rolls

Energen Starch Reduced Rolls, each	23	0·5

Snacks

Cereal, fruit & nut bars and slices, per bar or slice
Holly Mill

Carob Chip Bar	145	0·5

	Calories	Fibre g
Cereal, fruit & nut bars and slices (Holly Mill), *cont.*		
Cereal & Nut Crunchy Bar	115	0·5
Crunchy Slice	185	1·0
Fruit & Nut Slice	175	1·0
Muesli Slice	215	1·0
Oat, Apple & Raisin Slice	165	1·0
Oat, Apricot & Almond Slice	175	1·0
Protein Slice	175	0·5
Roasted Peanut Bar	155	0·5
Sesame Bar	125	1·0
Jordans		
Original Crunchy Bar,		
Honey & Almond	150	0·5
Original Crunchy Bar,		
Honey & Coconut	145	1·0
Lynn Valley Wholefoods,		
Peanut & Raisin Bar	170	2·5
Prewett's		
Apple & Date Dessert Bar	120	4·0
Banana Dessert Bar	75	2·5
Date & Fig Dessert Bar	125	3·5
Fruit & Bran Bar	85	5·0
Fruit & Nut Dessert Bar	130	4·0
Muesli Fruit Bar	125	3·5
Quaker		
Harvest Crunch Bar, Almond Variety	90	1·0
Harvest Crunch Bar, Peanut Variety	90	1·0
Fruit and nut mixtures		
Cheshire Wholefoods		
Trail Pack, Fruit & Nut Mix,		
100g pack	535	5·0
Trail Pack with coconut and banana,		
56g pack	240	3·0
T. G. Smith (Liverpool) Limited		
Tropical Treat, 100g pack	410	8·0

	Calories	*Fibre g*
Savoury snacks		
Allinson Wheateats, per 21g packet	90	0·5
Soups		
Lentil		
Baxter's Lentil, 15oz (425g) can	200	9·0
Campbell's		
Condensed Lentil, 4·9oz (140g) can,		
makes 9·8oz (280g)	130	5·5
Condensed Lentil, 10½oz (298g) can,		
makes 21oz (596g)	280	12·0
Granny Soup, Lentil,		
15oz (425g) can	240	10·0
Heinz Lentil, 10·6oz (300g) can	180	6·0
Minestrone		
Batchelor's Minestrone, packet,		
makes 1 pint	155	2·5
Crosse & Blackwell Box Soup,		
Minestrone, makes 1 pint	80	3·5
Knorr Minestrone, packet,		
makes 1½ pints	225	4·5
Sainsbury's Minestrone, packet,		
makes 1 pint	120	4·0
Pea		
Baxter's Pea & Ham, 15oz (425g)	225	10·0
Campbell's		
Condensed Pea & Ham,		
10½oz (298g) can, makes 21oz (596g)	400	13·0
Main Course Pea & Ham,		
15oz (425g) can	350	9·0
Heinz Pea & Ham, 10·6oz (300g) can	200	7·0
Vegetable		
Heinz Vegetable & Lentil Big Soup,		
15·3oz (435g) can	210	8·9

	Calories	Fibre g
Soya and Cereal Protein Foods		

Savoury mixes, per packet or can unless stated otherwise

Brooke Bond Oxo

	Calories	Fibre g
Beanfeast, Bolognese, 4oz (113g) pack	330	10·0
Beanfeast, Mexican Chilli, 4oz (113g) pack	330	17·0
Beanfeast, Mild Curry, 4oz (113g) pack	320	10·0
Beanfeast, Paella Style, 4oz (113g) pack	350	13·5
Beanfeast, Soya Mince with Onion, 4oz (113g) pack	375	10·0
Beanfeast, Supreme, 4oz (113g) pack	335	13·5

Direct Foods

	Calories	Fibre g
Protoveg, Natural, Unflavoured, 4½oz (127g) carton	370	4·0
Protoveg, Flavoured (Beef, Ham, Pork Style), 4½oz (127g) carton	360	4·5
Protoveg Menu, Farmhouse Soya Stew Mince, 4oz (113g) carton	405	3·5
Protoveg Menu, Minced Soya & Onion Mix, 5oz (142g) carton	510	3·5
Protoveg Menu, Soya Bolognese Mix, 4oz (113g) carton	390	5·5
Protoveg Menu, Soya Mince with Vegetables, 4oz (113g) carton	395	4·0
Protoveg Menu, Burgamix, 6½oz (184g) pack	995	9·0
Protoveg Menu, Sosmix, 6½oz (184g) pack	960	5·5
Protoveg Menu, Jumbo Grills, 8oz (227g) carton	750	4·0
Protoveg Menu, Jumbo Grills Flavouring, per oz (28g)	68	0·7

	Calories	Fibre g
Protoveg Menu, Vegetable Curry, 112g pack	400	4·0
Protoveg Menu, Vegetable Goulash, 112g pack	395	3·5
Mr Fritzi Fry's Sausage Mix, 8oz (227g) pack	1,210	13·0
Mr Fritzi Fry's Savoury Mix (Burga Style), 8oz (227g) pack	1,075	8·0
Mr Fritzi Fry's Hawaiian Croquettes (Fishcake Style), 8oz (227g) pack	850	7·5
Granose		
Beef Flavour Chunks, per oz (28g) dry weight	95	0·9
Beef Flavour Mince, per oz (28g) dry weight	95	0·9
Bologna, 10oz (283g) can	475	4·0
Bologna, 15oz (425g) can	710	6·5
Bolognese Sauce, 10oz (284g) can	170	1·5
Cannelloni, 14oz (397g) can	300	1·0
Chicken Flavour Pie Filling, 10oz (284g) can	165	1·5
Goulash, 10oz (284g) can	155	1·5
Nutloaf, 15oz (425g) can	750	14·5
Nuttolene, 15oz (425g) can	1,265	14·5
Protose, 15oz (425g) can	675	14·5
Ravioli, 15oz (425g) can	270	2·5
Sausalatas, 10oz (284g) can	390	4·0
Sausalatas, 15oz (425g) can	580	6·0
Sausalene, 10oz (284g) can	555	7·5
Sausfry, per oz (28g) dry weight	140	2·6
Saviand, 10oz (284g) can	565	4·5
Savoury Cuts, 7½oz (213g) can	185	0·5
Savoury Cuts, 15oz (425g) can	375	1·0
Savoury Pudding, 11oz (312g) can	645	4·5
Savoury Pudding, Chicken Flavour, 11oz (312g) can	510	3·0

	Calories	Fibre g
Savoury mixes (Granose) *cont.*		
Soya Beans in Tomato Sauce,		
7½oz (213g) can	365	7·5
Soya Beans in Tomato Sauce,		
15oz (425g) can	725	15·5
Tenderbits, 7½oz (213g) can	170	0·5
Vegetable Pâté, per oz (28g)	85	1·0
Prewett's		
5 Cereal Savoury Mix, per oz (28g)		
dry weight	97	2·5
5 Cereal Savoury Mix, 300g pack	1,025	24·0

Spreads

Sunwheel Natural Foods		
Peanut Butter, Crunchy and Smooth,		
per oz (28g)	169	1·4
Sesame Spread,		
per oz (28g)	177	1·6
Sunflower Spread,		
per oz (28g)	175	1·1

Vegetables, Canned

Artichoke hearts		
Wardour Artichoke Hearts, 14oz (400g)	115	2·5

Baked beans with tomato sauce		
Armour Baked Beans with Tomato		
Sauce, 7¾oz (220g)	140	16·0
Chef Baked Beans with 4 Pork		
Sausages, 7¾oz (220g)	270	13·5
Crosse & Blackwell Baked Beans with		
Tomato Sauce, 15½oz (439g)	280	32·0
Heinz		
Baked Beans with Tomato Sauce,		
5·29oz (150g)	110	11·0

	Calories	*Fibre g*
Baked Beans with Tomato Sauce, 7·9oz (225g)	160	16·5
Baked Beans with Tomato Sauce, 15·9oz (450g)	325	33·5
Baked Beans with Pork Sausages, 7·9oz (225g)	285	11·5
Curried Beans with Sultanas, 7·9oz (225g)	195	16·5
S & W Barbecue Beans Chuckwagon Style in Tomato Sauce, 15½oz (439g)	315	33·0
Safeway		
Baked Beans with Tomato Sauce, 7¾oz (220g)	140	16·0
Baked Beans with Tomato Sauce, 15¾oz (447g)	285	32·5
Sainsbury's		
Baked Beans with Tomato Sauce, 7¾oz (220g)	155	16·0
Baked Beans and Sausages, 7¾oz (220g)	340	12·0
Tesco Baked Beans, 15oz (425g)	270	31·0
Waitrose Baked Beans, 5½oz (156g)	100	11·5

Barlotti beans

Vulcano Barlotti Beans, 15oz (425g)	215	17·0

Broad beans

Hartley's Broad Beans, 10oz (283g)	100	7·5
Smedley Broad Beans, 10oz (283g)	90	7·5
Waitrose Broad Beans, 10oz (283g)	120	10·5

Butter beans

Batchelor's Butter Beans, 7½oz (213g)	115	6·5
Hartley's Butter Beans, 10oz (283g)	175	8·5
Safeway Butter Beans, 7½oz (213g)	115	6·5
Sainsbury's Butter Beans, 7¾oz (220g)	125	6·5
Tesco Butter Beans, 7½oz (213g)	125	7·0

	Calories	Fibre g
Cannellini beans (white kidney beans)		
Batchelor's Cannellini Beans,		
7·9oz (223g)	125	10·0
Bonduelle White Kidney Beans in		
Tomato Sauce, 14½oz (411g)	295	20·0
Vulcano White Kidney (Cannellini),		
15oz (425g)	240	18·5
Green beans		
Bonduelle		
Golden, Cut, 7¼oz (205g)	25	4·5
Whole Green Beans, 14½oz (411g)	20	9·5
Heley Cut Green Beans, 14½oz (411g)	50	7·5
Safeway		
Sliced Green Beans, 9½oz (269g)	20	3·5
Whole Green Beans, 14oz (397g)	15	7·0
Sainsbury's		
Cut Green Beans, 10oz (283g)	30	5·5
Cut Stringless Green Beans,		
14oz (397g)	40	7·5
Smedley Cut Green Beans, 10oz (283g)	15	5·0
Talpe Cut Green Beans, 14oz (397g)	35	6·5
Tesco Cut Green Beans, 10oz (283g)	30	5·5
Lima beans		
S & W Lima Beans, 16oz (454g)	310	26·5
Red kidney beans		
Batchelor's Red Kidney Beans,		
7·9oz (223g)	120	9·5
Pickerings Red Kidney Beans,		
15·9oz (450g)	240	19·0
S & W Red Kidney Beans, 8¾oz		
(248g)	130	11·5
Sainsbury's Red Kidney Beans,		
15½oz (439g)	230	19·0
Smedley Red Kidney Beans,		
10oz (283g)	260	20·0

	Calories	Fibre g
Stokeley Red Kidney Beans, 15oz (425g)	225	18·0
Tesco Red Kidney Beans, 15oz (425g)	285	19·5
Beetroot		
Baxter's		
Baby Beets, pickled, 12oz (340g)	155	8·5
Sliced Beets, pickled, 11¾oz (333g)	100	5·7
Brussels sprouts		
Bonduelle Brussels Sprouts, 14½oz (411g)	50	8·5
Talpe Continental Cuisine Brussels Sprouts, 14oz (397g)	45	7·5
Carrots		
Sainsbury's		
Sliced Carrots, 10½oz (298g)	35	6·5
Whole Carrots, 10½oz (298g)	30	6·5
Young Carrots, 7oz (198g)	25	4·5
Smedley		
Sliced Carrots, 10½oz (298g)	35	6·5
Whole Carrots, 10½oz (298g)	30	6·5
Mixed vegetables		
Sainsbury's Mixed Vegetables (peas, carrots, turnips, potato), 10½oz (298g)	95	9·5
Smedley Mixed Vegetables (peas, swede, potato, carrot), 10oz (283g)	125	7·0
Tesco Mixed Vegetables (peas, carrots, potato, swede), 10oz (283g)	125	7·0
Mushrooms		
Chesswood		
Button Mushrooms in Brine, 7½oz (213g)	15	3·0

	Calories	Fibre g
Mushrooms (Chesswood), *cont.*		
Sliced Large Mushrooms in Brine, 7½oz (213g)	15	4·0
Sliced Mushrooms in Creamed Sauce, 7½oz (213g)	190	2·0
Small Whole Mushrooms in Brine, 7½oz (213g)	15	3·0
Sainsbury's Small Whole Mushrooms, 7½oz (213g)	15	3·5
Talpe Continental Cuisine Mushrooms, 7oz (198g)	15	3·0
Chick peas		
Bonduelle Chick Peas, 400g	275	14·5
Napolina Chick Peas, 15oz (425g)	275	14·5
Vulcano Chick Peas, 15oz (425g)	270	14·5
Garden peas and petit pois		
Bonduelle Petit Pois, 14½oz (411g)	125	13·5
Hartley's Garden Peas, 10oz (283g)	85	11·5
Safeway Petit Pois, 7oz (198g)	55	8·5
Sainsbury's		
Garden Peas, 5oz (142g)	45	6·5
Garden Peas, 10oz (283g)	90	13·0
Smedley		
Garden Peas, 5oz (142g)	60	4·5
Garden Peas, 10oz (283g)	125	9·5
Tesco		
Garden Peas, 10oz (283g)	85	13·0
Petit Pois, 10oz (283g)	90	13·0
Mushy peas		
Batchelor's Mushy Peas, 10·7oz (304g)	240	22·0
Sainsbury's Mushy Processed Peas, 10oz (283g)	220	23·0
Smedley Mushy Processed Peas, 10oz (283g)	240	9·0

	Calories	*Fibre g*
Tesco Mushy Processed Peas, 10oz (283g)	225	23·5
Pease pudding		
Pickering's		
Pease Pudding, 7½oz (213g)	290	11·0
Pease Pudding, 15oz (425g)	585	21·5
Sainsbury's		
Pease Pudding, 7¾oz (220g)	290	11·0
Pease Pudding, 15½oz (439g)	605	22·5
Processed and marrowfat peas		
Batchelor's Bigga Processed Peas, 10oz (283g)	150	15·0
Farrow's Giant Marrowfat Processed Peas, 4·97oz (141g)	70	6·5
International Processed Peas, 10oz (283g)	115	13·5
Safeway		
Marrowfat Processed Peas, 10oz (283g)	115	13·0
Processed Peas, 10oz (283g)	130	14·0
Sainsbury's		
Processed Peas, 10oz (283g)	130	14·0
Small Processed Peas, 10oz (283g)	145	14·5
Smedley Processed Peas, 10oz (283g)	190	10·5
Tesco Processed Peas, 10oz (283g)	140	15·5
Potatoes		
Sainsbury's New Potatoes, 10oz (283g)	115	5·5
Smedley New Potatoes, 10oz (283g)	135	3·5
Yeoman New Potatoes, mint flavour, 19oz (539g)	190	9·0
Spinach		
Bonduelle		
Chopped Spinach, 7¼oz (205g)	55	11·5
Leaf Spinach, 14½oz (411g)	65	13·5

	Calories	Fibre g
Spinach, *cont.*		
Lockwood's Leaf Spinach, 9½oz (269g)	40	7·0
Smedley Spinach, chopped leaf,		
9oz (258g)	30	7·5
Talpe Chopped Spinach, 14oz (397g)	90	20·0
Sweetcorn		
Bonduelle Sweetcorn Kernels,		
12oz (340g)	220	16·5
Green Giant		
Mexicorn Golden Corn,		
whole kernels with peppers,		
7oz (198g)	150	10·5
Niblets Golden Corn, whole kernel,		
7oz (198g)	150	11·0
Kounty Kist Sweetcorn Kernels,		
12oz (340g)	200	17·5
Mexicana Sweetcorn with Peppers,		
11½oz (325g)	200	15·0
Sainsbury's		
Sweetcorn & Peppers, 12oz (340g)	230	17·5
Whole Kernel Sweetcorn, 7oz (198g)	150	11·5
Whole Kernel Sweetcorn,		
11½oz (326g)	250	18·5
Tesco Sweetcorn Kernels, 12oz (340g)	260	18·0
Tomatoes		
Mon Jardin Chopped Tomatoes,		
14oz (400g)	50	3·5
Napolina		
Peeled Plum Tomatoes, 8oz (227g)	25	2·0
Peeled Plum Tomatoes, 14oz (397g)	50	3·5
Regatta		
Italian Peeled Tomatoes, 8oz (227g)	25	2·0
Italian Peeled Tomatoes, 14oz (397g)	50	3·5
Sainsbury's Israeli Peeled Tomatoes,		
1lb 3oz (539g)	65	5·0

	Calories	Fibre g
Salads		
Bonduelle Mexican Salad		
(sweetcorn, peas, peppers),		
14½oz (411g)	165	15·5
Green Giant American Bean Salad,		
1lb 1oz (482g)	245	13·5
Heinz Vegetable Salad, 7¼oz (206g)	305	5·0

Vegetables, Dried

Whitworths		
Mixed Vegetables, per oz (28g) dry	75	7·0
Mushrooms, per oz (28g) dry	40	7·5
Peppers, per oz (28g) dry	60	3·5
Sliced Onion, per oz (28g) dry	85	4·5

Vegetables, Frozen

For basic frozen vegetables (e.g. peas) refer to Your Basic Calorie and Fibre Chart.

Stir-fry vegetables		
Birds Eye		
Continental Stir Fry Vegetables,		
10oz (284g), after frying	250	6·5
Country Style Stir Fry Vegetables,		
10oz (284g), after frying	250	6·5
Mediterranean Stir Fry Vegetables,		
10oz (284g), after frying	300	6·5
St Michael		
Brown Pack, 10oz (284g), as sold	90	6·0
Red Pack, 10oz (284g), as sold	80	10·0
Yellow Pack, 10oz (284g), as sold	130	8·0

Vegetable mixtures		
Birds Eye		
Casserole Vegetables, 8oz (227g)	80	5·5
Cauliflower, Peas and Carrots,		
8oz (227g)	80	9·5

	Calories	Fibre g
Vegetable mixtures (Birds Eye), *cont.*		
Original Mixed Vegetables, 4oz (113g)	60	5·5
Original Mixed Vegetables, 8oz (227g)	120	11·0
Peas, Sweetcorn and Peppers, 8oz (227g)	120	13·0
Rice, Peas and Mushrooms, 8oz (227g)	350	9·5
Rice, Sweetcorn and Peppers, 8oz (227g)	340	5·0
Ross		
Farmhouse Mixed Vegetables, 8oz (227g)	115	11·0
Mixed Vegetables, 8oz (227g)	125	12·5
Stewpack, 8oz (227g)	40	4·5

Wheatgerm

	Calories	Fibre g
Wheatgerm, per oz (28g)		
Allinson Wheatgerm (stabilized)	89	0·7
Bemax		
Crunchy	85	2·1
Natural Wheat Germ	85	2·1
Cheshire Wholefoods Wheatgerm	90	0·9
Froment Stabilized Wheatgerm	95	0·8
Granose Wheatgerm	102	2·0
Jordans Natural Wheatgerm	100	0·5
Kretschmer Wheatgerm (lightly toasted)	100	0·6

Drinks Calorie Guide

Drinks do not supply you with dietary fibre and do little, if anything, to satisfy the appetite – mostly passing through the stomach in a matter of minutes. That is why, in terms of weight control, it is generally better to eat a piece of fruit than to drink the juice.

There are many drinks, however, which are calorie-free and can be consumed with absolute freedom. These are listed on pages 61–62. Other drinks supply calories that must be included as part of your daily total.

Because alcoholic drinks lack nutritional value, those allowing themselves a little alcohol while following the F-Plan are recommended to have a minimum 1,000 calories (or 850 in the special circumstances described in Chapter 9) of food and drink, and add the alcohol-supplied calories to this total (see pages 63 and 64 for advice and instructions). There are very few people who would not achieve a speedy weight loss on a fibre-rich 1,200 calories a day, for instance, so you can ensure your nutrients by eating sufficient food and then allowing that little extra calorie ration for alcohol.

Many of the drinks listed here are not particularly recommended for F-Plan dieters; but they are included on the basis that if you are going to feel deprived without any one particular food or drink, it is better to include a little, while slimming, than to put too much strain on your will-power.

You will find an honest and realistic guide to alcohol calories here. We say 'honest' because a great deal of self-deception goes on in counting drinks calories during dieting. Pub measures can be relied upon for both meanness and accuracy. Home measures rarely can. It is so easy to count the calories for a single and then pour out very much more. And it is very dreary to have to measure precisely every tot or glass of wine.

For this reason, the number of calories in a whole bottle is often the safest and easiest guide to accuracy – and the most restraining influence – for home consumption. If you drink vodka, for instance, first decide how much to allow yourself for the week – perhaps a quarter or a half bottle. Then set that quantity aside in a separate bottle. Those are your alcoholic calories for the week, and when you've finished that's your lot – so an over-indulgent Monday could lead to a dry Saturday and Sunday. This way there is just no chance of making a multiplicity of little calorie mistakes with each drink, which could add up to many extra calories in a week.

With wines, the number of calories in a whole bottle tends to be the best guide, too. The size and fullness of different glasses of wine varies a great deal. Most people will either share a bottle of wine between two, with a meal, or perhaps share just half a bottle if they are dieting. Even from the sight of a glass of wine served in a restaurant or bar it is fairly easy to assess how many such glasses you would get from one bottle. Rather easier than thinking in terms of fluid ounces, for most of us!

So, in this chart, calories are given for full bottles as well as for full measures where applicable. There is a variation of about 50 calories between different bottles of wine in the groups we list together. For instance, sweet white wines will range from 600 to 650 calories. Unkindly, and to be on the safe side, we list the higher figure.

Drinks Calorie Chart

	Calories
Aperitifs, per bar measure	
Campari (50ml)	115
per bottle	1,840
Cinzano	
Bianco (50ml)	80
Rosso (50ml)	75
Dubonnet	
Dry (50ml)	55
per bottle	905
Red (50ml)	75
per bottle	1,255
Martini	
Bianco (50ml)	75
per bottle	1,255
Extra Dry (50ml)	55
per bottle	905

Beer, Cider and Lager, per ½ pint (284ml)	
bitter	90
brown ale	85
cider	100
home-brewed beer	120
lager	90
light ale	75
mild ale	75
non-alcoholic lager (e.g. Barbican)	45
pale ale	90
special brew lager (e.g. Carlsberg Special Brew)	200

Beverages	
cocoa, 1 rounded teaspoon (10ml)	20
drinking chocolate, 1 rounded teaspoon (10ml)	20
Horlicks, malted milk, 1 rounded teaspoon (10ml)	20

	Calories
Beverages, *cont*.	
milk	
fresh, whole, pasteurized, sterilized, homogenized, longlife (UHT), or untreated farm milk, ½ pint (284ml)	180
fresh, semi-skimmed (e.g. Light Gold), ½ pint (284ml)	140
fresh, skimmed (e.g. Sainsbury's Vitapint Skimmed), ½ pint (284ml)	90
dried, skimmed, 1 rounded teaspoon (10ml)	10
Ovaltine, 1 heaped teaspoon (10ml)	25
tea, without milk, per cup	0

Fizzy Drinks and Mixers	
All 'low-calorie' labelled drinks (e.g. Energen One Cal Drinks, Diet Pepsi, Slimline Tonic) contain negligible calories	
American ginger ale, 4fl. oz (113ml)	40
Bitter lemon, 4fl. oz (113ml)	40
Coca Cola	
11½fl. oz (325ml) can	140
6½fl. oz (185ml) bottle	80
dry ginger ale, 4fl. oz (113ml)	40
lemonade, ¼ pint (142ml)	50
orangeade, 4fl. oz (113ml)	55
Pepsi Cola	
11½fl. oz (325ml) can	135
6fl. oz (170ml) bottle	70
Schweppes Slimline Shandy, 8½fl. oz (241ml) bottle	15
soda water, per glass	0
tonic water, 4fl. oz (113ml)	40

Fruit Juices, per 4fl. oz (113ml) glass	
apple	40
grape	60

	Calories
grapefruit	
bottled, sweetened	65
canned, unsweetened	35
canned, sweetened	45
in a carton (e.g. Just Juice)	25
frozen, reconstituted	45
orange	
bottled, sweetened	70
canned, unsweetened	35
canned, sweetened	55
in a carton (e.g. Just Juice)	40
frozen, reconstituted	60
pineapple	
canned, sweetened	65
bottled, sweetened	65
tomato, bottled or canned	25

Fruit Squashes and Cordials, per fl. oz (28ml), undiluted	
blackcurrant	
cordial	30
health drinks (e.g. Ribena)	85
lemon	
barley water	30
squash or drink	30
lime juice cordial	25
orange squash or drink	35
whole grapefruit drink	30

Liqueurs, per bar measure	
Benedictine (25ml)	90
Cointreau (25ml)	85
Crème de Menthe (25ml)	80
Drambuie (25ml)	85
Grand Marnier (25ml)	80
Kirsch (25ml)	50
Tia Maria (25ml)	75

	Calories
Port and Sherry	
sherry	
cream (50ml), small schooner	65
per bottle	1,100
dry (50ml), small schooner	55
per bottle	750
medium (50ml), small schooner	60
per bottle	820
port (50ml)	75
Spirits	
brandy, per bar measure (25ml)	50
gin, per bar measure (25ml)	50
rum, per bar measure (25ml)	50
vodka, per bar measure (25ml)	50
whisky, per bar measure (25ml)	50
brandy, gin, rum, vodka and whisky, per bottle	1,675
Wine	
red, per 4fl. oz (113ml) glass	
dry	80
sweet	95
rosé, per 4fl. oz (113ml) glass	80
white, per 4fl. oz (113ml) glass	
dry	75
sparkling	90
sweet	100

Your basic calorie and fibre chart

This is the chart to use for measuring and calculating various quantities of foods, and for adding up your own recipes and day's meals.

In this chart calorie and fibre values are given per oz (28g) of food. More precise fibre and calorie figures are given here (as opposed to rounded figures in the other charts, which suffice when dealing with larger total quantities).

Your Basic Calorie and Fibre Chart

Food	Calories per oz (28g)	Fibre g per oz (28g)
All Bran	70	7·9
Almond paste	124	1·8
Almonds, shelled, whole or ground	158	4·1
Apples eating, raw		
weighed with skin and core	10	0·6
flesh only	13	0·6
cooking		
raw, flesh only	10	0·7
baked or stewed without sugar	9	0·6
Apricots fresh		
raw, weighed with stones	7	0·5
stewed, without sugar, weighed with stones	6	0·4
dried		
raw	51	6·7
no-need-to-soak (e.g. Whitworths), raw	44	6·0
stewed without sugar	18	2·5
canned in syrup	30	0·4
Arrowroot	99	0·8
Artichokes, globe, boiled	4	0·3

Food	Calories per oz (28g)	Fibre g per oz (28g)
Asparagus, boiled	5	0·4
Aubergines, raw, flesh only	4	0·7
Avocado, flesh only	62	0·6
Bacon		
collar joint		
raw, lean and fat	89	0
boiled, lean and fat	91	0
lean only	53	0
gammon joint		
raw, lean and fat	66	0
boiled, lean and fat	75	0
boiled, lean only	47	0
gammon rashers		
grilled, lean and fat	64	0
grilled, lean only	48	0
back rashers		
raw, lean and fat	120	0
grilled, lean and fat	113	0
fried, lean and fat	130	0
middle rashers		
raw, lean and fat	119	0
grilled, lean and fat	116	0
fried, lean and fat	134	0
streaky rashers		
raw, lean and fat	116	0
grilled, lean and fat	118	0
fried, lean and fat	139	0
Baking powder	46	0
Bananas		
weighed with skin	13	0·6
flesh only	22	1·0

Food	Calories per oz (28g)	Fibre g per oz (28g)
Barcelona nuts, shelled	179	2·9
Barley, pearl		
raw	100	1·8
boiled	34	0·6
Bean sprouts		
raw	8	0·3
canned	3	0·8
boiled	10	0·3
Beans		
adzuki, dry weight	91	7·0
baked, canned in tomato sauce	18	2·0
black-eyed, dry weight	97	7·2
broad, boiled	13	1·2
butter		
dry weight	76	6·0
boiled	27	1·4
French, boiled	2	0·9
haricot		
dry weight	76	7·2
boiled	26	2·0
mung, dry weight	65	6·2
red kidney		
dry weight	76	7·0
boiled or canned drained	25	2·3
runner		
raw	7	0·8
boiled	5	1·0
soya		
dry weight	112	1·2
boiled	37	0·4
Beef		
beefburgers, frozen		
raw	74	0·1

Food	Calories per oz (28g)	Fibre g per oz (28g)
Beef, *cont.*		
fried	74	0·1
brisket		
raw	70	0
boiled	91	0
corned, canned	61	0
forerib		
raw	81	0
roast	98	0
roast, lean only	63	0
mince		
raw	62	0
stewed	64	0
rump steak		
raw	55	0
fried	69	0
fried, lean only	53	0
grilled	61	0
grilled, lean only	47	0
silverside		
salted, boiled	68	0
salted, boiled, lean only	48	0
sirloin		
raw	76	0
roast	80	0
roast, lean only	54	0
stewing steak		
raw	49	0
stewed	62	0
topside		
raw	50	0
roast	60	0
roast, lean only	44	0
Beef sausages		

Food	Calories per oz (28g)	Fibre g per oz (28g)
raw	84	0
fried	75	0
grilled	74	0
Beetroot		
raw	8	0·9
boiled	12	0·7
Bemax (wheatgerm)	97	2·1
Bilberries, raw	16	2·0
Biscuits		
cream crackers	123	0·8
digestive		
plain	132	1·5
chocolate	138	1·0
ginger nuts	128	0·6
matzo	108	1·1
oatcakes	123	1·1
rye crispbread	90	3·3
semi-sweet	128	0·6
short-sweet	131	0·5
wafers, filled	150	0·4
water biscuits	123	0·9
wheat, starch-reduced crispbread	109	1·4
Black pudding, fried	85	0·2
Blackberries		
raw	8	2·0
stewed without sugar	7	1·8
Blackcurrants		
raw	8	2·4
stewed without sugar	7	2·1
Bloater, grilled, weighed with bones	52	0

Food	Calories per oz (28g)	Fibre g per oz (28g)
Bovril	49	0
Brain		
calf and lamb, raw	31	0
calf, boiled	43	0
lamb, boiled	35	0
Bran, wheat	58	12·3
Brawn	43	0
Brazil nuts, shelled	173	2·5
Bread		
brown	62	1·4
currant	70	0·5
Hi Bran	57	3·1
malt	69	1·4
soda, white	74	0·6
wheatgerm (e.g. Hovis, Vitbe)	64	1·3
white	65	0·8
wholemeal	60	2·4
Bread rolls		
brown		
crusty	81	1·7
soft	79	1·5
white		
crusty	81	0·9
soft	85	0·8
wholemeal (e.g. Allinson)	60	2·4
starch-reduced	108	0·6
Bread sauce	31	0·1
Breadcrumbs, white, dried	99	1·0
Broccoli tops		
raw	6	1·0
boiled	5	1·1

Food	Calories per oz (28g)	Fibre g per oz (28g)
Brussels sprouts		
raw	7	1·2
boiled	5	0·8
Buns, currant	85	0·5
Butter	207	0
Cabbage		
red, raw	6	1·0
savoy		
raw	7	0·9
boiled	3	0·7
spring, boiled	2	0·6
white, raw	6	0·8
winter		
raw	6	1·0
boiled	4	0·8
Cakes		
fruit		
plain	99	0·8
rich	93	1·0
rich, iced	99	1·0
madeira	110	0·4
sponge		
with fat	130	0·3
without fat	84	0·3
jam-filled	85	0·3
Carrots		
old		
raw	6	0·8
boiled	5	0·9
young, boiled	6	0·8
canned, drained	5	1·0

Food	Calories per oz (28g)	Fibre g per oz (28g)
Cashew nuts	157	4·0
Cauliflower		
raw	4	0·6
boiled	3	0·5
Celeriac, boiled	4	1·4
Celery		
raw	2	0·5
boiled	1	0·6
Cheese		
Baby Bel	80	0
Brie	88	0
Caerphilly	101	0
Camembert	84	0
Cheddar	115	0
cheese spread	79	0
Cheshire	95	0
cottage cheese	27	0
cream cheese	123	0
curd cheese	40	0
Danbo	98	0
Danish Blue	103	0
Double Gloucester	105	0
Edam	88	0
Emmenthal	115	0
Fetta	54	0
Gorgonzola	112	0
Gouda	100	0
Gruyère	115	0
Jarlsberg	95	0
Lancashire	109	0
Lymeswold	115	0
Mycella	110	0

Food	Calories per oz (28g)	Fibre g per oz (28g)
Parmesan	114	0
Philadelphia, soft cheese	90	0
processed, full fat	87	0
Quark		
less than 1% butter fat	22	0
less than 5% butter fat	33	0
less than 12% butter fat	47	0
Red Leicester	120	0
Roquefort	99	0
Sage Derby	112	0
skimmed-milk soft cheese	25	0
soft cheese, full fat	110	0
St Paulin	98	0
Stilton	130	0
Tome au Raisin	74	0
Wensleydale	115	0
Cherries		
eating, raw	11	0·4
cooking, raw	11	0·4
stewed without sugar, weighed with stones	9	0·3
glacé	59	0·4
Chestnuts, shelled	48	1·9
Chicken		
light meat only, raw	32	0
dark meat only, raw	35	0
light and dark meat mixed		
raw	34	0
no skin, boiled	51	0
no skin, roast	41	0
meat and skin, roast	60	0
Chicory, raw	3	0·4

Food	Calories per oz (28g)	Fibre g per oz (28g)
Chinese leaves	3	0·6
Chips, fried in deep fat	71	0·6
Chips (grill), frozen, grilled	40	0·6
Chips (oven), frozen, baked in oven	55	0·6
Chocolate		
drinking	102	0
milk	148	0
plain	147	0
Chocolates, fancy and filled	129	0
Choux pastry, cooked	92	0·4
Christmas pudding	85	0·6
Cockles, boiled, without shells	13	0
Cocoa powder	87	0
Coconut		
fresh	98	3·8
milk	6	0
desiccated	169	6·6
Cod		
fillets		
raw	21	0
boneless, baked	27	0
boneless, poached	26	0
boneless, steamed	23	0
fried in batter	56	0
frozen steaks, uncooked	19	0
steaks, fresh or frozen, grilled	27	0
smoked		
raw	22	0
poached	28	0

Food	Calories per oz (28g)	Fibre g per oz (28g)
Cod liver oil	252	0
Coffee		
ground, roasted, dry weight	80	0
instant powder or granules	28	0
Coffee and chicory essence	61	0
Coley		
raw	20	0
steamed, weighed with bones and skin	24	0
Condensed milk		
whole, sweetened	90	0
skimmed, sweetened	75	0
Corn oil	252	0
Corn-on-the-cob		
kernels only, raw	36	1·0
kernels only, boiled	34	1·3
Corned beef	61	0
Cornflakes	103	0·8
Cornflour	99	0·8
Courgettes		
raw	5	0·5
boiled	2	0·3
Cow's milk, fresh, whole	18	0
Crab		
boiled, meat only	36	0
canned	23	0
Cranberries, raw	4	1·2

Food	Calories per oz (28g)	Fibre g per oz (28g)
Cream		
double	125	0
half	35	0
single	59	0
soured	59	0
sterilized, canned	64	0
whipping	93	0
Crispbread		
rye	90	3·3
wheat, starch-reduced	109	1·4
Crisps, potato	149	3·2
Cucumber	3	0·1
Currants, dried	68	1·8
Custard		
egg	33	0
made with powder	33	0
Custard powder	99	0·8
Damsons		
raw	10	1·0
stewed without sugar	8	0·9
Dates		
dried		
no stones	69	2·4
weighed with stones	60	2·1
chopped and sugar-rolled	77	2·0
Dogfish (rock salmon), fried in batter	74	0·1
Dried milk, cow's		
whole	137	0
skimmed	99	0

Food	Calories per oz (28g)	Fibre g per oz (28g)
Dripping, beef	249	0
Duck		
raw, meat only	34	0
roast		
meat only	53	0
meat, fat and skin	95	0
Eel, stewed, flesh only	56	0
Egg		
whole, raw, without shell	41	0
boiled	41	0
fried	65	0
poached	43	0
Egg white, raw	10	0
Egg yolk, raw	95	0
Eggplant, see **Aubergines**		
Endive, raw	3	0·6
Evaporated milk, whole, unsweetened	44	0
Figs		
green, raw	11	0·7
dried		
raw	60	5·2
stewed without sugar	33	2·9
Fish fingers		
frozen	50	0·2
grilled without fat	50	0·2
fried	65	0·2
Flaky pastry, cooked	158	0·6

Food	Calories per oz (28g)	Fibre g per oz (28g)
Flour		
brown (85% extraction)	92	2·1
patent (40% extraction)	97	0·8
rye (100% extraction)	94	3·3
white		
bread-making (72% extraction)	94	0·8
household, plain	98	1·0
household, self-raising	94	1·0
wholemeal (100% extraction)	89	2·7
Frankfurters	77	0·3
Fruit gums	48	0
Fruit salad		
canned	27	0·3
dried, stewed without sugar	29	2·2
Gammon, *see under* **Bacon**		
Gelatine	95	0
Glacé cherries, *see under* **Cherries**		
Glucose, liquid	89	0
Goat's milk	20	0
Golden syrup	83	0
Goose, roast, meat only	89	0
Gooseberries		
green		
raw	5	0·9
stewed without sugar	4	0·8
ripe, raw	10	1·0
Grapefruit		
fresh		
weighed with skin and pips	3	0·1

Food	Calories per oz (28g)	Fibre g per oz (28g)
flesh only	6	0·2
canned in natural juice	11	0·1
canned in syrup	17	0·1
Grapefruit juice, canned		
unsweetened	9	0
sweetened	11	0
Grapenuts	99	2·0
Grapes		
black, raw	14	0·1
white (green), raw	17	0·3
Greengages		
raw, weighed with stones	12	0·7
stewed without sugar, weighed with stones	11	0·6
Groundnut (peanut) oil	252	0
Grouse, roast		
meat only	48	0
weighed with bone	32	0
Guavas, canned	17	1·0
Haddock fillets		
fresh		
raw	20	0
fried, weighed without bones	49	0
steamed, weighed without bones	27	0
smoked, steamed, weighed without bones	28	0
Halibut		
raw	26	0
steamed, flesh only	37	0

Food	Calories per oz (28g)	Fibre g per oz (28g)
Ham		
boiled, lean only	47	0
cooked and vacuum-packed	40	0
canned	33	0
Ham and pork, chopped, canned	76	0
Hare, stewed, weighed with bone	39	0
Hazelnuts, shelled	106	1·7
Heart		
lamb, raw	33	0
sheep, roast	66	0
ox		
raw	30	0
stewed	50	0
pig, raw	26	0
Herring		
raw, flesh only	66	0
coated in oatmeal, fried	66	0·4
grilled, flesh only	56	0
Honey, in jars	81	0
Horseradish, raw	17	2·3
Ice cream		
dairy	47	0
non-dairy	46	0
Jam		
fruit with edible seeds (e.g. raspberry)	73	0·3
stone fruit (e.g. plum)	73	0·3
Jelly		
packet cubes	73	0
made up with water	17	0

Food	Calories per oz (28g)	Fibre g per oz (28g)
Kidney		
lamb		
raw	25	0
fried	43	0
ox		
raw	24	0
stewed	48	0
pig		
raw	25	0
stewed	43	0
Kipper, baked		
flesh only	57	0
weighed with bones	31	0
Lady's fingers, see **Okra**		
Lamb		
breast		
raw, lean and fat, no bone	106	0
roast, lean and fat, no bone	115	0
roast, lean only	71	0
cutlets		
raw, lean and fat, weighed without bone	108	0
grilled, lean and fat, weighed without bone	104	0
grilled, lean and fat, weighed with bone	68	0
grilled, lean only	62	0
leg		
raw, lean and fat, weighed without bone	67	0
roast, lean and fat, weighed without bone	74	0

Food	Calories per oz (28g)	Fibre g per oz (28g)
Lamb, *cont.*		
roast, lean only	53	0
loin chops		
raw, lean and fat, weighed without bone	106	0
grilled, lean and fat, weighed without bone	99	0
grilled, lean and fat, weighed with bone	78	0
lean only	62	0
scrag and neck		
raw, lean and fat, weighed without bone	88	0
stewed, lean and fat, weighed without bone	82	0
stewed, lean only, weighed with fat and bone	71	0
shoulder		
raw, lean and fat, weighed without bone	88	0
roast, lean and fat, weighed without bone	88	0
roast, lean only	55	0
Lard	250	0
Laverbread (cooked, puréed seaweed, coated in oatmeal)	15	0·9
Leeks		
raw	9	0·9
boiled	7	1·0
Lemon curd		
starch base	79	0·1
home-made	81	0

Food	Calories per oz (28g)	Fibre g per oz (28g)
Lemon juice, fresh	2	0
Lemon sole		
raw	23	0
fried coated in crumbs, weighed with bones	48	0·1
steamed, weighed without bones	25	0
Lemons, whole, including skin	4	1·4
Lentils		
raw	85	3·3
split, boiled	28	1·0
Lettuce, raw	3	0·4
Liquorice Allsorts	88	0
Liver		
calf		
raw	43	0
fried	71	0
chicken		
raw	38	0
fried	54	0
lamb		
raw	50	0
fried	65	0
ox		
raw	46	0
stewed	55	0
Liver sausage	87	0·1
Loganberries		
raw	5	1·7
stewed without sugar	4	1·6
canned in syrup	28	0·9

Food	Calories per oz (28g)	Fibre g per oz (28g)
Longlife milk	18	0
Low-fat spread (e.g. Outline, St Ivel Gold)	102	0
Luncheon meat, canned	88	0·1
Lychees		
raw	18	0·1
canned	19	0·1
Macaroni		
white		
raw	104	0·8
boiled	33	0·3
wholewheat		
raw	97	2·8
boiled	32	0·9
Mackerel		
fresh		
raw	62	0
fried, flesh only	53	0
kippered, raw	62	0
hot smoked, as sold	70	0
Maize oil	252	0
Mandarin oranges, canned	16	0·1
Mangoes		
raw	17	0·4
canned	22	0·3
Margarine, all brands, hard, soft and polyunsaturated	210	0
Marmalade	73	0·2

Food	Calories per oz (28g)	Fibre g per oz (28g)
Marmite	50	0
Marrow		
raw	4	0·5
boiled	2	0·2
Marzipan	124	1·8
Mayonnaise	201	0
Medlars, raw, flesh only	12	2·9
Melon		
cantaloup		
raw, weighed with skin	4	0·2
raw, flesh only	7	0·3
yellow, honeydew		
raw, weighed with skin	4	0·2
raw, flesh only	6	0·3
water		
raw, weighed with skin	3	0·1
raw, flesh only	6	0·3
Milk		
fresh		
whole, pasteurized, sterilized, homogenized, longlife (UHT) or untreated farm milk	18	0
whole, Channel Islands	21	0
semi-skimmed (e.g. Light Gold)	14	0
skimmed (e.g. Sainsbury's Vitapint Skimmed)	9	0
condensed		
whole, sweetened	90	0
skimmed, sweetened	75	0
evaporated, whole, unsweetened	44	0

Food	Calories per oz (28g)	Fibre g per oz (28g)
Milk, *cont.*		
dried		
whole, not made up	137	0
skimmed (e.g. Marvel), not made up	95	0
skimmed with added vegetable fat		
(e.g. Cadbury's Pint Size), not		
made up	140	0
skimmed with added vegetable fat,		
made up with water	14	0
cultured buttermilk	10	0
goat's milk	20	0
soya milk, diluted as instructed	18	0
Mincemeat	66	0·9
Minestrone soup, dried	83	1·8
Muesli	103	2·0
Mulberries, raw	10	0·5
Mushrooms		
raw	4	0·7
fried	59	1·1
Mussels		
raw, weighed without shells	18	0
boiled, weighed without shells	24	0
Mustard and cress, raw	3	1·0
Nectarines		
raw, flesh and skin, no stones	14	0·7
raw, whole fruit weighed with stone	13	0·6
Oatcakes	123	1·1

Food	Calories per oz (28g)	Fibre g per oz (28g)
Oatmeal, raw	112	2·0
Okra (Lady's fingers), raw	5	0·9
Olive oil	252	0
Olives, in brine		
weighed with stones	23	1·0
weighed without stones	29	1·2
Onions		
raw	6	0·4
boiled	4	0·4
fried	97	1·3
spring, raw	10	0·9
Orange juice		
fresh	11	0
canned		
unsweetened	9	0
sweetened	14	0
Oranges		
whole, weighed with peel and pips	7	0·4
flesh only	10	0·6
Ovaltine	106	0
Oxo cubes	64	0
Oxtail, stewed, weighed on the bone	26	0
Oysters, raw		
weighed with shell	2	0
weighed without shell	14	0
Papaya (pawpaw), canned	18	0·1
Parsley, raw	6	2·5

Food	Calories per oz (28g)	Fibre g per oz (28g)
Parsnips		
raw	14	1·1
boiled	16	0·7
Partridge, roast		
meat only	59	0
weighed on the bone	36	0
Passion fruit (Granadilla)		
raw, weighed with skin	4	1·9
Pastry, see **Choux pastry, Flaky pastry, Shortcrust pastry**		
Pawpaw, see **Papaya**		
Peaches		
fresh raw, flesh only	10	0·4
raw, weighed with stone	9	0·3
dried		
raw	59	4·0
stewed without sugar	22	1·5
canned	24	0·3
Peanut butter	174	2·1
Peanut oil	252	0
Peanuts		
fresh	160	2·3
roasted	160	2·3
Pearl barley, see **Barley, pearl**		
Pears		
eating		
flesh only	11	0·6
weighed with skin and core	8	0·5

Food	Calories per oz (28g)	Fibre g per oz (28g)
cooking		
raw, flesh only	10	0·8
stewed without sugar	8	0·7
canned	22	0·5
Peas		
fresh		
raw	19	1·5
boiled	15	1·5
frozen		
raw	15	2·2
boiled	11	2·2
canned		
garden	13	1·8
processed	22	2·2
dried		
raw	80	4·7
boiled	29	1·3
split, dried		
raw	87	3·3
boiled	33	1·4
chick		
raw	90	4·2
boiled	30	1·7
red pigeon, raw	84	4·2
Pepper, green		
raw	4	0·3
boiled	4	0·3
Peppermints	110	0
Pheasant, roast		
meat only	60	0
weighed with bone	38	0
Piccalilli	9	0·5

Food	Calories per oz (28g)	Fibre g per oz (28g)
Pickle, sweet	38	0·5
Pigeon, roast		
meat only	64	0
weighed with bone	28	0
Pilchards, canned in tomato sauce	35	0
Pineapple		
fresh, no skin and core	13	0·3
canned	22	0·3
Pineapple juice, canned	15	0
Plaice		
raw, flesh only	25	0
fried in batter	78	0·2
fried in crumbs	64	0·1
steamed, flesh only	26	0
Plantain		
green		
raw	31	1·6
boiled	34	1·8
ripe, fried	75	1·6
Plums		
Victoria dessert, raw, weighed with stones	10	0·6
cooking		
raw, weighed with stones	6	0·6
stewed without sugar, weighed with stones	7	0·6
Polony	79	0·2
Pomegranate pulp	22	0·3

Food	Calories per oz (28g)	Fibre g per oz (28g)
Pork		
belly rashers		
raw, lean and fat	107	0
grilled, lean and fat	111	0
chops		
loin, raw, lean and fat, weighed		
without bone	92	0
loin, grilled, lean and fat, weighed		
without bone	93	0
loin, grilled, lean and fat, weighed		
with bone	72	0
loin, grilled, lean only	63	0
loin, grilled, lean only, weighed with		
fat and bone	37	0
leg		
raw, lean and fat	75	0
roast, lean and fat	80	0
roast, lean only	52	0
Pork sausages		
raw	103	0·1
fried	89	0·1
grilled	89	0·1
Porridge (oatmeal made up with water)	12	0·2
Porridge oats	113	2·0
Potatoes		
old		
raw, peeled	24	0·6
boiled	22	0·3
mashed	33	0·3
baked, weighed with skin	24	0·7
baked, flesh only	29	0·7
roast	44	0·6

Food	Calories per oz (28g)	Fibre g per oz (28g)
Potatoes, *cont.*		
chip, medium-thick cut	71	0·6
new		
boiled	21	0·6
canned, drained	15	0·7
instant powder		
dry	89	4·6
made up	20	1·0
crisps	149	3·2
Prawns, boiled, shelled	30	0
Prunes		
dried		
raw, with stones	38	3·8
no-need-to-soak (e.g. Whitworths),		
raw	33	3·4
stewed without sugar	21	2·1
Puffed wheat	91	4·3
Pumpkins, raw	4	0·1
Quinces, raw, flesh only	7	1·8
Rabbit		
raw, meat only	35	0
stewed		
meat only	50	0
weighed on the bone	25	0
Radishes, raw	4	0·3
Raisins, dried	69	1·9
Raspberries		
raw	7	2·1

Food	Calories per oz (28g)	Fibre g per oz (28g)
stewed without sugar	7	2·2
canned in syrup	24	1·4
Ready Brek	109	2·1
Redcurrants		
raw	6	2·3
stewed without sugar	5	2·0
Rhubarb		
raw	2	0·7
stewed without sugar	2	0·7
stewed with sugar	13	0·6
Ribena, undiluted	64	0
Rice Krispies	104	1·3
Rice		
brown		
raw	100	1·2
boiled	36	0·4
white		
raw	103	0·7
boiled	34	0·2
Rice pudding		
home-made	37	0·1
canned	25	0·1
Rock salmon, fried in batter	74	0·1
Roe		
cod, hard		
raw	32	0
fried	57	0
herring, soft		
raw	22	0
fried	68	0

Food	Calories per oz (28g)	Fibre g per oz (28g)
Rosehip syrup, undiluted	65	0
Rye crispbread	90	3·3
Rye flour	94	3·3
Safflower seed oil	252	0
Sago, raw	99	0·8
Saithe (coley) raw	20	0
steamed, no bones	28	0
Salad cream	90	0
Salami	137	0
Salmon fresh, raw	51	0
steamed, flesh only	55	0
canned	43	0
smoked	40	0
Salsify, boiled	5	0·3
Sardines canned in oil		
fish only	61	0
fish plus oil	94	0
canned in tomato sauce	50	0
Sausages, see **Beef sausages, Pork sausages**		
Saveloy	73	0·1
Scallops, steamed, no shells	29	0
Scampi, in breadcrumbs, fried	88	0·3

Food	Calories per oz (28g)	Fibre g per oz (28g)
Scones, made from white flour	104	0·6
Scotch pancakes (drop scones)	79	0·4
Sea-kale, boiled	2	0·3
Semolina, raw	98	0·8
Semolina pudding	37	0·1
Shortbread, made from white flour	141	0·6
Shortcrust pastry made from white flour		
raw	127	0·6
cooked	148	0·7
made from wholemeal flour		
raw	119	1·6
cooked	140	1·9
Shredded wheat	91	3·4
Shrimps boiled, shelled	33	0
canned	26	0
Skate, fried in batter	56	0·1
Skimmed milk, cow's fresh	9	0
dried	99	0
Soda bread, *see under* **Bread**		
Sole, lemon, *see* **Lemon sole**		
Soya bean curd	21	0·3
Soya bean oil	252	0
Soya beans, yellow, dried	112	1·2

Food	Calories per oz (28g)	Fibre g per oz (28g)
Soya flour		
full fat	125	3·3
low fat	99	4·0
Spaghetti		
white		
raw	106	0·8
boiled	33	0·2
brown wholewheat		
raw	97	2·8
boiled	32	0·9
canned in tomato sauce	17	0·3
Special K	109	0·5
Spinach, boiled	8	1·8
Sprats, fried, whole fish	109	0
Spring greens, boiled	3	1·1
Sprouts, brussels, *see* **Brussels sprouts**		
Strawberries		
raw	7	0·6
canned in syrup	23	0·3
Suet		
block	251	0
shredded	231	0
Suet pudding, sweet, steamed	93	0·3
Sugar		
demerara	110	0
white (caster, granulated, icing)	110	0
soft brown	110	0
Sugar puffs	97	1·7

Food	Calories per oz (28g)	Fibre g per oz (28g)
Sultanas, dried	70	2·0
Sunflower seed oil	252	0
Sunflower seeds	137	1·0
Swedes		
raw	6	0·8
boiled	5	0·8
Sweetbread, lamb		
raw	37	0
fried, coated in egg and breadcrumbs	64	0·1
Sweetcorn		
raw, kernels only	36	1·0
boiled, kernels only	34	1·3
canned	21	1·6
Sweet potatoes		
raw, flesh only	25	0·7
boiled, flesh only	24	0·6
Syrup, golden	83	0
Tangerines		
flesh only, no peel or pips	10	0·5
weighed with peel and pips	6	0·4
Tapioca, raw	100	0·8
Toffees, mixed	120	0
Tomato chutney	43	0·5
Tomato juice, canned	4	0
Tomatoes		
raw	4	0·4
canned	3	0·3

Food	Calories per oz (28g)	Fibre g per oz (28g)
Tongue		
canned	60	0
lamb, raw	54	0
sheep, stewed	81	0
ox		
pickled, raw	61	0
pickled, boiled	82	0
Treacle, black	72	0
Tripe		
dressed	17	0
stewed	28	0
Trout, brown, steamed, weighed with bones	25	0
Tuna		
canned in brine	33	0
canned in oil	81	0
Turnip tops, boiled	3	1·1
Turnips		
raw, flesh only	6	0·8
boiled, flesh only	4	0·6
Turkey		
raw		
meat only	30	0
meat and skin	40	0
roast		
meat only	39	0
meat and skin	48	0
light meat	37	0
dark meat	41	0
UHT milk, *see under* **Milk**		

Food	Calories per oz (28g)	Fibre g per oz (28g)
Veal		
cutlet, coated in egg and breadcrumbs, fried	60	0
fillet		
raw	31	0
roast	64	0
jellied, canned	35	0
Vegetable oils	252	0
Venison, roast, meat only	55	0
Vinegar	1	0
Walnuts, shelled	147	1·5
Watercress	4	0·9
Weetabix	95	3·6
Wheatgerm	100	0·6
Wheatgerm oil	252	0
Whelks, boiled, no shells	25	0
White pudding	126	1·0
White sauce		
savoury	42	0·1
sweet	48	0·1
Whitebait, whole fish, fried	147	0
Whitecurrants		
raw	7	1·9
stewed without sugar	6	1·6
Whiting		
fried, coated in crumbs, weighed with bones	48	0·1
steamed, weighed with bones	18	0

Food	Calories per oz (28g)	Fibre g per oz (28g)
Wholemeal bread, *see under* **Bread**		
Wholemeal flour, *see under* **Flour**		
Winkles, boiled, no shells	21	0
Yam		
raw, flesh only	37	1·1
boiled, flesh only	33	1·1
Yeast		
bakers', compressed	15	1·9
dried	47	6·1
Yogurt, low fat		
natural	15	0
flavoured	23	0
fruit	27	0
hazelnut	30	0·5
Yorkshire pudding	60	0·3

F-Plus

SIMPLY F-PLAN

The menus in this section provide the types of meals which have proved most popular with F-Plan dieters: plenty of nice ideas but never too much fuss or effort in shopping or cooking. The menus all follow the basic F-Plan rules (see Chapter 19) and are divided into three meals a day, plus a snack. All the means are quick and simple to prepare and the foods are readily available.

The section is divided up into two parts; 1,000 calories and 1,250 calories daily, all providing 35–50g fibre. They are designed for a fast weight loss with the minimum of fuss.

SPECIAL DIET NOTES

1. Begin by deciding which daily calorie total will give you a satisfactory weight loss. You will find guidance in Chapter 9.

2. Select the menus from those of your chosen daily calorie total for one week at a time so that you can plan the shopping and always have the right foods available.

3. Vary the menus chosen to ensure that you eat a wide variety of foods.

4. Do *not* swap individual meals from one menu to another since all the menus have been carefully calorie and fibre calculated for a full day.

5. Make up the Fibre-Filler for your daily allowance either daily or for several days in one batch following the recipe on p. 65.

6. Allow yourself as much tea and coffee *without sugar* (sweeteners can be used) as you wish throughout the day *as long as* you use only the skimmed milk which remains from your daily allowance after you have had your Fibre-Filler. In addition you can drink as much water and drinks labelled 'low-calorie' as you wish. Alcoholic

drinks are not included in these menus; however, should you feel the need for an occasional alcoholic drink see the advice on alcoholic drinks on p. 63.

1,000 CALORIE MENU   1

	Calories	Fibre (g)
Daily allowance: Fibre-Filler (p. 65), ½ pint (285ml) skimmed milk, an orange and an apple or pear	400	20
Breakfast Half portion of Fibre-Filler with milk from allowance		
Lunch * Pizza Toasts		
An orange from allowance	325	8·5
Evening meal 1 packet frozen cod in butter or cheese sauce, cooked 4oz (115g) fresh or frozen peas, boiled 4oz (115g) carrots, boiled		
An apple or pear from allowance	275	12·5
Snack Remaining portion Fibre-Filler with milk from allowance		
TOTAL	1,000	41

* Pizza Toasts

Serves 1

2 large thin slices (1½oz, 32g each) Hi-Bran bread
2 small tomatoes, sliced
salt and freshly ground pepper
¼ teaspoon dried thyme or mixed herbs
2oz (55g) Edam cheese, grated
2 stuffed olives, sliced

Toast the two slices of bread on both sides. Cover both slices of toast with the sliced tomatoes. Season well and sprinkle over the herbs. Top with the grated cheese and garnish with the slices of olive. Grill until the cheese is melted. Serve hot.

1,000 CALORIE MENU   2

	Calories	Fibre (g)
Daily allowance: Fibre-Filler (p. 65), ½ pint (285ml) skimmed milk, an orange and an apple or pear	400	20

Breakfast
Half portion of Fibre-Filler with milk from allowance

Lunch
4oz (115g) cottage cheese (natural or with chives or with onion and peppers or with pineapple) served with 3oz (85g) cooked beetroot, diced, mixed with 2oz (55g) mushrooms, sliced, 1 large stick celery, finely chopped, and 2 tablespoons oil-free French dressing
a few sprigs of watercress

	Calories	Fibre (g)
An apple or pear from allowance	175	4·5

	Calories	Fibre (g)

Evening meal
* Baked Jacket Potato with Kidneys
2oz (55g) firm white cabbage, shredded
and tossed with 2 teaspoons oil-free
French dressing   425   10·5

Snack
Remaining portion of Fibre-Filler with
milk from allowance

TOTAL	1,000	35

* Baked Jacket Potato with Kidneys

Serves 1

7oz (200g) potato
2 lamb's kidneys, skinned, core removed and chopped
1 small onion, chopped
4oz (115g) canned tomatoes, drained and chopped
4 tablespoons juice from canned tomatoes
dash of Worcestershire sauce
salt and pepper
1oz (30g, 1 rounded tablespoon) frozen peas

Scrub the potato well, then bake by one of the following methods:
   1. Place the potato in the centre of a moderately hot oven (200°C,
400°F, gas 6) for 45 minutes or until soft when pinched.
   2. Place the potato in a pan of water, bring to the boil, then
simmer gently for 20 minutes. Drain. Place the potato in a moderately hot oven (190°C, 375°F, gas 5) for 10–15 minutes to crisp
the skin.
   3. Prick well all over and cook in a microwave oven on full
power for 4 minutes, turning after 2 minutes.

Meanwhile place the lamb's kidneys, onion, canned tomatoes and
juice in a small pan. Add the Worcestershire sauce and salt and

pepper. Heat to boiling point, cover and simmer gently for 15 minutes. Stir in the peas and heat through. Cut the baked potato in half lengthwise and scoop out some of the flesh. Mix it with the hot kidney mixture and pile back into the potato jacket. Serve with shredded white cabbage.

1,000 CALORIE MENU   3

	Calories	Fibre (g)
Daily allowance: Fibre-Filler (p.65), ½ pint (285ml) skimmed milk, an orange and an apple or pear	400	20
Breakfast Half portion Fibre-Filler with milk from allowance		
Lunch * Kidney Bean Soup 1 large thin slice (1⅛oz. 32g) Hi-Bran bread		
An apple or pear from allowance	190	14
Evening meal * Cheese and Sweetcorn Omelet 1 average-sized tomato, fresh or grilled without fat		
150g carton low-fat natural yogurt with orange from allowance and artificial sweetener, if necessary	410	4
Snack Remaining portion Fibre-Filler with milk from allowance		
TOTAL	1,000	38

* Kidney Bean Soup

Serves 1

4oz (115g) canned red kidney beans, drained
1oz (30g) chopped onion
1 large stick celery, chopped
7½fl oz (215ml) beef stock made from ½ beef stock cube
1 bay leaf
salt and pepper
¼ teaspoon chilli powder

Put all the ingredients in a saucepan. Bring to the boil, cover and
simmer for 30 minutes. Remove the bay leaf and serve the soup as
it is, or purée in a blender if preferred.

* Cheese and Sweetcorn Omelet

Serves 1

2 eggs (size 3)
salt and pepper
a dash of Worcestershire sauce
½oz (7g) low-fat spread
2oz (55g) canned sweetcorn, drained
1oz (30g) green pepper, finely chopped
1oz (30g) Edam cheese, grated

Beat the eggs, 2 tablespoons water, seasoning and Worcestershire
sauce together. Grease a non-stick omelet pan with the low-fat
spread and heat. Pour in the eggs and cook gently until almost set.
Sprinkle over the sweetcorn, green pepper and grated cheese. Heat
under the grill until the cheese begins to melt. Fold the omelet and
serve.

1,000 CALORIE MENU 4

	Calories	Fibre (g)
Daily allowance: Fibre-Filler (p. 65), ½ pint (285ml) skimmed milk, an orange and an apple or pear	400	20

	Calories	Fibre (g)

Breakfast
Half portion of Fibre-Filler with milk from
allowance

Lunch
8oz (225g) canned baked beans in tomato
sauce, heated and served on 1 large thin
slice (1½oz, 32g) Hi-Bran bread, toasted and
garnished with 1 average-sized tomato, cut
into wedges

An orange from allowance   235   20·5

Evening meal
1 bacon steak (3½oz, 100g raw weight),
grilled
3½oz (100g) canned pease pudding
4oz (115g) Brussels sprouts, boiled

2oz (55g) vanilla ice-cream   365   8·5

Snack
Remaining portion Fibre-Filler with milk
from allowance

An apple or pear from allowance

TOTAL	1,000	49

1,000 CALORIE MENU   5

	Calories	Fibre (g)

Daily allowance: Fibre-Filler (p. 65), ½ pint
(285ml) skimmed milk, an orange and an
apple or pear   400   20

	Calories	Fibre (g)

Breakfast
Half portion of Fibre-Filler with milk from allowance

An orange from allowance

Lunch
* Tuna Salad Sandwich

An apple or pear from allowance	250	7

Evening meal
8oz (225g) (raw weight) chicken leg joint, grilled and skin removed
6oz (170g) potato, baked in its jacket (p. 31) with 1 tablespoon oil-free French dressing

2 oz (55g) fresh or frozen peas, boiled	350	9

Snack
Remaining portion Fibre-Filler with milk from allowance

TOTAL	**1,000**	**36**

* Tuna Salad Sandwich

Serves 1

2 large thin slices (1¼oz, 35g each) wholemeal bread
1 tablespoon low-calorie salad dressing
2oz (55g) tuna, canned in brine, flaked
1 lettuce leaf
1 tomato, sliced
a few slices of cucumber

Spread both slices of bread with the salad dressing and fill with the remaining ingredients.

1,000 CALORIE MENU   6

	Calories	Fibre (g)
Daily allowance: Fibre-Filler (p. 65), ½ pint (285ml) skimmed milk, an orange and an apple or pear	400	20

Breakfast
Half portion Fibre-Filler with milk from allowance

An orange from allowance

Lunch
2 Energen F-Plan Diet Brancrisps, topped with 2oz (55g) cottage cheese, natural, mixed with ½oz (15g) stoned dates, chopped, and ½oz (15g) shelled walnuts, chopped

1 large stick celery, cut into pieces

| An apple or pear from allowance | 210 | 5·5 |

Evening meal
* Egg Florentine

| * Poached Citrus Plums | 390 | 12 |

Snack
Remaining portion of Fibre-Filler with milk from allowance

| TOTAL | 1,000 | 37·5 |

* Egg Florentine

Serves 1

5oz (140g) frozen cut-leaf spinach, thawed
1 egg (size 3)

2½oz (70g) natural low-fat yogurt
¼ teaspoon prepared mustard
salt and pepper
½oz (15g) Cheddar cheese, grated
½oz (15g) wholemeal breadcrumbs

Heat the thawed spinach gently (without adding butter) in a small pan or in a microwave oven, then spoon into the bottom of a small fireproof dish. Poach the egg and place on top of the spinach. Blend the yogurt with the made mustard and seasoning to taste, and spoon over the egg. Mix the grated cheese and breadcrumbs and sprinkle over the top. Heat under a grill until the topping is crisp and brown.

* Poached Citrus Plums

Serves 1

4oz (115g) sweet plums
4 tablespoons fresh orange juice
1 level teaspoon sugar (optional)
1 level dessertspoon flaked almonds

Wash the plums and place in a pan with the orange juice. Cover with a tight-fitting lid and heat gently for 5 minutes. Add the sugar, if liked. Serve hot or cold sprinkled with the flaked almonds.

1,000 CALORIES MENU   7

	Calories	Fibre (g)
Daily allowance: Fibre-Filler (p. 65), ½ pint (285ml) skimmed milk, an orange and an apple or pear	400	20

Breakfast
Half portion Fibre-Filler with milk from allowance

An orange from allowance

	Calories	Fibre (g)

Lunch
* Lentil and Vegetable Soup
2 Energen F-Plan Diet Brancrisps

An apple or pear from allowance	220	10·5

Evening meal
3oz (85g) sliced lean boiled ham served with
* Coleslaw and 2 average-sized tomatoes,
sliced
A bunch of watercress
A few cucumber slices
A few lettuce leaves
1 large thin slice (1¼oz, 35g) wholemeal
bread spread with ¼oz (7g) low-fat spread

4oz (115g) green grapes	380	10·5

Snack
Remaining portion Fibre-Filler with milk
from allowance

TOTAL	1,000	41

* Lentil and Vegetable Soup

Serves 1 (several portions can be made at one time and frozen until required)

1½oz (45g) red lentils
1oz (30g) onion, chopped
2oz (55g) carrot, sliced
1 large stick celery, chopped
1 chicken or ham stock cube. dissolved in ¾ pint (425ml) boiling
　　water
salt and pepper

Put all the ingredients in a pan. Bring to the boil, cover and simmer gently for 1 hour.

* Coleslaw

Serves 1

3oz (85g) firm white cabbage, shredded
1 level tablespoon finely chopped onion
2oz (55g) carrot, grated
2 tablespoons oil-free French dressing

Mix the cabbage, onion and carrot together. Add the dressing and toss well.

1,000 CALORIE MENU   8

	Calories	Fibre (g)
Daily allowance: Fibre-Filler (p. 65), $\frac{1}{2}$ pint (285ml) skimmed milk, an orange and an apple or pear	400	20
Breakfast Half portion of Fibre-Filler with milk from allowance		
Lunch * Crunchy Sardine Sandwich An apple or pear from allowance	235	6·5
Evening meal * Baked Jacket Potato with Chicken Liver Filling 2oz (55g) runner beans, boiled An orange from allowance	365	9
Snack Remaining portion Fibre-Filler with milk from allowance		
TOTAL	1,000	35·5

* Crunchy Sardine Sandwich

Serves 1
2 large thin slices (1½oz, 35g each) wholemeal bread
1 tablespoon low-calorie salad dressing
1 sardine in tomato sauce
1oz (30g) raw bean sprouts
1 tablespoon chopped green pepper

Spread the bread with the salad dressing. Mash the sardine and spread on one slice of bread. Top with bean sprouts and green pepper and the second slice of bread. Cut into four sandwiches.

* Baked Jacket Potato with Chicken Liver Filling

Serves 1

7oz (200g) potato
4oz (115g) chicken livers, chopped
1oz (30g) finely chopped onion
1oz (30g) canned sweetcorn
salt and pepper
1 level teaspoon tomato purée

Bake the potato following one of the methods on p. 31. Place the chicken livers, onion, sweetcorn and 4 tablespoons water in a small pan. Add the salt, pepper and tomato purée. Heat to simmering point, cover and simmer gently for 5 minutes. Cut the potato in half lengthwise and scoop out some of the flesh. Mix with the chicken liver mixture and pile back into the potato jacket. Serve at once.

1,000 CALORIE MENU   9

	Calories	Fibre (g)
Daily allowance: Fibre-Filler (p. 65), ½ pint (285ml) skimmed milk, an orange and an apple or pear	400	20

	Calories	Fibre (g)

Breakfast
Half portion Fibre-Filler with milk from
allowance

Lunch
* Mushroom and Tomato Scramble on Toast

An orange from allowance   325   9

Evening meal
6oz (170g) cod or haddock fillets, brushed
with ¼oz (7g) low-fat spread and grilled
4oz (115g) peas, boiled
2oz (55g) raw bean sprouts, blanched
4oz (115g) canned tomatoes, heated

5½oz (155g) banana   275   13·5

Snack
Remaining portion Fibre-Filler with milk
from allowance

TOTAL	1,000	42·5

* Mushroom and Tomato Scramble on Toast

Serves 1

2 large thin slices (1⅛oz, 32g each) Hi-Bran bread
2fl oz (55ml) skimmed milk, additional to allowance
2oz (55g) mushrooms, sliced
2 eggs (size 3)
salt and pepper
1 average-sized tomato, chopped
1 tablespoon chopped parsley (optional)

Toast both sides of bread. Put the milk and mushrooms in a pan. Heat gently for 3 minutes. Beat the eggs with the seasoning and stir into the mushrooms. Cook, stirring continuously until the eggs are creamy. Stir in the chopped tomato. Top the two slices of toast with the mushroom and tomato scramble. Sprinkle with chopped parsley, if liked.

1,000 CALORIE MENU   10

	Calories	Fibre (g)
Daily allowance: Fibre-Filler (p. 65), ½ pint (285ml) skimmed milk, an orange and an apple or pear	:00	20
Breakfast Half portion of Fibre-Filler with milk from allowance		
An orange from allowance		
Lunch * Creamy Spinach Soup 2 Energen F-Plan Diet Brancrisps		
An apple or pear from allowance	175	11·5
Evening meal * Savoury Mince Half a medium packet Smash Potato Pieces made up with boiling water, no butter 4 oz (115g) Brussels sprouts, boiled		
2oz (55g) blackberries stewed with 4oz (115g) cooking apple, peeled, cored and sliced, 2 tablespoons water and 1½ teaspoons sugar	425	18

Calories   Fibre (g)

Snack
Remaining portion Fibre-Filler with milk
from allowance

TOTAL	1,000	49·5

* Creamy Spinach Soup

Serves 1 (several portions can be made up at one time and frozen until required)

5oz (140g) frozen cut-leaf spinach, thawed
7½fl oz (215ml) skimmed milk (additional to allowance)
3 level teaspoons Mornflake Oatbran and Oatgerm *or* fine oatmeal
salt and pepper
grated nutmeg

Put the spinach, milk and Oatbran and Oatgerm or fine oatmeal in a pan. Bring to the boil and simmer for 3 minutes. Purée in a blender and season to taste with salt, pepper and grated nutmeg.

* Savoury Mince

Serves 1

4oz (115g) lean minced beef
1 small onion, peeled and finely chopped
1 stick celery, finely chopped
¼ beef stock cube, dissolved in 2½ oz (70ml) boiling water
salt and pepper
pinch of mixed herbs
1 level teaspoon tomato purée
1oz (30g) frozen peas

Fry the minced beef in a non-stick saucepan until well browned. Drain off all the fat which runs out of the meat. Add the onion, celery and stock to the meat in the pan and bring to the boil, stirring. Reduce the heat, season to taste with salt and pepper and add the herbs and tomato purée and stir. Cover and simmer for 30 minutes, stirring occasionally and adding more water if it begins to boil dry. Stir in the peas and heat through for 5 minutes.

1,250 CALORIE MENU   1

	Calories	Fibre (g)
Daily allowance: Fibre-Filler (p. 65), $\frac{1}{2}$ pint (285ml) skimmed milk, an orange and an apple or pear	400	20
Breakfast Half portion Fibre-Filler with milk from allowance		
1 large thin slice (1$\frac{1}{8}$oz, 32g) Hi-Bran bread, spread with $\frac{1}{4}$oz (7g) low-fat spread and 1 level teaspoon honey or marmalade	105	3·5
Lunch * Corned Beef and Baked Bean Sandwich		
2oz (55g) raw carrot sticks		
An apple or pear from allowance	235	10·5
Evening meal * Ham and Pepper Omelet 4oz (115g) frozen mixed vegetables, boiled		
8oz (225g) can Koo Peach Slices in Apple Juice 1$\frac{1}{2}$oz (45g) vanilla ice-cream	510	8·5

Calories   Fibre (g)

Snack
Remaining portion Fibre-Filler with milk
from allowance

An orange from allowance

TOTAL   1,250   42·5

* Corned Beef and Baked Bean Sandwich

Serves 1

2 large thin slices (1¼oz, 32g each) Hi-Bran bread
1 tablespoon tomato sauce
1oz (30g) corned beef
1oz (30g) canned baked beans in tomato sauce
pepper
a few slices of cucumber

Spread the slices of bread with the tomato sauce. Mash the corned
beef with the baked beans and pepper to taste. Spread over one
slice of the bread. Top with cucumber slices and cover with the
second slice of bread. Cut into four sandwiches.

* Ham and Pepper Omelet

Serves 1

2 eggs (size 3)
salt and pepper
¼oz (7g) low-fat spread
2oz (55g) boiled lean ham, chopped
1½oz (45g) chopped green pepper

Beat the eggs with 2 tablespoons water and salt and pepper to
taste. Grease a non-stick omelet pan with the low-fat spread and
heat. Pour in the egg mixture and cook gently until almost set.

Sprinkle over the chopped ham and green pepper and heat under the grill for 1 minute. Fold the omelet and serve.

1,250 CALORIE MENU 2

	Calories	Fibre (g)
Daily allowance: Fibre-Filler (p. 65), ½ pint (285ml) skimmed milk, an orange and an apple or pear	400	20

Breakfast
Half portion Fibre-Filler with milk from allowance

1 large thin slice (1½oz, 35g) wholemeal bread, toasted and spread with ¼oz (7g) low-fat spread	100	3

Lunch
2 Energen F-Plan Diet Brancrisps, spread with 1oz (30g) peanut butter and topped with 1 tomato, sliced, a few slices cucumber and ½ carton of mustard and cress

An average-sized banana (6oz, 170g)	315	9

Evening meal
* Frankfurter Salad

150g carton low-fat fruit-flavoured yogurt

An apple or pear from allowance	435	9

Snack
Remaining portion Fibre-Filler with milk from allowance

TOTAL	1,250	41

* **Frankfurter Salad**

Serves 1

7½oz (215g) can butter beans, drained
2oz (55g) frankfurter, sliced
1 small green pepper, seeds removed and chopped
1oz (30g) radishes, sliced
2–3 spring onions, chopped
3 tablespoons oil-free French dressing
a few lettuce leaves

Put the butter beans, frankfurter, green pepper, radishes and spring onions into a bowl. Add the French dressing and toss well. Serve on a bed of lettuce leaves.

1,250 CALORIE MENU   3

	Calories	Fibre (g)
Daily allowance: Fibre-Filler (p. 65), ½ pint (285ml) skimmed milk, an orange and an apple or pear	400	20
Breakfast Half portion of Fibre-Filler with milk from allowance		
Lunch * Bean and Ham Toppers An orange from allowance	330	21
Evening meal * Macaroni Cheese 5oz (140g) green grapes	520	9
Snack Remaining portion Fibre-Filler with milk from allowance		

	Calories	Fibre (g)
An apple or pear from allowance		
TOTAL	1,250	50

* Bean and Ham Toppers

Serves 1

1 wholemeal round bread roll (2oz, 55g)
½ teaspoon made mustard
8oz (225g) canned baked beans in tomato sauce
1oz (30g) boiled lean ham, chopped

Split the bread roll and spread both cut surfaces with the mustard. Heat the baked beans and pile on top of the two halves of the bread roll. Sprinkle the chopped ham over the beans and serve.

* Macaroni Cheese

Serves 1

2oz (55g) wholewheat macaroni
½oz (15g) wholemeal flour
¼ pint (140ml) skimmed milk (additional to allowance)
¼oz (7g) low-fat spread
salt and pepper
¼ teaspoon made mustard
1oz (30g) Cheddar cheese, grated
1 average-sized tomato, sliced

Boil the macaroni in salted water for 12 minutes or until tender; drain. Put the flour, milk and low-fat spread into a saucepan and heat, whisking continuously until it boils and thickens. Season to taste with salt and pepper. Add the mustard and half the cheese. Stir the macaroni into the sauce. Pour into an ovenproof dish. Top with the tomato slices and the remaining grated cheese.

Heat under the grill until the cheese is melted and beginning to brown.

1,250 CALORIE MENU   4

	Calories	Fibre (g)
Daily allowance: Fibre-Filler (p. 65), ½ pint (285ml) skimmed milk, an orange and an apple or pear	400	20

Breakfast
Half portion of Fibre-Filler with milk from allowance

Lunch
* Mushrooms and Sweetcorn on Toast

1 Jordans Original Crunchy Bar, Honey & Coconut

An apple or pear from allowance	345	8·5

Evening meal
* Sardine Salad
8oz (225g) potato, baked in its jacket (see p. 328 for baking instructions) topped with 2 tablespoons low-fat natural yogurt mixed with 1 teaspoon tomato purée and salt and pepper to taste

An orange from allowance	505	12

Snack
Remaining portion Fibre-Filler with milk from allowance

TOTAL	1,250	40·5

* Mushrooms and Sweetcorn on Toast

Serves 1

1 large thin slice (1½oz, 35g) wholemeal bread
2oz (55g) button mushrooms
4fl oz (115ml) skimmed milk (additional to allowance)
2 teaspoons cornflour
1 tablespoon low-fat natural yogurt
2oz (55g) canned sweetcorn
salt and pepper
a dash of Worcestershire sauce

Toast the bread on both sides. Poach the mushrooms in 3fl oz (85ml) of the milk for 5 minutes. Blend the cornflour with the remaining milk and stir into the mushrooms. Bring to the boil, stirring, and cook for 2 minutes until thickened. Add the yogurt and sweetcorn. Season to taste with salt and pepper and stir in the Worcestershire sauce. Heat gently for 2 minutes. Serve the mushrooms and sweetcorn mixture on the toast.

* Sardine Salad

Serves 1

4½oz (130g) canned sardines in tomato sauce
a few lettuce leaves
2 large sticks celery, chopped
2oz (55g) carrot, grated
2oz (55g) fresh garden peas or thawed frozen peas
1 tablespoon oil-free French dressing

Arrange the sardines on the lettuce leaves. Mix the celery, carrot and peas with the French dressing and serve with the sardines.

1,250 CALORIE MENU   5

	Calories	Fibre (g)
Daily allowance: Fibre-Filler (p. 65), ½ pint (285ml) skimmed milk, an orange and an apple or pear	400	20

	Calories	Fibre (g)
Breakfast		
Half portion of Fibre-Filler with milk from allowance		
1 large thin slice (1½oz, 35g) wholemeal bread, toasted and spread with ¼oz (7g) low-fat spread and 2 level teaspoons honey or marmalade	130	3
Lunch		
1 egg (size 3), hard-boiled, served with a few lettuce leaves, a small bunch of watercress, 2oz (55g) grated carrot mixed with ½oz (15g) raisins, a few radishes and spring onions and 1 tablespoon low-calorie salad dressing		
150g carton low-fat fruit-flavoured yogurt	285	4·5
Evening meal		
* Grilled Lamb Chop with Savoury Topping 4oz (115g) fresh or frozen peas, boiled 3oz (85g) carrots, boiled		
An orange from allowance	435	14·5
Snack		
Remaining portion Fibre-Filler with milk from allowance		
An apple or pear from allowance		
TOTAL	1,250	42

* **Grilled Lamb Chop with Savoury Topping**

Serves 1

1 lamb loin chop (5oz, 140g raw weight)

1 small onion, sliced
4oz (115g) canned tomatoes, chopped
salt and pepper
a dash of Worcestershire sauce
½oz (15g) wholemeal breadcrumbs
a generous pinch of dried mixed herbs

Grill the lamb chop until cooked through. Meanwhile heat the
sliced onion, canned tomatoes, salt and pepper together in a pan
for 5 minutes, or until the onion is softened. Put half the onion and
tomato mixture in a small heatproof dish. Put the grilled lamb
chop on top and spoon over the remaining onion and tomato
mixture. Mix the breadcrumbs with the mixed herbs and sprinkle
evenly over the top of the chop. Heat under the grill until the
breadcrumbs are crisp and browned.

1,250 CALORIE MENU   6

	Calories	Fibre (g)
Daily allowance: Fibre-Filler (p. 65), ½ pint (285 ml) skimmed milk, an orange and an apple or pear	400	20

Breakfast
Half portion Fibre-Filler with milk from
allowance

1 Ryvita crispbread, brown or original, spread with 1 level teaspoon honey or marmalade (no butter)	40	1

Lunch
* Crunchy Salad with Ham
2 Ryvita crispbreads, brown or original,
spread with ¼oz (7g) low-fat spread

An orange from allowance	260	10

	Calories	Fibre (g)
Evening meal		
2 pork sausages (2oz, 55g each), grilled		
1 average-sized tomato, halved, grilled		
without fat		
8oz (225g) canned baked beans in tomato		
sauce, 5oz (140g) boiled potatoes, mashed,		
using skimmed milk from allowance and no		
butter *or* half medium packet Smash Potato		
Pieces, made up without butter	550	19

Snack
Remaining portion Fibre-Filler with milk
from allowance
An apple or pear from allowance

	Calories	Fibre (g)
TOTAL	1,250	50

* Crunchy Salad with Ham

Serves 1

4oz (115g) red cabbage, shredded
1 carrot, grated
1 leek (green part removed), thinly sliced
1 tablespoon oil-free French dressing
1 tablespoon low-calorie salad dressing
2oz (55g) boiled lean ham, sliced

Mix the red cabbage, carrot and leek together. Add the French dressing and salad dressing and toss well until thoroughly blended. Serve with the slices of ham.

1,250 CALORIE MENU   7

	Calories	Fibre (g)
Daily allowance: Fibre-Filler (p. 65),		
½ pint (285ml) skimmed milk, an orange		
and an apple or pear	400	20

	Calories	Fibre (g)

Breakfast
Half portion Fibre-Filler with milk from
allowance

1 egg (size 3), poached and served on
1 large thin slice (1¼oz, 35g) wholemeal
bread, toasted ... 155 ... 3

Lunch
* Cauliflower Soup
2 Energen F-Plan Diet Brancrisps, spread
with ¼oz (7g) low-fat spread

1 apple or pear from allowance ... 155 ... 6·5

Evening meal
2 bacon steaks (3½oz, 100g each), grilled
without added fat, served with 2 pineapple
rings, canned in natural juice, grilled
3oz (85g) canned sweetcorn
4oz (115g) runner beans, boiled
2 Energen F-Plan Diet Brancrisps, spread
with ¼oz (7g) low-fat spread and served
with 1oz (30g) Edam cheese and 1 large
stick celery ... 540 ... 12·5

Snack
Remaining portion Fibre-Filler with milk
from allowance

TOTAL	1,250	42

* Cauliflower Soup

Serves 1

6oz (170g) cauliflower, broken into florets

1oz (30g) onion, chopped
½ chicken stock cube
1 level tablespoon dried skimmed milk powder
salt and pepper
2 level teaspoons grated Parmesan cheese

Put the cauliflower and onion into a small saucepan. Dissolve the
stock cube in ½ pint (285ml) boiling water and add to the pan.
Cook until the vegetables are tender, about 15–20 minutes. Sieve
or purée the soup in a blender. Return to the pan. Beat in the dried
skimmed milk and season to taste with salt and pepper. Reheat
gently. Serve topped with the Parmesan cheese.

1,250 CALORIE MENU   8

This menu is suitable for vegetarians

	Calories	Fibre (g)
Daily allowance: Fibre-Filler (p. 24), ½ pint (285ml) skimmed milk, an orange and an apple or pear	400	20
Breakfast Half portion of Fibre-Filler with milk from allowance		
1 egg (size 3), boiled and served with 1 Ryvita crispbread, brown or original, spread with ¼oz (7g) low-fat spread	130	1
Lunch 2oz (55g) flat round wholemeal roll (bap), split and filled with 1oz (30g) peanut butter, 2oz (55g) grated carrot and 1 lettuce leaf		
An orange from allowance	305	8·5

	Calories	Fibre (g)
Evening meal		
* Ratatouille au Gratin		
4oz (115g) fresh or frozen raspberries or strawberries		
1oz (30g) vanilla ice-cream	415	19·5/
		13·5
Snack		
Half portion Fibre-Filler with milk from allowance		

TOTAL	1,250	49/43

* Ratatouille au Gratin

Serves 1

1 small aubergine (6oz, 170g)
salt and pepper
1 medium onion (3oz, 85g), peeled and sliced
1 courgette (5oz, 140g), sliced
2 average-sized tomatoes, sliced
½ teaspoon dried mixed herbs
2oz (55g) Edam cheese, grated
1 large thin slice (1¼oz, 35g) wholemeal bread

Slice the aubergine into ¼ inch (6mm) slices. Sprinkle the cut surfaces with salt, then leave to stand for 30 minutes to draw out the juices. Rinse the aubergine, drain and dry. Put aubergine slices, onion, courgette, tomatoes and mixed herbs in an ovenproof dish. Season to taste with salt and pepper. Sprinkle the grated cheese on top of the vegetables. Bake at 180°C (350°F, gas 4) for 30 minutes, until the vegetables are tender. Serve with the bread to mop up the juices.

1,250 CALORIE MENU   9

This menu is suitable for vegetarians

	Calories	Fibre (g)
Daily allowance: Fibre-Filler (p. 24), ½ pint (285ml) skimmed milk, an orange and an apple or pear	400	20

Breakfast
Half portion Fibre-Filler with milk from allowance

An average-sized banana (6oz, 170g)	80	3·5

Lunch
* Cheese and Apple Sandwich

150g carton low-fat fruit-flavoured yogurt	365	7

Evening meal
* Layered Bean Casserole

An orange from allowance	325	19·5

Snack
Remaining portion Fibre-Filler with milk from allowance

A cup of chocolate, made up from 1 rounded teaspoon drinking chocolate and 6fl oz (170ml) skimmed milk, additional to allowance	80	0

TOTAL	1,250	50

* Cheese and Apple Sandwich

Serves 1

1 tablespoon low-calorie salad dressing
1oz (30g) Edam cheese, grated
2 large thin slices (1½oz, 32g each) Hi-Bran bread
eating apple from allowance

Mix the salad dressing with the grated cheese and spread over both slices of bread. Cut the apple in half. Core one half and then slice thinly. Arrange the apple slices over one of the cheese-covered slices of bread and top with the second slice of bread. Cut into four sandwiches. Cut the remaining half apple into wedges and eat with the sandwich.

* Layered Bean Casserole

Serves 1

2oz (55g) canned red kidney beans, drained
7½oz (215g) canned butter beans, drained
6oz (170g) canned tomatoes, chopped
1oz (30g) finely chopped onion
salt and pepper
pinch of dried basil
4½oz (130g) canned chopped-leaf spinach, drained
grated nutmeg
1 small packet (25g) crisps, any flavour, crushed

Spoon the red kidney beans into the bottom of a small ovenproof casserole. Cover with the butter beans. Mix the tomatoes with the onion, salt, pepper and basil, and spoon over the beans. Spread the spinach over the top and sprinkle on a little grated nutmeg. Cover and bake at 190°C (375°F, gas 5) for 35 minutes. Uncover and sprinkle over the crushed crisps. Return to the oven for 5 minutes, uncovered. Serve hot.

1,250 CALORIES MENU   10

This menu is suitable for vegetarians

	Calories	Fibre (g)
Daily allowance: Fibre-Filler (p. 65). ½ pint (285ml) skimmed milk, an orange and an apple or pear	400	20

Breakfast
Whole portion Fibre-Filler with milk from
allowance

Lunch
7½oz (215g) canned spaghetti in tomato
sauce, heated and covered with 1 sliced
tomato and ½oz (15g) grated Edam
cheese

An apple or pear from allowance   195   3

Evening meal
* Vegetable Paella

Fruit salad made with 2oz (55g) grapes,
1 orange from allowance, segmented,
1 average-sized banana (6oz, 170g), sliced,
and 2fl oz (55ml) apple juice   545   16

Snack
150g carton low-fat natural yogurt with
2 teaspoons clear honey   110   0

| TOTAL | 1,250 | 39 |

* Vegetable Paella

Serves 1

2oz (55g) brown long-grain rice
1 small onion, chopped
1 small green pepper (4oz, 115g), seeds removed and chopped
2 average-sized tomatoes, chopped
1oz (30g) mushrooms, sliced
1oz (30g) fresh or frozen peas
¼ teaspoon dried thyme or marjoram
½ teaspoon grated lemon rind
salt and pepper
1oz (30g) roasted peanuts or cashew nuts

Put the rice, onion, pepper, tomatoes, mushrooms, peas, 8fl oz
(225ml) boiling water and herbs into a saucepan. Bring to the boil,
stir well and cover and simmer gently for about 25 minutes until
the rice is tender. Add more water during cooking if the rice mixture becomes too dry. Stir in the grated lemon rind and salt and
pepper to taste. Turn out on a serving dish and sprinkle the nuts
over the top.

F-PLAN FOR
WORKING WOMEN

All the menus in this section include a packable lunch, making them ideal for women who are out at work all day. The easiest and often the only way to stick to your diet when you have to eat lunch at work is to take your own meal with you. Those who think that packed lunches must always be sandwiches will be pleasantly surprised to find that the lunches given here also include salads, soups, crispbreads with toppings, pizza and filled rolls. All are easy to pack and eat, as long as you remember to pack any necessary items of cutlery. Hot soups can easily be carried in a thermos flask; only ready prepared canned soups have been included since working women do not have time to cook home-made soups before leaving for work in the morning, and it is unwise to keep home-made soup warm in a thermos flask from the previous evening.

The meals for the rest of the day in each menu are breakfast (either Fibre-Filler or Energen F-Plan Crunchy Bran Muesli), evening meal (usually something quick and easy since most working people have little time for meal preparation after work) and a snack which can be eaten any time during the evening.

The menus are divided into two sections of 1,000 and 1,250 calories. Half the menus in each section contain Fibre-Filler in the daily allowance as in all basic F-Plan diets and the remaining menus contain Energen F-Plan Crunchy Bran Muesli in the daily allowance so that you can decide which suits you best or use both, on different days, to provide variety.

While the menus with the packed lunches are just right for weekdays or working days you might like to have something different at the weekend. You will find plenty of choice for weekend menus in the 'Simply F-Plan' (p. 325) and the 'Keen Cook's F-Plan' (p. 416) menus.

SPECIAL DIET NOTES

1. Decide on your daily calorie allowance, either 1,000 calories or 1,250 calories, which will depend on how fast you want your

weight loss to be, how overweight you are and the amount of physical work you do.

2. Include as many different menus as possible from the selection provided, to keep your diet interesting and nutritious.

3. Do not swap individual meals from one menu to another since all the menus have been carefully calorie and fibre counted.

4. Drink as much sugarless tea and coffee as you like, either black or with the skimmed milk which remains from your daily allowance after using it on the Fibre-Filler or muesli. You can use artificial sweeteners. In addition you can drink unlimited amounts of canned and bottled low-calorie labelled drinks (e.g. Tab, Diet Pepsi Cola, Low-Calorie Bitter Lemon) and also water and soda water. In fact it is often helpful to have a low-calorie fizzy drink when your willpower is flagging, since such drinks can make you feel full. Alcoholic drinks have not been included in these menus. However, there may be occasions when you feel you must have an alcoholic drink; in this case, select a 1,000-calorie menu and allow yourself drinks to the value of 200 or 250 calories from the chart on p. 281.

1,000 CALORIE MENU   1

	Calories	Fibre (g)
Daily allowance: Fibre-Filler (p. 24), ½ pint (285ml) skimmed milk, an orange and an apple or pear	400	20
Breakfast Half portion of Fibre-Filler with milk from allowance		
Office or work lunch * Sardine and Cucumber Sandwich 2oz (55g) carrot sticks 1 large stick celery, cut into short sticks An apple or pear from allowance	225	8·5

	Calories	Fibre (g)

Evening meal
1 chicken leg joint (8oz, 225g raw weight),
grilled and then skin removed
4oz (115g) canned sweetcorn
4oz (115g) mushrooms, poached in a little
stock, *or* 7½oz (215g) canned button
mushrooms in brine, heated

2oz (55g) vanilla ice-cream served with
orange from allowance, segmented, and
1oz (30g) black grapes   375   9·5

Suppertime snack
Remaining portion of Fibre-Filler with milk
from allowance

TOTAL	1,000	38

* **Sardine and Cucumber Sandwich**

Serves 1

2 large thin slices (2½oz, 70g) wholemeal bread
1·23oz (35g) pot Shippams Sardine Spread with Tomato
1oz (30g) cucumber, sliced
salt and pepper

Spread both slices of the bread with the sardine spread. Fill with
the cucumber slices and season with salt and pepper. Cut into four.

1,000 CALORIE MENU   2

	Calories	Fibre (g)

Daily allowance: Fibre-Filler (p. 65),
½ pint (285ml) skimmed milk, an orange
and an apple or pear   400   20

	Calories	Fibre (g)

Breakfast
Half portion of Fibre-Filler with milk from
allowance

Office or work lunch
* Ham and Fruit Salad
2 Energen F-Plan Diet Brancrisps, spread
with ½oz (7g) low-fat spread

An orange from allowance	190	6·5

Evening meal
* Cheesy Fish and Tomato Pie
4oz (115g) frozen mixed cauliflower, peas
and carrots

An apple or pear from allowance	410	11

Suppertime snack
Remaining portion of Fibre-Filler with milk
from allowance

TOTAL	**1,000**	**37·5**

* Ham and Fruit Salad

Serves 1

1oz (30g) sliced boiled lean ham
1 small red-skinned eating apple, additional to allowance
2 teaspoons lemon juice
1oz (30g) black grapes, halved and pips removed
2 sticks celery, chopped
1 tablespoon oil-free French dressing
salt and pepper
a few lettuce leaves

Remove any fat and chop the ham. Core and chop the apple and toss in the lemon juice to prevent browning. Mix the chopped apple with the halved grapes, celery, French dressing and salt and pepper to taste. Arrange the lettuce leaves in the bottom of a plastic carton. Spoon the apple and grape mixture into the carton and top with the chopped ham. Remember to take a fork to work.

* Cheesy Fish and Tomato Pie

Serves 1

6oz (170g) packet frozen cod in mushroom sauce
half medium packet Smash Potato Pieces
1 tomato, sliced
2 tablespoons grated Parmesan cheese

Cook the frozen cod in sauce as directed on the packet. Make up the potato pieces with boiling water as directed (do not add butter). Pipe or spoon the potato around the edges of an individual ovenproof dish. Remove the fish and sauce from the bag and flake the fish into the sauce. Spoon into the potato border. Cover the fish with tomato slices and sprinkle over the grated cheese. Heat through under a hot grill until the cheese is beginning to brown.

1,000 CALORIE MENU   3

	Calories	Fibre (g)
Daily allowance: Fibre-Filler (p. 65), ½ pint (285ml) skimmed milk, an orange and an apple or pear	400	20

Breakfast
Half portion of Fibre-Filler with milk from allowance

	Calories	Fibre (g)

Office or work lunch
2 Energen F-Plan Diet Brancrisps
4oz (115g) Eden Vale Coleslaw in
Vinaigrette
1oz (30g) German salami, sliced
(Pack the ingredients separately to avoid
the crispbreads becoming soggy; at
lunchtime spoon the coleslaw over the
crispbreads and top with sliced salami.)

	Calories	Fibre (g)
An apple or pear from allowance	200	7·5

Evening meal
* Jacket Potato with Sausage Topping
3½oz (100g) baked beans in tomato sauce

	Calories	Fibre (g)
An orange from allowance	400	12·5

Suppertime snack
Remaining portion of Fibre-Filler with milk
from allowance

	Calories	Fibre (g)
TOTAL	1,000	40

* Jacket Potato with Sausage Topping

Serves 1

7oz (200g) potato
2 beef chipolata sausages
1oz (30g) Bicks Corn Relish

Bake the potato following one of the methods on p. 328. Grill the beef chipolatas until well done. Cut the baked potato in half lengthwise and scoop out some of the flesh. Mix with the corn relish and pile back into the potato jacket. Arrange one chipolata sausage on the top of each half jacket potato. Serve with heated baked beans.

1,000 CALORIE MENU   4

	Calories	Fibre (g)
Daily allowance: Fibre-Filler (p. 65), ½ pint (285ml) skimmed milk, an orange and an apple or pear	400	20

Breakfast
Half portion of Fibre-Filler with milk from
allowance

Office or work lunch
1 egg (size 3), hard-boiled and shelled
Salad: a bunch of watercress, a few spring
onions or onion rings, 1 stick celery,
chopped, 1 carrot cut into small sticks, a
few cucumber slices, 1 tomato cut into
wedges and 1 tablespoon oil-free French
dressing
(Put all the salad vegetables into a plastic
container and toss in the French dressing.
Seal the container and take to work with
the egg wrapped separately.)
2 Energen F-Plan Diet Brancrisps, spread
with ½oz (7g) low-fat spread

An apple or pear from allowance	190	6·5

Evening meal
* Spaghetti with Tuna Sauce

2 Energen F-Plan Diet Brancrisps, spread
with 1 triangle cheese spread and topped
with mustard and cress

An orange from allowance	410	9

	Calories	Fibre (g)
Suppertime snack Remaining portion of Fibre-Filler with milk from allowance		
TOTAL	1,000	35·5

* **Spaghetti with Tuna Sauce**

Serves 1

2oz (55g) wholewheat spaghetti
5oz (140g) canned tomatoes with juice
1 tablespoon finely chopped onion
a pinch dried basil or oregano
3½oz (100g) canned tuna in brine, drained
salt and pepper

Boil the spaghetti in salted water for about 12 minutes or until just tender. Meanwhile, purée the canned tomatoes in a blender or mash well with a fork. Place in a small saucepan with the onion and herbs. Bring to the boil, cover and simmer for 5 minutes. Flake the tuna and add to the sauce in the pan with salt and pepper to taste. Stir well and continue to heat for 3 minutes. Drain the spaghetti and arrange on a serving dish. Spoon the tuna sauce over the spaghetti and serve.

1,000 CALORIE MENU   5

	Calories	Fibre (g)
Daily allowance: Fibre-Filler (p. 24), ½ pint (285ml) skimmed milk, an orange and an apple or pear	400	20

Breakfast
Half portion of Fibre-Filler with milk from
allowance

	Calories	Fibre (g)

Office or work lunch
10·6oz (300g) can Heinz Lentil Soup
2 Energen F-Plan Diet Brancrisps, lightly
spread with Marmite or yeast extract
(Heat the soup and carry to work in a
vacuum flask; wrap the crispbreads.
Remember to take a spoon.)

An orange from allowance	225	8

Evening meal
* Watercress and Herb Omelet
4oz (115g) fresh or frozen peas

7½oz (220g) can Boots Shapers Peaches in Low-Calorie Syrup	375	12

Suppertime snack
Remaining portion of Fibre-Filler with milk
from allowance

An apple or pear from allowance

TOTAL	1,000	40

* Watercress and Herb Omelet

Serves 1

3 eggs (size 3)
salt and pepper
1 tablespoon chopped fresh chives and parsley, mixed
¼oz (7g) low-fat spread
1oz (30g) watercress, chopped

Beat the eggs with 1 tablespoon cold water, salt, pepper and fresh
herbs. Grease a non-stick omelet pan or small frying pan with the
low-fat spread and heat. Pour in the egg mixture and cook until the
bottom of the omelet is set and beginning to brown and the top is still
slightly runny. Sprinkle the watercress over the centre of the omelet.
Fold the omelet and turn out on a warm plate. Serve with peas.

1,000 CALORIE MENU   6

	Calories	Fibre (g)
Daily allowance: 2 tubs Energen F-Plan Crunchy Bran Muesli, ½ pint (285ml) skimmed milk, an orange and an apple or pear	420	20

Breakfast
1 tub Energen F-Plan Crunchy Bran
Muesli with milk from allowance

An orange from allowance

Office or work lunch
* Peanut Butter and Salad Lunch Roll
1 carrot cut into sticks
1 large stick celery, cut into small sticks

An apple or pear from allowance	235	9

Evening meal
6oz (170g) pack Birds Eye Cod in Cheese
Sauce, cooked
4oz (115g) frozen mixed peas, sweetcorn
and peppers
4oz (115g) cabbage, boiled

125g carton Waistline Reduced Calorie Yogurt, black cherry or prune	345	9·5

Suppertime snack
1 tub Energen F-Plan Crunchy Bran
Muesli with milk from allowance

TOTAL	1,000	38·5

* Peanut Butter and Salad Lunch Roll

Serves 1

1 wholemeal lunch roll or bap (2oz, 55g)
½oz (15g) peanut butter
1 tomato, sliced
a few slices cucumber
¼ carton mustard and cress

Split the wholemeal roll in two and spread the bottom half with
the peanut butter. Top with the sliced tomato, cucumber and mustard and cress. Replace the top half of the roll. Wrap in cling film.

1,000 CALORIE MENU   7

	Calories	Fibre (g)
Daily allowance: 2 tubs Energen F-Plan Crunchy Bran Muesli, ½ pint (285ml) skimmed milk, an orange and an apple or pear	420	20
Breakfast 1 tub Energen F-Plan Crunchy Bran Muesli with milk from allowance		
An orange from allowance		
Office or work lunch * Cottage Cheese and Grape Salad 2 Energen F-Plan Diet Brancrisps		
An average-sized banana (6oz, 170g)	290	7
Evening meal * Cauliflower with Chicken Liver and Mushroom Sauce 3½oz (100g) canned sweetcorn		
An apple or pear from allowance	290	12·5

	Calories	Fibre (g)
Suppertime snack 1 tub Energen F-Plan Crunchy Bran Muesli with milk from allowance		
TOTAL	1,000	39.5

* Cottage Cheese and Grape Salad

Serves 1

4oz (115g) carton natural cottage cheese
3oz (85g) black grapes, halved and pips removed
1 large stick celery, chopped
salt and pepper
a few lettuce leaves, shredded

Mix the cottage cheese with the halved grapes, chopped celery and seasoning to taste. Line a plastic carton with shredded lettuce and spoon the cottage cheese and grape salad on top. Seal; take a fork to eat it with.

* Cauliflower with Chicken Liver and Mushroom Sauce

Serves 1

4oz (115g) chicken livers, chopped
½ small onion, peeled and chopped
½ clove garlic, crushed (optional)
1 carrot, grated
½ chicken stock cube
salt and pepper
2oz (55g) mushrooms, chopped
6oz (170g) cauliflower, broken into florets

Put the chicken livers, onion, garlic and carrot in a small saucepan. Dissolve the stock cube in 3½fl oz (100ml) boiling water and pour into the pan. Add salt and pepper. Bring to the boil, cover and simmer gently for 20 minutes. Add the mushrooms and simmer for a further 5 minutes. Meanwhile, cook the cauliflower in boiling, salted water until just tender, then drain. Arrange the cauliflower on a serving dish and pour over the chicken liver and mushroom sauce.

1,000 CALORIE MENU 8

	Calories	Fibre (g)
Daily allowance: 2 tubs Energen F-Plan Crunchy Bran Muesli, ½ pint (285ml) skimmed milk, an orange and an apple or pear	420	20

Breakfast
1 tub Energen F-Plan Crunchy Bran
Muesli with milk from allowance

An orange from allowance

Office or work lunch
* Salmon Pâté and Watercress Lunch Roll

An apple or pear from allowance	190	5·5

Evening meal
3½oz (100g) bacon steak, grilled without fat
2 tomatoes, grilled without fat
8oz (225g) canned baked beans with
tomato sauce

Half medium packet Smash Potato Pieces, made up with water (no butter)	390	23

Suppertime snack
1 tub Energen F-Plan Crunchy Bran
Muesli with milk from allowance

TOTAL	1,000	48·5

* Salmon Pâté and Watercress Lunch Roll

Serves 1

1 wholemeal lunch roll or bap (2oz, 55g)
1·23oz (35g) pot Shippams Salmon Pâté Spread
a small bunch of watercress
1 teaspoon low-calorie salad dressing

Split the roll in half. Spread the salmon spread on the bottom half
of the roll. Cover generously with sprigs of watercress. Spread the
low-calorie salad dressing on the top half of the roll and place on
top of watercress. Wrap in cling film.

1,000 CALORIE MENU   9

	Calories	Fibre (g)
Daily allowance: 2 tubs Energen F-Plan Crunchy Bran Muesli, ½ pint (285ml) skimmed milk, an orange and an apple or pear	420	20

Breakfast
1 tub of Energen F-Plan Crunchy Bran
Muesli with milk from allowance

An orange from allowance

Office or work lunch
10·6oz (300g) can Heinz Pea & Ham Soup
2 Energen F-Plan Diet Brancrisps, without
spread
(Heat the soup and pour into a vacuum
flask; wrap the crispbreads. Remember to
take a spoon.)

An apple or pear from allowance	245	9

	Calories	Fibre (g)
Evening meal		
* Chicken with Raisin Coleslaw Vinaigrette		
2 Energen F-Plan Diet Brancrisps, spread with 1 triangle cheese spread and topped with sliced cucumber	335	8·5
Suppertime snack		
1 tub Energen F-Plan Crunchy Bran Muesli with milk from allowance		

	Calories	Fibre (g)
TOTAL	1,000	37·5

* **Chicken with Raisin Coleslaw Vinaigrette**

Serves 1

1 chicken leg joint (8oz, 225g raw weight)
3oz (85g) white cabbage, shredded
1 medium carrot, grated
1 large stick celery, finely chopped
½oz (15g) raisins
2 tablespoons oil-free French dressing

Grill the chicken joint without added fat, turning over until cooked through. To make the coleslaw, mix the cabbage, carrot, celery, raisins and French dressing until well blended. Remove the skin from the grilled chicken joint and serve with the coleslaw.

1,000 CALORIE MENU		**10**

	Calories	Fibre (g)
Daily allowance: 2 tubs Energen F-Plan Crunchy Bran Muesli, ½ pint (285ml) skimmed milk, an orange and an apple or pear	420	20

	Calories	Fibre (g)

Breakfast
1 tub Energen F-Plan Crunchy Bran
Muesli with milk from allowance

Office or work lunch
2 pork chipolata sausages, well grilled and
then left to go cold
8oz (226g) carton Eden Vale Coleslaw with
Low Calorie Dressing
(Wrap the sausages separately and take to
work with the salad. Remember to take a
fork.)

An apple or pear from allowance	245	4·5

Evening meal
* Baked Jacket Potato with Cheesy Filling
4oz (115g) canned baked beans with
tomato sauce

An orange from allowance	335	13·5

Suppertime snack
1 tub Energen F-Plan Crunch Bran
Muesli with milk from allowance

TOTAL	1,000	38

* Baked Jacket Potato with Cheesy Filling

Serves 1

7oz (200g) potato
2oz (55g) cottage cheese (natural or with chives or with onion
and peppers)
½oz (15g) Bicks Corn Relish
salt and pepper
2 level teaspoons grated Parmesan cheese

Bake the potato following one of the methods on p. 328. Cut the potato in half lengthwise and scoop out some of the flesh. Add the cottage cheese, corn relish and salt and pepper to taste to the potato flesh and mash together. Pile the cheese and potato mixture back into the potato jacket. Sprinkle 1 teaspoon Parmesan cheese over the top of each half of jacket potato and then heat through under the grill until the cheese begins to brown. Serve hot.

1,250 CALORIE MENU   1

	Calories	Fibre (g)
Daily allowance: Fibre-Filler (p. 65), ½ pint (285ml) skimmed milk, an orange and an apple or pear	400	20
Breakfast Half portion of Fibre-Filler with milk from allowance		
An orange from allowance		
Office or work lunch * Devilled Egg Sandwich		
125g carton Waistline Reduced Calorie Yogurt, black cherry, strawberry or prune		
An apple or pear from allowance	345	7·5
Evening meal * Thatched Cod and Broccoli 4oz (115g) fresh or frozen broad beans, boiled		
3½oz (100g) green grapes	455	14

	Calories	Fibre (g)
Suppertime snack		
Remaining portion of Fibre-Filler with milk from allowance		
1 Energen F-Plan Diet Brancrisp, spread with 2 level tablespoons Waistline Country Vegetable Spread	50	1·5

TOTAL	1,250	43

* Devilled Egg Sandwich

Serves 1

1 tablespoon low-calorie salad dressing
½ teaspoon Worcestershire sauce
1 medium carrot, grated
2 large thin slices (2½oz, 70g) wholemeal bread
1 egg (size 3), hard-boiled and sliced
¼ carton mustard and cress

Mix the low-calorie salad dressing with the Worcestershire sauce and grated carrot. Divide between the two slices of bread and spread over the bread. Arrange the egg slices and mustard and cress over one slice of bread and cover with the second slice. Cut into four; wrap in cling film for carrying.

* Thatched Cod and Broccoli

Serves 1

6oz (170g) frozen broccoli
6oz (170g) pack frozen cod in cheese or butter sauce
salt and pepper
1oz (30g) fresh wholemeal breadcrumbs
½oz (15g) grated Cheddar cheese

Cook the broccoli and the cod according to pack instructions. Drain the broccoli and season with salt and pepper. Place in a shallow ovenproof dish. Put the cod and sauce on top of the broccoli. Mix the breadcrumbs with the grated cheese and sprinkle on top. Heat under the grill until the topping is crisp and golden brown.

1,250 CALORIE MENU   2

	Calories	Fibre (g)
Daily allowance: Fibre-Filler (p. 65), $\frac{1}{2}$ pint (285 ml) skimmed milk, an orange and an apple or pear	400	20

Breakfast
Half portion of Fibre-Filler with milk from allowance

1 large thin slice wholemeal bread, toasted and spread with $\frac{1}{4}$oz (7g) low-fat spread and 1 level teaspoon marmalade or honey	115	3

Office or work lunch
1 Wimpy hamburger with bun

An orange from allowance	325	1·5

Evening meal
1 pork chop (7oz, 200g raw weight), well grilled and with fat cut off after grilling, served with 1 ring of pineapple from a can of pineapple in natural juice, heated through under grill
4oz (115g) mushrooms, poached in a little stock *or* 7½oz (215g) canned button mushrooms in brine, heated through and drained
4oz (115g) frozen peas, boiled

An apple or pear from allowance	410	12·5

	Calories	Fibre (g)
Suppertime snack Remaining portion of Fibre-Filler with milk from allowance		
TOTAL	1,250	37

1,250 CALORIE MENU   3

	Calories	Fibre (g)
Daily allowance: Fibre-Filler (p. 65), ½ pint (285ml) skimmed milk, an orange and an apple or pear	400	20
Breakfast Half portion Fibre-Filler with milk from allowance		
A large banana (7½oz. 215g)	95	4·5
Office or work lunch * Corned Beef and Corn Relish Lunch Roll 2oz (55g) carrot, cut into sticks		
An orange from allowance	310	8
Evening meal * Grilled Spiced Chicken with Stir-Fry Vegetables		
An apple or pear from allowance	445	6·5
Suppertime snack Remaining portion of Fibre-Filler with milk from allowance		
TOTAL	1,250	39

* Corned Beef and Corn Relish Lunch Roll

Serves 1

1 wholemeal lunch roll or bap (2oz, 55g)
¼oz (7g) low-fat spread
2oz (55g) corned beef, sliced
1oz (30g) Bicks Corn Relish
a few sprigs of watercress

Split the wholemeal roll in two and spread the cut surfaces lightly with low-fat spread. Arrange the sliced corned beef on the bottom half of the roll and top with corn relish and sprigs of watercress. Replace the top half of the roll. Wrap in cling film.

* Grilled Spiced Chicken with Stir-Fry Vegetables

Serves 1

1 chicken leg joint (8oz, 225g raw weight)
1oz (30g) Branston Spicy Sauce
10oz (285g) pack Birds Eye Continental Stir-Fry Vegetables

Remove the skin from the chicken leg joint and brush all over with the sauce. Cook on a piece of foil under the grill, turning once or twice, until cooked through. Meanwhile cook the vegetables according to the pack instructions. Serve with the grilled chicken.

1,250 CALORIE MENU   4

	Calories	Fibre (g)
Daily allowance: Fibre-Filler (p. 65), ½ pint (285ml) skimmed milk, an orange and an apple or pear	400	20

Breakfast
Half portion of Fibre-Filler with milk from allowance
1 egg (size 3), poached and served on 1
large thin slice (1¼oz, 35g) wholemeal

	Calories	Fibre (g)
bread, toasted and spread with 1 tablespoon tomato ketchup	170	3

Office or work lunch
15·3oz (435g) can Heinz Vegetable & Lentil
Big Soup
2 Energen F-Plan Diet Brancrisps, lightly
spread with Marmite or yeast extract
(Heat the soup and carry to work in a
vacuum flask; wrap the crispbreads.)

An apple or pear from allowance	255	11

Evening meal
5oz (140g) lamb loin chop, well grilled
4oz (115g) Brussels sprouts, boiled
4oz (115g) carrots, boiled

4oz (115g) canned pineapple slices in natural juice	415	7·5

Suppertime snack
Remaining portion Fibre-Filler with milk
from allowance

2oz (55g) carrot sticks	10	1·5

TOTAL	1,250	43

1,250 CALORIE MENU 5

	Calories	Fibre (g)
Daily allowance: Fibre-Filler (p. 65), ½ pint (285ml) skimmed milk, an orange and an apple or pear	400	20

	Calories	Fibre (g)
Breakfast		
Half portion Fibre-Filler with milk from allowance		
1 large thin slice (1¼oz, 35g) wholemeal bread, toasted and spread with ½oz (7g) low-fat spread and 1 level teaspoon marmalade or honey	115	3
Office or work lunch		
2oz (55g) boiled lean ham with any fat trimmed off		
2 Energen F-Plan Diet Brancrisps, spread with ½oz (7g) low-fat spread mixed with a little made mustard		
8oz (226g) carton Eden Vale Coleslaw in Vinaigrette		
(Pack the ham slices and crispbreads separately and leave the coleslaw in its carton. Place the ham slices on the crispbreads to eat; pack a fork for the salad.)		
An apple or pear from allowance	195	6·5
Evening meal		
* Baked Jacket Potato with Egg and Tomato Filling		
4oz (115g) canned baked beans with tomato sauce		
2oz (55g) vanilla ice-cream served with the orange from allowance, segmented	460	14
Suppertime snack		
Remaining portion Fibre-Filler with milk from allowance		
An average-sized banana (6oz, 170g)	80	3·5
TOTAL	1,250	47

* Baked Jacket Potato with Egg and Tomato Filling

Serves 1

7oz (200g) potato
1 egg (size 3)
2 tablespoons skimmed milk from allowance
¼oz (7g) low-fat spread
salt and pepper
1 medium tomato or 1 canned tomato, chopped

Bake the potato in the oven at 200°C (400°F, gas 6) for 45 minutes or until soft when pinched. Scramble the egg with the skimmed milk, low-fat spread and salt and pepper in a small saucepan. Stir in the chopped tomato and heat through. Cut the potato in half lengthwise and scoop out some of the flesh. Mash the potato flesh and mix with the scrambled egg and tomato. Pile back into the potato jacket and serve.

1,250 CALORIE MENU 6

This menu is suitable for vegetarians

	Calories	Fibre (g)
Daily allowance: 2 tubs Energen F-Plan Crunchy Bran Muesli, ½ pint (285 ml) skimmed milk, an orange and an apple or pear	420	20

Breakfast
1 tub Energen F-Plan Crunchy Bran Muesli with milk from allowance

An orange from allowance

Office or work lunch
* Waldorf Salad

1 Quaker Harvest Crunch Bar, almond or peanut	340	9

	Calories	Fibre (g)
Evening meal		
* One Pan Pasta Dish	420	6

Suppertime snack
1 tub Energen F-Plan Crunchy Bran
Muesli with milk from allowance

An apple or pear from allowance

TOTAL	1,250	35

* Waldorf Salad

Serves 1

3oz (85g) red cabbage, shredded
1 large stick celery, chopped
1 small (about 4oz, 115g) green eating apple, additional to
   allowance, cored and chopped
2 teaspoons lemon juice
1oz (30g) walnuts, shelled, roughly chopped
2 tablespoons low-calorie salad dressing

Mix the red cabbage and celery together. Toss the apple in the
lemon juice and then add to the cabbage and celery with the
walnuts and the salad dressing. Mix well until the salad ingredients
are thoroughly blended. Pack in a plastic carton and seal with a
lid. Pack a fork.

* One Pan Pasta Dish

Serves 1

1oz (30g) wholewheat spaghetti or macaroni
½oz (15g) low-fat spread
1 small onion, peeled and chopped
2oz (55g) mushrooms, sliced
1 medium tomato, chopped
2 eggs (size 3)

4 tablespoons skimmed milk, additional to allowance
salt and pepper
½oz (15g) grated mature Cheddar cheese

Boil the spaghetti or macaroni in salted water for about 12 minutes or until just tender. Heat the low-fat spread in a pan, add the onion and cook gently until soft. Add the mushrooms and tomato and cook for a further 3–4 minutes. Add the drained cooked spaghetti or macaroni and heat through. Beat the eggs with the milk and salt and pepper. Pour over the pasta mixture and cook over a low heat, stirring continuously, until sauce begins to thicken. Do not allow to boil. Remove from heat and serve immediately, sprinkled with the grated cheese.

1,250 CALORIE MENU   7

This menu is suitable for vegetarians

	Calories	Fibre (g)
Daily allowance: 2 tubs Energen F-Plan Crunchy Bran Muesli, ½ pint (285ml) skimmed milk, an orange and an apple or pear	420	20
Breakfast 1 tub Energen F-Plan Crunchy Bran Muesli with milk from allowance 1 Energen F-Plan Diet Brancrisp, spread with 1 level teaspoon honey	35	1
Office or work lunch 1 sachet Batchelors Slim-a-Soup, beef and tomato or chicken and golden vegetable Cheese, tomato and cucumber sandwich: 2 large thin slices (2½oz, 70g) wholemeal bread, spread with 1 triangle cheese spread and filled with 1 medium tomato, sliced and a few slices of cucumber		
An apple or pear from allowance	240	7

	Calories	Fibre (g)
Evening meal		
* Vegetable and Cheese Pie		
2 Energen F-Plan Diet Brancrisps, spread		
with Marmite or yeast extract		
An orange from allowance	480	15·5
Suppertime snack		
1 tub Energen F-Plan Crunchy Bran		
Muesli with milk from allowance		
125g carton Waistline Reduced Calorie yogurt,		
any fruit flavour	75	0

TOTAL	**1,250**	**43·5**

* Vegetable and Cheese Pie

Serves 1

½oz (15g) low-fat spread
½oz (15g) wholemeal flour
¼ pint (140ml) skimmed milk, additional to allowance
salt and pepper
¼ teaspoon made mustard
1oz (30g) mature Cheddar cheese, grated
7½oz (215g) canned butter beans
4oz (115g) frozen mixed vegetables

Put the low-fat spread, flour and milk into a small saucepan and heat gently, whisking continuously, until the mixture boils and thickens. Season to taste with salt and pepper and stir in the mustard and half the grated cheese. Remove from the heat. Heat the can of butter beans and drain. Cook the frozen mixed vegetables according to instructions and drain. Mix the butter beans and mixed vegetables with the cheese sauce and turn into a small ovenproof dish. Sprinkle over the remaining grated cheese and heat under the grill until the cheese is melted and beginning to brown.

1,250 CALORIE MENU   8

	Calories	Fibre (g)
Daily allowance: 2 tubs Energen F-Plan Crunchy Bran Muesli, ½ pint (285ml) skimmed milk, an orange and an apple or pear	420	20

Breakfast
Both tubs Energen F-Plan Crunchy Bran Muesli with milk from allowance

Office or work lunch
1 McCain Deep 'n' Delicious Ham & Mushroom Pizza, cooked according to instructions, cooled, cut into four pieces and wrapped
Mixed salad: a few lettuce leaves, shredded, 1 tomato, cut into wedges, a few cucumber slices, a few spring onions, chopped
(Pack in a plastic carton.)

An apple or pear from allowance	205	3

Evening meal
* Bean and Frankfurter Supper

2oz (55g) vanilla ice-cream, served with an orange from allowance, cut into segments	510	20

Suppertime snack
1 large thin slice (1¼oz, 35g) wholemeal bread, toasted and spread with 1 triangle

cheese spread	115	3

TOTAL	1,250	46

* Bean and Frankfurter Supper

Serves 1

8oz (225g) canned baked beans with tomato sauce
1 teaspoon Worcestershire sauce
½ teaspoon made mustard
1 tablespoon finely chopped onion
1 canned tomato, chopped
2 tablespoons tomato juice from canned tomatoes
2oz (55g) frankfurter, sliced
1 large thin slice (1¼oz, 35g) wholemeal bread

Mix all the ingredients together in a saucepan. Heat to simmering point, cover and cook over a gentle heat for 15 minutes. Meanwhile, toast the slice of bread. Pile the bean and frankfurter mixture on the toast.

1,250 CALORIE MENU   9

	Calories	Fibre (g)
Daily allowance: 2 tubs Energen F-Plan Crunchy Bran Muesli, ½ pint (285ml) skimmed milk, an orange and an apple or pear	420	20
Breakfast 1 tub Energen F-Plan Crunchy Bran Muesli with milk from allowance 1 egg (size 3), poached and served on 1 large thin slice (1¼oz, 35g) wholemeal bread, toasted and spread with ¼oz (7g) low-fat spread	180	3
Office or work lunch Cottage cheese and date sandwich: 2 large thin slices (2½oz, 70g) wholemeal bread filled with 2oz (55g) natural cottage cheese mixed with 1oz (30g) chopped stoned dates		
An apple or pear from allowance	275	8·5

	Calories	Fibre (g)
Evening meal		
* Tuna and Sweetcorn in Seafood Sauce with Cauliflower		
8oz (226g) can Koo Peach Slices in Apple Juice		
2 tablespoons low-fat natural yogurt	375	9
Suppertime snack		
1 tub Energen F-Plan Crunchy Bran Muesli with milk from allowance		
An orange from allowance		
TOTAL	1,250	40·5

* Tuna and Sweetcorn in Seafood Sauce with Cauliflower

Serves 1

half packet Knorr Seafood Sauce Mix
¼ pint (140ml) skimmed milk, additional to allowance
3½oz (100g) canned tuna in brine, drained and flaked
2oz (55g) canned sweetcorn kernels
6oz (170g) cauliflower, broken into florets

Put the sauce mix into a small saucepan and add a little of the milk. Blend to a smooth cream, then stir in the remaining milk. Bring slowly to the boil, stirring continuously. Lower the heat, continue to stir and simmer for 3 minutes. Add the flaked tuna and sweetcorn to the sauce and heat through. Cook the cauliflower in boiling salted water until just tender, about 10 minutes. Drain well and arrange on a serving dish. Pour the sauce over the cauliflower and serve immediately.

1,250 CALORIE MENU   10

	Calories	Fibre (g)
Daily allowance: 2 tubs Energen F-Plan Crunchy Bran Muesli, ½ pint (285ml) skimmed milk, an orange and an apple or pear	420	20
Breakfast 2 tubs Energen F-Plan Crunchy Bran Muesli with milk from allowance		
Office or work lunch * Kidney Beans, Mushroom, Sweetcorn and Cheese Salad		
An orange from allowance	215	11·5
Evening meal * Liver and Bacon in a Pot Half a medium packet Smash Potato Pieces made up with boiling water as instructed (no butter) *or* 5oz (140g) potatoes, boiled and mashed with a little skimmed milk from allowance (no butter)	455	8
Suppertime snack 1 large thin slice (1¼oz, 35g) wholemeal bread, toasted, topped with 1oz (30g) Edam cheese, grated and heated under the grill until the cheese has melted	160	3
TOTAL	1,250	42·5

* Kidney Beans, Mushroom, Sweetcorn and Cheese Salad

Serves 1

3oz (85g) canned red kidney beans, drained
2oz (55g) button mushrooms, sliced
2oz (55g) canned sweetcorn kernels
1oz (30g) Edam cheese, diced
2 tablespoons oil-free French dressing

Mix all the ingredients together well. Pack in a plastic carton. Remember to pack a fork.

* Liver and Bacon in a Pot

Serves 1

½oz (7g) low-fat spread
1 rasher streaky bacon, rind removed and chopped
1 medium carrot, sliced
1 small onion, peeled and sliced
4oz (115g) lamb's liver, thinly sliced
8oz (225g) canned tomatoes
a pinch of dried thyme
salt and pepper

Melt the low-fat spread in a saucepan and add the bacon, carrot and onion. Cover and cook gently for 5 minutes, shaking the pan from time to time. Turn into a small ovenproof casserole and lay the liver slices on top. Chop the tomatoes in their juice and spoon over the liver. Sprinkle over the thyme and season well with salt and pepper. Cover and cook in a slow oven at 150°C (300°F, gas 2) for 1 hour. Serve with mashed potato.

SNACK EATER'S
F-PLAN

Many women who are at home most of the day tend to eat frequent snacks. If this pattern of eating is your norm, these menus of five small snack meals a day will provide your easiest F-Plan method. And there is no harm – you may even lose weight slightly faster – in eating little and often, as long as your total food and fibre intake is correct for the day.

The menus all follow the basic F-Plan rules (p. 91). The snack meals are all simple and quick to prepare, both to reduce to a minimum the time spent in the kitchen and because snack eaters and nibblers tend to prefer more or less instant foods.

As with the 'Simply F-Plan' menus these snack eater's menus are divided into two sections – menus providing 1,000 calories and menus providing 1,250 calories daily – to enable you to choose menus which will result in the best weight loss for you.

SPECIAL DIET RULES

1. Decide which daily calorie total will give you the best weight loss. For guidance on the most suitable daily calorie allowance for you, see Chapter 9.

2. Plan ahead and select at least two or three menus, preferably one week's menus, at a time to enable you to shop for the foods you need.

3. Make sure that you eat a variety of foods by selecting several different menus each week, to be sure that you are getting all the nutrients you need for good health.

4. The five snack meals from your daily menu can be eaten in any order and at any time of day you wish. However, it is inadvisable to swap one snack meal from one menu with a meal from another menu, since this will usually alter the amount of calories and fibre which have been carefully counted for each full day's menu.

5. Drinks can be taken at any time during the day and in any

quantity provided that you stick to unsugared tea and coffee, either black or with skimmed milk from the daily allowance (reserve some to eat with the Fibre-Filler), low-calorie-labelled bottled and canned drinks, and water. If you feel the need to have an alcoholic drink occasionally then see the advice given on p. 63 and select a drink from the chart on p. 281–4.

1,000 CALORIE MENU   1

	Calories	Fibre (g)
Daily allowance: Fibre-Filler (p. 24), ½ pint (285 ml) skimmed milk, an orange and an apple or pear	400	20

Meal 1
Half portion of Fibre-Filler with milk from allowance

Meal 2
1 egg (size 3), poached and served on 1 large thin slice (1½oz, 35g) wholemeal bread, toasted and spread with ¼oz (7g) low-fat spread

Meal 3
10·6oz (300g) can Heinz Lentil Soup,
1 Energen F-Plan Diet Brancrisp, spread with
2 level tablespoons Waistline Low Calorie
Vegetable Spread, any variety

An apple or pear from allowance	230	7

Meal 4
2 frozen cod fish cakes, grilled without fat,
1 medium tomato, halved and grilled without fat

	Calories	Fibre (g)
4oz (115g) frozen peas, boiled	190	12

Meal 5
Remaining portion of Fibre-Filler with milk
from allowance

An orange from allowance

	Calories	Fibre (g)
TOTAL	1,000	42

1,000 CALORIE MENU   2

	Calories	Fibre (g)
Daily allowance: Fibre-Filler (p. 65), ½ pint (285ml) skimmed milk, an orange and an apple or pear	400	20

Meal 1
Half portion of Fibre-Filler with milk from
allowance

An orange from allowance

Meal 2
Cottage cheese and cucumber sandwich:
2 large thin slices (2½oz, 70g) wholemeal
bread filled with 2oz (55g) cottage cheese
(natural, with chives, with onions and
peppers, or with pineapple), salt and pepper
to taste and 1oz (30g) sliced cucumber   210   6

Meal 3
150g carton low-fat natural yogurt mixed
with an average-sized banana (6oz, 170g),
sliced and 2 walnut halves, chopped   190   4

	Calories	Fibre (g)

Meal 4
1 frozen beefburger, well grilled
1 medium tomato, grilled without fat
4oz (115g) baked beans in tomato sauce   200   9

Meal 5
Remaining portion of Fibre-Filler with milk
from allowance

An apple or pear from allowance

TOTAL	1,000	39

1,000 CALORIE MENU   3

	Calories	Fibre (g)

Daily allowance: Fibre-Filler (p. 65),
½ pint (285 ml) skimmed milk, an orange
and an apple or pear   400   20

Meal 1
Half portion of Fibre-Filler with milk from
allowance

An orange from allowance

Meal 2
2 Energen F-Plan Diet Brancrisps, each
topped with 1 medium tomato, sliced,
1 sardine canned in tomato sauce and 1 small
gherkin, chopped

An apple or pear from allowance   165   4

	Calories	Fibre (g)
Meal 3		
7½oz (215g) canned prunes in syrup with 1 tablespoon natural yogurt	245	9
Meal 4		
1 frozen cod steak, covered with 1 tablespoon chopped onion, 4oz (115g) canned tomatoes, salt and pepper to taste and a pinch of mixed herbs, covered and baked at 180°C (350°F, gas 4) for 25 minutes		
4oz (115g) frozen mixed vegetables, boiled	155	6·5
Meal 5		
Remaining portion of Fibre-Filler with milk from allowance		
1 Energen F-Plan Diet Brancrisp, spread with Marmite or yeast extract and topped with 2oz (55g) grated carrot	35	2·5
TOTAL	1,000	42

1,000 CALORIE MENU   4

	Calories	Fibre (g)
Daily allowance: Fibre-Filler (p. 65), ½ pint (285 ml) skimmed milk, an orange and an apple or pear	400	20

Meal 1
Half portion of Fibre-Filler with milk from allowance

	Calories	Fibre (g)
1 Energen F-Plan Diet Brancrisp, spread with half a 1¼oz (35g) pot Princes Salmon Spread and topped with a little mustard and cress	40	1

Meal 2
2 rashers streaky bacon, well grilled, served with 4oz (115g) baked beans in tomato sauce and 1 tomato, halved — **180**, **9**

Meal 3
4oz (115g) carton cottage cheese (natural, with chives, with onions and peppers or with pineapple)
Salad: a few lettuce leaves, a 1 inch (2·5cm) piece of cucumber, sliced, 1 medium tomato, sliced, 2 spring onions, chopped *or* ½oz (15g) onion rings, 1oz (30g) green or red pepper, chopped, 1 stick celery, chopped and 1 tablespoon oil-free French dressing, 1 Energen Brancrisp crispbread — **165**, **4**

Meal 4
1 small packet (25g) potato crisps, any flavour
2 large sticks celery, cut into small sticks

125g carton Waistline Reduced Calorie Yogurt, any fruit flavour — **215**, **5**

Meal 5
Remaining portion of Fibre-Filler with milk from allowance

	Calories	Fibre (g)
An orange and an apple or pear from allowance		
TOTAL	**1,000**	**39**

1,000 CALORIE MENU   5

	Calories	Fibre (g)
Daily allowance: Fibre-Filler (p. 65), ½ pint (285ml) skimmed milk, an orange and an apple or pear	400	20

Meal 1
Half portion of Fibre-Filler with milk from allowance

An orange from allowance

Meal 2
Ham and pickle sandwich: 2 large thin slices (2½oz, 70g) wholemeal bread spread with 1oz (30g) sweet pickle and filled with 1oz (30g) sliced ham and a few cucumber slices

An apple or pear from allowance   235   6·5

Meal 3
Mexican omelet: beat 2 eggs (size 3), with 2 tablespoons water and salt and pepper. Grease a small non-stick omelet pan with a little low-fat spread. Heat the pan, add the egg mixture and cook until the egg is just set. Spoon 2oz (55g) canned sweetcorn with

	Calories	Fibre (g)
peppers into the centre. Fold the omelet in half and serve with a bunch of watercress	220	4

Meal 4
8oz (225g) canned pear halves in apple juice
1 tablespoon low-fat natural yogurt — 115 — 4

Meal 5
Remaining portion of Fibre-Filler with milk from allowance

1 large stick celery filled with 1oz (30g) cottage cheese — 30 — 1

TOTAL	**1,000**	**35·5**

1,000 CALORIE MENU — 6

	Calories	Fibre (g)
Daily allowance: Fibre-Filler (p. 65), ½ pint (285ml) skimmed milk, an orange and an apple or pear	400	20

Meal 1
Half portion of Fibre-Filler with milk from allowance

1 average-sized banana (6oz, 170g) — 80 — 3·5

Meal 2
1 sachet Batchelors Slim-A-Soup, golden vegetable, made up with boiling water
2 Energen F-Plan Diet Brancrisps, each spread with 1 level tablespoon Waistline Low Calorie Vegetable Spread, any variety, and topped with 2oz (55g) grated carrot — 125 — 4

	Calories	Fibre (g)
Meal 3 150g carton low-fat fruit-flavoured yogurt mixed with 2 level tablespoons Toasted Bran		
An orange from allowance	145	2
Meal 4 6oz (170g) pack frozen cod in mushroom sauce, cooked		
4oz (115g) frozen peas, boiled	250	9
Meal 5 Remaining portion of Fibre-Filler with milk from allowance		
An apple or pear from allowance		
TOTAL	1,000	38·5

1,000 CALORIE MENU   7

	Calories	Fibre (g)
Daily allowance: Fibre-Filler (p. 65), ½ pint (285ml) skimmed milk, an orange and an apple or pear	400	20
Meal 1 Half portion of Fibre-Filler served with 125g carton Waistline Reduced Calorie Yogurt, prune flavour	75	0
Meal 2 1 egg (size 3), boiled and served with 1 large thin slice (1¼oz, 35g) wholemeal bread spread with ¼oz (7g) low-fat spread		
An orange from allowance	180	3

	Calories	Fibre (g)

Meal 3
4oz (115g) cottage cheese, natural, mixed
with an apple or pear from allowance,
cored and chopped and 1oz (30g) sultanas
or raisins, served on a bed of lettuce
leaves and garnished with 2oz (55g) carrot,
grated

	Calories	Fibre (g)
grated	200	4

Meal 4
Bean and tomato hot-pot: heat 4oz (115g)
canned baked beans in tomato sauce with
8oz (225 g) canned tomatoes, a generous
dash of Worcestershire sauce and salt and
pepper to taste. Grill 1 rasher streaky bacon
until crisp. Pour the bean and tomato
hot-pot into a soup bowl and crumble the
bacon over the top

bacon over the top	145	10

Meal 5
Remaining portion of Fibre-Filler with milk
from allowance

TOTAL	1,000	37

1,000 CALORIE MENU   **8**

	Calories	Fibre (g)

Daily allowance: Fibre-Filler (p. 65),
½ pint (285ml) skimmed milk, an orange
and an apple or pear

and an apple or pear	400	20

Meal 1
Half portion of Fibre-Filler with milk from
allowance

	Calories	Fibre (g)
Meal 2		
1 Prewett's Fruit & Bran Bar		
An average-sized banana (6oz, 170g)	165	8·5
Meal 3		
1 packet Birds Eye Braised Kidneys in Gravy		
4oz (115g) cabbage, boiled		
An orange from allowance	215	3
Meal 4		
10·6oz (300g) can Heinz Lentil Soup		
An apple or pear from allowance	180	6
Meal 5		
Remaining portion of Fibre-Filler with milk from allowance		
1 Energen F-Plan Diet Brancrisp, spread with half a 1¼oz (35g) pot Princes Salmon Spread and topped with a little mustard and cress	40	1
TOTAL	1,000	38·5

1,000 CALORIE MENU   9

	Calories	Fibre (g)
Daily allowance: Fibre-Filler (p. 65), ½ pint (285ml) skimmed milk, an orange and an apple or pear	400	20

Meal 1
Half portion of Fibre-Filler with milk from allowance

An orange from allowance

	Calories	Fibre (g)
Meal 2		
8oz (225g) canned baked beans in tomato sauce served on 1 large thin slice (1¼oz, 35g) wholemeal bread, toasted	235	19·5
Meal 3		
2oz (55g) peeled prawns, served with a few lettuce leaves, small bunch watercress, 1 inch (2·5cm) cucumber, sliced, 1 medium tomato, sliced, 1 large stick celery, chopped, 1oz (30g) green pepper, sliced, and 1 tablespoon oil-free French dressing		
An apple or pear from allowance	95	4
Meal 4		
7¼oz (220g) Boots Shapers Apricots in Low-Calorie Syrup 2oz (55g) vanilla ice-cream 2 level tablespoons Toasted Bran (Top the canned apricots with the ice-cream and sprinkle with the Toasted Bran.)	150	5
Meal 5		
Remaining portion of Fibre-Filler with milk from allowance		
150g carton low-fat fruit-flavoured yogurt	120	0
TOTAL	1,000	48·5

1,000 CALORIE MENU   10

	Calories	Fibre (g)
Daily allowance: Fibre-Filler (p. 65), ½ pint (285ml) skimmed milk, an orange and an apple or pear	400	20

	Calories	Fibre (g)

Meal 1
Half portion of Fibre-Filler with milk from
allowance

Meal 2
1 large thin slice (1¼oz, 35g) wholemeal
bread, toasted, topped with 1 medium
tomato, sliced, sprinkled with a pinch
dried thyme and salt and pepper and
covered with 1oz (30g) mature Cheddar
cheese, grated. Heat through under grill
until the cheese is melted and beginning to
brown

An apple or pear from allowance   200   4

Meal 3
8oz (226g) carton Eden Vale Coleslaw in
Vinaigrette
2oz (55g) boiled lean ham
1oz (30g) pickled beetroot
1 Energen F-Plan Diet Brancrisp   200

Meal 4
2oz (55g) vanilla ice-cream
An orange from allowance, segmented

1 Prewett's Banana Dessert Bar   170   2·5

Meal 5
Remaining portion of Fibre-Filler with milk
from allowance

1 Energen F-Plan Diet Brancrisp, spread
with Marmite or yeast extract and topped
with 1 chopped pickled onion or 1oz (30g)
chopped green pepper   30   1·5

TOTAL	1,000	36

1,250 CALORIE MENU   1

	Calories	Fibre (g)
Daily allowance: Fibre-Filler (p. 65), ½ pint (285ml) skimmed milk, an orange and an apple or pear	400	20

Meal 1
Half portion of Fibre-Filler with milk from allowance

1 large thin slice (1¼oz, 35g) wholemeal bread, spread with ¼oz (7g) low-fat spread and 1 level teaspoon honey or marmalade	115	3

Meal 2
2 frozen fish fingers, grilled without fat
4oz (115g) canned tomatoes, heated
4oz (115g) button mushrooms poached in
stock *or* 7½oz (215g) canned button

mushrooms in brine, heated and drained	125	4

Meal 3
150g carton low-fat natural yogurt with an
apple or pear from allowance, cored and
chopped

1oz (30g) raisins or sultanas	150	2

Meal 4
8oz (225g) frozen shepherd's pie
4oz (115g) frozen peas, boiled
4oz (115g) carrots, boiled

An orange from allowance	355	13

	Calories	Fibre (g)

Meal 5
Remaining portion of Fibre-Filler with milk
from allowance

2 Energen F-Plan Diet Brancrisps, spread with
1·23oz (35g) Shippams Beef & Tomato
Country Pot Paste and topped with 1
medium tomato, sliced ... 105 ... 3

TOTAL	1,250	45

1,250 CALORIE MENU   2

	Calories	Fibre (g)

Daily allowance: Fibre-Filler (p. 65),
½ pint (285ml) skimmed milk, an orange
and an apple or pear ... 400 ... 20

Meal 1
Half portion of Fibre-Filler with milk from
allowance

An average-sized banana (6oz, 170g) ... 80 ... 3·5

Meal 2
2 large thin slices (2½oz, 70g) wholemeal
bread, toasted and spread with 2oz (55g)
cottage cheese mixed with 1oz (30g) corn
relish and topped with 2 medium tomatoes,
sliced and heated through under the grill

An apple or pear from allowance ... 255 ... 9

Meal 3
Remaining portion of Fibre-Filler with milk
from allowance

An orange from allowance

	Calories	Fibre (g)
Meal 4		
4oz (115g) lamb's liver, sliced, brushed with		
1 teaspoon oil and grilled		
1 rasher streaky bacon, well grilled		
1 medium tomato, halved and grilled		
without fat		
4oz (115g) cabbage, boiled	315	4
Meal 5		
10·6oz (300g) can Heinz Lentil Soup		
1 Energen F-Plan Diet Brancrisp	200	7

TOTAL	1,250	43·5

1,250 CALORIE MENU		**3**

	Calories	Fibre (g)
Daily allowance: Fibre-Filler (p. 65),		
½ pint (285ml) skimmed milk, an orange		
and an apple or pear	400	20
Meal 1		
Half portion of Fibre-Filler with milk from		
allowance		
2 Energen F-Plan Diet Brancrisps, spread with		
¼oz (7g) low-fat spread and 2 level teaspoons		
honey or marmalade	100	2
Meal 2		
Banana, honey and raisin sandwich: 2 large		
thin slices (2½oz, 70g) wholemeal bread,		
filled with 6oz (170g) banana, mashed with		
2 level teaspoons honey and mixed with		
1oz (30g) raisins		
An apple or pear from allowance	330	11·5

	Calories	Fibre (g)

Meal 3
1 McCain Deep 'n' Delicious Ham &
Mushroom Pizza
small bunch of watercress

| 1 medium tomato | 200 | 3·5 |

Meal 4
7½oz (215g) canned spaghetti in tomato
sauce topped with ½oz (15g) grated Edam
cheese and heated under grill until cheese

| melts | 190 | 2 |

Meal 5
Remaining portion of Fibre-Filler with milk
from allowance

An orange from allowance, segmented and
mixed with 3 level tablespoons low-fat

| natural yogurt | 30 | 0 |

| **TOTAL** | 1,250 | 39 |

1,250 CALORIE MENU   4

	Calories	Fibre (g)

Daily allowance: Fibre-Filler (p. 65),
½ pint (285ml) skimmed milk, an orange

| and an apple or pear | 400 | 20 |

Meal 1
Half portion of Fibre-Filler with milk from
allowance

An orange from allowance

Meal 2
1 Prewett's Muesli Fruit Bar

	Calories	Fibre (g)
125g carton Waistline Reduced Calorie Fruit Yogurt, any flavour	200	3·5

Meal 3

| 1 frozen beefburger, well grilled and served in a 2oz (55g) wholemeal bap or soft roll, spread with 1oz (30g) sweet pickle; serve with a small bunch of watercress and 1 medium tomato | 295 | 7 |

Meal 4

Remaining portion of Fibre-Filler with milk from allowance

| 2 Energen F-Plan Diet Brancrisps, each spread with 1 tablespoon Waistline Low Calorie Vegetable Spread, any flavour, and topped with 1 medium tomato, sliced | 85 | 2 |

Meal 5

1 chicken leg joint (8oz, 225g raw weight), grilled and skin removed
4oz (115g) canned sweetcorn, drained
4oz (115g) Brussels sprouts, boiled

| An apple or pear from allowance | 270 | 9·5 |

| TOTAL | 1,250 | 42 |

1,250 CALORIE MENU 5

	Calories	Fibre (g)
Daily allowance: Fibre-Filler (p. 65), ½ pint (285ml) skimmed milk, an orange and an apple or pear	400	20

	Calories	Fibre (g)

Meal 1
Half portion of Fibre-Filler with milk from
allowance

1 large thin slice (1¼oz. 35g) wholemeal
bread, toasted and spread with ¼oz (7g)
low-fat spread and 1 level teaspoon honey
or marmalade   115   3

Meal 2
4oz (115g) cottage cheese (natural or with
chives, or with onions and peppers, or with
pineapple)
Coleslaw: 2oz (55g) finely shredded white
cabbage, mixed with 2oz (55g) grated carrot,
½oz (15g) raisins and 1 tablespoon
low-calorie salad dressing   200   4

Meal 3
4oz (115g) canned pineapple slices in
natural juice
2oz (55g) vanilla ice-cream
2 level tablespoons Toasted Bran
(Serve pineapple with ice-cream topped
with bran.)   195   3

Meal 4
2 pork sausages, grilled
4oz (115g) baked beans in tomato sauce

An orange from allowance   340   8

Meal 5
Remaining portion of Fibre-Filler with milk
from allowance

An apple or pear from allowance

TOTAL   1,250   38

1,250 CALORIE MENU   6

	Calories	Fibre (g)
Daily allowance: Fibre-Filler (p. 65), ½ pint (285ml) skimmed milk, an orange and an apple or pear	400	20

Meal 1
Half portion Fibre-Filler with milk from allowance

| 1 large thin slice (1¼oz, 35g) wholemeal bread, toasted, spread with Marmite or yeast extract and topped with 4oz (115g) canned tomatoes | 90 | 4 |

Meal 2
1 egg (size 3), hard-boiled, halved and served with half a 7¼oz (206g) can Heinz Vegetable Salad, a few lettuce leaves, a few sprigs of watercress, and 1 tomato, sliced

| 1 Energen F-Plan Diet Brancrisp | 265 | 5 |

Meal 3
| 1 Quaker Harvest Crunch Bar, almond or peanut, served with 2 oz (55g) vanilla ice-cream and an orange from allowance | 185 | 1 |

Meal 4
1 bacon steak (3½oz, 100g raw weight), well grilled, served with 1 pineapple ring from can of pineapple slices in natural juice 4 oz (115g) canned sweetcorn kernels
| 4oz (115g) Brussels sprouts, boiled | 245 | 10 |

Meal 5
Remaining portion of Fibre-Filler with milk from allowance

	Calories	Fibre (g)
1 Energen F-Plan Diet Brancrisp, spread with 1 triangle (½oz, 15g) cheese spread and topped with a few slices of cucumber		
An apple or pear from allowance	65	1·5
TOTAL	**1,250**	**41·5**

1,250 CALORIE MENU 7

	Calories	Fibre (g)
Daily allowance: Fibre-Filler (p. 65), ¼ pint (285ml) skimmed milk, an orange and an apple or pear	400	20

Meal 1
Half portion of Fibre-Filler with milk from allowance

An average-sized banana (6oz, 170g)	80	3·5

Meal 2
Sardines and tomato on toast: 2 large thin
slices (2½oz, 70g) wholemeal bread,
toasted, each slice topped with 1 medium
tomato, sliced, a pinch of dried thyme and 2
sardines in tomato sauce, heated through

under the grill	390	8

Meal 3
4oz (115g) cottage cheese (natural, with
chives, with onions and peppers or with
pineapple)
1 large stick celery, cut into small sticks
2oz (55g) carrot, cut into sticks

An apple or pear from allowance	125	2·5

	Calories	Fibre (g)
Meal 4		
1 pack Birds Eye Gravy and Lean Roast Chicken		
4oz (115g) frozen peas, boiled		
1oz (30g) button mushrooms, poached in a little stock or sliced and cooked with peas	255	9·5

Meal 5
Remaining portion of Fibre-Filler with milk from allowance

An orange from allowance

TOTAL	1,250	43·5

1,250 CALORIE MENU 8

	Calories	Fibre (g)
Daily allowance: Fibre-Filler (p. 24), ½ pint (285 ml) skimmed milk, an orange and an apple or pear	400	20

Meal 1
Half portion of Fibre-Filler with milk from allowance

2 Energen F-Plan Diet Brancrisps, spread with ¼oz (7g) low-fat spread and 2 teaspoons honey	100	2

Meal 2
170g carton Eden Vale Chicken and Sweetcorn Salad
A small bunch of watercress

An apple or pear from allowance	270	3

	Calories	Fibre (g)

Meal 3
1 small (25g) packet potato crisps, any
flavour
1 sachet Batchelors Slim-A-Soup, any
flavour, made up

An orange from allowance	170	3

Meal 4
Egg florentine: thaw and heat 5oz (140g)
frozen cut-leaf spinach (don't add butter),
season to taste with salt and pepper and
grated nutmeg. Place in a small ovenproof
dish. Top with 1 egg (size 3), poached,
covered with 3 level tablespoons natural
yogurt, and sprinkle over 1oz (30g) grated
Edam cheese; heat under grill until cheese

begins to melt	230	7·5

Meal 5
Remaining portion of Fibre-Filler with milk
from allowance

An average-sized banana (6oz, 170g)	80	3·5

TOTAL	1,250	39

1,250 CALORIE MENU		**9**

	Calories	Fibre (g)

Daily allowance: Fibre-Filler (p. 65),
½ pint (285ml) skimmed milk, an orange and

an apple or pear	400	20

	Calories	fibre (g)
Meal 1		
Half portion of Fibre-Filler with milk from allowance		
125g carton Waistline Reduced Calorie Fruit Yogurt, any flavour	75	0
Meal 2		
7oz (200g) canned macaroni cheese		
2 medium tomatoes		
An apple or pear from allowance	275	2
Meal 3		
1 Quaker Harvest Crunch Bar, almond or peanut		
An average-sized banana (6oz, 170g)	170	4·5
Meal 4		
2 frozen Realeat Vegeburgers, grilled without fat		
4 oz (115g) canned baked beans in tomato sauce		
An orange from allowance	300	14
Meal 5		
Remaining portion of Fibre-Filler with milk from allowance		
1 Energen F-Plan Diet Brancrisp, spread with Marmite or yeast extract		
1 large stick celery	30	2
TOTAL	**1,250**	**42·5**

1,250 CALORIE MENU   10

	Calories	Fibre (g)
Daily allowance: Fibre-Filler (p. 65), ½ pint (285ml) skimmed milk, an orange and an apple or pear	400	20

Meal 1
Half portion of Fibre-Filler with milk from
allowance

1 large thin slice (1¼oz, 35g) wholemeal
bread, toasted, spread with ¼oz (7g) low-fat
spread and 1 level teaspoon honey or
marmalade   115   3

Meal 2
Cottage cheese and date sandwich: 2 large
thin slices (2½oz, 70g) wholemeal bread,
filled with 2oz (55g) cottage cheese mixed
with 1oz (30g) stoneless dates, chopped

An orange from allowance   275   8·5

Meal 3
8oz (226g) can Koo Peach Slices in Apple
Juice
2 level tablespoons low-fat natural yogurt   115   2·5

Meal 4
Mushroom omelet with vegetables: beat 2
eggs (size 3) with 2 tablespoons water, salt
and pepper to taste and a pinch of dried
mixed herbs. Grease a small non-stick omelet
pan with ¼oz (7g) low-fat spread. Pour in
the egg mixture and cook until just set.
Spoon 7½oz (215g) canned sliced large
mushrooms in brine (drained and heated)

	Calories	Fibre (g)
over half the omelet. Fold the other half over the mushrooms and turn out on a warmed plate. Serve with 4oz (115g) frozen mixed peas, sweetcorn and peppers, boiled		
An apple or pear from allowance	260	10·5

Meal 5
Remaining portion of Fibre-Filler with milk from allowance

Chocolate drink made from 1 rounded teaspoon drinking chocolate and 6½fl oz (185ml) skimmed milk additional to allowance	85	0

TOTAL	1,250	44·5

KEEN COOK'S F-PLAN

F-Plan slimmers who are also keen cooks may wish to spend more time preparing their food than the majority of slimmers. If you are a keen cook (male or female) and can resist the temptation to nibble while in the kitchen, you will find plenty of choice of attractive, tasty dishes to prepare in these menus.

All the recipes are for two, since if you are going to take time preparing a dish it is more worthwhile if you are sharing it with at least one other person. The ingredients can be increased proportionally if you are feeding more than two people.

Since keen cooks usually prefer to spend most of their time preparing one main meal, these menus provide simple, light meals during the day, saving most of the calorie allowance for the main evening meal. A late afternoon snack has been included in each menu to help you avoid hunger pangs and to reduce the temptation to nibble while preparing your evening meal.

The menus are divided into three sections: 1,000 calories, 1,250 calories and 1,500 calories daily. The lower calorie menus are suitable for women and the 1,500 calorie menus are mainly for men.

SPECIAL DIET NOTES

1. As always, begin by deciding which daily calorie total will give you a satisfactory weight loss. You will find guidance in Chapter 9.

2. Plan at least two or three days ahead, preferably one week ahead, and arrange your shopping so that you always have the right foods available.

3. Make sure that you eat a wide variety of foods to give a balanced healthy diet – select several different menus, preferably all different, each week.

4. Make up the Fibre-Filler for your daily allowance either daily or for several days in one batch, following the recipe on p. 65.

5. Drink as much sugarless tea and coffee as you wish throughout the day as long as you use only the skimmed milk from your daily allowance. Artificial sweeteners can be used. Water and drinks labelled 'low-calorie' can also be drunk in unlimited quantities, but alcoholic drinks must be limited, see p. 63.

1,000 CALORIE MENU   1

	Calories	Fibre (g)
Daily allowance: Fibre-Filler (p. 65), ½ pint (285ml) skimmed milk, an orange and an apple or pear	400	20

Breakfast
Half portion of Fibre-Filler with milk from allowance

An orange from allowance

Lunch
Banana and honey sandwich: 2 large thin slices (1¼ oz, 35g each) wholemeal bread filled with 1 medium banana (6oz, 170g), mashed with 2 level teaspoons honey

An apple or pear from allowance	260	9·5

Late afternoon
Remaining portion Fibre-Filler with milk from allowance

Evening meal
* Stuffed Aubergine
Mixed salad: 1 tomato, quartered, a few sprigs of watercress, a few chicory leaves,

	Calories	Fibre (g)
1oz (30g) green pepper, chopped, 2–3 spring onions, chopped, with 1 tablespoon oil-free French dressing		
2 Energen F-Plan Diet Brancrisps, each spread with ½ triangle (¼oz, 7g) cheese spread and topped with mustard and cress or sliced cucumber	340	13
TOTAL	1,000	42·5

* Stuffed Aubergine

Serves 2

1 medium aubergine (12oz, 340g)
½oz (15g) low-fat spread
2oz (55g) onion, chopped
2 medium tomatoes (4oz, 115g), chopped
1 large thin slice (1½oz, 35g) wholemeal bread
4 tablespoons skimmed milk, additional to allowance
2oz (55g) boiled lean ham, chopped
generous pinch of dried mixed herbs
salt and freshly ground pepper
1oz (30g) Cheddar cheese, grated

Preheat the oven to 180°C (350°F, gas 4). Cut the aubergine in half lengthwise and scoop out the flesh from the centre of each half using a teaspoon. Chop the flesh. Heat the low-fat spread in a saucepan and fry the chopped onion and tomatoes gently for 5 minutes. Break up the bread, place in a basin with the milk and leave to soak for 5 minutes, then squeeze dry and add to the chopped onion mixture with the chopped ham and aubergine flesh. Stir in the mixed herbs and season well with salt and pepper. Divide the mixture in half and pile into the aubergine shells. Place in an ovenproof dish and cover with foil. Bake in the oven for 1½ hours. Remove the foil and sprinkle over the grated cheese. Return to the oven for a further 15 minutes until the cheese is melted and beginning to brown. Serve hot.

1,000 CALORIE MENU   2

	Calories	Fibre (g)
Daily allowance: Fibre-Filler (p. 65), ½ pint (285ml) skimmed milk, an orange and an apple or pear	400	20

Breakfast
Half portion of Fibre-Filler with milk from allowance

Lunch
Ham salad: 2oz (55g) boiled lean ham with 1 medium tomato, 2oz (55g) Chinese leaves, shredded, a small bunch of watercress, 2oz (55g) carrot, grated, and 1 large stick celery, chopped

An apple or pear from allowance	130	5·5

Late afternoon
Remaining portion of Fibre-Filler with milk from allowance

Evening meal
* Stuffed Plaice with Lemon and Prawn Sauce
4oz (115g) broccoli, boiled
1 large thin slice (1¼oz, 35g) wholemeal bread spread with ¼oz (7g) low-fat spread

An orange from allowance	470	12

TOTAL	1,000	37.5

* Stuffed Plaice with Lemon and Prawn Sauce

Serves 2

4 fillets plaice (3oz, 85g each), skinned

Stuffing
2oz (55g) wholemeal breadcrumbs
1oz (30g) onion, peeled and finely chopped
1oz (30g) carrot, peeled and finely grated
2oz (60g) mushrooms, finely chopped
juice and rind of half a lemon
a pinch of lemon thyme
salt and pepper

Sauce
½oz (15g) wholemeal flour
½oz (15g) low-fat spread
¼ pint (140ml) skimmed low-fat milk
1 tablespoon lemon juice
4oz (115g) prawns
1 teaspoon chopped fresh parsley
salt and pepper

Preheat the oven to 190°C (375°F, gas 5). Mix the stuffing ingredients together. Spread the stuffing over the fillets of plaice and fold in half. Place in an ovenproof dish, cover and bake for 20 minutes or until the fish is tender. Meanwhile, prepare the sauce: put the flour, low-fat spread and milk into a saucepan and heat gently, stirring continuously, until it comes to the boil and thickens. Add the lemon juice, prawns and parsley, and cook over a low heat for 5 minutes. Season to taste. Arrange the stuffed fillets of plaice on two serving plates and pour over the sauce.

1,000 CALORIE MENU   3

	Calories	Fibre (g)
Daily allowance: Fibre-Filler (p. 65), ½ pint (285ml) skimmed milk, an orange and an apple or pear	400	20

	Calories	Fibre (g)

Breakfast
Half portion of Fibre-Filler with milk from
allowance

An orange from allowance

Lunch
2 Energen F-Plan Diet Brancrisps, spread
with 1oz (30g) low-fat cottage cheese
and topped with 1oz (30g) sliced
cucumber and 1oz (30g) corn relish

An apple or pear from allowance   130   3·5

Late afternoon
Remaining portion of Fibre-Filler with milk
from allowance

Evening meal
8oz (225g) slice cantaloup, honeydew or
yellow melon topped with half a glacé
cherry

* Spinach and Cheese Soufflé
4oz (115g) frozen mixed peas, sweetcorn
and peppers, boiled   470   13

TOTAL	1,000	36·5

* Spinach and Cheese Soufflé

Serves 2

4oz (115g) cooked or frozen (thawed) spinach, finely chopped
4oz (115g) cooked potato, mashed
2oz (55g) mature Cheddar cheese, grated
salt and freshly ground pepper

1oz (30g) wholemeal flour
1oz (30g) low-fat spread
¼ pint (140ml) skimmed low-fat milk
2 eggs (size 3), separated

Preheat the oven to 220°C (425°F, gas 7). Place the spinach,
potato, cheese and salt and pepper in a bowl and mix thoroughly.
Leave to one side. Put the flour, low-fat spread and milk into a
small saucepan and heat gently, stirring all the time, until the
sauce thickens. Remove from the heat and beat in the egg yolks,
then stir in the spinach mixture. Whisk the egg whites until they
form a soft peak and fold into the rest of the ingredients. Pour into
a 1½ pint (850ml) soufflé dish and bake in the oven for 25–30
minutes or until it is golden brown and well risen. Serve immediately.

1,000 CALORIE MENU   4

	Calories	Fibre (g)
Daily allowance: Fibre-Filler (p. 65), ½ pint (285ml) skimmed milk, an orange and an apple or pear	400	20

Breakfast
Half portion of Fibre-Filler with milk from
allowance

An orange from allowance

Lunch
Toasted cheese and date sandwich: fill
2 large thin slices (1¼ oz, 35g each)
wholemeal bread with 1oz (30g) curd
cheese mixed with 1oz (30g) finely
chopped stoned dates. Toast the
sandwich on both sides, cut into four and
serve

| An apple or pear from allowance | 260 | 8·5 |

	Calories	Fibre (g)

Late afternoon
Remaining portion of Fibre-Filler with milk
from allowance

Evening meal
* Minted Watercress and Cucumber Soup
1 Energen F-Plan Diet Brancrisp

8oz (225g) chicken leg joint, grilled
and skin removed, served hot or cold
* Kidney Bean, Onion and Cauliflower

	Calories	Fibre (g)
Salad	340	12·5
TOTAL	1,000	41

* Minted Watercress and Cucumber Soup

Serves 2

1 bunch (2oz, 55g) watercress
4oz (115g) cucumber, roughly chopped
1 small (3oz, 85g) onion, peeled and chopped
1 small (2oz, 55g) potato, peeled and cut into
four
salt and freshly ground pepper
1 teaspoon chopped fresh mint
3 tablespoons low-fat natural yogurt

Place the watercress, cucumber, onion and potato in a medium-sized saucepan with ½ pint (285ml) water, bring to the boil. Reduce the heat and simmer for 15 minutes. Allow to cool for a few minutes then sieve or purée in a blender. Season to taste, add the mint and 2 tablespoons low-fat yogurt and stir thoroughly. Chill in the refrigerator. To serve, pour into two soup bowls and pour the remaining yogurt in a spiral pattern in the centre of each bowl of soup.

* Kidney Bean, Onion and Cauliflower Salad

Serves 2

6oz (170g) canned red kidney beans, drained and rinsed
4 spring onions, chopped
6oz (170g) raw cauliflower, broken into florets
½ clove garlic, crushed
1 tablespoon oil-free French dressing
1 tablespoon lemon juice

Mix the kidney beans, chopped spring onions and cauliflower
florets together in a salad bowl. Mix the garlic with the French
dressing and lemon juice and pour over the salad vegetables. Toss
well until thoroughly mixed. Allow to stand for 10 minutes before
serving.

1,000 CALORIE MENU   5

	Calories	Fibre (g)
Daily allowance: Fibre-Filler (p. 65), ½ pint (285ml) skimmed milk, an orange and an apple or pear	400	20

Breakfast
Half portion Fibre-Filler with milk from
allowance

An orange from allowance

Lunch 2 Energen F-Plan Diet Brancrisps, topped with 2oz (55g) cottage cheese mixed with ½oz (15g) raisins and ½oz (15g) chopped walnuts		
An apple or pear from allowance	210	4

Late afternoon
Remaining portion Fibre-Filler with milk
from allowance

	Calories	Fibre (g)
Evening meal * Kidney Risotto		
4oz (115g) fresh or frozen (thawed) raspberries with 1 level teaspoon sugar	390	17
TOTAL	1,000	41

* Kidney Risotto

Serves 2

1 teaspoon vegetable oil
3oz (85g) brown rice
1 small (3oz, 85g) onion, peeled and
    chopped
1 small (3oz, 85g) red pepper, deseeded and
    chopped
½ pint (285ml) beef stock, made from ½ beef
    stock cube
4 lamb's kidneys (8 oz, 225g), cored and chopped
4oz (115g) frozen peas, thawed
4oz (115g) courgette, thinly sliced, tossed in
    1–2 tablespoons oil-free French dressing
1 level teaspoon grated Parmesan cheese

Heat the oil in a medium-sized saucepan and gently fry the rice, onion and pepper for 3–4 minutes. Add the beef stock and bring to the boil. Reduce the heat and simmer for 25 minutes. Meanwhile quickly brown the kidneys in a non-stick frying pan over a medium heat. Add the kidneys and peas to the rice mixture and simmer for a further 10–15 minutes or until the rice has absorbed most of the stock. Arrange the courgette slices around the edge of two serving plates and spoon the risotto into the centre. Sprinkle with Parmesan cheese.

1,250 CALORIE MENU   1

	Calories	Fibre (g)
Daily allowance: Fibre-Filler (p. 65), ½ pint (285ml) skimmed milk, an orange and an apple or pear	400	20

Breakfast
Half portion of Fibre-Filler with milk
from allowance

An orange from allowance

Lunch
Liver pâté and cress sandwich: 2 large thin
slices (1¼oz, 35g each) wholemeal
bread, filled with 1½oz (40g) sliced liver
sausage and a thick layer of watercress
sprigs

An apple or pear from allowance   285   7

Late afternoon
Remaining portion of Fibre-Filler with
milk from allowance

Evening meal
* Soufflé Omelet Filled with Prawns,
Sweetcorn and Tomato
4oz (115g) broccoli, boiled
5oz (140g) new potatoes, boiled

2oz (55g) portion vanilla ice-cream
served with 1 medium banana (6oz, 170g),
sliced   565   15

| TOTAL | 1,250 | 42 |

* Soufflé Omelet Filled with Prawns, Sweetcorn and Tomato

Serves 2

Filling
2oz (55g) prawns
4oz (115g) canned sweetcorn kernels
1 medium (2oz, 55g) tomato, chopped
1 small (3oz, 85g) onion, peeled and chopped
a large pinch of mixed dried herbs

Omelet
3 eggs (size 3), separated
salt and freshly ground pepper
1 teaspoon vegetable oil
1½oz (45g) mature Cheddar cheese, grated

Place the prawns, sweetcorn, tomato, onion and herbs in a
saucepan, cover and cook over a medium heat for 10–15 minutes
or until the onion is soft. Prepare the omelet: whisk the egg yolks,
2 tablespoons warm water and salt and pepper together. Whisk
the egg whites until they form soft peaks, then fold evenly into the
whisked yolks. Heat the oil in a large frying pan or omelet pan and
pour the egg mixture into it, spreading it out evenly. Cook gently
for 5–7 minutes, until the underneath is golden brown, put under
a preheated moderate grill for 4–5 minutes until the omelet is set
and is lightly brown on the surface. Spoon the prawn, sweetcorn
and tomato filling on top of one half of the omelet, sprinkle with
the grated cheese. Fold in half and slide on to a hot plate. Cut into
two portions and serve at once.

1,250 CALORIE MENU   **2**

	Calories	Fibre (g)
Daily allowance: Fibre-Filler (p. 65), ½ pint (285ml) skimmed milk, an orange and an apple or pear	400	20

	Calories	Fibre (g)

Breakfast
Half portion of Fibre-Filler with milk from
allowance

An orange from allowance

Lunch
2 Energen F-Plan Diet Brancrisps, topped
with 1 hard-boiled egg (size 3), chopped
and mixed with 2 tablespoons low-calorie
salad dressing, salt and pepper and ¼
carton mustard and cress

An apple or pear from allowance	180	2·5

Late afternoon
Remaining portion of Fibre-Filler with milk
from allowance

Evening meal
* Chicken and Grapes with Mushroom
Sauce
7oz (200g) potato, baked in its jacket
  (p. 31)
4oz (115g) Brussels sprouts

4oz (115g) fresh or frozen raspberries with 125g carton Waistline Reduced Calorie Fruit Yogurt, any flavour	670	21

TOTAL	1,250	43·5

* Chicken and Grapes with Mushroom Sauce

Serves 2

2 chicken pieces (8oz, 225g each)
2oz (55g) frozen sweetcorn kernels

4oz (115g) mushrooms, sliced
4fl oz (115ml) dry white wine
3½fl oz (100ml) chicken stock using ½ chicken stock cube
salt and pepper

Sauce
1oz (30g) wholemeal flour
½oz (15g) low-fat spread
salt and pepper
4oz (115g) green grapes, cut in half and deseeded

Preheat the oven to 200°C (400°F, gas 6). Remove the skin from
the chicken joints and place them in an ovenproof dish with the
sweetcorn, mushrooms, wine, chicken stock and salt and pepper.
Cover and bake in the oven for 40–55 minutes or until the chicken
is tender. Remove the chicken from the dish, place on a serving
dish and keep warm. Strain the stock into a saucepan but reserve
the mushrooms and sweetcorn. To the stock add the flour, low-fat
spread and salt and pepper. Stir over a gentle heat until it thickens.
Add the grapes, sweetcorn and mushrooms, and mix thoroughly.
Pour over the chicken and serve.

1,250 CALORIE MENU   3

	Calories	Fibre (g)
Daily allowance: Fibre-Filler (p. 24), ½ pint (285ml) skimmed milk, an orange and an apple or pear	400	20
Breakfast Half portion of Fibre-Filler with milk from allowance		
1 large thin slice (1¼oz, 35g) wholemeal bread, toasted and spread with ¼oz (7g) low-fat spread and 2 level teaspoons honey or marmalade	130	3

	Calories	Fibre (g)

Lunch
7fl oz (200ml) carton Ambrosia Yogurt
Juice, raspberry, strawberry, peach or
black cherry

1 Jordans Original Crunchy Bar, Honey
& Almond

An apple or pear from allowance · 270 · 0·5

Late afternoon
Remaining portion of Fibre-Filler with milk
from allowance

Evening meal
* Trout Kiev
8oz (225g) frozen peas, sweetcorn and
peppers

An orange from allowance · 450 · 16·5

TOTAL · 1,250 · 40

---

* **Trout Kiev**

Serves 2

2 trout (7oz, 200g each after gutting), cleaned
2 teaspoons vegetable oil

Stuffing
2oz (55g) canned sweetcorn kernels
2 level tablespoons ground almonds
1oz (30g) low-fat spread
1 clove garlic, crushed
2 tablespoons lemon juice

Garnish
lemon slices
½oz (15g) toasted flaked almonds

Wipe the trout. Mix all the stuffing ingredients together and use to stuff the two trout. Brush the skin with the oil and place on a foil-lined grill rack. Cook under a moderate grill for 8–10 minutes on each side or until the fish is cooked right through and the juices of the stuffing start to run out. Place on a hot serving dish and garnish with the lemon slices and toasted flaked almonds.

1,250 CALORIE MENU 4

	Calories	Fibre (g)
Daily allowance: Fibre-Filler (p. 65), ½ pint (285ml) skimmed milk, an orange and an apple or pear	400	20
Breakfast Half portion of Fibre-Filler with milk from allowance		
An orange from allowance		
Lunch * Mushrooms on Toast		
An apple or pear from allowance	250	6
Late afternoon Remaining portion of Fibre-Filler with milk from allowance		
Evening meal ½ grapefruit, decorated with ½ glacé cherry		
* Liver Stroganoff 4oz (115g) cauliflower, boiled		
* Blackberry and Apple Fool	600	12
TOTAL	1,250	38

* Mushrooms on Toast

Serves 1

2 large thin slices (1¼oz, 35g each) wholemeal bread
4oz (115g) button mushrooms
4fl oz (115ml) skimmed milk, additional to allowance
2 level teaspoons cornflour
a dash of Worcestershire sauce
salt and pepper
a few sprigs of watercress

Toast both sides of bread. Poach the mushrooms in the skimmed milk for 5 minutes. Blend the cornflour with a little cold water and stir into the mushrooms. Bring to the boil, stirring, and cook for 2 minutes until thickened. Add the Worcestershire sauce and seasoning to taste. Serve on the two slices of toast garnished with sprigs of watercress.

* Liver Stroganoff

Serves 2

1 teaspoon vegetable oil
8oz (225g) lamb's liver, cut into thin strips
1 small (3oz, 85g) onion, peeled and chopped
4oz (115g) mushrooms, sliced
¼ pint (140ml) beef stock, made from ½ beef stock cube
2 tablespoons dry sherry
3 tablespoons low-fat natural yogurt
3oz (85g) green tagliatelle or noodles, cooked and drained
chopped fresh parsley

Heat the oil in a medium-sized saucepan, add the liver and onion and fry gently for 3–4 minutes. Stir in the mushrooms, beef stock and sherry, bring to the boil. Reduce the heat and simmer for 12–15 minutes or until the liver is tender. Remove from the heat and stir in 2 tablespoons yogurt. Arrange the tagliatelle or noodles around the edges of two warmed plates and spoon the liver mixture into the centre. Garnish with the remaining yogurt and the chopped parsley.

* Blackberry and Apple Fool

Serves 2

4oz (115g) blackberries
8oz (225g) cooking apple, peeled, cored and
    sliced
1 level tablespoon sugar
two 125g cartons Waistline Reduced Calorie
    Natural Yogurt

Stew the blackberries and apple with 4 tablespoons water in a
covered pan until tender. Add the sugar and purée in a blender
with the yogurt. Serve cold.

1,250 CALORIE MENU   5

	Calories	Fibre (g)
Daily allowance: Fibre-Filler (p. 65), ½ pint (285ml) skimmed milk, an orange and an apple or pear	400	20

Breakfast
Half portion of Fibre-Filler with milk from
allowance

Lunch
1 sachet Batchelors Slim-A-Soup, any
flavour
2 Energen F-Plan Diet Brancrisps, topped
with 2oz (55g) cottage cheese (natural,
with chives or with onions and peppers)
and 2 medium tomatoes, sliced   155   3·5

Late afternoon
Remaining portion of Fibre-Filler with milk
from allowance

	Calories	Fibre (g)
Evening meal		
* Apricot Stuffed Lamb Chops		
4oz (115g) carrots, boiled		
4oz (115g) cabbage		
* Flambé Bananas	695	18
TOTAL	1,250	41·5

* Apricot Stuffed Lamb Chops

Serves 2

2 lean lamb loin chops (5oz, 140g each)

Stuffing
1½oz (40g) dried apricots, finely chopped
1½oz (40g) wholemeal breadcrumbs
1oz (30g) onion, finely chopped
1oz (30g) walnuts, finely chopped
2 tablespoons beaten egg
a large pinch of dried marjoram
salt and pepper

Preheat the oven to 190°C (375°F, gas 5). Using a sharp knife cut a horizontal pocket in each chop from the fat edge towards the bone. Mix all the stuffing ingredients together. Fill the pocket in each chop with some of the stuffing. Form the remaining stuffing into small balls. Place the chops and stuffing balls into a shallow ovenproof dish. Cover and cook in the oven for 40–45 minutes or until the lamb is tender and cooked through. Serve hot.

* Flambé Bananas

Serves 2

2 medium bananas (6oz, 170g each)
3 tablespoons unsweetened orange juice

1 level teaspoon clear honey
¼ teaspoon ground cinnamon
1 tablespoon Grand Marnier or brandy
1oz (30g) walnuts, chopped

Place the bananas in a medium-sized saucepan or frying pan with
the orange juice, honey and cinnamon. Bring to the boil, reduce
the heat and simmer gently for 3–4 minutes or until the bananas
are tender. Place with the juice on a serving dish. Heat the Grand
Marnier or brandy, then set alight. While flaming pour over the
bananas, and leave until flames die out. Sprinkle with the chopped
walnuts.

1,250 CALORIE MENU   6

	Calories	Fibre (g)
Daily allowance: Fibre-Filler (p. 24), ½ pint (285ml) skimmed milk, an orange and an apple or pear	400	20

Breakfast
Half portion of Fibre-Filler with milk from
allowance

An orange from allowance

Lunch
Banana, raisin and almond sandwich:
2 large thin slices (1¼oz, 35g each)
wholemeal bread filled with 6oz (170g)
banana mashed with 2 teaspoons
honey and mixed with 1oz (30g) raisins
and ¼oz (7g) flaked almonds

An apple or pear from allowance	370	12·5

Late afternoon
Remaining portion of Fibre-Filler with milk
from allowance

	Calories	Fibre (g)
Evening meal		
* Crab and Apple Cocktail		
6oz (170g) gammon rasher, well grilled,		
served with 1 ring pineapple, from a can		
of pineapple in natural juice, heated		
through under grill		
4oz (115g) broccoli, boiled		
4oz (115g) broad beans, boiled	480	12·5
TOTAL	**1,250**	**45**

* Crab and Apple Cocktail

Serves 2

3oz (85g) crab meat
1 medium (5oz, 140g) eating apple (additional to allowance),
   cored and chopped
1oz (30g) canned sweetcorn kernels

Dressing
1 level teaspoon tomato purée
2 dessertspoons low-calorie salad dressing
a pinch of dry mustard
1 teaspoon lemon juice
1 teaspoon skimmed low-fat milk

Garnish
a few lettuce leaves, shredded
1 medium (2oz, 55g) tomato, sliced
lemon wedges

Place the crab, apple and sweetcorn in a medium-sized bowl and mix well. Mix all the dressing ingredients together and stir into the crab mixture. Line two glass dishes with shredded lettuce and pile the crab and apple mixture on top. Garnish with the tomato and lemon. Chill.

1,250 CALORIE MENU 7

	Calories	Fibre (g)
Daily allowance: Fibre-Filler (p. 65), ½ pint (285ml) skimmed milk, an orange and an apple or pear	400	20

Breakfast
Whole portion of Fibre-Filler with milk from allowance

Lunch
Creamed mushrooms on toast: 1 large thin slice (1¼oz, 35g) wholemeal bread, toasted and topped with 7½oz (213g) can Chesswood Sliced Mushrooms in Creamed Sauce, heated and mixed with 2½ level tablespoons bran and 1 tablespoon Worcestershire sauce

| An apple or pear from allowance | 300 | 8 |

Late afternoon
1 Jordans Original Crunchy Bar, Honey & Coconut

| An orange from allowance | 145 | 1 |

Evening meal
* Tropical Melon

* Chicken and Fruit Salad

| 2 Energen F-Plan Diet Brancrisps, spread with ¼oz (7g) low-fat spread | 405 | 8 |

| TOTAL | 1,250 | 37 |

* Tropical Melon

Serves 2

1lb 4oz (570g) water melon, rind and pips removed, flesh cut into 1in (2·5cm) cubes

1 tablespoon white rum
1 tablespoon unsweetened orange juice
2 level teaspoons desiccated coconut

Place the melon in a mixing bowl with the rum and orange juice and mix well. Cover and leave to stand for 1 hour in a cool place. Divide equally between two glass dishes and sprinkle with the coconut. Serve chilled.

* Chicken and Fruit Salad

Serves 2

6oz (170g) cooked chicken with all skin removed
2 rings pineapple from a can of pineapple rings in natural
   juice
4oz (115g) green grapes, halved and pips removed
150g carton low-fat natural yogurt
1 tablespoon lemon juice
salt and pepper
a few lettuce leaves
4oz (115g) cucumber, sliced
4oz (115g) canned sweetcorn kernels

Dice the chicken into bite-sized pieces and chop the pineapple rings. Place in a bowl with the grapes. Mix the yogurt with the lemon juice and season well with salt and pepper. Stir into the chicken mixture. Arrange a bed of lettuce leaves on two plates, divide the chicken and fruit salad equally between the two plates and pile into the centre. Arrange a ring of sliced cucumber around the edge and then spoon a thin ring of sweetcorn kernels on top of the cucumber slices.

1,250 CALORIE MENU   **8**

	Calories	Fibre (g)
Daily allowance: Fibre-Filler (p. 65),		
½ pint (285ml) skimmed milk, an orange		
and an apple or pear	400	20

	Calories	Fibre (g)
Breakfast		
Half portion of Fibre-Filler with milk from allowance		
An average-sized banana (6oz, 170g)	80	3·5
Lunch		
8oz (225g) canned baked beans in tomato sauce heated and topped with ½oz (15g) Edam cheese, grated		
An orange from allowance	205	16·5
Late afternoon		
Remaining portion of Fibre-Filler with milk from allowance		
Evening meal		
* Steak Kebabs		
Green salad: a few lettuce leaves, a few slices of cucumber, a small bunch of watercress		
An apple or pear from allowance	565	8
TOTAL	1,250	48

* Steak Kebabs

Serves 2

Marinade
1 tablespoon vegetable oil
2 tablespoons red wine
1 tablespoon low-calorie salad dressing

8oz (225g) rump steak, cut into ¾in (2cm) cubes
6 button onions or spring onion bulbs (2oz, 55g)
2 medium (4oz, 115g) tomatoes, each cut into four

3oz (85g) button mushrooms
1 small (3oz, 85g) green pepper, cut into 1in (2·5cm) pieces
6 bay leaves

To serve
4oz (115g) brown rice, boiled
2oz (55g) canned sweetcorn kernels, heated

Mix the marinade ingredients together. Place the cubes of steak in
the marinade and leave, covered, for approximately 1 hour. Then
thread the steak on to two long or four medium skewers, alternat-
ing with the onions, tomato, mushrooms, green pepper and bay
leaves. Cook under a preheated moderate grill for 15 minutes,
turning several times and brushing with the marinade. Mix the
rice with the sweetcorn and spoon on to a warm serving dish.
Place the kebabs on top and serve.

1,250 CALORIE MENU   9

	Calories	Fibre (g)
Daily allowance: Fibre-Filler (p. 65), ½ pint (285ml) skimmed milk, an orange and an apple or pear	400	20

Breakfast
Whole portion of Fibre-Filler with milk from
allowance

Lunch
Mushroom scramble on toast: poach 2oz
(55g) mushrooms, sliced, in 2fl oz (55ml)
skimmed milk (additional to allowance) in a
saucepan. Add 2 eggs (size 3), beaten, with
salt and pepper and cook gently, stirring,
until the eggs are creamy. Serve on 1 large
thin slice (1¼oz, 35g) wholemeal bread,
toasted

An orange from allowance   265   4·5

	Calories	Fibre (g)
Late afternoon		
1 small packet (25g) potato crisps		
1 apple or pear from allowance	130	3
Evening meal		
* Ham with Bean Salad		
* Fruited Orange Sorbet	455	15·5
TOTAL	**1,250**	**43**

* Ham with Bean Salad

Serves 2

6oz (170g) boiled lean ham, sliced
4oz (115g) French beans
2 large sticks celery, chopped
1oz (30g) onion, finely chopped
15½oz (440g) canned red kidney beans, drained
1 small green pepper (3oz, 85g), seeds removed and sliced
5 tablespoons oil-free French dressing
salt and pepper
a small bunch of watercress

Remove all visible fat from the meat. Cook the French beans in salted water until just tender, drain and rinse under cold water to cool. Cut the French beans into bite-sized pieces and mix in a salad bowl with the celery, onion, red kidney beans and green pepper. Add the dressing and salt and pepper to taste and mix well. Serve the salad with the sliced ham and garnish with watercress.

* Fruited Orange Sorbet

Serves 2

¼ pint (140ml) unsweetened orange juice or unsweetened passion fruit and orange juice

1oz (30g) granulated sugar
1oz (30g) sultanas
1 large (8oz, 225g) orange
1 egg white

To decorate
1 glacé cherry, halved
2 mint leaves

Place the orange juice, sugar and sultanas into a saucepan and heat until the sugar dissolves. Allow to cool. Cut the orange in half and cut out the flesh, reserve the two halves of orange skin. Purée the orange flesh in a blender and stir into the orange juice. Pour into a freezer container and freeze until granular. Beat with a fork. Whisk the egg white until it forms soft peaks, then fold in the orange mixture. Return to the freezer container and freeze until hard. To serve, spoon into the two halves of orange skin. Decorate each with half a glacé cherry and a mint leaf.

1,500 CALORIE MENU   1

	Calories	Fibre (g)
Daily allowance: Fibre-Filler (p. 65), ½ pint (285ml) skimmed milk, an orange and an apple or pear	400	20

Breakfast

Half portion of Fibre-Filler with milk from allowance		
1 egg (size 3), boiled and served with 1 large thin slice (1½oz, 35g) wholemeal bread, spread with ¼oz (7g) low-fat spread	180	3

Lunch
Cheese and pineapple on toast: 1 large thin slice (1¼oz, 35g) wholemeal bread, toasted,

	Calories	Fibre (g)

and covered with 1oz (30g) grated Cheddar
cheese and 1 ring pineapple from a can of
pineapple in natural juice. Heat through
under a hot grill until cheese has melted.
Garnish with a few sprigs of watercress

An apple or pear from allowance	225	3·5

Late afternoon
Remaining portion of Fibre-Filler with milk
from allowance

Evening meal
* Tuna Pasties
* Orange and Watercress Salad

150g carton low-fat raspberry-flavoured yogurt served with 6oz (170g) banana, peeled and sliced	695	11·5

TOTAL	1,500	38

* Tuna Pasties

Serves 2

Pastry
4oz (115g) wholemeal flour
pinch of salt
1½oz (45g) low-fat spread
½oz (15g) margarine

Filling
3½oz (100g) canned tuna in brine, drained and
  flaked
1½oz (45g) mature Cheddar cheese, grated
1 teaspoon tomato purée

1 teaspoon low-calorie salad dressing
1 medium (2oz, 55g) tomato, chopped
1 medium (5oz, 140g) eating apple, additional to allowance,
    cored and chopped
freshly ground pepper

For brushing
½ teaspoon salt in 3 tablespoons warm water

Preheat the oven to 200°C (400°F, gas 6). Place the wholemeal
flour, salt, low-fat spread and margarine in a mixing bowl and rub
the ingredients together using the fingertips until the mixture resembles breadcrumbs. Mix in enough cold water to form a soft
dough, lightly knead, then cut into two. Roll out each half to a 7in
(17·5cm) circle. Mix all the filling ingredients together. Divide the
filling equally between the two pastry circles. Damp the edges with
water, then bring up the edges to meet in the middle to form a
pasty shape. Flute the joined edges using a finger and a thumb.
Place on a baking sheet and brush with the salt and water. Bake in
the oven for 25–30 minutes or until the pastry is golden brown.
Serve hot or cold.

* Orange and Watercress Salad

Serves 2

2 medium-sized oranges (1 orange from allowance)
a large bunch of watercress
2 tablespoons lemon juice
salt and pepper
a few lettuce leaves

Cut the peel and pith off the orange using a sharp stainless steel
knife. Cut the orange segments out from the membranes. Divide
the watercress into sprigs, discarding any yellowed leaves, and mix
with the orange segments, lemon juice and seasoning to taste.
Line two individual salad bowls with lettuce leaves and spoon in
the orange and watercress salad.

1,500 CALORIE MENU   2

	Calories	Fibre (g)
Daily allowance: Fibre-Filler (p. 65), ½ pint (285ml) skimmed milk, an orange and an apple or pear	400	20

Breakfast
Half portion of Fibre-Filler with milk from allowance

1 large thin slice (1½oz, 35g) wholemeal bread, toasted and spread with ½oz (7g) low-fat spread and 2 level teaspoons honey or marmalade	130	3

Lunch
2oz (55g) wholemeal bap or lunch roll, split and filled with 1 hard-boiled egg (size 3), chopped and mixed with 1 tablespoon low-calorie salad dressing and ¼ carton mustard and cress

1 large digestive biscuit

An apple or pear from allowance	295	6

Late afternoon
Remaining portion of Fibre-Filler with milk from allowance

Evening meal
* Vegetable and Ham Gougère		
* Ice-cream and Orange Sundae	675	12·5

TOTAL	1,500	41·5

*Vegetable and Ham Gougère

Serves 2

Filling
7½oz (215g) canned butter beans, drained
2oz (55g) frozen peas, boiled
4oz (115g) cauliflower, broken into small florets and boiled
2oz (55g) carrot, sliced and boiled
2oz (55g) mushrooms, sliced
2oz (55g) boiled ham, chopped
1oz (30g) wholemeal flour
1oz (30g) low-fat spread
7fl oz (200ml) skimmed low-fat milk
salt and freshly ground pepper
1oz (30g) mature Cheddar cheese, grated

Choux pastry
1½oz (40g) low-fat spread
2oz (55g) wholemeal flour
1 egg (size 3), beaten

Preheat the oven to 220°C (425°F, gas 7). Place the butter beans, peas, cauliflower, carrot, mushrooms and ham into a bowl and mix well. Put the flour, low-fat spread, milk and salt and pepper into a small pan. Stir over a gentle heat until it thickens. Add the vegetable and ham mixture and mix thoroughly. Pour into a 1½ pint (850ml) ovenproof dish, sprinkle with the grated cheese and leave to one side. To make the choux pastry, put 3½fl oz (100ml) water and the low-fat spread into a small saucepan; bring to the boil. Stir in the flour all at once and beat well until the mixture leaves the sides of the saucepan clean. Remove from the heat and gradually beat in the egg. Using a ½in (1cm) nozzle, pipe the choux pastry round the edge of the filling. Bake in the hot oven for 15 minutes, then reduce the heat to 190°C (375°F, gas 5) and cook for a further 15 minutes, or until the cheese is beginning to brown. Serve hot.

* Ice-cream and Orange Sundae

Serves 2

4oz (115g) vanilla ice-cream
2 medium oranges (1 from allowance), segmented
½oz (15g) Jordans Original Crunchy with Bran and Apple

Divide the ice-cream in scoops equally between two sundae glasses
in layers, with the orange segments and Original Crunchy with
Bran and Apple. Serve at once.

1,500 CALORIE MENU   3

	Calories	Fibre (g)
Daily allowance: Fibre-Filler (p. 65), ½ pint (285ml) skimmed milk, an orange and an apple or pear	400	20

Breakfast
Whole portion of Fibre-Filler with milk from
allowance

Lunch
Cottage cheese and coleslaw salad: 4oz
(115g) low-fat cottage cheese (natural,
with onion and peppers or with pineapple),
served with 8oz (226g) carton Eden Vale
Coleslaw with Low Calorie Dressing and
with 1 medium tomato, quartered

An orange from allowance	235	5

Late afternoon
1 small packet (25g) potato crisps

An apple or pear from allowance	130	3

	Calories	Fibre (g)

Evening meal
½ grapefruit decorated with ½ glacé cherry
* Gammon with Somerset Sauce
4oz (115g) broad beans, boiled
4oz (115g) cauliflower, boiled

2 Energen F-Plan Diet Brancrisps with
1½oz (45g) Camembert, Brie or Edam cheese
1 large stick celery   735   13

TOTAL   1,500   41

*Gammon with Somerset Sauce

Serves 2

2 gammon rashers or steaks (6oz, 170g each)

Sauce
5fl oz (140ml) dry cider and 4 tablespoons water
1 small (6oz, 170g) cooking apple, cored and chopped
1 oz (30g) raisins
4 cloves
¼ teaspoon dry mustard
1 level teaspoon cornflour, blended with 1 teaspoon water

Garnish
8 slices of a red eating apple dipped in lemon juice,
   additional to allowance

Make cuts in the fat of the gammon rashers or steaks to prevent
curling during cooking. Grill under a preheated moderate grill for
8–10 minutes on each side or until the fat is well browned. Meanwhile, make the sauce: put all the ingredients into a medium-sized
saucepan and bring to the boil, stirring continuously. Reduce the
heat and simmer for 15 minutes. Arrange the gammon rashers on
a serving dish and spoon the sauce over them. Garnish with the
sliced apple.

1,500 CALORIE MENU   4

	Calories	Fibre (g)
Daily allowance: Fibre-Filler (p. 65), ½ pint (285ml) skimmed milk, an orange and an apple or pear	400	20
Breakfast Whole portion of Fibre-Filler with milk from allowance		
Lunch Cottage cheese and carrot sandwich: 2 large thin slices (1¼oz, 35g each) wholemeal bread filled with 2oz (55g) cottage cheese with chives mixed with 2oz (55g) carrot, grated, and 1 tablespoon low-calorie salad dressing	235	7·5
Late afternoon Jordans Original Crunchy Bar, Honey & Coconut		
An orange from allowance	145	1
Evening meal 1 chicken leg joint (8oz, 225g raw weight), baked in the oven and skin removed before serving 7oz (200g) potato baked in its jacket (see p. 31), split and topped with 1 table-spoon cottage cheese with chives mixed with 2 tablespoons oil-free French dressing 4oz (115g) frozen mixed peas, sweetcorn and peppers, boiled * Lemon Cheesecake	720	14·5
TOTAL	1,500	43

* Lemon Cheesecake

Serves 2

Base
3 large wheatmeal digestive biscuits, crushed
½oz (15g) low-fat spread

Filling
2oz (55g) low-fat cottage cheese, sieved
2 level tablespoons caster sugar
1 egg (size 3), separated
juice and grated rind of ½ lemon
2 level teaspoons powdered gelatine
4 tablespoons low-fat natural yogurt

Decoration
2 kiwi fruit, peeled and sliced

Place the crushed biscuits and low-fat spread in a saucepan and heat until they are thoroughly mixed. Divide equally between two individual glass dishes or tip into a 6in (15cm) flan ring on a baking tray; press down well. Leave in a cool place. Beat together the cottage cheese, sugar and egg yolk until smooth, add the lemon juice and grated rind. Dissolve the gelatine in 2 tablespoons water in a heatproof bowl over hot water. Stir into the cheese mixture with the yogurt. Whisk the egg white until it forms soft peaks, then fold into the other ingredients and pour over the biscuit base. Leave in a cool place to set. Decorate with sliced kiwi fruit.

1,500 CALORIE MENU   5

	Calories	Fibre (g)
Daily allowance: Fibre-Filler (p. 65), ½ pint (285ml) skimmed milk, an orange and an apple or pear	400	20

	Calories	Fibre (g)

Breakfast
Whole portion of Fibre-Filler with milk from
allowance

Lunch
* Minestrone Soup
2oz (55g) wholemeal lunch roll or bap,
spread with ½oz (7g) low-fat spread

An apple or pear from allowance	360	15

Late afternoon
1 large thin slice (1¼oz, 35g) wholemeal
bread, spread with ½oz (7g) low-fat spread
and 2 level teaspoons honey

An orange from allowance	130	3

Evening meal
8oz (225g) rump steak, grilled and all fat
trimmed off
Mixed salad: few lettuce leaves, 1oz (30g)
cucumber, sliced, 1 medium tomato, sliced,
1oz (30g) green pepper, sliced, 1oz (30g)
onion rings, a few sprigs of watercress and
1 tablespoon oil-free French dressing

* Raspberry Sundae	610	11

TOTAL	1,500	49

* Minestrone

Serves 2

2oz (55g) onion, coarsely grated or finely chopped
4oz (115g) carrot, coarsely grated
4oz (115g) parsnip, coarsely grated

1 chicken stock cube
½ pint (285ml) tomato juice
2oz (55g) wholewheat macaroni
4oz (115g) cabbage, finely shredded
salt and pepper
1 tablespoon chopped fresh parsley
2 level tablespoons grated Parmesan cheese

Put the onion, carrot and parsnip into a saucepan. Dissolve the chicken stock cube in ½ pint (285ml) boiling water and add to the vegetables in the pan with the tomato juice and macaroni. Bring to the boil, stir well, cover and simmer gently for 15 minutes. Add the cabbage, bring back to the boil and cook, covered, for a further 5–10 minutes until the cabbage is tender. Season to taste with salt and pepper and stir in the chopped parsley. Serve in two soup bowls and sprinkle 1 tablespoon cheese over each bowl. Serve hot.

* Raspberry Sundae

Serves 2

Jelly
8oz (225g) raspberries, fresh or frozen
½oz (15g) soft brown sugar
2 level teaspoons powdered gelatine, dissolved in 2 tablespoons
   water

Topping
3¼oz (90g) petit suisse cheese
3 tablespoons low-fat natural yogurt
1 level dessertspoon caster sugar

Place the raspberries, sugar and 7fl oz (200ml) water in a small saucepan and bring to the boil. Reduce the heat and simmer gently for 2–3 minutes. Remove from the heat and cool for a few minutes. Stir in the dissolved gelatine and pour into two sundae glasses. Leave to set, tilted on one side so the jelly sets at an angle. Meanwhile blend the petit suisse cheese, yogurt and caster sugar together. When the raspberry jelly is set, spoon half the topping into each glass on top of the jelly. Serve at once.

CANNED AND PACKAGED F-PLAN

As the title suggests, these menus contain a large number of ready-prepared canned and packaged convenience foods for those whose lifestyle leaves little time or inclination for food preparation. While they follow most of the basic F-Plan diet rules, the daily allowance has been adjusted so that packaged cereals can be used in place of Fibre-Filler to cut out the need to weigh out and make up the ingredients. Adequate food storage space, especially a food freezer, is an advantage when following these menus unless you can shop frequently.

To enable both men and women to use these menus, a choice of menus providing 1,000 calories, 1,250 calories and 1,500 calories daily has been given. All you have to do is to decide which daily calorie total will suit you best, i.e. give you the most satisfactory weight loss. You could find that if you are strict from Monday to Friday, i.e. selecting menus from the 1,000 calories section, you will be able to allow yourself to be a little more generous at the weekends and choose menus from the 1,250 calories or 1,500 calories section, and still achieve a satisfactory weight loss.

If you find that you long for the occasional alcoholic drink or bar of chocolate and can only stick to a diet which allows you to indulge occasionally, turn to the 1,500 calories menus. However, it may be necessary to limit strictly the number of days when you allow yourself an intake of 1,500 calories if your weight loss is slow.

SPECIAL DIET NOTES

1. Select the menus for at least one week at a time so that you can plan the shopping and always have the right foods available.

2. The daily allowance for all the 1,000 calories and 1,250 calories menus includes one tub Energen F-Plan Crunchy Bran Muesli in place of Fibre-Filler. The 1,500 calories menus have a high-fibre breakfast cereal with dried fruit for breakfast and no Fibre-Filler has been included in the daily allowance.

3. All the menus include ½ pint (285ml) skimmed milk and two whole fresh fruits (one orange and an apple or pear) in the daily allowance.

4. Use your skimmed milk allowance with the Crunchy Bran Muesli or cereal and in tea and coffee.

5. Tea and coffee are unlimited as long as you don't add sugar (artificial sweeteners can be used). In addition you can drink unlimited amounts of those drinks labelled 'low-calorie', and water.

6. The menus are divided into breakfast, a light meal, a main meal and an any-time snack or drink. You can eat these meals in any order you wish throughout the day, but eat *only* those meals/snacks and/or drinks included in your chosen menu.

1,000 CALORIE MENU   1

	Calories	Fibre (g)
Daily allowance: 2 tubs Energen F-Plan Crunchy Bran Muesli, ½ pint (285ml) skimmed milk, two items of fruit	420	20

Breakfast
1 tub Energen F-Plan Crunchy Bran Muesli with milk from allowance

Light meal
10·6oz (300g) can Heinz Lentil Soup
1 Allinson's wholemeal snack roll (1½oz, 42g)

| An apple or pear from allowance | 270 | 9·5 |

Main meal
Individual pack of Birds Eye Gravy & Lean Roast Chicken

	Calories	Fibre (g)
8oz (225g) Birds Eye Cauliflower, Peas & Carrots		
An orange from allowance	270	9·5
Any-time snacks 1 tub of Energen F-Plan Crunchy Bran Muesli with milk from allowance		
1 Boots Second Nature Wholemeal Hazelnut Biscuit	40	0·5
TOTAL	1,000	39·5

1,000 CALORIE MENU   2

	Calories	Fibre (g)
Daily allowance: 2 tubs Energen F-Plan Crunchy Bran Muesli, ½ pint (285ml) skimmed milk, two items of fruit	420	20
Breakfast 1 tub Energen F-Plan Crunchy Bran Muesli with milk from allowance		
An orange from allowance		
Light meal 2 large thin slices (1½oz, 35g each) wholemeal bread filled with the contents of a 1½oz (35g) pot of Princes Crab Pâté and 1oz (30g) watercress		
2oz (55g) carrot sticks	215	8·5

	Calories	Fibre (g)
Main meal		
3oz (85g) sliced corned beef		
8oz (226g) carton Eden Vale Coleslaw in Vinaigrette		
Mixed salad: a few lettuce leaves, 1oz (30g) cucumber, sliced, 2 average tomatoes, sliced, 2 spring onions, chopped, 1oz (30g) green or red pepper, sliced and chopped with 1 tablespoon Waistline Oil-Free French Dressing		
2 Energen F-Plan Diet Brancrisps, spread with ¼oz (7g) low-fat spread	365	11
Any-time snacks		
1 tub Energen F-Plan Crunchy Bran Muesli with milk from allowance		
An apple or pear from allowance		

TOTAL	1,000	39·5

1,000 CALORIE MENU 3

	Calories	Fibre (g)
Daily allowance: 2 tubs Energen F-Plan Crunchy Bran Muesli, ½ pint (285ml) skimmed milk, two items of fruit	420	20
Breakfast		
1 tub Energen F-Plan Crunchy Bran Muesli with milk from allowance		

1 large thin slice (1¼oz, 35g) wholemeal

	Calories	Fibre (g)
bread, toasted and spread with ¼oz (7g) low-fat spread and Marmite or savoury yeast extract	105	3

Light meal
1 large thin slice (1¼oz, 35g) wholemeal bread, toasted and topped with 8oz (225g) canned baked beans in tomato sauce — 235 — 19·5

Main meal
1 packet Birds Eye Chicken & Mushroom Casserole.
4oz (115g) frozen Brussels sprouts, boiled
4oz (115g) canned new potatoes

An orange from allowance — 240 — 6·5

Any-time snacks
1 tub Energen F-Plan Crunchy
Bran Muesli with milk from
allowance

TOTAL	1,000	49

1,000 CALORIE MENU   4

	Calories	Fibre (g)
Daily allowance: 2 tubs Energen F-Plan Crunchy Bran Muesli, ½ pint (285ml) skimmed milk, two items of fruit	420	20

Breakfast
Both tubs of Energen F-Plan Crunchy
Bran Muesli with milk from allowance

	Calories	Fibre (g)

Light meal
2 Energen F-Plan Diet Brancrisps, spread with
the contents of a 1·23oz (35g) pot of
Shippams Chicken & Bacon Country Pot
Paste and each topped with an average-
sized tomato, sliced, and a little mustard
and cress

	Calories	Fibre (g)
An apple or pear from allowance	120	4

Main meal
13·6oz (385g) pack Marco & Carlo Spaghetti
Bolognese (whole pack)
4oz (115g) frozen peas, boiled

An average-sized banana (6oz, 170g)	460	14

Any-time snack
An orange from allowance

TOTAL	1,000	38

1,000 CALORIE MENU   5

	Calories	Fibre (g)
Daily allowance: 2 tubs Energen F-Plan Crunchy Bran Muesli, ½ pint (285ml) skimmed milk, two items of fruit	420	20

Breakfast
Both tubs Energen F-Plan Crunchy Bran
Muesli with milk from allowance

	Calories	Fibre (g)
Light meal		
4oz (115g) carton cottage cheese with onion and peppers		
8oz (226g) carton Eden Vale Coleslaw in Vinaigrette		
An apple or pear from allowance	190	6·5
Main meal		
15oz (425g) can Campbell's Main Course Pea & Ham Soup		
1 Energen F-Plan Diet Brancrisp		
An orange from allowance	375	10·5
Any-time snacks		
2oz (55g) carrot sticks		
1 large stick celery	15	2·5
TOTAL	1,000	39·5

1,000 CALORIE MENU   6

	Calories	Fibre (g)
Daily allowance: 2 tubs Energen F-Plan Crunchy Bran Muesli, ½ pint (285ml) skimmed milk, two items of fruit	420	20

Breakfast
1 tub Energen F-Plan Crunchy Bran
Muesli with milk from allowance

Light meal
150g carton fruit-flavoured low-fat yogurt

	Calories	Fibre (g)
1 Quaker Harvest Crunch Bar, almond or peanut		
An orange from allowance	210	1
Main meal 1 egg (size 3), poached 2 rashers streaky bacon, grilled crisp 8oz (225g) canned baked beans in tomato sauce		
An apple or pear from allowance	340	16·5
Any-time snacks 1 tub Energen F-Plan Crunchy Bran Muesli with milk from allowance		
1 Energen F-Plan Diet Brancrisp, spread with Marmite or yeast extract	30	1·5
TOTAL	1,000	39

1,000 CALORIE MENU   7

	Calories	Fibre (g)
Daily allowance: 2 tubs Energen F-Plan Crunchy Bran Muesli, ½ pint (285ml) skimmed milk, two items of fruit	420	20
Breakfast 1 tub Energen F-Plan Crunchy Bran Muesli with milk from allowance		

	Calories	Fibre (g)
Light meal		
15·3oz (435g) can Heinz Vegetable & Lentil Big Soup		
An apple or pear from allowance	210	9
Main meal		
1 pack Birds Eye Cod in Cheese Sauce		
4oz (115g) Birds Eye Peas, Sweetcorn & Peppers, boiled		
Half medium pack Smash Potato Pieces, made up with boiling water (no butter)	360	12
Any-time snacks		
1 tub Energen F-Plan Crunchy Bran Muesli with milk from allowance		
2 large sticks celery	10	2
TOTAL	**1,000**	**43**

1,250 CALORIE MENU   1

	Calories	Fibre (g)
Daily allowance: 2 tubs Energen F-Plan Crunchy Bran Muesli, ½ pint (285ml) skimmed milk, two items of fruit	420	20

Breakfast
Both tubs of Energen F-Plan Crunchy Bran
Muesli with milk from allowance

Light meal
Peanut salad sandwich: 2 large thin slices

	Calories	Fibre (g)
(1½oz, 35g each) wholemeal bread spread with 1oz (30g) peanut butter and filled with 1 lettuce leaf, 1 tomato, sliced, a few slices of cucumber and a few sprigs of watercress		
An orange from allowance	340	9·5

Main meal

15oz (425g) can Campbell's Steak & Kidney Stew		
8oz (225g) Birds Eye Cauliflower, Peas & Carrots		
Half packet Smash Potato Pieces, made up with boiling water (no butter)	425	14

Any-time snacks

1 Energen F-Plan Diet Brancrisp, spread with 1 triangle cheese spread		
An apple or pear from allowance	65	1·5

TOTAL	1,250	45

1,250 CALORIE MENU   2

	Calories	Fibre (g)
Daily allowance: 2 tubs Energen F-Plan Crunchy Bran Muesli, ½ pint (285ml) skimmed milk, two items of fruit	420	20

Breakfast
Both tubs Energen F-Plan Crunchy Bran Muesli with milk from allowance

An orange from allowance

	Calories	Fibre (g)
Light meal		
1 large thin slice (1¼oz, 35g) wholemeal bread topped with 1oz (30g) Cheddar cheese, grated and mixed with 1oz (30g) sweet pickle and grilled until cheese melts		
2 average-sized tomatoes		
a small bunch of watercress		
An apple or pear from allowance	250	6
Main meal		
10½oz (300g) Findus Cottage Pie		
4oz (115g) frozen peas, boiled		
150g carton low-fat fruit-flavoured yogurt	500	9
Any-time snack		
1 piece Allinson Wholemeal Shortbread	80	1
TOTAL	1,250	36

1,250 CALORIE MENU   3

	Calories	Fibre (g)
Daily allowance: 2 tubs Energen F-Plan Crunchy Bran Muesli, ½ pint (285ml) skimmed milk, two items of fruit	420	20
Breakfast		
Both tubs Energen F-Plan Crunchy Bran Muesli with milk from allowance		
Light meal		
10·6oz (300g) can Heinz Pea & Ham Soup		
2 Energen F-Plan Diet Brancrisps		
An apple or pear from allowance	245	9·5

	Calories	Fibre (g)
Main Meal 1 Findus Savoury Barbecue Beef French Bread Pizza Salad: a few lettuce leaves, 1 tomato, sliced, 1oz (30g) cucumber, sliced, a small bunch of watercress, 1oz (30g) green pepper, sliced, dressed with 1 tablespoon low-calorie oil-free French dressing		
10oz (283g) can John West Peach Slices in Fruit Juice	540	8·5
Any-time snacks An orange from allowance		
1 Boots Second Nature Bran Biscuit	45	1·5
TOTAL	1,250	39·5

1,250 CALORIE MENU   4

	Calories	Fibre (g)
Daily allowance: 2 tubs Energen F-Plan Crunchy Bran Muesli, ½ pint (285ml) skimmed milk, two items of fruit	420	20
Breakfast Both tubs Energen F-Plan Crunchy Bran Muesli with milk from allowance		
Light meal Bacon and green pepper sandwich: 2 slices (1¼oz, 35g each) wholemeal bread filled with 1⅞oz (53g) pot Princes Smokey Bacon Spread and 1½oz (45g) chopped green pepper		
An orange from allowance	280	6·5

	Calories	Fibre (g)

Main meal
1 Findus All Beef Quarter Pounder
(beefburger), well grilled
Half 10·7oz (304g) can Batchelor's Mushy
Peas
3½oz (100g) canned small whole
mushrooms in brine

150g carton low-fat fruit-flavoured yogurt	460	12·5

Any-time snacks
An apple or pear from allowance

| 1 Quaker Harvest Crunch Bar, almond
or peanut	90	1

TOTAL	1,250	40

1,250 CALORIE MENU   5

	Calories	Fibre (g)
**Daily allowance: 2 tubs Energen F-Plan
Crunchy Bran Muesli, ½ pint (285ml)
skimmed milk, two items of fruit**	420	20

Breakfast
Both tubs Energen F-Plan Crunchy Bran
Muesli with milk from allowance

Light meal
Creamy mushrooms on toast: 1 large thin
slice (1¼oz, 35g) wholemeal bread, toasted
and topped with 7½oz (215g) canned sliced
mushrooms in creamed sauce, mixed with 1
level tablespoon bran and 1 tablespoon

	Calories	Fibre (g)
Worcestershire sauce and heated through		
A small bunch of watercress		
An apple or pear from allowance	285	7

Main meal
2 sausalatas from 10oz (283g) can Granose
Sausalatas, grilled
Half medium packet Smash Potato Pieces,
made up without butter
8oz (225g) Birds Eye Peas & Baby Carrots

	Calories	Fibre (g)
150g carton low-fat natural yogurt with 1 level teaspoon honey or soft brown sugar	395	22

Any-time snacks
1 choc ice (chocolate covered ice-cream bar)
or 1 Cadbury's Fudge Bar

	Calories	Fibre (g)
An orange from allowance	150	0

	Calories	Fibre (g)
TOTAL	**1,250**	**49**

1,250 CALORIE MENU   6

	Calories	Fibre (g)
Daily allowance: 2 tubs Energen F-Plan Crunchy Bran Muesli, ½ pint (285ml) skimmed milk, two items of fruit	420	20

Breakfast
1 tub Energen F-Plan Crunchy Bran
Muesli with milk from allowance

1 egg (size 3), poached and served on

	Calories	Fibre (g)
1 large thin slice (1½oz, 35g) wholemeal bread, toasted	155	3

Light meal
2 sardines in tomato sauce
Half 7½oz (206g) can Heinz Vegetable
Salad
A few lettuce leaves
1 average-sized tomato

An apple or pear from allowance	270	3·5

Main meal
1 pack Birds Eye Liver with Onion & Gravy
Half medium packet Smash Potato Pieces,
made up without butter
Half 10oz (283g) can Hartley's or Smedley's
broad beans

An orange from allowance	350	9

Any-time snacks
1 tub Energen F-Plan Crunchy Bran
Muesli with milk from allowance

1 small (4oz, 115g) banana	55	2·5

TOTAL	**1,250**	**38**

1,250 CALORIE MENU 7

	Calories	Fibre (g)
Daily allowance: 2 tubs Energen F-Plan Crunchy Bran Muesli, ½ pint (285ml) skimmed milk, two items of fruit	420	20

	Calories	Fibre (g)

Breakfast
1 tub Energen F-Plan Crunchy Bran
Muesli with milk from allowance

1 large thin slice (1¼oz, 35g) wholemeal bread,
toasted and spread with ¼oz (7g) low-fat spread
and 1 level teaspoon honey or marmalade   115   3

Light meal
1 McCain Deep 'n' Delicious Cheese & Onion
or Cheese & Tomato Pizza
4oz (115g) canned baked beans in tomato
sauce

An orange from allowance   270   9·5

Main meal
Mushroom omelet: 2 eggs (size 3), beaten
with 2 tablespoons water, salt and pepper
and a pinch of mixed herbs. Cook in ½oz
(7g) low-fat spread in a non-stick omelet pan
and fill with the contents of a 7½oz (213g)
can Chesswood Sliced Large Mushrooms in
Brine, drained
Half 7oz (198g) can Green Giant Mexicorn
Golden Corn

150g carton low-fat fruit-flavoured yogurt
with 7¾oz (220g) can Boots Shapers Pears
in Low-Calorie Syrup   445   12·5

Any-time snacks
1 tub Energen F-Plan Crunchy Bran
Muesli with milk from allowance

An apple or pear from allowance

TOTAL   1,250   45

1,500 CALORIE MENU   1

	Calories	Fibre (g)
Daily allowance: ½ pint (285ml) skimmed milk, two items of fruit	200	5
Breakfast 2oz (55g) Allinson Crunchy Bran with ½oz (15g) sultanas or raisins and milk from allowance	165	16·5
Light meal 7½oz (215g) canned spaghetti in tomato sauce, topped with 1 egg (size 3), poached		
1 Jordans Original Crunchy Bar, Honey & Coconut		
1 average-sized banana (6oz, 170g)	435	6·5
Main meal 10oz (284g) pack Birds Eye Mediterranean Stir-Fry Vegetables, fried and mixed with 7oz (200g) canned tuna in brine, drained and flaked		
An orange from allowance	530	6·5
Any-time snacks An apple of pear from allowance		
2 Energen F-Plan Diet Brancrisps, spread with Princes Beef or Fried Chicken Spread (1¼oz, 35g) pot, and topped with 1oz (30g) sweet pickle	170	3
TOTAL	1,500	37·5

1,500 CALORIE MENU   2

	Calories	Fibre (g)
Daily allowance: ½ pint (285ml) skimmed milk, two items of fruit	200	5

Breakfast
1½oz (45g) Kellogg's All-Bran with 1oz (30g) Whitworth's (no-need-to-soak) dried apricots, chopped, and milk from allowance | 150 | 18

Light meal
1 pot Golden Wonder Chicken & Mushroom Pot Noodle

An apple or pear from allowance | 380 | 8·5

Main meal
14oz (397g) tray Birds Eye Captain's Pie (cod in butter sauce topped with potato and a sprinkling of Cheddar cheese)
4oz (115g) frozen peas, boiled

8oz (227g) can Koo Peach Slices in Apple Juice
2oz (55g) portion vanilla ice-cream | 670 | 13

Any-time snack and drinks
An orange from allowance

2 bar measures of spirits (gin, rum, vodka or whisky) with low-calorie mixers *or*
1 glass (4fl oz, 115ml) sweet white wine *or*
other drinks chosen from chart (p. 281)
to value of 100 calories | 100 | 0

| TOTAL | 1,500 | 44·5 |

1,500 CALORIE MENU   3

	Calories	Fibre (g)
Daily allowance: ½ pint (285ml) skimmed milk, two items of fruit	200	5
Breakfast 2oz (55g) Allinson Crunchy Bran with ½oz (15g) sultanas or raisins and milk from allowance	165	16·5
Light meal 15oz (425g) can Baxter's or Campbell's Granny Lentil Soup 2 Energen F-Plan Diet Brancrisps An apple or pear from allowance	285	12·5
Main meal Half 14·8oz (419g) tray frozen Marco & Carlo Lasagne, cooked Half 1lb 1oz (482g) can Green Giant American Bean Salad Half 8oz (227g) can Del Monte Pineapple Slices in Natural Juice 150g carton Eden Vale Natural Yogurt with Honey	560	8
Any-time snacks and drinks Drink(s) from chart (p. 281) to value of 160 calories 1 small (25g) packet potato crisps, any flavour An orange from allowance	290	3
TOTAL	1,500	45

1,500 CALORIE MENU   4

	Calories	Fibre (g)
Daily allowance: ½ pint (285ml) skimmed milk, two items of fruit	200	5

Breakfast
1½oz (45g) Kellogg's All-Bran with 1oz
(30g) Whitworth's (no-need-to-soak) dried
apricots, chopped, and milk from allowance   150   18

Light meal
Crab and salad sandwich: 2 large thin
slices (1¼oz, 35g each) wholemeal bread
filled with contents of 1½oz (42g) can John
West Dressed Crab, 1 tablespoon low-
calorie salad dressing, 1 lettuce leaf, 1
tomato, sliced, a few slices of cucumber, a
few sprigs of watercress

1 Prewett's Fruit & Nut Dessert Bar

An orange from allowance   380   11

Main meal
1 individual Birds Eye Frozen Chicken &
Mushroom Pie, cooked
8oz (225g) Birds Eye frozen Cauliflower,
Peas & Carrots

2oz (55g) vanilla ice-cream with an
average-sized banana (6oz, 170g), sliced   605   15

Any-time snacks
An apple or pear from allowance

1 Cadbury's Crunchie, large *or* Rowntree
Mackintosh Walnut Whip, Plain Chocolate

	Calories	Fibre (g)
Vanilla *or* St Michael Milk Chocolate Wafer Bar (30g)	165	0
TOTAL	1,500	49

1,500 CALORIE MENU 5

	Calories	Fibre (g)
Daily allowance: ½ pint (285ml) skimmed milk, two items of fruit	200	5

Breakfast

	Calories	Fibre (g)
2oz (55g) Allinson Crunchy Bran with ½oz (15g) sultanas or raisins and milk from allowance	165	16·5

Light meal

8oz (225g) canned baked beans in tomato sauce

2oz (55g) frozen beefburger, grilled

	Calories	Fibre (g)
An orange from allowance	290	16·5

Main meal

1 Bowyer's individual (5oz, 142g) pork pie
Mixed salad: 1 average-sized tomato, sliced, a few spring onions, 1oz (30g) cucumber, sliced, a few sprigs of watercress, a few lettuce leaves, 1oz (30g) green pepper, sliced, and 1 tablespoon oil-free French dressing

	Calories	Fibre (g)
150g carton low-fat fruit-flavoured yogurt	705	4

	Calories	Fibre (g)

Any-time snacks and drinks
An apple or pear from allowance

1 Energen F-Plan Diet Brancrisp, spread
with 1 triangle cheese spread and topped
with a few sprigs of watercress or slices of
cucumber

	Calories	Fibre (g)
1 drink chosen from chart (p. 281) to the value of 75 calories	140	2·5
TOTAL	1,500	44·5

1,500 CALORIE MENU   6

	Calories	Fibre (g)
Daily allowance: ½ pint (285ml) skimmed milk, two items of fruit	200	5

Breakfast
| 1½oz (45g) Kellogg's All-Bran with 1oz (30g) Whitworth's (no-need-to-soak) dried apricots, chopped, and milk from allowance | 150 | 18 |

Light meal
Chicken and ham with tomato sandwich:
2 large thin slices (1¼oz, 35g each)
wholemeal bread, filled with Shippams
Chicken & Ham Paste, 1·23oz (35g) pot,
and 1 large tomato, sliced
1 small packet (25g) potato crisps, any
flavour

| An apple or pear from allowance | 360 | 10 |

	Calories	Fibre (g)
Main meal		
1 pack Birds Eye Braised Kidneys in Gravy		
Half medium packet Smash Potato Pieces, made up without butter		
4oz (115g) frozen mixed vegetables (Birds Eye or Ross)		
1 individual Birds Eye Trifle or Super Mousse	500	10·5
Any-time snacks and drinks		
An orange from allowance		
1 Quaker Harvest Crunch Bar, almond or peanut		
Drinks chosen from chart (p. 281) to the value of 200 calories	290	1

TOTAL	1,500	44·5

F-PLAN FOR MEN

Although most men could achieve a very successful weight loss on any of the 1,500 calorie menus in this book, these menus have been especially designed to take into account their different life-styles. The menus which total between 1,200 and 1,300 calories are intended for the drinking man, allowing him to 'spend' between 200 and 300 calories (to bring the daily total up to 1,500 calories) on alcoholic drinks (see chart, p. 281). Those menus with meals eaten in a restaurant, etc., have an *approximate* calorie and fibre total, since it is impossible to calculate the value of such meals accurately.

Varied eating habits have been taken into account in these menus. Although breakfasts have been included each day, if you are a non-breakfast eater you can keep this meal until later in the day. Various types of lunches – for example, packed lunches, café, restaurant, business, pub and Sunday/weekend lunches – have been included to cater for different needs. Some of the evening meals are easy-cook meals which might better suit the bachelor; others are suitable for the married man who eats his meals with his family. The recipes are all planned to serve one person, but the recipe ingredients can easily be multiplied by the number of people eating together, when appropriate.

Some variation from the basic F-Plan rules will be found in the 'daily allowances', since some men lack the time to make Fibre-Filler and others find skimmed milk unacceptable. In case anyone should be tempted to give up the diet for either of these reasons, half the menus do not include Fibre-Filler and a few menus include whole milk (in place of skimmed milk) in the daily allowance.

SPECIAL DIET NOTES

1. Decide whether or not you wish to include one or two alcoholic drinks in your daily menus.

2. On the days when you can do without alcohol, choose your menus from the 1,500 calorie daily menus.

3. Choose your menus from the 1,200–1,300 calorie menus on days when you know you will want an alcoholic drink, and decide which drinks you will have using the chart (p. 281).

4. Make sure that you 'spend' only an additional 200–300 calories on drinks if you want to achieve a good weight loss.

5. Select menus for at least two or three days, preferably one week at a time, so that you can plan to have the right foods ready at the right time.

6. Don't just choose one menu and repeat it every day. Use a variety of menus which will ensure a variety of foods and hence a variety of nutrients, which is essential for good health.

7. The daily allowance' of essential basic F-Plan diet foods varies throughout the menus, so ensure that you know what is included in the 'daily allowance' of each menu you select.

8. Non-alcoholic drinks, such as sugarless tea and coffee, either black or with skimmed or whole milk from the daily allowance, low-calorie labelled bottled and canned drinks, and water can be drunk in unlimited amounts at any time of the day.

1,500 CALORIE MENU   1
(no additional alcohol)

	Calories	Fibre (g)
Daily allowance: Fibre-Filler (p. 65), ½ pint (285ml) skimmed milk, an orange and an apple or pear	400	20

Breakfast
Whole daily portion of Fibre-Filler with milk
from allowance

	Calories	Fibre (g)

Lunch (to carry to work)
* Ham Double-Decker Sandwich

1 small packet (25g) potato crisps, any
flavour

An apple or pear from allowance	445	13·5

Evening meal
8oz (225g) chicken leg joint, grilled or oven
baked without added fat
7oz (200g) potato, baked in its jacket (see
p. 31 for cooking instructions), served
with ½oz (15g) low-fat spread
4oz (115g) Brussels sprouts, boiled
4oz (115g) carrots, boiled

2oz (55g) vanilla ice-cream with 2 wafers

An orange from allowance	655	11·5

TOTAL	1,500	45

* Ham Double-Decker Sandwich

Serves 1

3 large thin slices (1¼oz, 35g each) wholemeal bread
a little made mustard
1oz (30g) sliced boiled lean ham
¼ carton mustard and cress
¼oz (7g) low-fat spread
1 medium tomato, sliced
a few slices of cucumber
a few lettuce leaves
salt and pepper

Spread one slice of the bread with a little made mustard, top with the slice of boiled ham and the mustard and cress. Spread the second slice of bread lightly with half the low-fat spread and place spread side up on the ham. Cover with slices of tomato, cucumber and lettuce leaves. Season to taste. Spread the third slice of bread with the remaining low-fat spread and place spread side down on top of the sandwich. Cut into four small sandwiches and pack.

1,500 CALORIE MENU   2
(no additional alcohol)

	Calories	Fibre (g)
Daily allowance: Fibre-Filler (p. 65), $\frac{1}{2}$ pint (285ml) silver-top (whole pasteurized) milk, an orange and an apple or pear	490	20

Breakfast
Whole daily portion of Fibre-Filler with milk from allowance

An orange from allowance

Lunch (to carry to work)
* Crunchy Cheese and Tomato Rolls

2 fingers Kit Kat *or* 2 Hovis digestive biscuits

| An apple or pear from allowance | 490 | 12 |

Evening meal
6oz (170g) cod, haddock or coley fillets, brushed with 1 teaspoon cooking oil and grilled (serve with a wedge of lemon)
4oz (115g) frozen peas, boiled

	Calories	Fibre (g)
4oz (115g) canned tomatoes		
5oz (140g) boiled potatoes (no butter) *or* half medium-size packet Smash Potato Pieces, made up with boiling water (no butter)		
4oz (115g) canned pineapple slices in natural juice		
2oz (55g) portion vanilla ice-cream	520	12·5
TOTAL	1,500	44·5

* Crunchy Cheese and Tomato Rolls

Serves 1

2 wholemeal rolls, e.g. Allinson's (1½oz, 42g each)
1oz (30g) mature Cheddar cheese, grated
2 tablespoons low-calorie salad dressing
1 large stick celery, finely chopped
1 medium carrot, grated
2 medium tomatoes, sliced

Split the rolls. Mix the grated cheese with the salad dressing, finely chopped celery and grated carrot. Spread half the mixture over the cut surface of the bottom half of each roll. Cover each with sliced tomato and replace the top half of each roll. Pack.

1,500 CALORIE MENU   3
(no additional alcohol)

	Calories	Fibre (g)
Daily allowance: Fibre-Filler (p. 65), ½ pint (285ml) silver-top (whole pasteurized) milk, an orange and an apple or pear	490	20

	Calories	Fibre (g)

Breakfast
Whole daily portion of Fibre-Filler with
milk from allowance

Lunch (to carry to work)
2 * Sardine and Celery Sandwiches

An apple or pear from allowance	575	15

Evening meal
8oz (225g) individual frozen shepherd's pie
4oz (115g) cabbage, boiled
4oz (115g) carrots, boiled

1 Ryvita crispbread, brown or original,
with 1oz (30g) Edam, Brie, Camembert or
processed cheese (no butter)
2 sticks celery

An orange from allowance	435	10·5

TOTAL	1,500	45·5

* Sardine and Celery Sandwiches

Serves 1

4 large thin slices (1¼oz, 35g each) wholemeal bread
½oz (15g) low-fat spread
4½oz (130g) canned sardines in tomato sauce
½ teaspoon vinegar
2 large sticks celery, finely chopped
a few sprigs of watercress

Spread each of the slices of bread lightly with low-fat spread. Mash the sardines with the vinegar and mix with the chopped celery. Spread the sardine filling over two slices of bread. Cover with sprigs of watercress and top with the remaining slices of bread to make two rounds of sandwiches. Cut each sandwich into two or four pieces and pack.

1,500 CALORIE MENU   4
(no additional alcohol)

	Calories	Fibre (g)
Daily allowance: Fibre-Filler (p. 24), ½ pint (285ml) skimmed milk, an orange and an apple or pear	400	20

Breakfast
Whole daily portion of Fibre-Filler with
milk from allowance

**Business/restaurant lunch or evening
meal**
Slice (8oz, 225g) cantaloup, honeydew or
yellow melon (no sugar)
8oz (225g) steak, medium grilled
1 jacket baked potato, with a small pat of
butter or a foil-wrapped portion of butter
Green or mixed salad without dressing

1 glass (4fl oz, 115ml) dry red wine	approx. 890	8

Light meal
15·3oz (435g) can Heinz Vegetable &
Lentil Big Soup

An orange and an apple or pear from allowance	210	9

TOTAL	approx. 1,500	37

1,500 CALORIE MENU   5
(no additional alcohol)

	Calories	Fibre (g)
Daily allowance: Fibre-Filler (p. 65), ½ pint (285ml) skimmed milk, an orange and an apple or pear	400	20

	Calories	Fibre (g)

Breakfast
Whole daily portion of Fibre-Filler with
milk from allowance

Café/restaurant lunch
Mushroom omelet and chips

An apple or pear from allowance
(*Note.* If fresh fruit is not served in the café
or restaurant omit the dessert and eat the
fruit at home later in the day.)   approx. 600   3·5

Evening meal
* Kidney Bean, Cauliflower and Corned
Beef Salad

2 Ryvita crispbreads, brown or original,
with 1oz (30g) Edam, Brie, Camembert or
processed cheese (no butter)
2 sticks celery

An orange from allowance   500   18·5

TOTAL   approx. 1,500   42

---

* **Kidney Bean, Cauliflower and Corned Beef Salad**

Serves 1

4oz (115g) canned kidney beans, drained
4oz (115g) fresh cauliflower, broken into florets
2 or 3 spring onions, chopped *or* 1oz (30g) onion, sliced
3oz (85g) corned beef, diced
2oz (55g) green pepper, chopped

3 tablespoons oil-free French dressing
a pinch of curry powder
a few sprigs of watercress
2 small tomatoes, or 1 large one, cut in wedges

Put all the ingredients except the watercress and tomatoes into a bowl and toss until well mixed. Leave to stand for 30 minutes before serving. Serve garnished with sprigs of watercress and wedges of tomato.

1,500 CALORIE MENU   6
(no additional alcohol)

	Calories	Fibre (g)
Daily allowance: ½ pint (285ml) skimmed milk, an orange and an apple or pear	200	5
Breakfast		
1½oz (45g) All Bran or Bran Buds with ½oz (15g) sultanas and milk from daily allowance		
1 large thin slice (1¼oz, 35g) wholemeal bread, spread with ¼oz (7g) low-fat spread and 1 level teaspoon honey or marmalade	245	15
Lunch (to carry to work)		
* Prawn and Salad Double-Decker Sandwiches		
2 fingers Kit Kat or 2 Hovis digestive biscuits		
An apple or pear from allowance	460	10·5

	Calories	Fibre (g)

Evening meal

7oz (200g) raw weight pork chop, grilled,
with fat cut off before serving

1oz (30g) apple sauce
4oz (115g) button mushrooms, poached in
stock *or* 7½oz (215g) canned mushrooms in
brine
4oz (115g) frozen mixed peas, sweetcorn
and peppers, boiled
5oz (140g) boiled new potatoes *or* 7oz
(200g) canned new potatoes, drained (no
butter)

1 Ryvita crispbread (no butter)
½oz (15g) Edam, Brie, Camembert or
processed cheese
1 stick celery

An orange from allowance	595	16
TOTAL	1,500	46·5

* Prawn and Salad Double-Decker Sandwiches

Serves 1

3 large thin slices (1¼oz, 35g each) wholemeal bread
2 tablespoons low-calorie salad dressing
2 oz (55g) peeled prawns (fresh, frozen or canned)
a few sprigs of watercress
1 medium tomato, sliced
a few slices of cucumber

Spread all three slices of bread on one side with a little of the low-calorie salad dressing. Mix the prawns with the remaining salad dressing and use to cover one slice of the bread. Place second slice of bread on top of the prawns and cover with the watercress, tomato and cucumber. Place the final slice of bread, spread side down, on top of the sandwich. Cut into four small sandwiches and pack.

1,500 CALORIE MENU   7
(no additional alcohol)

	Calories	Fibre (g)
Daily allowance: ½ pint (285ml) skimmed milk, an orange and an apple or pear	200	5
Breakfast 2oz (55g) Prewett's Bran Muesli with milk from allowance		
An average-sized banana (6oz, 170g)	255	16
Lunch (to carry to work) Cheese and pickle bap: 2oz (55g) wholemeal bap (round flat roll), split and filled with 1oz (30g) piccalilli, chopped finely and mixed with 1oz (30g) Cheddar cheese, grated		
3oz (85g) carrots, cut into sticks 1 large stick celery, cut into short sticks 1 small packet (25g) potato crisps, any flavour		
An orange from allowance	400	12
Evening meal * Bacon and Liver Casserole 7oz (200g) baked jacket potato (baked in the oven with the casserole, see p. 328) 4oz (115g) canned tomatoes 4oz (115g) frozen peas, boiled		
An apple or pear from allowance	645	16
TOTAL	1,500	49

* Bacon and Liver Casserole

Serves 1

4oz (115g) pig's liver
1 level tablespoon cornflour
a generous pinch of dried mixed herbs
salt and pepper
2 rashers streaky bacon, rind removed
1 small (about 2oz, 55g) onion, sliced
¼ beef stock cube

Set the oven to 180°C (350°F, gas 4). Slice the liver. Mix the cornflour with the mixed herbs and a little salt and pepper. Toss the liver in the mixture. Cut each of the bacon rashers into three pieces. Arrange half the bacon pieces on the bottom of an ovenproof dish. Cover with half the onion slices, the liver, the rest of the onion slices and finally the remaining bacon pieces. Dissolve the stock cube in 6 tablespoons boiling water and pour over the ingredients in the dish. Cover with a tightly fitting lid or foil and cook in the oven for 1 hour.

1,500 CALORIE MENU   8
(no additional alcohol)

	Calories	Fibre (g)
Daily allowance: ½ pint (285ml) skimmed milk, an orange and an apple or pear	200	5
Breakfast 1½oz (45g) Allinson Crunchy Bran with 1oz (30g) dried apricots, chopped, and milk from allowance	145	22
Restaurant/café lunch Spaghetti bolognese		
Ice-cream	approx. 575	1·5

	Calories	Fibre (g)

Evening meal
* Fish bake
5oz (140g) boiled potatoes, mashed
without butter, or half medium packet
Smash Potato Pieces, made up with boiling
water (no butter)
4oz (115g) frozen peas, boiled

1 Ryvita crispbread, brown or original, no
butter
1oz (30g) Edam, Brie, Camembert or
processed cheese
2 sticks celery

	Calories	Fibre (g)
An orange and an apple or pear from allowance	580	14
TOTAL	approx. 1,500	42·5

* Fish Bake

Serves 1

two 4oz (115g) frozen cod, coley or haddock steaks, thawed
4·9oz (140g) can Campbell's Condensed Cream of Mushroom
  Soup
1 tablespoon skimmed milk from allowance
1 tablespoon finely chopped onion

Place the two thawed fish steaks in the bottom of a small ovenproof
dish. Put the soup into a pan, add the milk and chopped onion and
heat gently, stirring, until the soup is near boiling point. Pour over
the fish steaks and bake at 190°C (375°F, gas 5), for 30 minutes.
Serve hot.

1,500 CALORIE MENU   9
(no additional alcohol)

	Calories	Fibre (g)
Daily allowance: ½ pint (285ml) silver-top (whole pasteurized) milk, an orange and an apple or pear	290	5
Breakfast 1½oz (45g) All Bran or Bran Buds with ½oz (15g) sultanas and milk from allowance		
An orange from allowance	150	12
Lunch (to take to work) * Tuna and Sweetcorn Rolls 3oz (85g) carrots, cut into sticks 1 medium tomato, cut into wedges		
1 Jordans Original Crunchy Bar, Honey & Coconut .		
An apple or pear from allowance	500	13
Evening meal 14·8oz (419g) pack frozen Marco & Carlo Lasagne (whole pack, not half pack as suggested on the packet) 5oz (140g) frozen mixed cauliflower, peas and carrots, boiled		
An average-sized banana (6oz, 170g)	560	11
TOTAL	1,500	41

* Tuna and Sweetcorn Rolls

Serves 1

2 Allinson wholemeal snack rolls (1½oz, 42g each)
3½oz (100g) canned tuna in brine, drained

1oz (30g) Bicks Corn Relish
a few slices of cucumber

Split the bread rolls in half. Flake the tuna and mix with the corn relish. Spread the tuna mixture on the bottom half of each roll, cover with sliced cucumber and top with the remaining half of roll. Pack.

1,500 CALORIE MENU   10
(no additional alcohol)

	Calories	Fibre (g)
Daily allowance: ½ pint (285ml) silver-top (whole pasteurized) milk, an orange and an apple or pear	290	5
Breakfast 2oz (55g) Prewett's Bran Muesli with milk from allowance	175	12·5
Sunday lunch 3oz (85g) lean roast sirloin beef 2fl oz (55ml) thin fat-free gravy 4oz (115g) Brussels sprouts, boiled 4oz (115g) roast potato 4oz (115g) carrots, boiled		
* Banana Melba	610	16
Evening meal 1 McCain Deep 'n' Delicious Ham & Mushroom Pizza * Coleslaw		
2 Hovis digestive biscuits		
An orange and an apple or pear from allowance	425	9·5
TOTAL	1,500	43

* Banana Melba

Serves 1

2oz (55g) portion vanilla ice-cream
6oz (170g) banana
2oz (55g) fresh or frozen raspberries
1 rounded teaspoon icing sugar

Arrange the ice-cream on an oval flat dish. Peel the banana, cut it
in half and arrange the two halves on either side of the ice-cream.
Crush or liquidize the raspberries with the icing sugar and spoon
over the ice-cream. Serve at once.

* Coleslaw

Serves 1

4oz (115g) white cabbage, shredded
2oz (55g) carrot, grated
1oz (30g) onion, finely chopped
1 large stick celery, finely chopped
2 walnut halves, chopped
2 tablespoons low-calorie salad dressing

Mix all the ingredients together in a bowl thoroughly.

FOR THE DRINKING MAN   1
1,200–1,300 Calorie menu

	Calories	Fibre (g)
Daily allowance: Fibre-Filler (p. 65), ½ pint (285ml) skimmed milk, an orange and an apple or pear	400	20

Breakfast
Whole daily portion of Fibre-Filler with
milk from allowance

	Calories	Fibre (g)

Lunch (to carry to work)
* Liver Sausage and Beetroot Double-Decker
Sandwich

2 Hovis digestive biscuits

An apple or pear from allowance   465   11·5

Evening meal
* Continental Tuna Stir-fry

An orange from allowance   360   6·5

TOTAL   1,225   38

---

* **Liver Sausage and Beetroot Double-Decker Sandwich**

Serves 1

3 large thin slices (1½oz, 35g each) wholemeal bread
1oz (30g) thinly sliced liver sausage
¼ carton mustard and cress
½oz (7g) low-fat spread
1oz (30g) sliced pickled beetroot
2 lettuce leaves, shredded

Cover the first slice of bread with sliced liver sausage and mustard
and cress. Top with the second slice of bread. Spread the upper
surface of the second slice of bread with low-fat spread and one
side of the third slice of bread. Cover the second slice of bread with
sliced beetroot and shredded lettuce. Place the third slice of bread
spread side down, on top. Cut into four sandwiches. Pack.

* **Continental Tuna Stir-Fry**

Serves 1

10oz (284g) pack Birds Eye Continental Stir-Fry Vegetables
3½oz (100g) canned tuna in brine, drained

Cook the stir-fry vegetables according to pack instructions. Flake the tuna and stir into the vegetables and heat through. Turn out on to a warm serving dish and serve at once.

FOR THE DRINKING MAN   2
1,200–1,300 Calorie menu

	Calories	Fibre (g)
Daily allowance: Fibre-Filler (p. 65), ½ pint (285ml) skimmed milk, an orange and an apple or pear	400	20
Breakfast Whole daily portion of Fibre-Filler with milk from allowance		
An average-sized banana (6oz, 170g)	80	3·5
Lunch (to carry to work) * 2 Cottage Cheese and Celery Sandwiches		
An apple or pear from allowance	420	13
Evening meal 13·6oz (385g) pack Marco & Carlo Spaghetti Bolognese (whole pack, not half as pack suggests) Cucumber, tomato and celery salad: 2oz (55g) cucumber, sliced, with 2 medium tomatoes, sliced, and 1 large stick celery, diced and sprinkled with 1 tablespoon oil-free French dressing and a few chopped chives (optional)		
An orange from allowance	350	3

| **TOTAL** | 1,250 | 39·5 |

* Cottage Cheese and Celery Sandwiches

Serves 1

4oz (115g) cottage cheese (natural, with chives or with onions
    and peppers)
1 large stick celery, finely chopped
salt and pepper
4 large thin slices (1¼oz, 35g each) wholemeal bread
½ carton mustard and cress

Mix the cottage cheese with the chopped celery and salt and pepper
to taste. Fill two of the slices of bread with half of the cottage
cheese mixture and half the mustard and cress. Repeat with the
second two slices of bread to make two rounds of sandwiches. Cut
into smaller sandwiches; pack.

FOR THE DRINKING MAN   3
1,200–1,300 Calorie menu

	Calories	Fibre (g)
Daily allowance: Fibre-Filler (p. 65), ½ pint (285ml) skimmed milk, an orange and an apple or pear	400	20
Breakfast Whole daily portion of Fibre-Filler with milk from allowance 1 Ryvita crispbread, brown or original, spread with ¼oz (7g) low-fat spread and 1 teaspoon honey	65	1
Business/restaurant lunch or evening meal 8oz (225g) steak, medium grilled Green or mixed salad without dressing		
Fresh fruit salad without cream	approx. 520	7

	Calories	Fibre (g)
Drinks extra (see chart, p. 281)		

Light meal
Baked beans and egg on toast: 2 large
thin slices (1¼oz, 35g each) wholemeal
bread, toasted, 8oz (225g) canned baked
beans in tomato sauce and 1 egg (size 3),
poached

	Calories	Fibre (g)
An orange and an apple or pear from allowance	290	14

TOTAL	approx. 1,275	42

FOR THE DRINKING MAN   4
1,200–1,300 Calorie menu

	Calories	Fibre (g)
Daily allowance: Fibre-Filler (p. 65), ½ pint (285ml) skimmed milk, an orange and an apple or pear	400	20

Breakfast
Whole daily portion of Fibre-Filler with
milk from allowance

Pub or sandwich bar lunch
1 round of ham sandwiches (made from 2
large slices of bread, lightly buttered and
filled with ham)

1 small packet (25g) potato crisps, any flavour	approx. 515	5

Drinks extra (see chart, p. 281)

	Calories	Fibre (g)
Evening meal		
* Chicken Salad		
* Prune Compôte	335	16·5
TOTAL	approx. 1,250	41·5

* Chicken Salad

Serves 1

3oz (85g) cooked chicken
4oz (115g) red or white cabbage, shredded
1 tablespoon finely chopped onion
1 dessert apple from allowance, cored and chopped
2 teaspoons lemon juice
2 tablespoons oil-free French dressing
salt and pepper
a few chicory or lettuce leaves
a few sprigs of watercress
a few slices of cucumber

Remove any skin from the chicken and slice. Put the cabbage, onion and apple into a bowl. Add the lemon juice and oil-free French dressing and mix all together well. Season to taste with salt and pepper. Arrange the cabbage salad on a serving dish with the sliced chicken, chicory or lettuce leaves, sprigs of watercress and slices of cucumber.

* Prune Compôte

Serves 1

2oz (55g) dried prunes
4 drops angostura bitters (optional)
a strip of lemon peel
1 level teaspoon sugar
1 orange from allowance, segmented
1 small (5½oz, 155g) banana, peeled and sliced

Cover the prunes with cold water and leave to stand overnight. Place the prunes and liquid in a pan and add the angostura bitters, if used, and lemon peel. Cover with a lid and simmer for 20 minutes. Remove the lemon peel and stir in the sugar. If serving hot, add the orange segments and sliced banana, heat through and serve. If serving cold, allow the prunes to cool before adding the orange segments and sliced banana.

FOR THE DRINKING MAN 5
1,200–1,300 Calorie menu

	Calories	Fibre (g)
Daily allowance: Fibre-Filler (p. 65), ½ pint (285ml) skimmed milk, an orange and an apple or pear	400	20
Breakfast Whole daily portion of Fibre-Filler with milk from allowance		
Lunch (to carry to work or eat at home) 10·6oz (300g) can Heinz Lentil Soup (heat and carry to work in a flask)		
2 Ryvita crispbreads, brown or original, spread with Marmite or yeast extract 1oz (30g) Cheddar cheese		
An apple or pear from allowance	350	8
Evening meal * Mixed Vegetable Curry with Rice		
An orange from allowance	470	19
TOTAL	1,220	47

* Mixed Vegetable Curry with Rice

Serves 1

2oz (55g) brown rice
½oz (15g) low-fat spread
1 small onion, chopped
½ small cooking apple, peeled, cored and chopped
1–2 level teaspoons curry powder
1 level teaspoon plain flour
¼ pint (140ml) vegetable stock or water
1 level teaspoon tomato purée
1 teaspoon lemon juice
4oz (115g) canned red kidney beans
4oz (115g) frozen mixed cauliflower, peas and carrots, thawed
1oz (30g) mushrooms, sliced
salt and pepper

Boil the rice in lightly salted water for about 25 minutes or until tender. While the rice is cooking, melt the low-fat spread in a saucepan. Add the onion and apple and cook gently for 5 minutes. Stir in the curry powder and flour and cook for 2 minutes, stirring all the time. Add the water or stock, bring to the boil, stirring, then add the tomato purée and lemon juice. Cover and simmer for 5 minutes. Add the drained kidney beans, mixed vegetables and mushrooms. Bring to the boil, cover and simmer gently for 15 minutes. Season to taste with salt and pepper. Drain the rice and serve with the vegetable curry.

FOR THE DRINKING MAN   **6**
1,200–1,300 Calorie menu

	Calories	Fibre (g)
Daily allowance: ½ pint (285ml) skimmed milk, an orange and an apple or pear	200	5
Breakfast		
1½oz (45g) Allinson Crunchy Bran with 1oz (30g) dried apricots, chopped, and milk from allowance	145	22

	Calories	Fibre (g)
Restaurant/café lunch		
Tomato soup (or any other soup you wish)		
Chicken salad (no salad dressing)	**approx. 385**	3
Evening meal		
* Cheese and Spinach Omelet		
4oz (115g) canned baked beans in tomato sauce		
* Fruit Salad	520	17
TOTAL	approx. 1,250	47

* Cheese and Spinach Omelet

Serves 1

3 eggs (size 3)
half 10·6oz (300g) pack frozen cut-leaf spinach, thawed
salt and pepper
¼oz (7g) low-fat spread
1oz (30g) Cheddar cheese, grated

Lightly beat the eggs with 2 tablespoons water. Stir in the thawed spinach and salt and pepper. Grease a non-stick omelet pan or small frying pan with the low-fat spread and heat the pan. Pour in the egg and spinach mixture and heat until set. Sprinkle the grated cheese over the omelet and continue to heat for 1 minute. Fold the omelet in half and turn out on to a warm plate. Serve at once.

* Fruit Salad

Serves 1

1 orange from allowance, segmented
1 apple or pear from allowance, cored and diced or sliced
2oz (55g) black grapes, halved and pips removed
3fl oz (85ml) low-calorie ginger ale

¼oz (7g) flaked almonds

Mix the orange segments, diced or sliced apple or pear and grapes with the low-calorie ginger ale. Sprinkle over the flaked almonds and serve immediately.

FOR THE DRINKING MAN 7
1,200–1,300 Calorie menu

	Calories	Fibre (g)
Daily allowance: ½ pint (285ml) skimmed milk, an orange and an apple or pear	200	5
Breakfast 2oz (55g) Boots Second Nature Bran & Oat Crunch with milk from allowance	205	11
Lunch (to carry to work) Peanut butter and watercress sandwich: 2 large thin slices (1¼oz, 35g each) wholemeal bread, filled with ½oz (15g) peanut butter and sprigs of watercress		
2oz (55g) carrot, cut into sticks 1 large stick celery, cut into short sticks		
An apple or pear from allowance	260	10·5
Evening meal * Beef in Red Wine Sauce 6oz (170g) broccoli or Brussels sprouts, boiled		
1 Energen F-Plan Diet Brancrisp, spread with 1 triangle (½oz, 15g) cheese spread		
An orange from allowance	585	16
TOTAL	1,250	42·5

* Beef in Red Wine Sauce

Serves 1

4oz (115g) lean braising steak
7·9oz (225g) can Batchelors Cannellini Beans, drained
Half 13½oz (375g) can Homepride Red Wine Cook-in-Sauce

Arrange the piece of braising steak, either whole or in bite-sized pieces, in the bottom of a small ovenproof dish. Tip the beans over the steak. Spoon over the wine sauce. Cover with a lid or foil and bake in the oven at 180°C (350°F, gas 4) for 1½ hours.

FOR THE DRINKING MAN   8
1,200–1,300 Calorie menu

	Calories	Fibre (g)
Daily allowance: ½ pint (285ml) skimmed milk, an orange and an apple or pear	200	5
Breakfast 1½oz (45g) All Bran or Bran Buds with an average-sized banana (6oz, 170g), sliced and with milk from allowance	185	15·5
Lunch (to take to work) Beefburger with bun: split a 2oz (55g) wholemeal bap and spread the cut surfaces with 1 rounded tablespoon sweet pickle. Fill with a grilled beefburger, standard size (cold beefburgers are as tasty as hot ones)		
1 tomato 1 large stick celery, cut into short sticks		
An orange from allowance	315	7·5

	Calories	Fibre (g)

Evening meal
5oz (140g) lamb chump chop, well grilled
2 teaspoons mint sauce
7½oz (215g) canned butter beans, heated
4 oz (115g) canned tomatoes, heated
5oz (140g) boiled potatoes (no butter)
or half medium packet Smash Potato
Pieces, made up with boiling water (no
butter)

An apple or pear from allowance

1 Hovis digestive biscuit	600	10

TOTAL	1,300	38

FOR THE DRINKING MAN:
1,200–1,300 Calorie Menu

9

	Calories	Fibre (g)
Daily allowance: ½ pint (285ml) silver-top (whole pasteurized) milk, an orange and an apple or pear	290	5

Breakfast
2oz (55g) Allinson Crunchy Bran with milk from allowance	130	15·5

Restaurant/café lunch
Grilled Dover sole
Mixed salad without dressing

Fruit sorbet	approx. 620	2

	Calories	Fibre (g)
Evening meal		
Baked beans on toast: 1 large thin slice ($1\frac{1}{2}$oz, 35g) wholemeal bread, toasted, spread with $\frac{1}{4}$oz (7g) low-fat spread and topped with 8oz (225g) canned baked beans in tomato sauce, heated		
An orange and an apple or pear from allowance	260	19·5
TOTAL	approx. 1,300	42

FOR THE DRINKING MAN 10
1,200–1,300 Calorie menu

	Calories	Fibre (g)
Daily allowance: $\frac{1}{2}$ pint (285ml) silver-top (whole pasteurized) milk, an orange and an apple or pear	290	5
Breakfast		
$1\frac{1}{2}$oz (45g) All Bran or Bran Buds with $\frac{1}{2}$oz (15g) sultanas or raisins and milk from allowance	150	12

Sunday/weekend lunch
3oz (85g) portion roast chicken (meat only, with skin removed)
7oz (200g) jacket baked potato (for baking instructions see p. 31), served with $\frac{1}{4}$oz (7g) low-fat spread
$3\frac{1}{2}$oz (100g) canned sweetcorn
2oz (55g) button mushrooms poached in stock or seasoned water

8oz (225g) canned pear halves in apple juice

	Calories	Fibre (g)
1oz (30g, one small scoop) ice-cream *or* 1½ tablespoons single cream *or* half 150g carton low-fat natural yogurt	555	16

Evening meal
* Egg Salad
1 large thin slice (1¼oz, 35g) wholemeal
bread spread with ¼oz (7g) low-fat
spread

An orange and an apple or pear from allowance	255	6·5

TOTAL	1,250	39·5

* **Egg Salad**

Serves 1

1 egg (size 3), hard-boiled
2oz (55g) button mushrooms
1 tablespoon lemon juice
salt and pepper
a small bunch of watercress *or* a few lettuce leaves
1 tomato, sliced
2oz (55g) carrot, grated
1oz (30g) pickled beetroot, sliced or diced
1oz (30g) green pepper, sliced *or* 2oz (55g) cucumber, sliced
1 tablespoon low-calorie salad dressing

Shell and halve the egg. Slice the mushrooms and toss in the
lemon juice. Season to taste with salt and pepper. Arrange a bed of
watercress or lettuce on a plate, then arrange the halved egg,
mushrooms, sliced tomato, grated carrot, sliced or diced beetroot
and green pepper or cucumber on top. Pour the salad dressing
over the egg.

F-PLAN FOR CHILDREN

Most children need hardly know they are on a diet when following these menus, since the F-Plan allows children to eat the foods they most like.

Although most slimming diets which allow a daily intake of 1,500 calories are quite safe for school-age children to follow, they are rarely produced with children in mind and hence they do not include their favourite foods.

A daily calorie allowance of 1,500 will achieve a good weight loss for most boys; the weight loss for girls (unless heavily over-weight) may be less spectacular. As long as there is no further weight gain or, better still, if there is a steady (even if fairly small) weight loss, then you will have a chance to 'grow into your weight'.

The following menus follow the basic F-Plan diet rules, and include those foods which my testers and junior informers tell me are most popular with children. All the daily menus provide 1,500 calories and between 35g and 50g of fibre.

The first ten menus include a daily portion of Fibre-Filler (p. 65) in the daily allowance; however, since some children do not like Fibre-Filler and would find a diet including it every day to be quite unacceptable, there are ten daily menus without Fibre-Filler. These all contain a bran-based breakfast cereal which partly replaces the Fibre-Filler. Also in the daily allowance, all twenty menus include two whole pieces of fruit (an orange and an apple or pear) and one pint (570ml) skimmed milk. The quantity of milk has been increased from the basic F-Plan diet allowance to ensure that children obtain adequate amounts of nutrients for their growth requirements.

SPECIAL DIET NOTES

1. Choose a week's menus at one time so that the food can be bought in advance.

2. Don't swap meals from one day's menu to another. Stick to the chosen menus – there should be sufficient to choose from for you to avoid foods which you particularly dislike. However, the same menu every day will not provide you with sufficient variety of foods and will be very boring. You do need to use several menus if you are dieting for more than a few days.

3. The skimmed milk allowance is used on your breakfast cereal or Fibre-Filler and where necessary in a bed-time drink or to make the custard or sauce called for in some of the menus. However, there should be enough skimmed milk for you to use it in tea as well. (Children should not drink coffee.) Although tea is not mentioned in the menus you are allowed to drink as many cups of tea each day as you like as long as you do not add sugar and use only skimmed milk from your allowance.

4. You can drink canned and bottled drinks labelled *low-calorie* and as much water as you like throughout the day.

5. The daily menus are divided up into breakfast, mid-morning snack, lunch, after-school snack, dinner and a bed-time drink or snack. However, if this arrangement of meals does not fit in with your life-style then you can rearrange the meals (e.g. eat the evening meal at lunchtime and keep the mid-morning snack until lunchtime or the evening) as long as at the end of the day you have only eaten those foods on the daily menu.

6. Some of the lunches are suitable for packing so that they can be eaten at school or on a picnic. Soups and salads can be packed as well as sandwiches – just remember to take the right tools along to eat them with.

7. The after-school snack becomes a teatime snack at weekends.

8. Finally, eat more slowly than you usually do. Foods high in fibre need more chewing than low-fibre foods so you will probably slow down anyway. Slow eating means that you have time to enjoy your food and should feel more satisfied at the end of a meal, whereas if you gobble your food down you forget all too quickly that you have eaten and want more food.

9. Remember that if you stick to your diet you will not only be fitter and healthier but life will be more fun.

1,500 CALORIE MENU   1
with Fibre-Filler

	Calories	Fibre (g)
Daily allowances: Fibre-Filler, 1 pint (570ml) skimmed milk, two items of fruit	500	20

Breakfast
Half portion of Fibre-Filler with milk from allowance

An orange from allowance

Mid-morning snack		
1 Quaker Harvest Crunch Bar, peanut or almond	90	1

Lunch
* Peanut Butter and Cucumber Sandwich

2oz (55g) carrot, cut into sticks

An apple or pear from allowance	335	9·5

After-school snack
Remaining portion of Fibre-Filler with skimmed milk from allowance

Evening meal
2 frozen beefburgers, grilled
4oz (115g) canned baked beans in tomato sauce
4oz (115g) potatoes, boiled and mashed

2oz (55g) portion vanilla ice-cream with 2 wafers (optional)	535	9

	Calories	Fibre (g)
Bed-time drink		
A cup of chocolate – 2 rounded teaspoons drinking chocolate with milk from allowance	40	0
TOTAL	1,500	39·5

* **Peanut Butter and Cucumber Sandwich**

2 large thin slices (1½oz, 35g each) wholemeal bread
1oz (30g) peanut butter
a few slices of cucumber

Spread both slices of the bread with the peanut butter and sandwich together with slices of cucumber.

1,500 CALORIE MENU   2
with Fibre-Filler

	Calories	Fibre (g)
Daily allowances: Fibre-Filler, 1 pint (570ml) skimmed milk,	500	20
Breakfast		
Half portion of Fibre-Filler with milk from allowance		
1 large thin slice wholemeal bread, toasted and spread with ¼oz (7g) low-fat spread and Marmite or savoury yeast extract	110	3
Mid-morning snack		
1 Hovis digestive biscuit	55	0·5

	Calories	Fibre (g)
Lunch		
2 large pork sausages, grilled		
1 Ryvita crispbread, brown or original		
2 average-sized tomatoes		
1 large stick celery, cut into short lengths		
An apple or pear from allowance	315	3·5
After-school snack		
Remaining portion of Fibre-Filler with skimmed milk from allowance		
An orange from allowance		
Evening meal		
* Pasta with Meat Sauce		
1 average-sized banana (6oz, 170g)	480	12·5
Bed-time drink		
A cup of chocolate – 2 rounded teaspoons drinking chocolate with milk from allowance	40·	0
TOTAL	1,500	39·5

* Pasta with Meat Sauce

Serves 1 (several portions of the meat sauce can be made up at one time and frozen until required)

2oz (55g) wholewheat pasta rings, shells or spaghetti

Meat sauce
4oz (115g) lean minced beef
1oz (30g) onion, peeled and finely chopped
1 stick celery, finely diced
¼ beef stock cube, dissolved in 5 tablespoons boiling water
salt and freshly ground pepper

a pinch of mixed herbs
1 teaspoon tomato purée
1oz (30g) canned baked beans in tomato sauce

Fry the minced beef in a non-stick saucepan until well browned.
Drain off all the fat which has cooked out of the meat. Add the
onion, celery and stock to the meat in the pan and bring to the
boil, stirring. Reduce the heat, season to taste with salt and pepper
and add the herbs and tomato purée. Cover and simmer gently for
30 minutes, stirring occasionally and adding more water if necessary to prevent the mixture boiling dry. Boil the pasta in salted
water for about 12 minutes or until just tender. Drain and arrange
on a plate. Stir the baked beans into the meat sauce and heat
through for 2–3 minutes, then spoon over the pasta.

1,500 CALORIE MENU   3
with Fibre-Filler

	Calories	Fibre (g)
Daily allowances: Fibre-Filler, 1 pint (570ml) skimmed milk, two items of fruit	500	20
Breakfast Half portion of Fibre-Filler with milk from allowance 1 egg (size 3), boiled and served with 1 large thin slice wholemeal bread spread with a little Marmite or yeast extract	160	3
Mid-morning snack An apple or pear from allowance		
Lunch * Ham and Cheese Rolls * Corny Coleslaw 1 Ryvita crispbread, brown or original		
An orange from allowance	290	8

	Calories	Fibre (g)

After-school snack
Remaining portion of Fibre-Filler with
skimmed milk from allowance

Evening meal
2 fish fingers, grilled without fat
3oz (85g) frozen peas, boiled
4oz (115g) oven chips, baked or grilled

150g carton fruit-flavoured yogurt	510	9

Bed-time drink
A cup of chocolate – 2 rounded teaspoons
drinking chocolate with milk from

allowance	40	0

TOTAL	**1,500**	**40**

* Ham and Cheese Rolls

Serves 1

2oz (55g) cottage cheese with pineapple
½ carton mustard and cress
2 thin slices (2oz, 55g) boiled lean ham

Mix the cottage cheese with the chopped mustard and cress.
Divide equally between the two slices of ham and spread over
the ham. Roll up the ham and secure with a cocktail stick if
necessary.

* Corny Coleslaw

Serves 1

2oz (55g) firm white cabbage, shredded
2oz (55g) carrot, grated
2oz (55g) canned sweetcorn kernels, drained
1 tablespoon low-calorie salad dressing

Mix together the cabbage, carrot and sweetcorn. Then stir in the salad dressing.

1,500 CALORIE MENU   4
with Fibre-Filling

	Calories	Fibre (g)
Daily allowances: Fibre-Filler, 1 pint (570ml) skimmed milk, two items of fruit	500	20
Breakfast Half portion of Fibre-Filler with milk from allowance		
1 banana (7oz, 200g)	90	4
Mid-morning snack 1 Quaker Harvest Crunch Bar, peanut or almond	90	1
Lunch * 2 Cheese and Bean Snack Rolls		
2oz (55g) raw carrot, cut into sticks		
An apple or pear from allowance	345	12·5
After-school snack 1 packet Allinson Wheateats	90	0·5
Evening meal 2 chicken drumsticks (3½oz, 100g each before cooking), grilled		
2oz (55g) canned sweetcorn kernels		
2oz (55g) mushrooms, poached in a little stock or seasoned water		
2 average-sized tomatoes (4oz, 115g)		
A small bunch of watercress (1oz, 30g)		
Milk shake made from 1 sachet Kellogg's Two Shakes (any flavour) and ½ pint (285ml) skimmed milk from allowance	330	7

	Calories	Fibre (g)
Bed-time snack		
An orange from allowance		
1 Hovis digestive biscuit	55	0·5
TOTAL	1,500	45·5

* Cheese and Bean Snack Rolls

Serves 1

2 wholemeal snack rolls (1½oz, 45g each)
1oz (30g) mature Cheddar cheese, finely grated
2oz (55g) canned baked beans in tomato sauce
pepper to taste
a dash of Worcestershire sauce (optional)
½ carton mustard and cress

Split the rolls in half lengthwise. Mash the grated cheese and beans together using a fork. Season with pepper to taste and add the Worcestershire sauce if liked. Spread the cheese and bean mixture on the bottom half of each roll. Top with mustard and cress and the top half of each roll.

1,500 CALORIE MENU   5
with Fibre-Filler

	Calories	Fibre (g)
Daily allowances: Fibre-Filler, 1 pint		
(570ml) skimmed milk, two items of fruit	500	20
Breakfast		
Whole portion of Fibre-Filler with milk from allowance		
Mid-morning snack		
1 large thin slice wholemeal bread, toasted and spread with ¼oz (7g) low-fat spread and 2 level teaspoons honey	130	3

	Calories	Fibre (g)
Lunch		
* Star Wars Soup		
2 Ryvita crispbreads, brown or original		
An apple or pear from allowance	380	19
After-school snack		
1 Hovis digestive biscuit	55	0·5
Evening meal		
Average-sized lamb loin chop (5oz, 140g raw weight), grilled		
1 tablespoon mint sauce		
4oz (115g) Brussels sprouts or cabbage, boiled		
4oz (115g) frozen mixed vegetables, boiled		
An orange from allowance	395	7·5
Bed-time drink		
A cup of chocolate – 2 rounded teaspoons drinking chocolate with skimmed milk from allowance	40	0
TOTAL	1,500	50

* Star Wars Soup

Serves 1

8oz (225g) canned baked beans in tomato sauce
2oz (55g) carrot, grated
1 beef stock cube
freshly ground pepper
2 pork chipolata sausages

Put the baked beans and grated carrot into a saucepan. Dissolve the stock cube in ¼ pint (140ml) boiling water and stir into the beans and carrot in the pan. Bring to the boil, cover and simmer gently for 15–20 minutes. Meanwhile, grill the chipolata sausages until well done, then cut each sausage into three equal pieces. Add to the soup, season to taste, and add a little boiling water if the soup is too thick. Serve hot with crispbreads.

1,500 CALORIE MENU   6
with Fibre-Filler

	Calories	Fibre (g)
Daily allowances: Fibre-Filler, 1 pint (570ml) skimmed milk, two items of fruit	500	20
Breakfast Half portion of Fibre-Filler with milk from allowance		
An orange from allowance		
Mid-morning snack 1 small packet (25g) potato crisps	130	3
Lunch * Sardine Sandwich		
150g carton fruit-flavoured low-fat natural yogurt	400	6
After-school snack An apple or pear from allowance		
Evening meal * Meaty Jacket Potato 1oz (30g) pickled beetroot 5oz (140g) fruit-flavoured jelly	470	6·5

	Calories	Fibre (g)

Bed-time snack
Half portion of Fibre-Filler with milk from
allowance

TOTAL	1,500	35·5

* Sardine Sandwich

Serves 1

2 sardines, canned in tomato sauce
1oz (30g) cottage cheese
salt and pepper
2 large thin slices (1¼oz, 35g each) wholemeal bread
2 lettuce leaves
a few slices of cucumber

Mash the sardines with the cottage cheese and season to taste. Fill
the two slices of bread with the sardine mixture, lettuce and
cucumber. Cut into four sandwiches.

* Meaty Jacket Potato

Serves 1

7oz (200g) potato
4oz (115g) raw minced beef
1oz (30g) chopped onion
1oz (30g) finely chopped celery
1 teaspoon tomato paste or purée
salt and pepper

Scrub the potato well, then bake by one of the methods described
on p. 328. Meanwhile, fry the minced beef in a saucepan without
added fat until well browned. Drain off and discard the fat. Add the
onion, celery, tomato paste or purée and 4–5 tablespoons water.
Heat until boiling, then simmer, covered, for 15 minutes. Cut the

baked jacket potato in half lengthwise, scoop out some of the flesh and mix with the hot minced beef mixture. Season to taste. Pile back into the jackets and serve.

1,500 CALORIE MENU   7
with Fibre-Filler

	Calories	Fibre (g)
Daily allowances: Fibre-Filler, 1 pint (570ml) skimmed milk, two items of fruit	500	20

Breakfast
Half portion of Fibre-Filler with milk from allowance

1 large thin slice wholemeal bread, toasted and spread with $\frac{1}{4}$oz (7g) low-fat spread and Marmite or yeast extract   110   3

Mid-morning snack
An apple or pear from allowance

Lunch
1 Golden Wonder Chicken & Mushroom Pot Noodle *or* Spicy Curry Pot Noodle

An orange from allowance   380   8·5/
                                                          4·5

After-school snack
Half portion Fibre-Filler with milk from allowance

Evening meal
* Hungarian Liver
4oz (115g) cabbage, boiled   450   11

	Calories	Fibre (g)
Bed-time drink		
Orange Milky: mix 1fl oz (30ml) low calorie orange squash with ¼ pint (140ml) skimmed milk from allowance		
1 Hovis digestive biscuit	60	0·5
TOTAL	1,500	43/39

*Hungarian Liver

Serves 1

4oz (115g) pig's liver
1 level tablespoon wholemeal flour
½oz (15g) low-fat spread
1 small onion, thinly sliced
2oz (55g) mushrooms, sliced
¼ pint (140ml) beef stock made from ⅓ stock cube
1 level teaspoon tomato purée
1½oz (45g) wholewheat macaroni
1 tablespoon natural yogurt
¼ teaspoon lemon juice

Cut the liver into thin slices horizontally and then vertically. Toss in the wholemeal flour to coat. Heat the low-fat spread in a non-stick pan and cook the onion over a low heat until soft. Add the mushrooms and cook for a further 2–3 minutes. Add the liver and cook for 3 minutes. Stir in the stock and tomato purée. Bring to the boil, cover and simmer gently for 10 minutes. Meanwhile, cook the macaroni in fast boiling, lightly salted water for 12–15 minutes, until just soft. Drain the macaroni well and arrange on a serving plate. Spoon the liver mixture on top. Stir the yogurt and lemon juice together and spoon on top of the liver and pasta.

1,500 CALORIE MENU   8
with Fibre-Filler

	Calories	Fibre (g)
Daily allowances: Fibre-Filler, 1 pint (570ml) skimmed milk, two items of fruit	500	20

Breakfast
Half portion of Fibre-Filler with milk from allowance

| 2 rashers streaky bacon, well grilled and made into a sandwich with 1 large thin slice wholemeal bread spread with 1 teaspoon tomato ketchup or brown sauce | 180 | 3 |

Mid-morning snack
An apple or pear from allowance

Lunch
* Tuna Salad

| 1 Quaker Harvest Crunch Bar, peanut or almond | 400 | 9·5 |

After-school snack
Half portion of Fibre-Filler with milk from allowance

Evening meal
* One-Pan Supper

| 2oz (55g) vanilla ice-cream served with orange from allowance, cut into segments | 380 | 4·5 |

Bed-time drink

| A cup of chocolate – 2 rounded teaspoons drinking chocolate with milk from allowance | 40 | 0 |

| TOTAL | 1,500 | 37 |

* Tuna Salad

Serves 1

3½oz (100g) canned tuna in brine
1oz (30g) wholewheat pasta shells, cooked
3oz (85g) canned sweetcorn kernels with red and green pepper
1 stick celery, diced
2 level tablespoons low-fat natural yogurt
½ teaspoon lemon juice
salt and pepper

Flake the tuna into a bowl. Add the pasta, sweetcorn and celery
and mix well. Blend the yogurt with the lemon juice and add salt
and pepper to taste. Add to the tuna mixture and toss gently until
well mixed.

*One-Pan Supper

Serves 1

2 eggs (size 3)
salt and pepper
½oz (15g) low-fat spread
1oz (30g) chopped onion
1 small cooked potato (2oz, 55g), diced
1 average-sized fresh or canned tomato, chopped
1oz (30g) mushrooms, sliced
1oz (30g) cooked peas

Beat the eggs together with 2 tablespoons water and salt and
pepper to taste. Melt the low-fat spread in a non-stick frying pan.
Add the chopped onion, potato, tomato and mushrooms and cook
over a gentle heat for 5 minutes, stirring frequently. Add the peas,
then pour in the beaten egg. Cook over a moderate heat until the
egg mixture is set on the bottom, then place under a hot grill to set
the top and brown slightly. Turn out on to a warm plate and serve
immediately.

1,500 CALORIE MENU

9

with Fibre-Filler

	Calories	Fibre (g)
Daily allowances: Fibre-Filler, 1 pint (570ml) skimmed milk, two items of fruit	500	20
Breakfast Half portion of Fibre-Filler with milk from allowance		
1 average-sized banana (6oz, 170g)	80	3·5
Mid-morning snack Kit Kat, 2 fingers	110	0
Lunch * Ploughman's Rolls 2 average-sized tomatoes a small bunch of watercress		
An apple or pear from allowance	330	8·5
After-school snack Remaining portion of Fibre-Filler with milk from allowance		
Evening meal * Quick Fish Pie		
5oz (140g) fruit-flavoured jelly with orange from allowance, cut into segments	475	9·5
Bed-time drink Orange Milky: 1fl oz (30ml) low-calorie orange squash with ¼ pint (140ml) skimmed milk from allowance	5	0
TOTAL	1,500	41·5

* **Ploughman's Rolls**

Serves 1

2 large thin slices wholemeal bread (1¼oz, 35g each)
2 level tablespoons sweet pickle
2 pork chipolata sausages, well grilled

Flatten the two slices of bread by rolling with a rolling pin.
Spread each slice with a tablespoon of sweet pickle. Place a chipolata sausage along one end of each slice of bread and roll the
bread around the sausage. Secure with a cocktail stick if necessary.

* **Quick Fish Pie**

Serves 1

6oz (170g) packet frozen cod in cheese sauce
half medium packet Smash Potato Pieces
2oz (55g) frozen peas, boiled
½oz (15g) Cheddar cheese, grated

Cook the cod as directed on the packet. Make up the potato
pieces with boiling water as directed. (*Note.* Do not add butter.)
Pipe or spoon the potato around the edge of an individual flame-
proof dish. Place the peas in the bottom of the dish. Remove
the fish and sauce from the bag and flake the fish into the sauce.
Spoon over the peas. Top with the grated cheese and heat
through under a hot grill until the cheese has melted and is
lightly browned.

1,500 CALORIE MENU   10
with Fibre-Filler

	Calories	Fibre (g)
Daily allowances: Fibre-Filler, 1 pint (570ml) skimmed milk, two items of fruit	500	20

	Calories	Fibre (g)
Breakfast Half portion of Fibre-Filler with milk from allowance		
1 large thin slice wholemeal bread, toasted and spread with ¼oz (7g) low-fat spread and 2 level teaspoons honey	130	3
Mid-morning snack An apple or pear from allowance		
Lunch * Vegetable and Lentil Soup 2 Ryvita crispbreads, brown or original	225	10
After-school snack Kit Kat, 2 fingers		
An orange from allowance	110	0
Evening meal * Cheese Omelet 5oz (140g) frozen grill chips, grilled 2oz (55g) frozen peas, boiled	535	7·5
Bed-time snack Remaining portion of Fibre-Filler with milk from allowance		
TOTAL	1,500	42·5

* Vegetable and Lentil Soup

Serves 1 (several portions can be made up at one time and frozen in individual portions for future use)

1oz (30g) onion, sliced
2oz (55g) carrot, sliced

1 large stick celery, chopped
1½oz (45g) lentils
1 chicken or ham stock cube
salt and pepper

Put all the prepared vegetables in a pan with the lentils. Dissolve the stock cube in ¾ pint (425ml) boiling water. (*Note.* Vegetarians can omit the stock cube.) Add to the pan with salt and pepper to taste. Bring to the boil, cover and simmer gently for 1 hour.

* Cheese Omelet

Serves 1

2 eggs (size 3)
salt and pepper
¼oz (7g) low-fat spread
1oz (30g) Cheddar cheese, grated

Beat the eggs with 2 tablespoons water and seasoning to taste. Melt the low-fat spread in a non-stick omelet pan. Pour in the egg mixture and cook over a moderate heat until set. Sprinkle the cheese over the surface and allow to melt. Fold the omelet in half and turn out on to a warm plate. Serve at once.

1,500 CALORIE MENU   1
no Fibre-Filler

	Calories	Fibre (g)
Daily allowances: two items of fruit, 1 pint (570ml) skimmed milk	300	5
Breakfast 2oz (55g) Allinson Crunchy Bran with skimmed milk from allowance	130	15·5
Mid-morning snack An apple or pear from allowance		
1oz (30g) dried raisins	70	2

	Calories	Fibre (g)
Lunch		
* Pitta filled with corned beef, beetroot and cucumber		
An orange from allowance	350	3
After-school snack		
2 Ryvita crispbreads, brown or original, spread with 1 triangle cheese spread and topped with sliced cucumber or cress	95	2
Evening meal		
3½oz (100g) bacon steak, grilled without fat		
1 tablespoon brown sauce or tomato ketchup		
7oz (200g) potato, baked in its jacket (see p. 31)		
4oz (115g) canned baked beans in tomato sauce		
* Stewed Blackberries and Apple with Custard made with milk from allowance	505	14
Bed-time drink		
A cup of chocolate – 2 rounded teaspoons drinking chocolate with milk from allowance	40	0
TOTAL	**1,500**	**41·5**

* Pitta filled with Corned Beef, Beetroot and Cucumber

Serves 1

1 pitta (2oz, 55g)
2oz (55g) corned beef
1oz (30g) pickled beetroot, chopped
2oz (55g) cucumber, finely diced

Toast or bake the pitta until it puffs up to give a hollow centre. Cut the pitta in half. Mash the corned beef and mix with the chopped beetroot and cucumber. Fill the pitta with the corned beef mixture.

* Stewed Blackberries and Apple with Custard

Serves 1

2oz (55g) blackberries
4oz (115g) cooking apple, peeled, cored and sliced
3 level teaspoons granulated sugar
2 level teaspoons custard powder
4fl oz (115ml) skimmed milk from allowance

Stew the blackberries and apple with 2 tablespoons water in a covered pan until the fruit is tender. Stir in 1½ teaspoons of the sugar. Blend the custard powder and the remaining 1½ teaspoons of sugar with a little of the cold milk until smooth. Heat the remainder of the milk to boiling point in a small saucepan. Pour on to the blended custard powder, then return to the pan. Continue to heat, stirring continuously, until the custard has thickened. Serve with the fruit.

1,500 CALORIE MENU   2
no Fibre-Filler

	Calories	Fibre (g)
Daily allowances: two items of fruit, 1 pint (570ml) skimmed milk	300	5
Breakfast 2oz (55g) Kellogg's Sultana Bran with milk from allowance		
1 average-sized banana (6oz, 170g)	245	10·5
Mid-morning snack 2 Ryvita crispbreads, brown or original, each spread with 1 level tablespoon Waistline Low Calorie Vegetable Spread	80	2
Lunch * Welsh Soup with Wholemeal Croûtons		
An apple or pear from allowance	225	10

	Calories	Fibre (g)
After-school snack		
1 Jordans Original Crunchy Bar, Honey &		
Coconut	145	1
Evening meal		
* Egg and Beans with Cheese Crumble		
Topping		
2oz (55g) vanilla ice-cream served		
with orange from allowance, cut into		
segments	470	20·5
Bed-time snack and drink		
1 Ryvita crispbread spread with Marmite or		
yeast extract and topped with sliced		
cucumber		
Orange Milky: 1fl oz (30ml) low-calorie		
orange squash with ¼ pint (140ml)		
skimmed milk from allowance	35	1

TOTAL	1,500	50

* Welsh Soup with Wholemeal Croûtons

Serves 1 (several portions can be made up at one time and frozen in individual portions for future use)

5oz (140g) leeks, with coarse green leaves trimmed off
4oz (115g) peeled potato, thinly sliced or diced
½ chicken or vegetable stock cube
salt and pepper
1 large thin slice wholemeal bread (1½oz, 35g)

Slice the leek thinly and place in a pan with the potato. Dissolve the stock cube in ½ pint (285 ml) boiling water and pour into the pan. Season to taste with salt and pepper. Bring to the boil, cover and simmer gently for 20 minutes. Purée the soup in a blender or food processor. Reheat, check seasoning and thin with water, if necessary. Toast the slice of wholemeal bread on both sides and cut into small cubes (croûtons). Serve the soup with the croûtons sprinkled on top.

* Egg and Beans with Cheese Crumble Topping

Serves 1

8oz (225g) canned baked beans in tomato sauce
1 egg (size 3)
2 average-sized tomatoes (2oz, 55g each), sliced
1oz (30g) wholemeal breadcrumbs
½oz (15g) Cheddar cheese, grated

Heat the beans and poach the egg. Spoon half the beans into a small ovenproof dish. Place the poached egg on top and then spoon over the remaining beans. Cover with the sliced tomatoes. Mix the breadcrumbs with the cheese and sprinkle over the top. Grill until crisp and bubbly.

1,500 CALORIE MENU   3
no Fibre-Filler

	Calories	Fibre (g)
Daily allowances: two items of fruit, 1 pint (570ml) skimmed milk	300	5
Breakfast 1½oz (45g) Allinson Crunchy Bran with ½oz (15g) sultanas and milk from allowance	130	12·5
Mid-morning snack An apple or pear from allowance		
Lunch * Cheese with Nutty Coleslaw		
Orange from allowance	405	13

	Calories	Fibre (g)
After-school snack		
2 Hovis digestive biscuits	110	1·5
Evening meal		
1 frozen French bread pizza (any variety)		
Green salad: a few lettuce leaves, shredded,		
1oz (30g) sliced or diced cucumber,		
½ small green pepper, chopped, and a few		
sprigs of watercress		
4oz (115g) portion jelly		
1oz (30g) portion ice-cream	490	1·5
Bed-time snack		
1 Ryvita crispbread, brown or original,		
spread with 1 triangle cheese spread	65	1

TOTAL	1,500	34·5

* **Cheese with Nutty Coleslaw**

Serves 1

4oz (115g) firm white cabbage, shredded
2oz (55g) carrot, grated
2oz (55g) cooked peas
2oz (55g) canned sweetcorn kernels
1oz (30g) walnut pieces, roughly chopped
2 level tablespoons low-calorie salad dressing
1oz (30g) Edam cheese, grated

Mix the prepared vegetables and nuts together in a bowl. Stir in the salad dressing. Arrange the coleslaw on a plate and pile the grated cheese on top.

1,500 CALORIE MENU   4
no Fibre-Filler

	Calories	Fibre (g)
Daily allowances: two items of fruit, 1 pint (570ml) skimmed milk	300	5
Breakfast 2oz (55g) Kellogg's Sultana Bran with milk from allowance		
1 large thin slice wholemeal bread (1½oz, 35g) spread with ½oz (7g) low-fat spread and Marmite or yeast extract	275	10
Mid-morning snack An apple or pear from allowance		
Lunch 2 frozen beefburgers, grilled 4oz (115g) canned baked beans in tomato sauce		
An orange from allowance	330	8
After-school snack 1 large thin slice wholemeal bread (1½oz, 35g) spread with ½oz (7g) low-fat spread and 2 level teaspoons honey or jam	130	3
Evening meal * Individual Shepherd's Pie 4oz (115g) cabbage, boiled	425	9·5
Bed-time drink A cup of chocolate – 2 rounded teaspoons drinking chocolate with milk from allowance	40	0
TOTAL	1,500	35·5

* Individual Shepherd's Pie

Serves 1

4oz (115g) lean minced beef
1 small onion, finely chopped
2oz (55g) carrot, grated
1 level teaspoon plain flour
salt and freshly ground pepper
2½fl oz (70ml) beef stock made from ¼ beef stock cube
1 level tablespoon tomato purée
1oz (30g) cooked peas
6oz (170g) cooked potato, mashed
¼oz (7g) low-fat spread
1 tablespoon skimmed milk from allowance (optional)

Fry the minced beef in a pan until well browned, then drain off and discard fat which has cooked out of the meat. Add the onion, carrot, flour and salt and pepper to taste, to the meat in the pan. Blend the stock with the tomato purée and stir into the meat and vegetables. Heat to boiling point, stirring continuously, then cook for 5 minutes until the mixture thickens. Stir in the peas. Spoon into a small ovenproof dish. Cream the mashed potato with the low-fat spread and milk, if used. Spoon on top of the meat and fork the top. Bake at 200°C (400°F, gas 6), for 30 minutes or until the top is browned.

1,500 CALORIE MENU   5
no Fibre-Filler

	Calories	Fibre (g)
Daily allowances: two items of fruit, 1 pint (570ml) skimmed milk	300	5

Breakfast

1oz (30g) Bran Flakes with ½oz (15g) chopped dried apricots (no-need-to-soak variety) and milk from allowance		
1 egg (size 3), poached and served on 1 large thin slice (1¼oz, 35g) wholemeal bread, toasted, no butter	260	10

	Calories	Fibre (g)

Mid-morning snack
An orange from allowance

Lunch
* Cottage Cheese and Piccalilli Sandwiches
4oz (115g) carrot, cut into sticks

150g carton fruit-flavoured yogurt	350	10·5

After-school snack
An apple or pear from allowance

Evening meal
* Macaroni and Vegetable Cheese Bake
Green salad: a few lettuce leaves, shredded,
1oz (30g) sliced or diced cucumber, ½ small
green pepper, chopped, and a few sprigs of
watercress

1 frozen chocolate éclair, thawed	550	12.5

Bed-time drink
A cup of chocolate – 2 rounded teaspoons
drinking chocolate with milk from

allowance	40	0

TOTAL	**1,500**	**38**

* **Cottage Cheese and Piccalilli Sandwiches**

Serves 1

2oz (55g) cottage cheese (natural, with chives or with onion and
    peppers)
1oz (30g) piccalilli, chopped
2 large thin slices (1¼oz, 35g each) wholemeal bread

Mix the cottage cheese with the piccalilli and sandwich between
the two slices of bread. Cut into four.

* Macaroni and Vegetable Cheese Bake

Serves 1

1½oz (45g) wholewheat macaroni
4oz (115g) frozen mixed vegetables
½oz (15g) wholemeal flour
¼ pint (140ml) skimmed milk from
   allowance
½oz (7g) low-fat spread
salt and pepper
¼ teaspoon made mustard
1oz (30g) Cheddar cheese, grated

Boil the macaroni in lightly salted water for 12 minutes or until just tender. Drain well. Cook the vegetables as directed and drain. Put the flour, milk and low-fat spread in a saucepan and heat, whisking continuously until it boils and thickens. Season to taste with salt and pepper. Add the mustard and half the cheese. Stir the macaroni and vegetables into the sauce. Turn into an ovenproof dish. Sprinkle over the remaining cheese. Cook in a moderately hot oven (200°C, 400°F, gas 6) for 20 minutes or until the cheese is browned.

1,500 CALORIE MENU   6
no Fibre-Filler

	Calories	Fibre (g)
Daily allowances: two items of fruit, 1 pint (570ml) skimmed milk	300	5
Breakfast		
1oz (30g) Bran Flakes with milk from allowance		
1 average-sized banana (6oz, 170g)	165	7·5

	Calories	Fibre (g)
Mid-morning snack		
1 Quaker Harvest Crunch Bar, almond or peanut		
An apple or pear from allowance	90	1
Lunch		
8oz (225g) canned baked beans in tomato sauce on 1 large thin slice (1¼oz, 35g) wholemeal bread, toasted	235	19·5
After-school snack		
150g carton fruit-flavoured yogurt	120	0
Evening meal		
* Oven-Baked Chicken and Chips		
2 average-sized tomatoes		
A bunch of watercress		
An orange from allowance	530	5·5
Bed-time snack and drink		
1 Hovis digestive biscuit		
Orange Milky – 1 fl oz (30ml) low-calorie orange squash with ¼ pint (140ml) skimmed milk from allowance	60	0·5
TOTAL	1,500	39

* Oven-Baked Chicken and Chips

Serves 1

8oz (225g) chicken joint
salt and pepper
6oz (170g) frozen oven chips

Season the chicken joint well, and wrap in foil to form a parcel.

Bake in a hot oven (220°C, 425°F, gas 7), for 45 minutes or
until tender. Place the chips on a baking tray and bake with the
chicken for the last 15–20 minutes. Unwrap the chicken and
remove and discard the skin. Serve with the chips.

1,500 CALORIE MENU   7
no Fibre-Filler

	Calories	Fibre (g)
Daily allowances: two items of fruit, 1 pint (570ml) skimmed milk	300	5
Breakfast 2oz (55g) Kellogg's Sultana Bran with milk from allowance	165	7
Mid-morning snack 1oz (30g) peanuts, mixed with 1oz (30g) raisins	230	4·5
Lunch * 2 Peanut Butter and Cress Snack Rolls 2oz (55g) carrot, cut into sticks An apple or pear from allowance	365	11
After-school snack 1 Quaker Harvest Crunch Bar, almond or peanut	90	1
Evening meal 6oz (170g) cod or haddock fillets brushed with ½oz (7g) low-fat spread and grilled 1 tomato, halved, grilled without fat 5oz (140g) boiled potato, mashed with 2 tablespoons milk from allowance 3oz (85g) frozen peas, cooked	310	9

	Calories	Fibre (g)
Bed-time drink:		
A cup of chocolate – 2 rounded teaspoons drinking chocolate with skimmed milk from allowance	40	0

	Calories	Fibre (g)
TOTAL	1,500	37·5

*Peanut Butter and Cress Snack Rolls

Serves 1

2 wholemeal snack rolls (1½oz, 45g each)
1oz (30g) peanut butter
1 carton mustard and cress

Split the two rolls lengthwise. Spread one half of each roll with peanut butter and top with mustard and cress. Replace the remaining half of each roll.

1,500 CALORIE MENU   8
no Fibre-Filler

	Calories	Fibre (g)
Daily allowances: two items of fruit, 1 pint (570ml) skimmed milk	300	5
Breakfast		
1½oz (45g) Allinson Crunchy Bran with ½oz (15g) sultanas and milk from allowance		
1 Ryvita crispbread spread with ¼oz (7g) low-fat spread and 1 level teaspoon honey or marmalade	200	13·5

	Calories	Fibre (g)
Mid-morning snack 2 Hovis digestive biscuits		
An orange from allowance	110	1·5
Lunch 1 egg (size 3), poached and served on 1 large thin slice (1¼oz, 35g) wholemeal bread, toasted and spread with ¼oz (7g) low-fat spread		
* Apricot Yogurt Dessert	380	12
After-school snack 1 frozen choc bar (ice-cream) *or* 3oz (85g) vanilla ice-cream	150	0
Evening meal * Liver and Mushroom Filled Jacket Potato 4oz (115g) canned tomatoes 4oz (115g) cabbage, boiled	360	9·5
Bed-time snack An apple or pear from allowance		
TOTAL	1,500	41·5

* Apricot Yogurt Dessert

Serves 1

150g carton low-fat natural yogurt
2oz (55g) dried apricots (no-need-to-soak variety), chopped
1 teaspoon clear honey

Mix the yogurt, chopped apricots and honey together. Leave to stand for at least 30 minutes to allow flavours to blend.

* Liver and Mushroom Filled Jacket Potato

Serves 1

7oz (200g) potato
4oz (115g) chicken livers, chopped
1 tablespoon finely chopped onion
1oz (30g) mushrooms, sliced
5 tablespoons skimmed milk from allowance
salt and pepper
a dash of Worcestershire sauce

Scrub the potato well and bake (see p. 328). Meanwhile place the chicken livers, onion, mushrooms and milk in a small pan. Heat to simmering point, cover and cook gently for 5 minutes. Cut the potato in half lengthwise and scoop out some of the flesh. Mix the flesh with the chicken liver mixture. Season to taste and add the Worcestershire sauce. Pile back into the potato jackets. Heat through in the oven for 5–10 minutes, if necessary.

1,500 CALORIE MENU   9
no Fibre-Filler

	Calories	Fibre (g)
Daily allowances: two items of fruit, 1 pint (570ml) skimmed milk	300	5
Breakfast 1½oz (45g) Allinson Crunchy Bran, topped with average-sized (6oz, 170g) banana, sliced, with milk from allowance	210	16
Mid-morning snack 1 small packet (25g) crisps, any flavour	130	3
Lunch * Tuna and Celery Sandwiches		
An apple or pear from allowance	215	7

	Calories	Fibre (g)
After-school snack		
2 Boots Second Nature Biscuits, any variety		
An orange from allowance	80	1
Evening meal		
* Chicken Risotto		
2 Ryvita crispbreads with ½oz (7g) low-fat spread and 1oz (30g) Edam cheese	490	7·5
Bed-time drink		
Milk shake – 1 sachet Kellogg's Two Shakes, any flavour, with milk from allowance	75	0
TOTAL	**1,500**	**39·5**

* Tuna and Celery Sandwiches

Serves 1

1oz (30g) canned tuna in brine, drained
1 stick celery, finely chopped
1 tablespoon low-calorie salad dressing
a pinch of curry powder (optional)
2 large thin slices (1¼oz, 35g each) wholemeal bread

Mash the tuna with a fork, then mix with the celery, salad dressing and curry powder, if used. Spread the tuna mixture on one slice of bread and top with the second slice. Cut diagonally into two or four.

* Chicken Risotto

Serves 1

2oz (55g) brown rice
1oz (30g) onion, finely chopped
2oz (55g) mushrooms, sliced

½ small green pepper, deseeded and chopped
1 tomato, skinned and chopped
½ chicken stock cube
a pinch of mixed herbs
salt and pepper
2oz (55g) cooked chicken

Place the rice, onion, mushrooms, pepper and tomato in a pan. Dissolve the stock cube in 8fl oz (225ml) boiling water and pour into the pan. Bring to the boil, add the mixed herbs and salt and pepper to taste. Stir well, reduce heat, cover and simmer until the stock is absorbed and the rice is tender, about 25 minutes. Remove any skin from the chicken and dice. Stir the chicken into the rice mixture and heat through gently for 5 minutes. Serve hot.

1,500 CALORIE MENU   10
no Fibre-Filler

	Calories	Fibre (g)
Daily allowances: two items of fruit, 1 pint (570ml) skimmed milk	300	5
Breakfast 2oz (55g) Kellogg's Sultana Bran with milk from allowance	165	7
Mid-morning snack 2 Boots Second Nature Biscuits, any variety	80	1
Lunch 2 frozen fish fingers, grilled without fat 8oz (225g) canned baked beans in tomato sauce		
An apple or pear from allowance	270	16·5
After-school snack 2oz (55g) slice fruit cake	200	1·5

	Calories	Fibre (g)
Evening meal		
* Cheese and Potato Pie		
* Raisin and Honey Stuffed Baked Apple	445	13
Bed-time drink		
A cup of chocolate – 2 rounded teaspoons		
drinking chocolate with milk from		
allowance	40	0

TOTAL	**1,500**	**44**

* Cheese and Potato Pie

Serves 1

6oz (170g) potato, peeled (weighed after peeling)
1 small onion (2oz, 55g), peeled and thinly sliced
1oz (30g) Cheddar cheese, grated
1oz (30g) sweetcorn kernels
salt and pepper
¼ pint (140ml) skimmed milk from allowance
½ level teaspoon Marmite or yeast extract

Slice the potato thinly. Arrange half the potato slices in the bottom of a small ovenproof dish. Top with half the sliced onion and half the cheese. Sprinkle over the sweetcorn. Season with salt and pepper to taste. Repeat the layers, using up the remaining potato, onion and cheese. Heat the milk and stir in the yeast extract. Pour over the cheese and vegetables. Cover and cook at 160°C (325°F, gas 3), for 1 hour. Serve hot.

* Raisin and Honey Stuffed Baked Apple

Serves 1

8oz (225g) cooking apple
1oz (30g) stoned raisins
1 teaspoon clear honey

Wash the apple and remove the core, leaving a hole for the filling.

Cut through the skin round the centre of the apple with a sharp knife to prevent it bursting during cooking. Place the apple in a small ovenproof dish. Mix the raisins with the honey and fill the hole with the raisins. Pour 2–4 tablespoons water round the apple. Cover with a lid or foil and bake at 160°C (325°F, gas 3) with the Cheese and Potato Pie for 45 minutes or until the apple is tender right through, but not overcooked. Serve hot or cold.

F-PLAN MENUS FOR FREEZER-OWNER COOKS

The inventor of the home freezer inadvertently invented the best slimming aid ever. Here's how to use it to maximum advantage, whether you cook and store F-Plan meals (pp. 544–81) or prefer to buy and store ready frozen convenience foods and follow the menus in the chapters on 'Canned and Packaged F-Plan Menus' (p. 453).

An enormously helpful way of ensuring that you stick to your diet is to plan ahead and prepare and store most of the foods you will need. One of the many advantages of this strategy is that when you start dieting you will be able to spend much less time in the kitchen, where the biscuit tin, bread bin and fridge door all seem to beckon to you, weakening your resolve. You are off to a head start if you stock your freezer with most if not all the sauces, soups, pizzas, flans, meat dishes and puds, packed in individual portions; you will then avoid all temptation to eat the wrong thing because you did not have time to shop for and cook the right thing.

The recipes for all the freezable dishes are given before the menus and not scattered throughout as in other sections, because freezer owners usually 'batch' cook in advance and then store the food until the day on which it is to be eaten. Recipes for four savoury sauces have been included, which can be used to liven up fish, meat and eggs with minimal effort. In addition to the home-cooked frozen foods in the menus one or two other foods commonly found in freezers – for example, ice-cream and frozen fruit, vegetables and fish – have been included. Should you be concerned that all the foods in these menus come from the freezer and that nothing is fresh, it will be reassuring to know that the menus follow all the basic F-Plan diet rules (p. 91) and contain the daily allowances of one portion of Fibre-Filler, an orange and an apple or pear and $\frac{1}{2}$ pint (285ml) skimmed milk. The menus also contain fresh bread, other fresh fruits, fresh vegetables, eggs, cheese and some fresh meat.

The menus are divided up into two parts; 1,000 calories and 1,250 calories daily, all providing 35–50g fibre.

Instructions have been included for reheating the frozen dishes in a microwave oven, as this is a particularly quick and convenient way of cooking or reheating frozen food.

SPECIAL DIET NOTES

1. Begin by deciding which daily calorie total will give you a satisfactory weight loss (See Chapter 19.)

2. Select the menus from your chosen daily calorie total for at least one week, preferably two or more, so that you can plan which dishes you need to prepare in advance and freeze. Remember to vary the menus and hence the foods to ensure that you are eating all the nutrients you need for good health.

3. Carry out as much cooking in advance of starting the diet as you can and have the dishes ready frozen in single portions.

4. Begin each day with Fibre-Filler (recipe on p. 65) from the daily allowance which you can prepare in 'batch' quantities too, if you wish.

5. Drink as much tea and coffee without sugar (artificial sweeteners can be used) as you wish each day, but remember to use only the skimmed milk from the daily allowance. In addition, drink as much water and drinks labelled 'low-calorie' as you wish. Alcoholic drinks have not been included in these menus. However, should you find it impossible to follow a diet which does not allow an occasional alcoholic drink, and if you are achieving a good weight loss, then you could try allowing yourself an increased calorie intake by selecting drinks from the chart (p. 281). However, it would be advisable to limit these to a daily total of 200 calories and if your weight loss stops then it will be necessary to leave out the drinks.

SAUCES

TOMATO SAUCE (30 calories, 2·5g fibre per portion)

6 portions

two 14oz (400g) cans tomatoes
1 large onion (6oz, 170g), peeled and chopped
1 large carrot (4oz, 115g), peeled and grated

1 stick celery
1 bay leaf
salt and pepper

Place all the ingredients in a medium-sized saucepan with $\frac{1}{4}$ pint
(140ml) water, bring to the boil, reduce the heat and simmer for
20 minutes. Remove the bay leaf and purée the sauce, either
through a sieve or in a blender. Season to taste.

To freeze
Leave to cool; divide equally between six polythene bags or individual freezer containers, seal, label and freeze.

To serve
Leave at room temperature for at least 3 hours, turn out into a
saucepan and heat gently until piping hot.
   or
Turn out frozen portion on to a dish, cover with cling film and
microwave on HIGH for $1\frac{1}{2}$ minutes; remove from the oven and
break up using a fork. Microwave on HIGH for a further $1\frac{1}{2}$ minutes.

BARBECUE SAUCE (40 calories, 1g fibre per portion)

6 portions

8oz (225g) unsweetened apple purée
6 level tablespoons tomato purée
2 teaspoons vinegar
2 teaspoons Worcestershire sauce
4 level teaspoons sugar
4oz (115g) mushrooms, finely chopped
salt and pepper
Place all the ingredients in a medium-sized saucepan, with 1
pint (570ml) water, bring to the boil, reduce the heat and simmer
for 20 minutes. Season to taste.

To freeze
Leave to cool; divide equally between six polythene bags or individual freezer containers, seal, label and freeze.

To serve

Leave at room temperature for at least 2½ hours, turn out into a saucepan and heat gently until piping hot.

  or

Turn out frozen portion on to a dish, cover with cling film and microwave on HIGH for 1½ minutes; remove from the oven and break up using a fork. Microwave on HIGH for a further 1½ minutes.

SWEET AND SOUR SAUCE (85 calories, 1g fibre per portion)

4 portions

8oz (225g) canned pineapple pieces in natural juice
1 tablespoon clear honey
1 tablespoon vinegar
2 level tablespoons cornflour
3 tablespoons soy sauce
1 green pepper (4oz, 115g after removing seeds), cut into thin strips
2oz (55g) carrot, peeled and cut into thin strips
salt and pepper

Drain the pineapple, reserving the juice. Make the juice up to 1 pint (570ml) with water, place in a saucepan with the honey and vinegar. Mix the cornflour and soy sauce together, add to the water and bring to the boil, stirring continuously. When it thickens, add the vegetables and pineapple, reduce the heat and simmer for 20–25 minutes.

To freeze

Leave to cool; divide equally between four polythene bags or individual freezer containers, seal, label and freeze.

To serve

Leave at room temperature for at least 3 hours, turn out into a saucepan and heat gently until piping hot.

or

Turn out frozen portion on to a dish, cover with cling film and microwave on HIGH for 1½ minutes; remove from the oven and break up using a fork. Microwave on HIGH for a further 1½ minutes.

CURRY SAUCE (100 calories, 3·5g fibre per portion)

6 portions

1 large onion (6oz, 170g), peeled and chopped
1 large stick celery, finely chopped
1 teaspoon vegetable oil
1 level tablespoon curry powder
2 level tablespoons piccalilli
1 cooking apple (8oz, 225g), peeled, cored and
  chopped
3oz (85g) dried lentils
1oz (30g) sultanas
1 tablespoon lemon juice

Gently fry the onion and celery in the oil for 3–4 minutes. Add the curry powder and piccalilli, mix well. Add ¾ pint (425ml) water and bring to the boil. Add the apple, lentils, sultanas and lemon juice, bring back to the boil, reduce the heat and simmer for 25–30 minutes or until the lentils are soft.

To freeze
Leave to cool; divide between six ¼ pint (140ml) containers (for example, empty yogurt cartons). Cover and seal, label and freeze.

To serve
Thaw at room temperature for at least 3 hours, empty into a saucepan, and heat gently until piping hot.
  or
Turn out frozen portion on to a dish, cover with cling film and microwave on HIGH for 1½ minutes. Remove and break up using a fork. Microwave on HIGH for a further 1½ minutes.

SOUPS

CREAMY PEA SOUP (90 calories, 7·5g fibre per portion)

5 portions

1lb (455g) fresh or frozen peas
1 large onion (6oz, 170g), peeled and chopped
1 tablespoon chopped fresh mint *or* 1 level teaspoon dried mint
1¼ pints (1l) chicken stock made from 2 chicken stock cubes
1 level teaspoon sugar
salt and pepper
1oz (30g) low-fat skimmed milk powder

Place the peas, onion, mint, stock and sugar in a saucepan. Season with salt and pepper. Bring to the boil, cover and simmer for 30 minutes. Purée in a blender or rub through a sieve. Blend the skimmed milk powder with a little of the soup and return to the saucepan with the remaining soup. Reheat gently without boiling.

To freeze
Leave to cool; divide equally between five ½ pint (285ml) containers. Cover, label and freeze.

To serve
Thaw at room temperature for 2 hours, turn into a saucepan and heat gently until piping hot.
   or
Turn out frozen portion into a bowl, cover with cling film and microwave on HIGH for 2 minutes; remove and break up using a fork. Microwave on HIGH for a further 2 minutes until piping hot.

CARROT AND LENTIL SOUP (120 calories, 7·5g fibre per portion)

4 portions

1¼ pints (565ml) chicken stock, made with 1 stock cube
12oz (340g) carrots, peeled and sliced
4oz (115g) lentils

1 large onion (6oz, 170g), peeled and chopped
1 stick celery
2 teaspoons lemon juice
1 tablespoon chopped parsley
salt and pepper

In a large saucepan bring the chicken stock to the boil. Add the
carrots, lentils, onion and celery, and simmer for 25 minutes or
until the vegetables are tender. Remove from the heat and purée
through a sieve or in a blender. Return to the saucepan and add
the lemon juice and parsley; season with salt and pepper to taste.

To freeze
Leave to cool; divide equally between four ½ pint (285ml) containers, cover, label and freeze.

To serve
Thaw at room temperature for at least 2½ hours. Empty soup into
a saucepan and heat gently until piping hot.
    or
Turn out frozen portion into a bowl, cover with cling film and
microwave on HIGH for 5 minutes, stirring after 2 and 4 minutes.

SWEETCORN POTAGE (155 calories, 5·5g fibre per portion)

6 portions

1½ pints (850ml) chicken stock, made with 2 chicken stock
    cubes
1lb 4oz (565g) potatoes, peeled and diced
1 large onion (6oz, 170g), peeled and chopped
10oz (285g) canned sweetcorn
4oz (115g) mushrooms, sliced
1 green pepper, deseeded and chopped
1oz (30g) low-fat dried milk powder
salt and pepper

Put the stock in a large saucepan and bring to the boil. Add the
potatoes, onion, sweetcorn, mushrooms and green pepper, and
simmer for 30 minutes or until the vegetables are soft. Remove

from the heat and allow to cool slightly; gradually stir in the milk powder. Season. Return to the heat and gently bring back to boiling point.

To freeze
Leave to cool; divide equally between six ½ pint (285ml) containers, cover, label and freeze.

To serve
Thaw at room temperature for at least 2¼ hours, empty into a saucepan and heat gently until piping hot.
   or
Turn out frozen portion into a bowl, cover with cling film and microwave on HIGH for 5 minutes, stirring after 2 and 4 minutes.

MAIN DISHES

COURGETTE AND SWEETCORN FLAN (225 calories, 4g fibre per portion)

6 portions

   Pastry
6oz (170g) wholemeal flour
3oz (85g) low-fat spread

   Filling
3oz (85g) onion, peeled and thinly sliced
3oz (85g) canned sweetcorn kernels
6oz (170g) courgette, thinly sliced
1 egg (size 2)
¼ pint (140ml) skimmed milk
¼ teaspoon mustard powder
salt and pepper
2oz (55g) mature Cheddar cheese, grated

Put the flour into a bowl and rub in the low-fat spread until the mixture resembles breadcrumbs. Stir in 3 tablespoons water and gather the dough together into a ball. Roll out the pastry (between two sheets of greaseproof paper for easier handling, if wished) and line an 8 inch (20cm) flan tin. Line the flan pastry with greaseproof paper and add some baking beans or bread crusts. Bake at 220°C (425°F, gas 7), for 10 minutes. Lift out the paper and beans and return the flan pastry to the oven for a further 5 minutes. Turn the oven down to 180°C (350°F, gas 4). Arrange the onion and sweetcorn in the bottom of the flan case. Arrange the courgette slices in overlapping circles on top of the sweetcorn and onion. Beat the egg, milk, mustard powder and salt and pepper together. Pour into the flan case. Bake in the oven for 15 minutes, then remove. Sprinkle the grated cheese over the top and return to the oven for a further 20 minutes or until the egg mixture is set and the cheese browned.

To freeze
Cool quickly, then cut into six equal pieces. Wrap each piece in foil, label and freeze.

To serve
Loosen foil wrapping and thaw at room temperature for 3 hours.

MEAT AND VEGETABLE LOAF (220 calories, 6g fibre per portion)

6 portions

4oz (115g) lentils
12oz (340g) lean minced beef
1 large onion, (6oz, 170g), peeled and chopped
4oz (115g) carrot, grated
6oz (170g) wholemeal breadcrumbs
3 level tablespoons tomato purée
1 level teaspoon mixed dried herbs
salt and pepper

Bring the lentils to the boil in ½ pint (285ml) water, then simmer gently for 25 minutes or until the lentils are soft. Preheat the oven to 180°F. gas 4). Lightly grease the sides of a 2lb (1 kg) loaf tin and place a piece of greaseproof or Bakewell paper in the bottom. Mix all the ingredients in a large bowl until they are evenly distributed. Put the mixture into the loaf tin; press down firmly using the back of a spoon. Bake in the middle of the oven for $1\frac{1}{2}$ hours or until the meat loaf is brown and firm to the touch.

To freeze
Leave to cool in the tin; turn out and cut into twelve slices. Pack two slices (separated by a piece of greaseproof paper) into six polythene bags or individual freezer containers; seal, label and freeze.

To serve
Thaw at room temperature for at least $3\frac{1}{2}$ hours; then either heat through in a hot oven or heat under the grill.
   or
Turn out the frozen slices on to a dish, cover with cling film and microwave on HIGH for 2 minutes, turn over and microwave for a further 2 minutes.

SARDINE AND TOMATO PIZZA (265 calories, 5g fibre per portion)

5 portions

8oz (225g) wholemeal flour
1 level teaspoon salt
$\frac{1}{2}$oz (15g) low-fat spread
1 sachet Harvest Gold Easy Blend Yeast

   Topping
1 level tablespoon tomato purée
$4\frac{1}{2}$oz (130g) canned sardines in tomato sauce
1 large onion (6oz, 170g), peeled and thinly sliced
6oz (170g) tomatoes, sliced
3oz (85g) Edam cheese, grated
$\frac{1}{2}$ teaspoon dried basil

Put the flour, salt and low-fat spread into a large mixing bowl and rub together until the mixture resembles breadcrumbs. Stir in the yeast and add $\frac{1}{4}$ pint (140ml) warm water to form a soft dough. Knead the dough for 5–7 minutes until smooth. Leave to prove (rise) in a lightly oiled polythene bag for 30 minutes or until it has doubled in size. Divide the dough into 5 portions, roll out each one to fit a 6 inch (15cm) round freezer container. Spread the tomato purée over them. Mash the sardines together with their sauce and place evenly over the tomato purée. Place the onion, tomato and cheese on each pizza, and sprinkle a little basil over the top.

To freeze
Open freeze, then when frozen, place with the container in a polythene bag, seal, label and freeze.

To serve
Defrost at room temperature for at least 2 hours, place in a pre-heated oven, 200°C (400°F, gas 6), for 15 minutes or until base is crusty.

BEEF AND BEAN CASSEROLE (195 calories, 6g fibre per portion)

4 portions

12oz (340g) stewing steak, fat removed, cut into 1 inch
   (2·5cm) cubes
1 large onion (6oz, 170g), peeled and chopped
1 large carrot (3oz, 85g), peeled and sliced
8oz (225g) canned baked beans in tomato sauce
1oz (30g) pearl barley
½ pint (285ml) beef stock, using 1 beef stock cube
1 teaspoon Worcestershire sauce
1 teaspoon vinegar
salt and pepper

Preheat the oven to 160°C (325°F, gas 3). Place the meat in a 2 pint (1l) ovenproof dish with the onion, carrot, baked beans and pearl barley. Mix together the beef stock, Worcestershire sauce and vinegar and pour over the meat. Season with salt and pepper. Cover and bake in the middle of the oven for 2 hours or until the meat and carrot are tender.

To freeze
Leave to cool; then divide equally between four polythene bags or four individual freezer containers. Seal, label and freeze.

To serve
Thaw at room temperature for at least 4 hours, empty into a saucepan and heat gently until piping hot.

or

Turn out frozen portion on to a dish. Cover with cling film and microwave on HIGH for 2 minutes; remove from the microwave and break up using a fork. Microwave on HIGH for a further 1½ minutes.

CHILI CON CARNE (245 calories, 9·5g fibre per portion)

4 portions

4oz (115g) red kidney beans, soaked overnight in water
1 large onion (6oz, 170g), peeled and chopped
8oz (225g) lean minced beef
2 large sticks celery, finely chopped
4oz (115g) mushrooms, sliced
2 level tablespoons tomato purée
1–2 level teaspoons chili powder, or to taste
14oz (400g) canned tomatoes
salt and pepper

Bring the kidney beans to the boil in lightly salted water and boil rapidly for 15 minutes; remove from the heat and drain. Gently fry the onion and minced beef, without added fat, for 2 to 3 minutes. To the meat mixture add the celery, mushrooms, tomato purée and chili powder, and mix thoroughly until the ingredients are evenly distributed. Pour in the tomatoes and ¼ pint (140ml) water, and add the kidney beans. Stir until the mixture is boiling. Reduce heat, cover and leave to simmer gently for approximately 1 hour or until the kidney beans are tender.

To freeze
Leave to cool; then divide equally between four polythene bags or four individual freezer containers. Seal, label and freeze.

To serve
Thaw at room temperature for at least 4 hours. Empty into a saucepan and heat gently until piping hot.
 or
Turn out frozen portion on to a dish. Cover with cling film and microwave on HIGH for 1½ minutes; remove from the microwave and break up using a fork. Microwave on HIGH for a further 1½ minutes.

FILLET OF PORK WITH PRUNES (260 calories, 6g fibre per portion)

4 portions

1lb (455g) lean pork fillet, fat removed, cut into 1 inch
 (2·5cm) cubes
4oz (115g) dried prunes, soaked overnight and
 drained
2oz (55g) raisins
1 cooking apple (8oz, 225g), cored and chopped
2 level tablespoons piccalilli

Preheat the oven to 180°C (350°F, gas 4). Place the meat in a 2 pint (1l) ovenproof dish with the prunes, raisins and apple. Mix the piccalilli with ½ pint (285ml) water and pour over the meat. Cover and bake in the middle of the oven for 1 hour or until the meat is tender.

To freeze
Leave to cool; then divide equally between four polythene bags or four individual freezer containers. Seal, label and freeze.

To serve
Thaw at room temperature for at least 4 hours, empty into a saucepan and heat gently until piping hot.
 or
Turn out frozen portion on to a dish, cover with cling film and microwave on HIGH for 1½ minutes. Remove from the microwave

and break up using a fork. Microwave on HIGH for a further 1½ minutes.

PAPRIKA CHICKEN (275 calories, 6g fibre per portion)

4 portions

2oz (55g) haricot beans, soaked overnight and drained
4 chicken pieces (weighing approximately 8oz, 225g each),
    skin removed
4oz (115g) frozen sweetcorn kernels
1oz (30g) brown rice
14oz (400g) canned tomatoes
¼ pint (140ml) chicken stock, made from ½ chicken stock
    cube
1 tablespoon vinegar
¼ teaspoon paprika

Preheat the oven to 190°C (375°F, gas 5). Place the haricot beans and skinned chicken pieces into a 3 pint (1¾l) ovenproof dish with the sweetcorn, rice and canned tomatoes. Mix together the stock, vinegar and paprika, and pour over the chicken joints. Cover and bake in the middle of the oven for 50–55 minutes or until the chicken and rice are tender.

To freeze
Leave to cool, then divide equally between four polythene bags or four individual freezer containers. Seal, label and freeze.

To serve
Thaw at room temperature for at least 4 hours, empty into an ovenproof dish and reheat at 200°C (400°F, gas 6), for 35–40 minutes.
    or
Turn out frozen portion on to a dish, cover with cling film and microwave on HIGH for 2 minutes. Take the chicken out and turn it over. Cook for a further 2 minutes on HIGH. Repeat this twice more.

LAMB WITH SPLIT PEAS (290 calories, 5·5g fibre per portion)

4 portions

8oz (225g) lean shoulder of lamb (weighed without the bone),
 cut into 1 inch (2·5cm) cubes
4oz (115g) dried split peas, soaked overnight in water
1 large onion (6oz, 170g), peeled and chopped
8oz (225g) carrots, peeled and sliced
2 bay leaves
½ teaspoon ground nutmeg
¾ pint (425ml) beef stock, made from 1 beef stock cube

Preheat the oven to 160°C (325°F, gas 3). Gently fry the lamb in a
non-stick pan, without added fat, until lightly browned. Drain off
and discard any fat which has cooked out of the meat. Place meat
in a 2 pint (1l) ovenproof dish, with the rest of the ingredients.
Cover the dish and bake in the middle of the oven for 2–2¼ hours
until the meat and carrots are tender.

To freeze
Leave to cool; then divide equally between four polythene bags or
four individual freezer containers. Seal, label and freeze.

To serve
Thaw at room temperature for at least 4 hours, empty into a
saucepan and heat gently until piping hot.
    or
Turn out frozen portion on to a dish, cover with cling film and
microwave on HIGH for 1½ minutes. Remove and break up using
a fork. Microwave on HIGH for a further 1½ minutes.

PUDDINGS

PEAR AND APRICOT MOUSSE (110 calories, 2g fibre per
portion)

6 portions

14½oz (410g) can pears in natural or fruit juice
14½oz (410g) can apricots in natural or fruit juice

3 eggs (size 3), separated
1 teaspoon clear honey
1 envelope or 3 level teaspoons powdered gelatine

Reserve 3 tablespoons juice from the can of pears and purée the pears and apricots with the remaining juice. Beat the egg yolks and honey with 1 teaspoon hot water until pale and creamy. Place the gelatine in a small heatproof bowl with the reserved juice. Stand the bowl in a saucepan of water and heat until the gelatine is dissolved. Cool slightly; stir into the egg yolk mixture with the fruit purée. Whisk the egg whites until stiff and gently fold into the mixture.

To freeze
Pour the mousse into six ½ pint (285ml) containers (for example, cottage cheese cartons). Cover, label and freeze.

To serve
Place in the refrigerator for 2½–3 hours.

PLUM CHARLOTTE (135 calories, 5·5g fibre per portion)

6 portions

1lb (455g) dessert plums, stoned
4oz (115g) wholemeal breadcrumbs
2oz (55g) Quaker Harvest Crunch with Bran and Apple
½ teaspoon ground cinnamon
grated rind of 1 orange
6 tablespoons fresh orange juice
2 level tablespoons soft brown sugar

Divide half the plums equally between six individual soufflé dishes or small foil basins and spread out over the bases. Mix the breadcrumbs, Harvest Crunch, cinnamon and grated orange rind together. Sprinkle half this mixture over the plums. Cover with the remaining plums, dividing them equally between the dishes and top with the remaining breadcrumb mixture. Mix the orange juice with the sugar and spoon an equal amount over the top of each charlotte. Stand the dishes on a baking tray and bake at 180°C (350°F, gas 4), for 30 minutes, until the top is crisp and browned. Serve hot.

To freeze
Cool as quickly as possible, cover with foil, label and freeze.

To serve
Thaw at room temperature for 2–3 hours, then heat through in the oven at 200°C (400°F, gas 6), for about 15 minutes or until hot.

RHUBARB AND BREAD PUDDING (150 calories, 4·5g fibre per portion)

6 portions

1lb 4oz (565g) rhubarb, cut into 1 inch (2·5cm) pieces
4 large slices (1¼oz, 35g each) wholemeal bread, each cut into
    9 squares
1oz (30g) sultanas
1½oz (35g) soft brown sugar
½ teaspoon ground ginger
¾ pint (425ml) skimmed milk
2 eggs (size 2)

Preheat the oven to 180°C (350°F, gas 4). Divide half the rhubarb between six individual freezer containers and cover each with three squares of bread. Sprinkle the sultanas over the bread and repeat the rhubarb and bread layers once more. Beat together the sugar, ginger, milk and eggs, and pour over the rhubarb and bread and leave to stand for 20–30 minutes. Bake in the oven for 30 minutes until the custard is set and rhubarb is soft.

To freeze
Leave to cool, cover, label and freeze.

To serve
Thaw at room temperature for 2 hours, uncover and then reheat at 200°C (400°F, gas 6) for about 15–20 minutes or until heated through.

TUTTI FRUTTI ICE-CREAM (155 calories, 3·5g fibre per portion)

1oz (30g) flaked almonds
1oz (30g) wholemeal breadcrumbs
½ pint (285ml) natural low fat yogurt
2oz (55g) dried apricots, finely chopped
1oz (30g) raisins
3 egg whites (size 3)
3oz (85g) soft brown sugar

Toast the flaked almonds and breadcrumbs under a hot grill until golden brown. Add to the yogurt with the dried apricots and raisins. Whisk the egg whites until stiff, add the sugar and whisk again until stiff. Fold the yogurt mixture into the whisked egg whites and pour into a rigid plastic container (for example an ice-cream carton). Freeze until just solid. Cut into six equal portions, wrap individually in cling film and place in a polythene bag; replace in the freezer.

To serve
Place in a refrigerator for 20–30 minutes before serving to allow the ice-cream to soften slightly.

BLACKBERRY AND APPLE CRUMBLE (195 calories, 7·5g fibre per portion)

5 portions

Crumble topping
4oz (115g) wholemeal flour
2oz (55g) low-fat spread
1oz (30g) soft brown sugar
1oz (30g) desiccated coconut

Filling
8oz (225g) blackberries
8oz (225g) cooking apples, peeled, cored and sliced
1 teaspoon clear honey

Put the flour and low-fat spread into a mixing bowl and rub together until the mixture resembles breadcrumbs. Stir in the sugar and coconut and leave to one side. Mix the blackberries, apple slices and honey together, and divide between five individual foil basins or dishes. Divide the crumble topping between each portion of fruit.

To freeze
Cover the uncooked crumbles, label and freeze.

To serve
Leave to defrost at room temperature for 2 hours; uncover and cook in a preheated oven 200°C (400°F, gas 6), for about 20 minutes or until crumble topping is browned.

1,000 CALORIE MENU   1

	Calories	Fibre (g)
Daily allowance: Fibre-Filler, ½ pint (285ml) skimmed milk, two items of fruit	400	20

Breakfast
Half portion of Fibre-Filler with milk from allowance

An orange from allowance

Lunch
1 portion Sweetcorn Potage (p. 549)
1 frozen Birds Eye Cod, Coley or Haddock Steak
(Thaw the fish steak with the Sweetcorn Potage then heat the two together in a saucepan until the fish is cooked and can be flaked into the potage. Serve hot.)

An apple or pear from allowance	200	7·5

	Calories	Fibre (g)

Evening meal
1 portion Fillet of Pork with Prunes
(p. 555)
4oz (115g) frozen Brussels sprouts, boiled
2oz (55g) carrots, boiled

1 portion Pear and Apricot Mousse
(p. 557)   400   13

Snack
Half portion of Fibre-Filler with milk from
allowance

TOTAL	1,000	40·5

1,000 CALORIE MENU   2

	Calories	Fibre (g)

Daily allowance: Fibre-Filler, ½ pint
(285ml) skimmed milk, two items of
fruit   400   20

Breakfast
Half portion of Fibre-Filler with milk from
allowance

An apple or pear from allowance

Lunch
1 egg (size 3), poached and served on
1 large thin slice (1¼oz, 35g) wholemeal
bread, toasted and spread with ¼oz (7g)
low-fat spread

1 portion Tutti Frutti Ice-cream (p. 560)   335   6·5

	Calories	Fibre (g)
Evening meal		
1 portion Chili con Carne (p. 554)		
4oz (115g) cabbage, boiled		
An orange from allowance	265	12·5
Snack		
Half portion of Fibre-Filler with milk from allowance		

	Calories	Fibre (g)
TOTAL	1,000	39

1,000 CALORIE MENU   3

	Calories	Fibre (g)
Daily allowance: Fibre-Filler, ½ pint (285ml) skimmed milk, two items of fruit	400	20
Breakfast		
Half portion of Fibre-Filler with milk from allowance		
An orange from allowance		
Lunch		
1 portion Carrot and Lentil Soup (p. 548)		
2 Energen F-Plan Diet Brancrisps, with 1oz (30g) Edam cheese		
An apple or pear from allowance	255	10
Evening meal		
1 bacon steak (3½oz, 100g raw weight), grilled without added fat		
1 portion Sweet and Sour Sauce (p. 546)		
3oz (85g) canned sweetcorn kernels		
4oz (115g) cauliflower, boiled		
4oz (115g) fresh or frozen raspberries with 1oz (30g) vanilla ice-cream	345	16·5

	Calories	Fibre (g)
Snack		
Half portion of Fibre-Filler with milk from allowance		
TOTAL	1,000	46·5

1,000 CALORIE MENU   4

	Calories	Fibre (g)
Daily allowance: Fibre-Filler, ½ pint (285ml) skimmed milk, two items of fruit	400	20

Breakfast
Half portion of Fibre-Filler with milk from allowance

An apple or pear from allowance

Lunch
1 (2oz, 55g) frozen beefburger, well grilled, served in a 2oz (55g) wholemeal lunch roll with 1 tablespoon piccalilli
Small bunch watercress and 1 average-sized tomato

An orange from allowance	260	7

Evening meal
1 packet Birds Eye Smoked Cod in Butter Sauce
6oz (170g) frozen mixed peas, sweetcorn and peppers

4oz (115g) fresh or frozen blackcurrants or blackberries stewed with a little water and sweetened with ½oz (7g) sugar   340   18·5/
                                                                                                                      17

	Calories	Fibre (g)
Snack		
Half portion of Fibre-Filler with milk from allowance		

	Calories	Fibre (g)
TOTAL	1,000	45·5/ 44

1,000 CALORIE MENU 5

	Calories	Fibre (g)
Daily allowance: Fibre-Filler, ½ pint (285ml) skimmed milk, two items of fruit	400	20

Breakfast
Half portion of Fibre-Filler with milk from allowance

An orange from allowance

Lunch
1 portion Creamy Pea Soup (p. 548)
1 rasher streaky bacon, well grilled and crumbled over the soup
1 Energen F-Plan Diet Brancrisp

	Calories	Fibre (g)
An apple or pear from allowance	165	10

Evening meal
1 portion Lamb with Split Peas (p. 557)
4oz (115g) Brussels sprouts, boiled
4oz (115g) potatoes, boiled and mashed with a little skimmed milk from allowance

	Calories	Fibre (g)
2oz (55g) green grapes	435	10·5

	Calories	Fibre (g)
Snack Remaining portion of Fibre-Filler with milk from allowance		

	Calories	Fibre (g)
TOTAL	1,000	40·5

1,000 CALORIE MENU   6

	Calories	Fibre (g)
Daily allowance: Fibre-Filler, ½ pint (285ml) skimmed milk, two items of fruit	400	20
Breakfast Half portion of Fibre-Filler with milk from allowance		
2oz (55g) green grapes	35	0·5
Lunch 1 portion Meat and Vegetable Loaf (p. 551) heated with 1 portion of Tomato Sauce (p. 544)		
2oz (55g) white cabbage, shredded, mixed with 2oz (55g) carrot, grated, and 1 tablespoon low-calorie salad dressing		
An orange from allowance	300	11·5
Evening meal 1 portion Sweetcorn Potage (p. 549) 2oz (55g) frozen prawns, thawed (Heat the Sweetcorn Potage with the prawns until piping hot.)		
1 Energen F-Plan Diet Brancrisp, spread with 1oz (30g) cottage cheese (with chives or with onion and peppers)		
An apple or pear from allowance	265	7

	Calories	Fibre (g)

Snack
Remaining portion of Fibre-Filler with milk
from allowance

	Calories	Fibre (g)
TOTAL	1,000	39

1,000 CALORIE MENU 7

	Calories	Fibre (g)
Daily allowance: Fibre-Filler, ½ pint (285ml) skimmed milk, two items of fruit	400	20

Breakfast
Half portion of Fibre-Filler with milk from
allowance

Lunch
1 portion Courgette and Sweetcorn Flan
(p. 550)
2oz (55g) carrot sticks
2oz (55g) celery sticks

An orange from allowance	240	6·5

Evening meal
1 portion Paprika Chicken (p. 556)
Half 10·6oz (300g) pack frozen cut-leaf
spinach, cooked without butter

1 Energen F-Plan Diet Brancrisp, spread
with 1oz (30g) cottage cheese (natural or
with chives or with onion and peppers or
with pineapple) and topped with 1oz (30g)
chopped green pepper or a few sprigs
watercress

An apple or pear from allowance	360	17

	Calories	Fibre (g)

Snack
Remaining portion of Fibre-Filler with milk
from allowance

TOTAL	1,000	43·5

1,000 CALORIE MENU   8

	Calories	Fibre (g)
Daily allowance: Fibre-Filler, ½ pint (285ml) skimmed milk, two items of fruit	400	20

Breakfast
Half portion of Fibre-Filler with milk from
allowance

Lunch
Curried egg on toast: 1 large thin slice
(1¼oz, 35g) wholemeal bread, toasted
and topped with 1 egg (size 3), poached
and 1 portion of Curry Sauce (p. 547)
heated

An apple or pear from allowance	255	6·5

Evening meal
1 portion Meat and Vegetable Loaf
(p. 551), heated
4oz (115g) baked beans
4oz (115g) mushrooms, poached in
stock
or 7½oz (215g) canned button
mushrooms in brine

An orange from allowance	305	17

	Calories	Fibre (g)
Snack Remaining portion of Fibre-Filler with milk from allowance		
1 Boots Second Nature Wholemeal Muesli Fruit Biscuit	40	0·5
TOTAL	1,000	44

1,000 CALORIE MENU   9

	Calories	Fibre (g)
Daily allowance: Fibre-Filler, ½ pint (285ml) skimmed milk, two items of fruit	400	20
Breakfast Half portion of Fibre-Filler with milk from allowance		
An orange from allowance		
Lunch 1 portion Carrot and Lentil Soup (p. 548) 2 Energen F-Plan Diet Brancrisps, spread with Marmite or yeast extract		
An average-sized banana (6oz, 170g)	250	12·5
Evening meal 1 portion Beef and Bean Casserole (p. 553) 4oz (115g) cauliflower, boiled 2oz (55g) runner beans, boiled		
1 portion Plum Charlotte (p. 558)	350	15·5

	Calories	Fibre (g)

Snack
Remaining portion of Fibre-Filler with milk
from allowance

An apple or pear from allowance

	Calories	Fibre (g)
TOTAL	1,000	48

1,000 CALORIE MENU   10

	Calories	Fibre (g)
Daily allowance: Fibre-Filler, ½ pint (285ml) skimmed milk, two items of fruit	400	20

Breakfast
Half portion of Fibre-Filler with milk from
allowance

Lunch
1 Sardine and Tomato Pizza (p. 552)
Green salad: a few lettuce leaves, a bunch
of watercress, a few slices of cucumber, a
few rings of green pepper and 1 tablespoon
oil-free French dressing

An orange from allowance	285	6·5

Evening meal
8oz (225g) chicken leg joint with all skin
removed
1 portion Curry Sauce (p. 547), thawed
(Cover the skinned chicken joint with the
curry sauce and bake in a covered dish at
200°C, 400°F, gas 6, for 45 minutes or
until the chicken is tender and cooked
through.)
3oz (85g) frozen peas, boiled

An apple or pear from allowance	315	10

	Calories	Fibre (g)

Snack
Half portion of Fibre-Filler with milk from
allowance

	Calories	Fibre (g)
TOTAL	1,000	36·5

1,250 CALORIE MENU 1

	Calories	Fibre (g)
Daily allowance: Fibre-Filler, ½ pint (285ml) skimmed milk, two items of fruit	400	20

Breakfast
Half portion of Fibre-Filler with milk from
allowance
1 large thin slice (1½oz, 35g) wholemeal
bread, toasted and spread with ¼oz (7g)
low-fat spread and 1 level teaspoon honey

or marmalade	115	3

Lunch
1 Sardine and Tomato Pizza (p. 552)
2oz (55g) white cabbage, shredded, mixed
with 2oz (55g) carrot, grated, and 1
tablespoon low-calorie salad dressing

An apple or pear from allowance	315	8

Evening meal
1 portion Paprika Chicken (p. 556)
4oz (115g) potatoes, boiled and mashed
with a little milk from allowance
4oz (115g) cabbage, boiled

An orange from allowance	380	10·5

	Calories	Fibre (g)
Snack Remaining portion of Fibre-Filler with milk from allowance		
1 Boots Second Nature Wholemeal Muesli Fruit Biscuit	40	0·5

TOTAL	1,250	42

1,250 CALORIE MENU   2

	Calories	Fibre (g)
Daily allowance: Fibre-Filler, $\frac{1}{2}$ pint (285ml) skimmed milk, two items of fruit	400	20
Breakfast Half portion of Fibre-Filler with milk from allowance		
1 average-sized banana (6oz, 170g)	80	3·5

Lunch
1 portion Carrot and Lentil Soup (p. 548)
1 large thin slice (1¼oz, 35g) wholemeal bread, toasted and spread with Marmite or yeast extract, cut into fingers and served with the soup

An apple or pear from allowance	200	10·5

Evening meal
7oz (200g) pork chop, grilled and fat trimmed off after grilling
1 portion Barbecue Sauce (p. 545), heated and served with pork chop
4oz (115g) frozen mixed peas, sweetcorn and peppers, boiled

	Calories	Fibre (g)
1 portion Tutti Frutti Ice-cream (p. 560) served with an orange from allowance, segmented	570	11

Snack
Remaining portion of Fibre-Filler with milk from allowance

TOTAL	1,250	45

1,250 CALORIE MENU   3

	Calories	Fibre (g)
Daily allowance: Fibre-Filler, ½ pint (285ml) skimmed milk, two items of fruit	400	20

Breakfast
Half portion of Fibre-Filler with milk from allowance

2 Energen F-Plan Diet Brancrisps, spread with ¼oz (7g) low-fat spread and 2 level teaspoons honey or marmalade	100	4·5

Lunch
1 large thin slice (1¼oz, 35g) wholemeal bread, toasted and topped with 1 average-sized tomato, sliced, a pinch of mixed herbs and 1oz (30g) grated Edam cheese, then heated under grill until the cheese is melted

An apple or pear from allowance	170	4

Evening meal
1 portion Beef and Bean Casserole (p. 553)

	Calories	Fibre (g)
7oz (200g) potato baked in its jacket (see p. 31 for baking instructions) 4oz (115g) Brussels sprouts, boiled		
1 portion Blackberry and Apple Crumble (p. 560)	580	21·5

Snack
Remaining portion of Fibre-Filler with milk
from allowance

An orange from allowance.

TOTAL	1,250	50

1,250 CALORIE MENU   4

	Calories	Fibre (g)
Daily allowance: Fibre-Filler, ½ pint (285ml) skimmed milk, two items of fruit	400	20

Breakfast
Half portion of Fibre-Filler with milk from
allowance

1 egg (size 3), boiled and served with 2 Energen F-Plan Diet Brancrisps, spread with ¼oz (7g) low-fat spread	150	2·5

Lunch
1 portion Sweetcorn Potage (p. 549)
1oz (30g) boiled lean ham, chopped
(Heat the Sweetcorn Potage and sprinkle
over the chopped ham.)

1 large thin slice (1¼oz, 35g)

	Calories	Fibre (g)
wholemeal bread spread with 1 triangle cheese spread		
An orange from allowance	285	10·5

Evening meal
6oz (170g) cod or haddock fillet topped
with 1 portion Tomato Sauce (p. 544) and
baked in the oven at 180°C (350°F, gas 4),
for 20 minutes or until the fish is cooked
through
4oz (115g) frozen peas, boiled
4oz (115g) cauliflower, boiled

	Calories	Fibre (g)
1 portion Tutti Frutti Ice-cream (p. 560) served with an apple or pear from allowance, cored and sliced	375	16·5

Snack
Remaining portion of Fibre-Filler with milk
from allowance
1 Boots Second Nature Wholemeal Muesli

	Calories	Fibre (g)
Fruit Biscuit	40	0·5
TOTAL	1,250	50

1,250 CALORIE MENU   5

	Calories	Fibre (g)
Daily allowance: Fibre-Filler, ½ pint (285ml) skimmed milk, two items of fruit	400	20

Breakfast
Half portion of Fibre-Filler with milk from
allowance

An orange from allowance

	Calories	Fibre (g)

Lunch
2 frozen beefburgers, grilled and served
with 1 portion Barbecue Sauce (p. 545),
heated
4oz (115g) canned baked beans in tomato
sauce

An apple or pear from allowance	375	9

Evening meal
1 portion Fillet of Pork with Prunes (p. 555)
4oz (115g) cabbage, boiled

1 portion Rhubarb and Bread Pudding
(p. 559) topped with 1oz (30g) vanilla
ice-cream	475	13·5

Snack
Remaining portion of Fibre-Filler with milk
from allowance

TOTAL	1,250	42·5

1,250 CALORIE MENU   6

	Calories	Fibre (g)
Daily allowance: Fibre-Filler, ½ pint (285ml) skimmed milk, two items of fruit	400	20

Breakfast
Half portion of Fibre-Filler with milk from
allowance
1 large thin slice (1¼oz, 35g) wholemeal
bread, toasted, spread with ¼oz (7g) low-fat
spread and 1 level teaspoon honey or
| marmalade | 115 | 3 |

	Calories	Fibre (g)
Lunch		
1 portion Courgette and Sweetcorn Flan (p. 550)		
A bunch of watercress		
2 average-sized tomatoes		
An apple or pear from allowance		
1 Boots Second Nature Wholemeal Muesli Fruit Biscuit	285	7
Evening meal		
1 portion Chili con Carne (p. 554)		
4oz (115g) cauliflower, boiled		
2oz (55g) runner beans, boiled		
1 portion Plum Charlotte (p. 558) topped with 1oz (30g) vanilla ice-cream	450	19
Snack		
Remaining portion of Fibre-Filler with milk from allowance		
An orange from allowance		
TOTAL	1,250	49

1,250 CALORIE MENU   7

	Calories	Fibre(g)
Daily allowance: Fibre-Filler, ½ pint (285ml) skimmed milk, two items of fruit	400	20
Breakfast		
Half portion of Fibre-Filler with milk from allowance		
1 average-sized banana (6oz, 170g)	80	3·5

	Calories	Fibre (g)

Lunch

1 portion Creamy Pea Soup (p. 548)

Cottage cheese sandwich: 2 large thin
slices (1¼oz, 35g each) wholemeal bread,
2 lettuce leaves, 2oz (55g) cottage cheese
(natural or with chives or with onion
and peppers or with pineapple)
(Arrange a lettuce leaf on 1 slice of bread,
top with the cottage cheese, the second
lettuce leaf and the second slice of bread.)

An orange from allowance	295	13·5

Evening meal

2 pork sausages (2oz, 55g each, raw
weight), grilled, served with 1 portion
Sweet and Sour Sauce (p. 546), heated
4oz (115g) cabbage, boiled
2oz (55g) canned sweetcorn kernels

An apple or pear from allowance	415	7·5

Snack

Remaining portion of Fibre-Filler with milk
from allowance

1 Energen F-Plan Diet Brancrisp, spread with 1 tablespoon low-calorie salad dressing, 1 tomato, sliced and a few slices cucumber	60	2

TOTAL	1,250	46·5

1,250 CALORIE MENU   8

	Calories	Fibre (g)
Daily allowance: Fibre-Filler, ½ pint (285ml) skimmed milk, two items of fruit	400	20

	Calories	Fibre (g)

Breakfast
Half portion of Fibre-Filler with milk from
allowance

1 egg (size 3), boiled 2 Energen F-Plan Diet Brancrisps, spread with ¼oz (7g) low-fat spread	150	2·5

Lunch
1 Sardine and Tomato Pizza (p. 552)
A small bunch of watercress
1oz (30g) pickled beetroot

An apple or pear from allowance	280	6·5

Evening meal
1 portion Lamb with Split Peas (p. 557)
4oz (115g) Brussels sprouts, boiled

1 portion Pear and Apricot Mousse (p. 557)	420	10·5

Snack
Remaining portion of Fibre-Filler with milk
from allowance

An orange from allowance

TOTAL	1,250	39·5

1,250 CALORIE MENU   9

	Calories	Fibre (g)
Daily allowance: Fibre-Filler, ½ pint (285ml) skimmed milk, two items of fruit	400	20

Breakfast
Half portion of Fibre-Filler with milk from
allowance

	Calories	Fibre (g)
1 large thin slice (1¼oz, 35g) wholemeal bread, toasted and spread with ¼oz (7g) low-fat spread and Marmite or yeast extract	105	3

Lunch
1 portion Carrot and Lentil Soup (p. 548)
2 Energen F-Plan Diet Brancrisps, spread with 1 triangle cheese spread

An apple or pear from allowance	205	10

Evening meal
4oz (115g) lamb's liver, sliced and brushed with 1 teaspoon oil and grilled
1 portion Sweet and Sour Sauce (p. 546)
4oz (115g) Birds Eye Frozen Rice, Peas and Mushrooms, cooked without added butter

An orange from allowance	500	6

Snack
Remaining portion of Fibre-Filler with milk from allowance

1 Boots Second Nature Wholemeal Muesli Fruit Biscuit	40	0·5

TOTAL	1,250	39·5

1,250 CALORIE MENU　　　　　　　　　10

	Calories	Fibre (g)
Daily allowance: Fibre-Filler, ½ pint (285ml) skimmed milk, two items of fruit	400	20

	Calories	Fibre (g)

Breakfast
Half portion of Fibre-Filler with milk from
allowance

| 1 large banana (7oz, 200g) | 95 | 4 |

Lunch
Prawn sandwich: 2 large thin slices (1¼oz,
35g each) wholemeal bread, spread with 1
tablespoon low-calorie salad dressing and
filled with 1oz (30g) frozen prawns,
thawed, 1 tomato, sliced, and a few sprigs
of watercress

| An apple or pear from allowance | 215 | 7 |

Evening meal
2 frozen Birds Eye Cod, Coley or Haddock
Steaks, thawed and covered with 1 portion
Curry Sauce (p. 547) and baked in the
oven in a covered dish at 190°C (375°F,
gas 5) for 25 minutes or until the fish is
cooked through
4oz (115g) mushrooms, poached in stock
or 7½oz (215g) canned button mushrooms
in brine
4oz (115g) runner beans, boiled

1 portion Blackberry and Apple Crumble
(p. 560) topped with 1oz (30g) vanilla

| ice-cream | 540 | 18 |

Snack
Remaining portion of Fibre-Filler with milk
from allowance

An orange from allowance

| TOTAL | 1,250 | 49 |

FOR THE BEST IN PAPERBACKS, LOOK FOR THE

In every corner of the world, on every subject under the sun, Penguins represent quality and variety – the very best in publishing today.

For complete information about books available from Penguin and how to order them, write to us at the appropriate address below. Please note that for copyright reasons the selection of books varies from country to country.

In the United Kingdom: For a complete list of books available from Penguin in the U.K., please write to *Dept EP, Penguin Books Ltd, Harmondsworth, Middlesex, UB7 0DA*

In the United States: For a complete list of books available from Penguin in the U.S., please write to *Dept BA, Viking Penguin, 299 Murray Hill Parkway, East Rutherford, New Jersey 07073*

In Canada: For a complete list of books available from Penguin in Canada, please write to *Penguin Books Canada Limited, 2801 John Street, Markham, Ontario L3R 1B4*

In Australia: For a complete list of books available from Penguin in Australia, please write to the *Marketing Department, Penguin Books Australia Ltd, P.O. Box 257, Ringwood, Victoria 3134*

In New Zealand: For a complete list of books available from Penguin in New Zealand, please write to the *Marketing Department, Penguin Books (N.Z.) Ltd, Private Bag, Takapuna, Auckland 9*

In India: For a complete list of books available from Penguin in India, please write to *Penguin Overseas Ltd, 706 Eros Apartments, 56 Nehru Place, New Delhi 110019*

PENGUIN HEALTH

Medicines: A Guide for Everybody   Peter Parish

This fifth edition of a comprehensive survey of all the medicines available over the counter or on prescription offers clear guidance for the ordinary reader as well as invaluable information for those involved in health care.

Pregnancy and Childbirth   Sheila Kitzinger

A complete and up-to-date guide to physical and emotional preparation for pregnancy – a must for all prospective parents.

The Penguin Encyclopaedia of Nutrition   John Yudkin

This book cuts through all the myths about food and diets to present the real facts clearly and simply. 'Everyone should buy one' – *Nutrition News and Notes*

The Parents' A to Z   Penelope Leach

For anyone with a child of 6 months, 6 years or 16 years, this guide to all the little problems involved in their health, growth and happiness will prove reassuring and helpful.

Jane Fonda's Workout Book

Help yourself to better looks, superb fitness and a whole new approach to health and beauty with this world-famous and fully illustrated programme of diet and exercise advice.

Alternative Medicine   Andrew Stanway

Dr Stanway provides an objective and practical guide to thirty-two alternative forms of therapy – from Acupuncture and the Alexander Technique to Macrobiotics and Yoga.

PENGUIN HEALTH

A Complete Guide to Therapy Joel Kovel

The options open to anyone seeking psychiatric help are both numerous and confusing. Dr Kovel cuts through the many myths and misunderstandings surrounding today's therapy and explores the pros and cons of various types of therapies.

Pregnancy Dr Jonathan Scher and Carol Dix

Containing the most up-to-date information on pregnancy – the effects of stress, sexual intercourse, drugs, diet, late maternity and genetic disorders – this book is an invaluable and reassuring guide for prospective parents.

Yoga Ernest Wood

'It has been asked whether in yoga there is something for everybody. The answer is "yes"' Ernest Wood.

Depression Ross Mitchell

Depression is one of the most common contemporary problems. But what exactly do we mean by the term? In this invaluable book Ross Mitchell looks at depression as a mood, as an experience, as an attitude to life and as an illness.

Vogue Natural Health and Beauty Bronwen Meredith

Health foods, yoga, spas, recipes, natural remedies and beauty preparations are all included in this superb, fully illustrated guide and companion to the bestselling *Vogue Body and Beauty Book*.

Care of the Dying Richard Lamerton

It is never true that 'nothing more can be done' for the dying. This book shows us how to face death without pain, with humanity, with dignity and in peace.

PENGUIN HEALTH

The Penguin Encyclopaedia of Nutrition   John Yudkin

This book cuts through all the myths about food and diets to present the real facts clearly and simply. 'Everyone should buy one' – *Nutrition News and Notes*

The Prime of Your Life   Dr Miriam Stoppard

The first comprehensive, fully illustrated guide to healthy living for people aged fifty and beyond, by top medical writer and media personality, Dr Miriam Stoppard.

A Good Start   Louise Graham

Factual and practical, full of tips on providing a healthy and balanced diet for young children, *A Good Start* is essential reading for all parents.

How to Get Off Drugs   Ira Mothner and Alan Weitz

This book is a vital contribution towards combating drug addiction in Britain in the eighties. For drug abusers, their families and their friends.

The Royal Canadian Airforce XBX Plan for Physical Fitness for Men
and **The Royal Canadian Airforce XBX Plan for Physical Fitness for Women**

Get fit and stay fit with minimum fuss and maximum efficiency, using these short, carefully devised exercises.

Pregnancy and Childbirth   Sheila Kitzinger

A complete and up-to-date guide to physical and emotional preparation for pregnancy – a must for prospective parents.

Alternative Medicine   Andrew Stanway

Dr Stanway provides an objective and practical guide to thirty-two alternative forms of therapy – from Acupuncture and the Alexander Technique to Macrobiotics and Yoga.

Naturebirth   Danaë Brook

A pioneering work which includes suggestions on diet and health, exercises and many tips on the 'natural' way to prepare for giving birth in a joyful relaxed way.

FOR THE BEST IN PAPERBACKS, LOOK FOR THE

GARDENING IN PENGUINS

The Adventurous Gardener   Christopher Lloyd

Prejudiced, delightful and always stimulating, Christopher Lloyd's book is essential reading for everyone who loves gardening. 'Get it and enjoy it' – *Financial Times*

The Magic Garden   Shirley Conran

The gardening book for the absolute beginner. 'Whether you have a window box, a patio, an acre or a cabbage patch . . . you will enjoy this' – *Daily Express*

The Cottage Garden   Anne Scott-James

'Her history is neatly and simply laid out; well-stocked with attractive illustrations' – *The Times*. 'The garden book I have most enjoyed reading in the last few years' – *Observer*

Growing Fruit   Mary Spiller

From blossom to harvest, through planting, pruning, picking and storing, in a small or large garden, plot or pot, here is an illustrated step-by-step guide to growing fruit of all kinds.

The Illustrated Garden Planter   Diana Saville

How to choose plants for your garden – to cover a wall, creep between paving, provide colour in summer – and to plan for collective effect or to overcome a difficult site. 650 plants are illustrated, in all over 900 described.

Organic Gardening   Lawrence D. Hills

The classic manual on growing fruit and vegetables without using artificial or harmful fertilizers. 'Enormous value . . . enthusiastic writing and off-beat tips' – *Daily Mail*

FOR THE BEST IN PAPERBACKS, LOOK FOR THE 🐧

GARDENING IN PENGUINS

The Penguin Book of Basic Gardening   Alan Gemmell

From the perfect lawn to the flourishing vegetable patch: what to grow, when to grow and how to grow it. Given the garden, a beginner can begin on the day he buys this book with its all-the-year-round Gardener's Calendar.

The Pip Book   Keith Mossman

All you need is a pip and patience . . . 'The perfect present for the young enthusiast, *The Pip Book* should ensure that even the most reluctant avocado puts down roots and sends up shoots' – *The Times*

The Town Gardener's Companion   Felicity Bryan

The definitive book for gardeners restricted by the dimensions of their gardens but unrestrained by their enthusiasm. 'A fertile source of ideas for turning a cat-ridden concrete backyard into a jungle of soothing green' – *Sunday Times*

Water Gardening   Philip Swindells

A comprehensive guide to the pleasures and uses of expanses of water, however great or small in the garden. Includes advice on aquatic and marginal plants and the management of ornamental fish.

Beat Garden Pests and Diseases   Stefan Buczacki

An invaluable book, covering all types of plants, from seedlings to root vegetables . . . there is even a section on the special problems of greenhouses.

The Englishman's Garden   Alvide Lees-Milne and Rosemary Verey

An entrancing guided tour through thirty-two of the most beautiful individual gardens in England. Each garden is lovingly described by its owner. Lavishly illustrated.

COOKERY IN PENGUINS

Jane Grigson's Vegetable Book   Jane Grigson

The ideal guide to the cooking of everything from artichoke to yams, written with her usual charm and depth of knowledge by 'the most engaging food writer to emerge during the last few years' – *The Times*

More Easy Cooking for One or Two   Louise Davies

This charming book, full of ideas and easy recipes, offers even the novice cook good wholesome food with the minimum of effort.

The Cuisine of the Rose   Mireille Johnston

Classic French cooking from Burgundy and Lyonnais, including the most succulent dishes of meat and fish bathed in pungent sauces of wine and herbs.

Good Food from Your Freezer   Helge Rubinstein and Sheila Bush

Using a freezer saves endless time and trouble and cuts your food bills dramatically; this book will enable you to cook just as well – perhaps even better – with a freezer as without.

An Invitation to Indian Cooking   Madhur Jaffrey

A witty, practical and delightful handbook of Indian cookery by the much loved presenter of the successful television series.

Budget Gourmet   Geraldene Holt

Plan carefully, shop wisely and cook well to produce first-rate food at minimal expense. It's as easy as pie!

FOR THE BEST IN PAPERBACKS, LOOK FOR THE

COOKERY IN PENGUINS

Mediterranean Food   Elizabeth David

Based on a collection of recipes made when the author lived in France, Italy, the Greek Islands and Egypt, this was the first book by Britain's greatest cookery writer.

The Complete Barbecue Book   James Marks

Mouth-watering recipes and advice on all aspects of barbecuing make this an ideal and inspired guide to *al fresco* entertainment.

A Book of Latin American Cooking   Elisabeth Lambert Ortiz

Anyone who thinks Latin American food offers nothing but *tacos* and *tortillas* will enjoy the subtle marriages of texture and flavour celebrated in this marvellous guide to one of the world's most colourful *cuisines*.

Quick Cook   Beryl Downing

For victims of the twentieth century, this book provides some astonishing gourmet meals – all cooked in under thirty minutes.

Josceline Dimbleby's Book of Puddings, Desserts and Savouries

'Full of the most delicious and novel ideas for every type of pudding' – *Lady*

Chinese Food   Kenneth Lo

A popular step-by-step guide to the whole range of delights offered by Chinese cookery and the fascinating philosophy behind it.

A New Book of Middle Eastern Food   Claudia Roden

'It has permanent value' – Paul Levy in the *Literary Review*. 'Beautifully written, interesting and evocative' – Josceline Dimbleby in the *Sunday Telegraph*. This revised and updated edition of *A Book of Middle Eastern Food* contains many new recipes and much more lore and anecdote of the region.

The Pleasure of Vegetables   Elizabeth Ayrton

'Every dish in this beautifully written book seems possible to make and gorgeous to eat' – *Good Housekeeping*

French Provincial Cooking   Elizabeth David

'One could cook for a lifetime on this book alone' – *Observer*

Jane Grigson's Fruit Book

Fruit is colourful, refreshing and life-enhancing; this book shows how it can also be absolutely delicious in meringues or compotes, soups or pies.

A Taste of American Food   Clare Walker

Far from being just a junk food culture, American cuisine is the most diverse in the world. Swedish, Jewish, Creole and countless other kinds of food have been adapted to the new environment; this book gives some of the most delicious recipes.

Leaves from Our Tuscan Kitchen   Janet Ross and Michael Waterfield

A revised and updated version of a great cookery classic, this splendid book contains some of the most unusual and tasty vegetable recipes in the world.